Second Edition

The History
of
Congressional
Apportionment

Charles M. Biles

Humboldt State University Press

HSU Library
1 Harpst Street
Arcata, California 95521-8299

hsupress@humboldt.edu

The cover background graphic is inspired by a graphic courtesy of The West Virginia Record, Chris Dickerson, editor, 13 April 2017. Originally accessed from http://wvrecord.com/stories/510653312-clay-co-high-students-win-we-the-people-competition.

Cover images were accessed on 19 July 2017.
- "Constitution We the People". Public domain. https://commons.wikimedia.org/wiki/File:Constitution_We_the_People.jpg
- https://pixabay.com/p-1937842/?no_redirect
- Public Domain. https://commons.wikimedia.org/wiki/File:Bill_of_Rights_Pg1of1_AC.jpg
- Cogswell, Ron. "House of Representatives Building and the East Portico of the U.S. Capitol -- Washington (DC) January 2013" *Flickr*. https://www.flickr.com/photos/22711505@N05/8395638677
- Harborfest, Boston. "Stars and Stripes." *Flickr*. https://www.flickr.com/photos/96644353@N02/8880731807
- Lemoine, Randy. "Statue of Liberty". Flickr. https://www.flickr.com/photos/19942094@N00/31585628982

Back cover image
- US Department of Agriculture. "d2700-2". 19 July 2017. *Flickr*. https://www.flickr.com/photos/usdagov/8411792021

ISBN-13: 978-1-947112-58-2

10 9 8 7 6 5 4 3 2 1

The History

of

Congressional Apportionment

Second Edition

By

Charles M. Biles

Humboldt State University Press

Dedication

This book is dedicated to those wonderful people who influenced and supported my interest in and study of congressional apportionment. Special thanks go to my fabulous wife Carolyn who never ceases to amaze me.

There are several professionals whose influence was so great that this work would never have been accomplished without them. I am indebted to Professor Tom Mays, Department of History at Humboldt State University, for the inspiration and the outlook he gave me on studying American history while I was a student in several of his classes. Ray Raphael taught me a special appreciation of early American history in his classes.

I am grateful to Professors Dale Oliver, Kami Larripa, Tim Lauck, Holland Heese, and Steven Margell at Humboldt State University; Professors John Martin, Dan Munton, Tim Melvin, Lin Ying, and Nat Wall at Santa Rosa Junior College; Professors Robin Carter and Levi Gill at College of the Redwoods; Ashlee Buzcek and Michael Chatfield at the Academy of the Redwoods; and Professors Debbie Simonson and Willie Gin at Sonoma State University for their trusting invitations for me to give guest presentations in their classes.

Further, I extend appreciation for timely encouragement to Professor Shannon Guerrero at Northern Arizona University who not only encouraged me to publish, but also utilized some of my materials in her class and further wrote a joint paper with me on congressional apportionment. My friend George Robinson persistently urged me to write something for a general audience.

I also acknowledge the special invitation and encouragement of Kyle Morgan, Scholarly Communications Librarian at Humboldt State University, who invited me to convert my series of decade-by-decade congressional apportionment essays into this book for HSU Press.

Finally, I want to thank and acknowledge readers and users of my materials on the history of congressional apportionment. Very special thanks go to Mr. Richard Schulze of Ames, Iowa, who shared his vast experience by not only calling attention to several errata items but by offering cogent suggestions for improving the referencing of the material. I deeply appreciate his attentive correspondence. Comments, suggestions, critiques, misprints, are welcome—please email me at cmb2@humboldt.edu.

Thank you.

Table of Contents

Preface

This work is devoted to the history of apportionment of the national House of Representatives in the United States. Congressional apportionment is a rich story in the evolution of one facet of American government. The early history involves many well-known figures including George Washington, Thomas Jefferson, Alexander Hamilton, John Adams, John Quincy Adams, Daniel Webster, and James K. Polk. The later history involves an interesting cast of characters from statisticians and mathematicians to presidents.

The problem of apportionment for the U.S. House of Representatives is deceptively easy to state: *how many representatives does each state get?* The U.S. Constitution simply states that this number shall be made based on population as enumerated by a decennial census.

At first it seems so obvious that a bright student could solve the problem. However, much of the complexity stems from a simple elementary school topic: how to round a decimal number. Resolution of this arithmetic problem with its resulting political consequences gives new meaning to the word *decimated*. Results of the process affect the political power structure of the country—it has even played a decisive role in who won a presidential election.

I first became interested in the history of congressional apportionment while taking *The Age of Jefferson to Jackson* from Professor Tom Mays at Humboldt State University in spring semester 2011. This was a 4-unit course, three units for lectures and one unit for a research project. Since the course spanned U. S. History from Washington to Polk, I selected the early history of congressional apportionment as my research project.

I chose this topic because, as a retired professor of mathematics, I wanted to study a subject in U. S. history where I could apply my mathematics background. I was lightly familiar with the mathematical problem of apportionment involving a fair distribution of resources. Also, general education mathematics textbooks displayed congressional apportionment as an illuminating example of a contemporary application.

As I progressed in my research, I noticed a huge disparity between the historical record and the accounts told in mathematics textbooks. Although the textbooks did an acceptable job of presenting the mathematics, the historical accounts were more fiction than fact. This led me to a study of congressional apportionment initiated by reading appropriate sections of the House and Senate journals from 1790 to 1842.

Although my original motivation was to conduct a class research project, I began to develop a series of decade-by-decade essays for use by mathematics professors. I believe that an application of mathematics should be as true to the application as it is to the mathematics. Mathematics texts begin by describing a mathematical apportionment problem as a distribution of a fixed number of integral resource units among a set of competing groups according to some measurable group asset. However, the congressional apportionment acts based on the censuses from 1790 to 1840 are not illustrations of a mathematical apportionment problem since there was no fixed number of House seats. The first congressional apportionment act that viewed apportionment as a fixed distribution problem was based on the 1850 census.

Textbooks define congressional apportionment methods as fixed resource distribution methods. Further, they attribute various methods to Jefferson, Hamilton, Adams, and Webster even though these men proposed no such methods. My project then evolved into constructing curricular materials which present congressional apportionment not as an application of but as a key motivator for mathematical apportionment. Those endeavors eventually led to this book.

The second edition was particularly motivated by reapportionment based on the 2020 census. Interest in the decade is further advanced by having a presidential election in a census year, a phenomenon that occurs once every 20 years. In addition to including reapportionment based on the 2020 census, the second edition reorganizes the first edition, deletes dead website links, updates some website links, and corrects several errors that eluded by my proofing of the first edition.

Chapter I

Congressional

Apportionment

Based on the

Census

1790

The First Congressional Reapportionment

MAP
SHOWING IN FIVE DEGREES OF DENSITY THE DISTRIBUTION
WITHIN THE TERRITORY EAST OF THE 100TH MERIDIAN
OF THE
POPULATION OF THE UNITED STATES
excluding Indians not taxed
Compiled from the Returns of Population at the First Census 1790.

Chapter 1

Congressional Apportionment Based on the Census: 1790
The First Congressional Reapportionment

Table of Contents

Chapter map source: U. S. Census Bureau, https://www.census.gov/history/img/1790-b.jpg

Introduction

The original apportionment of the House of Representatives was given in the Constitution which provided the number of House seats for the original 13 states upon ratification of the Constitution.[1] The Framers wanted apportionment to be based on population, but no national census was yet taken. Hence, an original apportionment, called the constitutional apportionment, was made based on population guestimates provided by delegates to the Constitutional Convention. The Constitution further directed that a census be taken within three years of the first meeting of Congress. The implication was clear: Congress should reapportion the House based on the census taken every ten years.

Apportionment based on the 1790 census was special from an historical perspective because it was the first one, so Congress had to figure out how to carry out the directives given in the Constitution. First, Congress had to construct the directives and mechanics of the 1790 census. Once the census data were reported, then how should one apportion the House based on the census? This first apportionment based on the census took almost six months. During that time, Congress found that apportionment was not a simple process. There were two approaches to apportionment whose natural norms of fairness conflicted with each other. There were devils in the details that the Framers had not anticipated.

---

[1] U. S. Constitution, Article I, Section 2, Paragraph 3.

Section 1.1: The Founding

Section 1.1.1   The Problem

Currently (2021) the House of Representatives has 435 members (Figure 1.1).[2] Different states are represented differently. Representation ranges from a minimum of 1 (AK, MT, WY, ND, SD, VT, DE) to a maximum of 53 (CA). The problem of determining how many representatives each state gets is called the **congressional apportionment problem**.

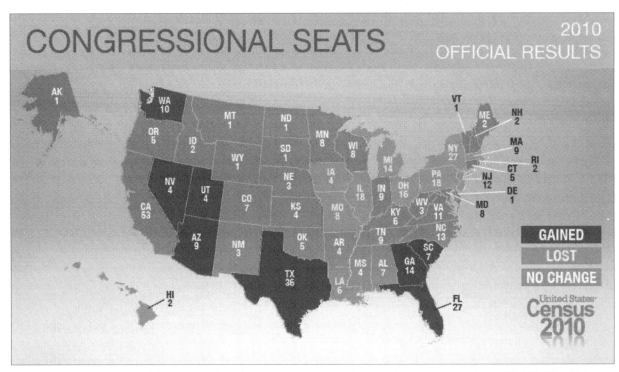

Figure 1.1. Apportionment of the 50 states based on the 2010 census. The apportionment population is 309,183,463 which yields an average congressional district size of 710,767.

We approach this problem as a story in U.S. History. Occasionally we view some details through a mathematical lens. A reader who feels uncomfortable with the mathematics may skip the nerd sections without interrupting the historical flow. However, understanding arithmetical processes (addition, subtraction, multiplication, and division) and working with decimal and whole numbers is assumed. Two arithmetical skills are needed: how to average two different positive numbers and how to round a decimal. The nerd explanations will add considerable insight for those comfortable with precalculus algebra along with the language and notation of basic set theory.

---

[2] http://commons.wikimedia.org/wiki/File:2010_census_reapportionment.jpg.

Primarily, the history of the congressional apportionment problem is a story about how American leaders have struggled with the conflicting forces of fairness and power. Since it is a story in history, we encourage the reader to activate two inquisitive viewpoints.

1. What was it like to live back then? Do not take today's values and outlooks and project them into the past. If you do, then you will be terrible at predicting history. Put yourself in the shoes of a person of the times. What was their environment like? What decisions did they have to make and what was their knowledge base? Then you may ask, what would I have done?

2. How did we get from then to now? Trace those key events, people, and forces at work that evolved yesterday into today.

To appreciate the apportionment map given in Figure 1.1, we first go back in time to Independence Hall, Philadelphia, Pennsylvania, in the summer of 1787. There the framers were meeting to construct the U.S. Constitution.

Section 1.1.2   The Constitution

Guidelines for apportionment are written in the Constitution, Article 1. After the short one-sentence preamble initiated by *We the People*, the first order of business is representation. The relevant material is displayed in Figure 1.2 (next page).

The term "legislative powers" refers to the law-making powers of the federal government. Federal legislative powers are invested in Congress. A key concept for the framers was that the members of Congress represent the country—but how? Should representation be based on geography, on population, on wealth, or on what? History books call the results of the debates *The Great Compromise*.[3] The compromise resulted in a bicameral legislature: a Senate with representation based on geography, and a House with representation based on "the people" as determined by a decennial enumeration of the population. Accordingly, each state has two senators. For the House, first a census is authorized; then, based on that census, "Representatives ... shall be apportioned among the several States ..., according to their respective Numbers." This is huge in that

> The United States in its Federal Government was the first nation of any importance to accept fully the principle of national representation on the basis of population in the constitution of its Lower House."[4]

The Constitution specifies several conditions for the House, including:

* Members shall be chosen every second year by the People;
* Representatives ... shall be apportioned ... according to their respective Numbers ...;

---

[3] Ray Raphael, *Constitutional Myths*, The New Press, New York (2013): 35-55.

[4] Edmond J. James, The First Apportionment of Federal Representatives in the United States, *Annals of the American Academy of Political and Social Science*, Vol. 9 (Jan. 1897):1-41.

- The actual Enumeration shall be made within three Years after the first Meeting of the Congress of the United States, and within every subsequent Term of ten Years;
- The Number of Representatives shall not exceed one for every thirty Thousand;
- But each State shall have at Least one Representative.

U. S. Constitution

Article I

Section 1
All legislative Powers herein granted shall be vested in a Congress of the United States, which shall consist of a Senate and House of Representatives.

Section 2
1: The House of Representatives shall be composed of Members chosen every second Year by the People of the several States, and the Electors in each State shall have the Qualifications requisite for Electors of the most numerous Branch of the State Legislature.

2: No Person shall be a Representative who shall not have attained to the Age of twenty five Years, and been seven Years a Citizen of the United States, and who shall not, when elected, be an Inhabitant of that State in which he shall be chosen.

3: **Representatives** and direct Taxes **shall be apportioned among the several States which may be included within this Union, according to their respective Numbers,** which shall be determined by adding to the whole Number of free Persons, including those bound to Service for a Term of Years, and excluding Indians not taxed, three fifths of all other Persons. **The actual Enumeration shall be made within three Years after the first Meeting of the Congress of the United States, and within every subsequent Term of ten Years, in such Manner as they shall by Law direct. The Number of Representatives shall not exceed one for every thirty Thousand, but each State shall have at Least one Representative;** and until such enumeration shall be made, the State of New Hampshire shall be entitled to chuse three, Massachusetts eight, Rhode-Island and Providence Plantations one, Connecticut five, New-York six, New Jersey four, Pennsylvania eight, Delaware one, Maryland six, Virginia ten, North Carolina five, South Carolina five, and Georgia three.

4: When vacancies happen in the Representation from any State, the Executive Authority thereof shall issue Writs of Election to fill such Vacancies.

5: The House of Representatives shall chuse their Speaker and other Officers; and shall have the sole Power of Impeachment.

Figure 1.2. Article 1, Sections 1 and 2 of the U. S. Constitution give the guidelines for the structure of the House and Senate.

Voters elect the members of the House in even-numbered years. The decennial census is conducted in each year ending in zero since the first census began in 1790. Otherwise, important questions went unanswered. Who are the "People" who choose the members of the House? Who is to be "enumerated" in the census? The answers have a convoluted and deep history all their own. Although these civil rights issues are not the main focus for this book, we need to be aware of them.

Exactly which "People" can do the choosing has been in a state of flux throughout American history. In 1790 general requirements for voting included white, male, at least 21 years of age, propertied, and Protestant.[5] Although voting rights now are expanded to include most citizens 18 years or older, voter suppression existed throughout U.S. history. Serious voter suppression occurred in Jim Crow laws.[6] Although Jim Crow laws are now repealed, voter suppression continues today under the guise of "voter identification" laws.[7]

The conduct of the census is a crucial preliminary step in determining apportionment for the House. There are not only the mechanics of counting people but also the identification of exactly who is to be counted. Controversy continues to this day. We caution that by today's standards there is no way to justify the exclusionary components "determined by adding to the whole Number of free Persons, including those bound to Service for a Term of Years, and excluding Indians not taxed, three fifths of all other Persons." The three-fifths rule was applied to the slave population. This exclusion was repealed in 1868 by the passage of the Fourteenth Amendment to the Constitution. A similar history exists with the Native American population which was not fully included into the apportionment census population until 1940.[8] Previous to the 1970 census no Americans living abroad were included in the enumeration. In 1970 the Census Bureau began to include "U.S. Armed Forces personnel, civilian U.S. federal employees, and dependents of both groups that were allocated to their home states were included in the populations of those states for apportionment purposes only."[9]

Controversy today exists over the inclusion of undocumented people. For example, in 2011 the state of Louisiana filed a complaint with the U. S. Supreme Court to "to declare that the inclusion of non-immigrant foreign nationals in the population figures used to apportion seats in the United States House of Representatives is unconstitutional and to enjoin Defendants to recalculate and submit new apportionment figures excluding such individuals."[10] Although the Supreme Court dismissed Louisiana's petition,[11] the controversy persists.[12] Another lightening rod issue centers on so-called Personhood Bills. Such bills seek to legally define that a person begins at conception. We leave it to the reader's imagination how such would be incorporated into the mechanics of the census. Although it is important to be aware of these related issues, we now return to our main focus: what is done with the census after it has been reported?

---

[5] http://www.crf-usa.org/bill-of-rights-in-action/bria-8-1-b-who-voted-in-early-america

[6] http://www.crf-usa.org/black-history-month/a-brief-history-of-jim-crow.

[7] http://www.pfaw.org/media-center/publications/new-face-jim-crow-voter-suppression-america

[8] https://www.census.gov/srd/papers/pdf/ev90-19.pdf

[9] http://www.census.gov/population/apportionment/about/history.html

[10] https://www.justice.gov/sites/default/files/osg/briefs/2011/01/01/140%2COriginal.resp.pdf

[11] *Louisiana v. Bryson*, 565 U.S. 1258 (2012);
https://www.abajournal.com/news/article/supreme_court_rejects_louisiana_bid_to_file_original_complaint_chall enging

[12] https://www.fairus.org/issue/societal-impact/illegal-immigrants-distort-congressional-representation-and-federal-programs

Section 1.2: The 1790 Census

Section 1.2.1   The Census

The 1st Congress authorized the first census to begin on 1 August 1790.[13] This made the United States the first country in history to authorize a regular enumeration of its residents for the purpose of establishing representation.[14] The 1st Congress also admitted Vermont as a new state and consented to recognize Kentucky as a new state to be admitted on 1 June 1792. Upon admission each state was allocated two representatives until reapportionment based on the census was completed.[15]

The first census was a joint venture between the three main branches of the federal government. The data were collected under the supervision of U.S. marshals, officers of the judicial branch. The marshals transmitted their results to the President. President Washington then passed the information to Secretary of State Thomas Jefferson who compiled the results. Hence, the legislative branch authorized and made the regulations for the first census; the judicial branch conducted the field work to make the enumeration; the executive branch processed the data and returned the results back to Congress.

The census took over a year and the results were submitted to the 1st session of the 2nd Congress on 28 October 1791. The Annals of Congress record the event as follows.

> A Message was received from the President of the United States, communicating a copy of the Enumeration of the Inhabitants of the United States, agreeable to the Census taken pursuant to a law of the Union.[16]

The Annals also supply a copy of the census results communicated to Congress (Table 1.2, next page).[17] However, the Total population column has not been adjusted for apportionment purposes in that the three-fifths rule has yet to be applied.

On what data did apportionment debates take place? This is not a simple question to answer. There are four reasonable data sets: Balinski and Young (Table 1.1 at right), the 1790 census data (Table 1.2), Thomas Jefferson (Table 1.3), and Fisher Ames (Table 1.4).

Table 1.1. Balinski and Young 1790 census.

State	Population
CT 5	236841
DE 1	55540
GA 3	70835
KY	68705
MD 6	278514
MA 8	475327
NH 3	141822
NJ 4	179570
NY 6	331589
NC 5	353523
PA 8	432879
RI 1	68446
SC 5	206236
VT 2	85533
VA 10	630560
US 67	3615920

---

[13] Statutes at Large, 1st Congress, 2nd Session, Ch. 2 (1790): 101-3.

[14] Carroll Wright, *The History and Growth of the U.S. Census*, Government Printing Office, Washington, D.C., 1900: 13; available as a public access ebook from Google books, https://play.google.com/books.

[15] Statutes at Large, 1st Congress, 3rd Session, Chap. IX (1791): 191.

[16] Annals of Congress, House of Representatives, 2nd Congress, 1st Session: 147.

[17] Annals of Congress, Senate, 2nd Congress, 1st Session: 17-18; https://www2.census.gov/prod2/decennial/documents/1790a.pdf.

Table 1.2. The 1790 census data as originally presented to Congress.

DISTRICTS.	Free white males of sixteen years, and upwards, including heads of families.	Free white males under sixteen years.	Free white females, including heads of families.	All other free persons.	Slaves.	Total.
Vermont	22,435	22,328	40,505	252	16	85,539
New Hampshire	36,086	34,851	70,160	630	158	141,885
{ Maine	24,384	24,748	46,870	538	none.	96,540 }
{ Massachusetts	95,453	87,289	190,582	5,463	none.	378,787 }
Rhode Island	16,019	15,799	32,652	3,407	948	68,825
Connecticut	60,523	54,403	117,448	2,808	2,764	237,946
New York	83,700	78,122	152,320	4,654	21,324	340,120
New Jersey	45,251	41,416	83,287	2,762	11,453	184,139
Pennsylvania	110,788	106,948	206,363	6,537	3,737	434,373
Delaware	11,783	12,143	22,384	3,899	8,887	59,094
Maryland	55,915	51,339	101,395	8,043	103,036	319,728
{ Virginia	110,936	116,135	215,046	12,866	292,627	747,610 }
{ Kentucky	15,154	17,057	28,922	114	12,430	73,677 }
North Carolina	69,988	77,506	140,710	4,975	100,572	393,751
South Carolina						
Georgia	13,103	14,044	25,739	398	29,264	82,548
Southwestern Territory	6,271	10,277	15,365	361	3,417	35,691
Northwestern Territory						

Whole number of Persons within the several Districts of the United States, according to an Act "providing for the Enumeration of the Inhabitants of the United States," passed March 1, 1790.

Balinski and Young is the seminal work in any serious study of apportionment. The Balinski and Young census data (Table 1.1, previous page) display a State column and a Population column. The State column lists the 14 states already admitted into the union at the start of the 2nd Congress along with Kentucky consented for admission. For convenience we also list the number of representatives each state had at the start of the 2nd Congress. The populations given are the apportionment populations for each state; i.e., the three-fifths rule has been applied to the resident slave population. Further, populations have been corrected for known historical errors.[18]

Despite the excellence of Balinski and Young's work there are difficulties in reading the historical record such as the House and Senate Journals and the Annals of Congress. Legislators at the time did not have corrected figures. There are variances in figures throughout the debates. For an historical study it helps to use the actual figures used by legislators in their arguments during the apportionment debates.

Accordingly, we seek to examine the historical arguments based on the figures used at the time. Of course, an obvious option is to use the census figures as originally reported to Congress by President Washington on 4 February 1791 (Table 1.2). The census figures are provided by federal judicial districts. Thus, Maine is combined with Massachusetts and Kentucky is combined with Virginia since Maine and Kentucky were not yet states, but Maine was a judicial district of Massachusetts and Kentucky a judicial district of Virginia. After

---

[18] Michael Balinski and H. Peyton Young, *Fair Representation: Meeting the Ideal of One Man, One Vote*, Second Edition, Brookings Institution Press, Washington, D. C.: 157-8.

applying the three-fifths rule we should have the apportionment population. Note that there is no population figure for South Carolina. At this point in time the census was incomplete for South Carolina. During the earlier stages of debate, assumptions for the population of South Carolina varied from 200000[19] to 240000[20]. The apportionment population for South Carolina, 206236, was finally reported to Congress on 5 March 1792.[21]

Kentucky was initially part of Virginia, but on 4 February 1791 Congress declared that the new state of Kentucky be formed and it was formally admitted to the Union on 1 June 1792.[22] On 25 February 1791 Congress allocated Vermont and Kentucky two representatives until reapportionment based on the 1790 census was complete.[23]

Another option is to use the numbers supplied by Jefferson in a report to President Washington analyzing the bill submitted 28 March 1792 for Washington's approval (Table 1.3).[24] Although Jefferson erroneously added rather than subtracted 2/5ths of the slave population for New York, it does not affect the results for comparing the apportionment proposals. However, the figures are from a letter sent to President Washington after passage of the congressional apportionment bill. One may prefer to use figures used by legislators during the formation of the bill.

Table 1.3. Jefferson's apportionment data.

State	Population
VT	85532
NH	141823
MA	475327
RI	68444
CN	235941
NY	352915
NJ	179556
PA	432880
DE	55538
MD	278513
VA	630558
KY	68705
NC	353521
SC	206236
GA	70843

Our final source is derived from Representative Fisher Ames (MA). On 19 December 1791 Mr. Ames gave a detailed analysis of the proposed apportionment bills and provided tables from which the apportionment populations can be derived (Table 1.4, next page).[25] For comparison we also provide the 1790 census data adjusted for apportionment with the data used by Mr. Ames. There are minor discrepancies which could reflect corrections as they became known, copy errors, computational errors, or communication errors. Fortunately, the discrepancies do not affect the final results. However, they help to explain when reading the historical record why, for example, a procedure sometimes yields a reported House size of 112 or 110 or 113.[26]

---

[19] Ibid: 188.

[20] Ibid: 149.

[21] Annals of Congress, Senate, 2nd Congress, 1st Session: 100.

[22] Statutes at Large, 1st Congress, 3rd Session, Statute III, Chap. IV: 189.

[23] Statutes at Large, 1st Congress, 3rd Session, Statute III, Chap. IX: 191.

[24] "Opinion on Apportionment Bill, 4 April 1792," Founders Online, National Archives (http://founders.archives.gov/documents/Jefferson/01-23-02-0324, ver. 2014-05-09). Source: *The Papers of Thomas Jefferson*, vol. 23, *1 January–31 May 1792*, ed. Charles T. Cullen. Princeton: Princeton University Press, 1990, pp. 370–377. Accessed from http://founders.archives.gov/documents/Jefferson/01-23-02-0324

[25] Annals of Congress, House of Representatives, 2nd Congress, 1st Session: 254-262.

[26] Ibid: 149, 155, 169, 243.

Table 1.4. Tabular population data for apportionment analysis from Representative Fisher Ames (MA).

States.	Members.	Numbers lost on each member by the bill.	Ratio of the House.	Lost numbers, or fractions.	Ratio by the amendment which adds seven members.	No. short of 30,000 for each member.
N. Hampshire	5	5,455	35,455	21,820	28,365	1,635
Massachusetts	16	1,919	31,919	25,327	29,924	291
Connecticut -	8	4,223	34,223	26,841	29,805	195
Vermont -	3	12,766	42,766	25,533	28,511	1,489
New Jersey -	6	5,911	35,911	29,559	29,826	174
North Carolina	12	2,138	32,138	23,522	29,460	540
Delaware -	2	25,539	55,539		27,769	2,231
	52	according to		the	amendment.	

" The following States, to which the rejected amendment makes no addition, stand thus :

States.	Members.	Ratio	Total loss by the ratio.
New York - - -	11	30,144	1,584
Pennsylvania - - -	14	30,919	12,866
Maryland - - -	9	30,946	8,514
Virginia - - -	21	30,026	546
	55		
Kentucky - - -	2	34,352	8,704
Georgia - - -	2	35,421	10,842
Rhode Island - - -	2	34,223	8,447"

State	Reported	Ames
VT	85530	85532
NH	141822	141780
MA	475327	478785
RI	68446	68446
CT	236840	239561
NY	331590	331584
NJ	179588	179555
PA	432878	432866
DE	55541	55539
MD	278514	278514
VA	630559	630546
KY	68705	68704
NC	353522	353518
SC		
GA	70842	70842
	3409705	3415772

Section 1.2.2   The Background

The House went to work on apportionment shortly after receiving the census report from President Washington. Members of the House were well aware of the constraints on House size imposed by the Constitution. First, each state shall have at least one representative. In 1791 this set a minimum House size at 15. The Constitution constrains the maximum size by "The Number of Representatives shall not exceed one for every thirty Thousand." Although it may take a couple of pots of coffee to decipher this constraint, for practical purposes it means that a representative can represent 30000 or more people but not less than 30000.

The 30000 constituency figure is interesting in itself. On the last day of the Constitutional Convention the figure was 40000. Although it was the last day, George Washington suggested that 40000 should be changed to 30000. This was Washington's only proposal during the convention. He restricted his role to presiding over the meetings, staying above the debates and issues. His mere suggestion was instantly adopted.[27]

---

[27] Edmond J. James, The First Apportionment of Federal Representatives in the United States, *Annals of the American Academy of Political and Social Science*, Vol. 9 (Jan. 1897): 18-19.

Members of Congress still had intense recollections from the ratification debates fresh in mind. Indicative of the issue is James Madison's writing in *The Federalist 55*.[28]

> The number of which the House of Representatives is to consist, forms another and a very interesting point of view, under which this branch of the federal legislature may be contemplated. Scarce any article, indeed, in the whole Constitution seems to be rendered more worthy of attention, by the weight of character and the apparent force of argument with which it has been assailed.

Even fresher for some congressmen were the debates in Congress over amendments to the Constitution. Delegates in several state conventions were persuaded to vote for ratification only under the promise that Congress would take swift action to include amendments guaranteeing citizen liberties. Accordingly, James Madison proposed a list of amendments. A revised list was incorporated in a resolution passed by Congress on 25 September 1789.[29] The approved resolution contained 12 articles submitted to the states for ratification as amendments. The first proposal, called Article the First, concerned apportionment.[30]

> Article the First . . . After the first enumeration required by the <u>first Article</u> of the Constitution, there shall be one Representative for every thirty thousand, until the number shall amount to one hundred, after which, the proportion shall be so regulated by Congress, that there shall be not less than one hundred Representatives, nor less than one Representative for every forty thousand persons, until the number of Representatives shall amount to two hundred, after which the proportion shall be so regulated by Congress, that there shall not be less than two hundred Representatives, nor more than one Representative for every fifty thousand persons.

The notion that "there shall be one Representative for every thirty thousand" appears to be a basic element in the thinking about the basis for calculation of apportionment. This amendment, as well as the proposed Article the Second, failed to pass ratification by the states. It is ironic that Article the First failed ratification by only one vote since Massachusetts was one of the states that did not ratify but was outspoken about guaranteeing adequate representation during the ratification. Article the Third through Article the Twelfth did pass ratification. They are now enshrined as the first ten amendments to the Constitution and are revered as the Bill of Rights.

A fascinating snippet of American history is that Article the Second was eventually ratified as The Twentieth-Seventh Amendment on 7 May 1992. As noted by Ray Raphael, "finally, 203 years later, one of the first amendments Congress proposed became the last (as of this date) to be ratified."[31]

---

[28] James Madison, The Total Number of the House of Representatives, *The Federalist No. 55*, Feb 13, 1788.
[29] http://teachingamericanhistory.org/bor/four-stages/
[30] http://avalon.law.yale.edu/18th_century/resolu02.asp
[31] Ray Raphael, *The U. S. Constitution: The Citizen's Annotated Edition*, Vintage Books, 2016: 136-138.

Section 1.2.3   The House Bill

On Friday, 28 October 1791, President Washington sent Congress a message communicating the results of the 1790 census. On Monday the House began debate. For almost all items about apportionment the House resolved itself into a Committee of the Whole. Mr. John Laurance (NY) (Figure 1.3.[32]) opened the discussion.[33] He observed that there were two items that needed attention: first, the apportionment ratio of representation; second, the incomplete census data from South Carolina. The state was given a time extension. Discussion proceeded with the understanding that the decided apportionment mechanism would be applied to that state when the census for South Carolina was completed.

Figure 1.3. John Laurance (NY).

The key item was the ratio of representation. The immediate topic of discussion was the pivotal constituency question: how many people should a congressman represent? Mr. Laurance proposed 30000. Subsequent debate included a ratio up to 40000 with some intermediate options. All options were in multiples of 1000. On both sides of the main issue (30000 or no) appeals were made to Article the First which already had received 9 votes toward ratification. Finally, after two weeks of debate a motion was made to make the ratio 30000; passed, 35-23. Representatives Page (VA), Murray (NY), and Macon (NC) were appointed as a committee to draft a bill based on the passed motion. The committee reported a bill to the House three days later. On 23 November a motion was made to amend the bill using the ratio 34000; failed, 21-38. The next day the House passed its apportionment bill 43-12.

There were two key mechanisms behind the House bill. First, it was initiated by the constituency question: how many people should a congressman represent? The answer is interchangeably referred to as the ratio of representation (ratio for short), the constituency, or the divisor. Their answer was 30000. Second, the ratio was divided into each state's population. The division produced two components: the whole number of multiples of the ratio and the remainder, better known in the congressional debates as the fraction. Hence, a state's apportionment is the result of a simple 2-step algorithm.

Step 1. Determine the ratio of representation.
Step 2. A state's apportionment is the whole number of multiples of the ratio in the state's population.

It is interesting to study the objections to using a divisor of 30000. Two main objections were summarized by John Steele (NY). First, he felt that the resulting House size was too large. Using a larger divisor would produce a smaller House size. Second, he felt that dropping the fractions left people unrepresented. For example, New Jersey's population was 179555. The

---

[32] Biographical Directory of the United States Congress, Public Domain, https://commons.wikimedia.org/w/index.php?curid=13286475.
[33] Annals of Congress, House of Representatives, 2nd Congress, 1st Session: 148-210.

ratio 30000 divides into the population 5 times leaving a fraction (remainder) of 29555. This provides New Jersey with 5 representatives but leaves 29555 people unrepresented. Mr. Steele sought, therefore, to use a divisor intermediate between 30000 and 40000 that might minimize this problem. He inquired, what ratio will leave the smallest fractions and fewest citizens "unrepresented?"[34] This concern may seem bizarre today, however it further demonstrates the priority that was given to representation in 1791.

The matter of the ratio of representation and its use in determining apportionment dismayed several congressmen as voiced by John Page (VA).[35]

> ... I feel myself more interested in the question than I ever was in any one I have had to decide on. Sir, it gave me pain to find those worthy members calculating and coldly applying the rules of arithmetic to a subject beyond the power of numbers to express the degree of its importance to their fellow-citizens.

Table 1.5 displays the results using the ratio of 30000. The Seats column denotes each state's apportionment which is the integer part of dividing 30000 into each state's population. The Fraction column is the remainder perceived as unrepresented people. The resulting House size is the sum of these apportionments. Since the data for South Carolina were not yet complete, the bill was sent to the Senate with the caveat that apportionment for South Carolina would be calculated using the same procedure once the census figures for that state were reported.

Note that the House size is only a result of the process. The House size never enters into the formulation of the apportionment algorithm, nor does the House size figure in the apportionment calculations. Assuming 200000 for South Carolina provides 6 seats yielding a total House size of 112.

Table 1.5. The House Bill.

State	Population	Seats	Fraction
VT	85532	2	25532
NH	141780	4	21780
MA	478785	15	28785
RI	68446	2	8446
CT	239561	7	29561
NY	331584	11	1584
NJ	179555	5	29555
PA	432866	14	12866
DE	55539	1	25539
MD	278514	9	8514
VA	630546	21	546
KY	68704	2	8704
NC	353518	11	23518
SC			
GA	70842	2	10842
	3415772	106	235772

The House passed its version of the apportionment bill on Thursday, 24 November 1791, by a vote of 43-12. That same day the House sent the bill to the Senate for concurrence.[36] It took almost a month from receiving the census to passing the House bill. If a congressman thought that this process was all rather easy, then that thinking was soon to be dashed.

---

[34] Annals of Congress, House of Representatives, 2nd Congress, 1st Session: 170-1.
[35] Ibid: 179.
[36] Senate Journal, 24 November 1791. Accessed from http://memory.loc.gov/cgi-bin/query/r?ammem/hlaw:@field%28DOCID+@lit%28sj001414%29%29

Section 1.2.4 The Senate Bill

The bill received by the Senate from the House on Thursday, 24 November 1791, was titled *An act apportioning representatives among the people of the several states, according to the first enumeration*. After reception the bill was read to the Senate. Protocol required three readings of a bill before a final vote for approval could be taken. The next day the Senate proceeded with the second reading and debate began. The debate continued on Monday. The Senate then decided to appoint a committee to study the issue and make recommendations. The committee members were Aaron Burr (NY), Oliver Ellsworth (CT), Pierce Butler (SC), Caleb Strong (MA), and James Monroe (VA).

Next Monday Mr. Ellsworth, on behalf of the committee, reported amendments to the full Senate. Debate ensued and continued the next day. On Wednesday a motion was made to amend the House bill by replacing the ratio of 30000 with 33000. A vote was postponed to consider a motion dealing with the House bill directly: retain the 30000 ratio, but rather than simply drop the fraction, award an additional seat for a sufficiently large fraction. Although the motion did not specify the method of rounding, results were consistent with the usual way of rounding (if the fractional part is less than 15000, then round down; otherwise, round up); failed, 9-15. A vote was taken on the original amendment to use a ratio of 33000; failed, 11-13. An amendment to use a ratio of 33000 with apportionments consistent with rounding the fractions in the usual way also failed, 9-15. Then a vote was taken on whether to agree to the apportionments given in the House bill; passed, 13-11.[37]

Table 1.6. The Senate Bill.

State	Population	Seats	Fraction
VT	85532	2	19532
NH	141780	4	9780
MA	478785	14	16785
RI	68446	2	2446
CT	239561	7	8561
NY	331584	10	1584
NJ	179555	5	14555
PA	432866	13	3866
DE	55539	1	22539
MD	278514	8	14514
VA	630546	19	3546
KY	68704	2	2704
NC	353518	10	23518
SC			
GA	70842	2	4842
	3415772	99	148772

Later, the Senate voted on an amendment to the House bill to use a ratio of 33000 and, although not explicitly stated, to drop all fractions. The vote was 12-12. Vice-President John Adams cast a tie-breaking vote in the affirmative; hence, the motion to amend passed 13-12. The Senate bill (Table 1.6) was sent to the House for concurrence.[38] The Seats column denotes each state's apportionment which is the integer part of dividing 33000 into each state's population. The Fraction column is the remainder perceived as unrepresented people.

On Friday, 9 December, the House received a message that the Senate passed the House bill with some amendments and that the Senate sought concurrence.[39] The House took up the

---

[37] Annals of Congress, Senate, 2nd Congress, 1st Session, 6 December 1791: 41-4. Accessed from https://memory.loc.gov/ammem/amlaw/lwaclink.html.
[38] Ibid: 44-47.
[39] Annals of Congress, House, 2nd Congress, 1st Session, 9 December 1791: 242.

request the following Monday. First, in response to the request for concurrence, Elbridge Gerry (MA) said that he was informed that the Senate wanted the 33000 divisor in order to "reduce the fractions."[40] Mr. Gerry moved to reject the Senate's amendment to replace 30000 by 33000. This launched two days of intense debate that exposed a variety of nuances associated with the apportionment algorithm and the results. On Wednesday a motion to concur with the Senate amendment failed by a close vote, 29-31.

In response the next day the Senate confirmed its original support for 33000 by the same vote as before, 12-12, with Vice-President Adams again breaking the tie to 13-12. The result was communicated to the House. On Monday, 19 December, the House spent the entire day on another in-depth discussion.[41] The day ended with two votes confirming the House's original ratio of 30000. The first vote was that the House should recede from disagreement with the Senate: yea 27, nay 33. The second vote was that the House should adhere to its disagreement with the Senate: yea 32, nay 27. The next day the Senate reaffirmed its position with its same vote. We thus find something new in our nation's history: congressional gridlock.

Section 1.2.5 The Jelly Bean Effect

The **Jelly Bean Effect** is the uncanny ability of human beings to recognize, often instantly, a disproportionate distribution of assets. The phenomenon is well-known among small children at Easter time. Even though too young to have learned to count, if a parent distributes jelly beans from a bag, one child knows immediately if another has received more jelly beans. The Jelly Bean Effect is especially relevant in a political distribution of resources. Politics is an interesting and unique blend of activities heavily influenced by undercurrents of fairness and power. Frequently, politicians mask concerns of power with speeches voicing concerns of fairness. To paraphrase an astute observation articulated by Balinski and Young, history attests to a politician's ingenuity for inventing rules of fairness when seats in a legislature are at stake.[42] We examine four manifestations of the Jelly Bean Effect in the apportionment debates: fractions and unrepresented populations, power, the quota rule, and constituency.

Fractions and Unrepresented Populations

The use of 30000 as the ratio by the House is easily understood in the context of the day. Where did the Senate's 33000 come from? Mr. Gerry (MA) opened the House discussion of the Senate bill, "The principle on which the amendment had taken place in the Senate, was to reduce the fractions which would result from the ratio proposed by the House … ."[43]

The fairness rule of "fewest fractions" was earlier noted by Hugh Williamson (NC) on 1 November during the House considerations of its original bill.[44]

---

[40] Annals of Congress, House of Representatives, 2nd Congress, 1st Session: 243. Accessed from http://memory.loc.gov/cgi-bin/ampage?collId=llac&fileName=003/llac003.db&recNum=119

[41] Ibid: 254-274.

[42] Michael Balinski and H. Peyton Young, *Fair Representation*, Second Edition, Brookings Institution Press: 10.

[43] Annals of Congress, House of Representatives, 2nd Congress, 1st Session: 243.

[44] Ibid: 154.

Mr. WILLIAMSON, after a few preliminary remarks on the several calculations that different members had made, and applying the various results to the population of the small States in particular, observed, that such a ratio should be adopted as would leave the fewest fractions, …

The thinking behind "fewest fractions" is fascinating. First, consider the House bill (see Table 1.5). For example, the population for Vermont is 85532. Giving Vermont 2 seats then leaves a fraction of 25532 unrepresented people. Adding all the state fractions leaves 255920 people "without representation." Similar analysis of the Senate bill, which uses 33000 per representative, yields only 150920 people unrepresented. This kind of thinking is solid evidence in support of Balinski and Young's observation that "history attests to the mathematical inventiveness of politicians when seats in a legislature at stake." It is amazing to conclude how one can provide more representation by providing fewer representatives.

For the most part, the debate over what divisor to use was restricted from 30000 to 40000 in increments of 1000. Analysis using Balinski and Young's 1790 census data verifies that the Senate divisor 33000 produced the "fewest fractions" with resulting smallest number of "unrepresented people" (Table 1.7). Underneath the Unrepresented figures in Table 1.7, the data from South Carolina are removed since the SC information was unknown at the time of the House-Senate impasse. The last row gives the unrepresented population figures using the Fisher Ames data set. Either way, using the Balinski and Young or the Ames census figures, d = 33000 yields the "fewest fractions" and least "unrepresented people."

Table 1.7. Analysis of fewest fractions.

State	Pop	d =	30000	31000	32000	33000	34000	35000	36000	37000	38000	39000	40000
CT	236841		26841	19841	12841	5841	32841	26841	20841	14841	8841	2841	36841
DE	55540		25540	24540	23540	22540	21540	20540	19540	18540	17540	16540	15540
GA	70835		10835	8835	6835	4835	2835	835	34835	33835	32835	31835	30835
KY	68705		8705	6705	4705	2705	705	33705	32705	31705	30705	29705	28705
MD	278514		8514	30514	22514	14514	6514	33514	26514	19514	12514	5514	38514
MA	475327		25327	10327	27327	13327	33327	20327	7327	31327	19327	7327	35327
NH	141822		21822	17822	13822	9822	5822	1822	33822	30822	27822	24822	21822
NJ	179570		29570	24570	19570	14570	9570	4570	35570	31570	27570	23570	19570
NY	331589		1589	21589	11589	1589	25589	16589	7589	35589	27589	19589	11589
NC	353523		23523	12523	1523	23523	13523	3523	29523	20523	11523	2523	33523
PA	432879		12879	29879	16879	3879	24879	12879	879	25879	14879	3879	32879
RI	68446		8446	6446	4446	2446	446	33446	32446	31446	30446	29446	28446
SC	206236		26236	20236	14236	8236	2236	31236	26236	21236	16236	11236	6236
VT	85533		25533	23533	21533	19533	17533	15533	13533	11533	9533	7533	5533
VA	630560		560	10560	22560	3560	18560	560	18560	1560	22560	6560	30560
US	3615920		**255920**	**267920**	**223920**	**150920**	**215920**	**255920**	**339920**	**359920**	**309920**	**222920**	**375920**
		no SC	229684	247684	209684	142684	213684	224684	313684	338684	293684	211684	375906
		Ames	229644	247644	209644	142644	213644	224644	313644	338644	293644	211644	369644

Power

The gridlock confrontation between the Senate and the House may also be understood as drama in the political struggle for power advantage. In this case note the difference in the basis of representation between the Senate and the House. In the Senate each state is regarded equally, each having two senators. Representation in the House is based on population, ranging from 1 representative for Delaware to 10 for Virginia. In comparing the House and Senate bills, note that nine states have the same apportionment (Table 1.8). For analysis purposes we include South Carolina with an estimated population of 200000.

Table 1.8. The original House and Senate bills.

State	House	Senate
VT	2	2
NH	4	4
MA	15	14
RI	2	2
CT	7	7
NY	11	10
NJ	5	5
PA	14	13
DE	1	1
MD	9	8
VA	21	19
KY	2	2
NC	11	10
SC	6	6
GA	2	2
	112	105

The nine states with the same number of representatives under both bills are VT, NH, RI, CT, NJ, DE, KY, SC, and GA. Accordingly, the power of these congressmen is slightly diluted under the House bill. Thinking like a senator and representing your state, one would expect around 8 of the states to vote for the Senate bill (KY was not yet formally admitted as a state; so, KY did not yet have senators and representatives in Congress). In contrast six states gain seats in comparison to the Senate bill: MA, NY, PA, MD, VA, and NC. These are the six largest states with 43 of the 67 votes in the House accounting for 64 per cent of the vote in the House. Others argued that the House bill added seven new seats, all going to the largest states. From the opposite side of the coin, as noted by Alexander White (VA), the Senate bill would "operate generally against the larger States."[45] This does not explain things exactly, but it may help explain the entrenched position of legislators. This power struggle between the states vs. the people was a serious concern for Johnathan Dayton (NJ).[46]

In addition, there were regional concerns. The 15 states were thought of in three main regions: New England (NH, VT, MA, CT, RI), Middle Atlantic (NY, PA, NJ), and South (DE, MD, VA, NC, SC, GA). In comparison with the House bill, some argued that the Senate bill took away 7 representatives: 4 from the South, but only 1 from New England and 2 from the Middle Atlantic. Hugh Williamson (NC) lamented "that the operation of the amendment [Senate Bill] was to diminish the fractions to the Eastward, and increase those to the Southward."[47] It was not lost on southerners that the vote in the Senate was close and along regional lines. The main vote was 12-12. The five New England states voted as a solid block and all ten New England senators voted "aye." They were joined by a senator from Delaware and a senator from New Jersey. Of the eight southern senators who voted, all voted "nay." The tie vote in the Senate was broken by Vice-President John Adams, from Massachusetts, who voted "aye." Hence, the Senate bill passed 13-12.[48]

---

[45] Annals of Congress, House of Representatives, 2nd Congress, 1st Session: 244.
[46] Ibid. 201-3.
[47] Ibid: 244.
[48] Annals of Congress, Senate, 2nd Congress, 1st Session: 46-7.

Quota Rule

The most effective move in breaking the gridlock was the introduction of the quota rule. The quota rule was based on a calculation known as the "Rule of Three."[49] To determine a state's fair share of the House, multiply the House size by each state's proportion of the population, (state population)/(national population). The quota rule is simply a formalization of the common sense notion that if a state has 10% of the population, then it should have 10% of the seats in the House.

Multiplying the House size by a state's proportion yields the state's quota considered to be the state's fair share of the House. This intuitive Jelly Bean rule applied as a rule of fairness is known today as the **quota rule**: a state's apportionment should be the state's quota rounded down (lower quota) or rounded up (upper quota). Any apportionment less than the lower quota gives the state fewer representatives than what the state deserves based on population. Similarly, any apportionment greater than the upper quota gives the state more representatives than what the state deserves. The concept was strongly advanced by Fisher Ames (MA). In analyzing the House bill with House size 112, Mr. Ames argued:[50]

> The Rule-of-Three will show what part of the representation any State shall have. … What part of one hundred and twelve members will Virginia have according to its people? The answer is easily found. Virginia, having six hundred and thirty thousand persons, … is entitled to nineteen members. The bill gives her twenty-one. Is that right? Who will say that the words or meaning of the Constitution are pursued? Are the Representatives, then, apportioned or disproportioned?

Mr. Ames did not win the battle of the day; however, the idea would eventually lead to a new bill that Congress would pass and send to President Washington for his approval.

We now formalize these ideas to analyze the House and Senate bills by applying the quota rule criterion of fairness. Both the House and Senate bills were created using a basic divisor method: first, decide on the constituency (House, 30000; Senate, 33000); second, each state's apportionment is the whole number of multiples of the constituency in the state's population. The sum of all the state apportionments is then the resulting House size.

The House size, once known, can be tested for fairness of allocation by applying the rule of three. First, determine each state's **proportion** defined as a state's population divided by the total U.S. population. Hence, the proportion is merely the state's fraction of the total population. A state's apportionment should reflect this same proportion for the House size. Accordingly, we define a state's **quota** as the House size, h, multiplied by the state's proportion. Hence,

$$state\ quota = h \times \frac{state\ population}{national\ population}$$

---

[49] Annals of Congress, House of Representatives, 2nd Congress, 1st Session: 255.
[50] Ibid: 254-63.

Alert Regarding Computations. The state quota involves a division. In 1791 congressmen did not have electronic computing devices. Computations had to be carried out by hand. Accordingly, divisions were performed by the process of long division. The answer was reported by displaying the whole number of multiples of the divisor along with the remainder. For example, 13 divided by 5 was reported as 2 with a remainder (fraction) of 3. Today, using a calculator we would view the decimal answer 2.6. In 1791, although computations were carried out by hand and division problems reported in the long division format, from this juncture on we will use the modern decimal reporting. Our reporting of the history will remain true to the historical record except that we will use decimal reporting to facilitate today's readers' understanding of the computations involved. In today's mathematics the answer to a division problem is called a quotient, just like the answer to an addition problem is a sum, the answer to a subtraction problem is a difference, and the answer to a multiplication problem is a product.

The name **rule of three** comes from the formula for computing the state quota. To make the computation, you need three quantities: House size, the state's population, and the national population. The populations are provided by the census. We now test the House and Senate bills (Table 1.9). The House bill produced a House size of 112. The results of multiplying 112 by each state's proportion are displayed in the Hquota column. The quota rule violation for Virginia is clear: Virginia's quota is 19.5314, yet the House bill gives Virginia 21 seats. In testing the Senate bill, one multiplies 105 by each state's proportion. The results (Squota column) appear favorable since there are no quota rule violations. However, there is an annoying feature. The rounding of the decimal quota numbers is consistent with apportionments made by the Senate bill except Virginia compared to Delaware or Vermont. Virginia is the only state with a decimal part under 0.5 whose apportionment is rounded up from the viewpoint of the quota. Delaware's apportionment is rounded down from the viewpoint of the quota although Delaware's decimal part is greater than 0.5; similarly for Vermont. From the viewpoint of the quotas, the Senate bill appears biased in favor of the largest state, Virginia, over the smallest state, Delaware.

Table 1.9. Quota Rule analysis of the House and Senate bills using the Fisher Ames apportionment census data.

State	Population	Hseats	Hquota	Sseats	Squota
VT	85532	2	2.6494	2	2.4838
NH	141780	4	4.3917	4	4.1172
MA	478785	15	14.8306	14	13.9036
RI	68446	2	2.1201	2	1.9876
CT	239561	7	7.4205	7	6.9567
NY	331584	11	10.2709	10	9.6290
NJ	179555	5	5.5618	5	5.2142
PA	432866	14	13.4082	13	12.5702
DE	55539	1	1.7203	1	1.6128
MD	278514	9	8.6271	8	8.0879
VA	630546	21	19.5314	19	18.3107
KY	68704	2	2.1281	2	1.9951
NC	353518	11	10.9504	10	10.2660
SC	200000	6	6.1951	6	5.8079
GA	70842	2	2.1944	2	2.0572
	3615772	112	112	105	105

Using the decimal approach to computation, the algorithm used to construct the House and Senate bills is called the **Jefferson Basic Divisor Method** and has three steps.

Step 1.   Decide the constituency, d.
Step 2.   Calculate each state's **quotient:** q = (state population)/d.
Step 3.   A state's apportionment is q rounded down.

Step 3 for a general basic divisor method reads: round the quotient decimal to obtain a state's apportionment. The use of Jefferson as a descriptive adjective for a basic divisor method specifies the decimal rounding mechanism that all quotient decimals are to be rounded down. However, one must keep in mind the constitutional minimum requirement that each state must be awarded at least one seat. The history of congressional apportionment supplies five different methods for rounding the quotient decimal in step 3.

The two anomalies exposed in the House and Senate bills by the quota rule preview the flaws in the Jefferson basic divisor method: the algorithm can lead to quota rule violations and can display biased favoritism. The Jefferson rounding method, when it displays bias, always displays the bias in favor of a larger state over a smaller state.

Constituency

Constituency (also known as the ratio or divisor) here means the number of people per congressman. Initially, this was the crucial question that inaugurated the apportionment process: how many people should a congressman represent? The predominant answers varied from 30000 to 40000 in increments of 1000. Then the issue became refined: 30000 (House bill) or 33000 (Senate bill).

The constituency issue became intermeshed with the House size issue since the House size is inversely related to the constituency—the larger the constituency, the smaller the House size. A constituency of 30000 led to a House with 112 members; 33000, 105 members. Several argued that 105 was too small. Ironically, the point that the current make-up of the House carried a constituency of nearly 53000 basically went unheeded. Further, Messrs. John Vining (DE), Benjamin Bourne (RI), and Elias Boudinot (NJ) spoke in support of a ratio of 34000 because it produced a House with 100 members.[51] Nice sounding and well-rounded numbers always seem to have an attraction.

Figure 1.4.   Fisher Ames (MA).

Fisher Ames (Figure 1.4[52]) gave a brilliant analysis of the House bill using constituency as a key to his argument. The House bill used the ratio of 30000. Mr. Ames noted that, for example, under the House bill, New Jersey would have a state

---

[51] Annals of Congress, House of Representatives, 2nd Congress, 1st Session: 188, 200, 203.
[52] Public Domain, https://commons.wikimedia.org/w/index.php?curid=20302265.

constituency of 35911: (NJ population)/(5 members) = 35911. This situation can be improved by rounding New Jersey's quotient up and awarding the state six seats, resulting in a state constituency of 29559. Obviously 29559 is closer to the initial ideal of 30000 than is 35911.[53]

This proposal uses some out-of-the-box thinking because, rather than simply dropping the quotient's decimal fraction, it chooses to round the quotient up if some criterion of fairness is met. Mr. Ames's proposal would have increased the apportionment for NH, MA, CT, VT, NJ, NC, and DE. The resulting adjustment would have increased the House size to 119. But the proposal ignited a controversy in another direction.

Mr. Ames's adjustment yielded a state constituency under 30000 for seven states. Was this constitutional? What about the Constitutional constraint that "The Number of Representatives shall not exceed one for every thirty Thousand, ..." Mr. Ames argued vigorously that the 30000 constraint applies only to the national population; it does not apply to each individual state. Since the House bill is based on a divisor of 30000, then round the quotient according to which option (round up or round down) yields a state constituency closest to the chosen ideal. Since a constituency of 30000 for each state cannot be achieved, then do the best you can.

Southerners became defensive. James Madison spoke against Mr. Ames's argument:[54]

> ... the idea of fractions was not then contended for, but has since become the very essence of the Opposition; and we are called on to violate the Constitution by adopting a measure that will give Representatives for those separate and distinct fractions in the respective States; and afterwards are told it is not to the fractional numbers in the States that they refer, but to the aggregate of the fractions in the United States.

Following Mr. Madison, Elias Boudinot (NJ) spoke in support of Mr. Ames that the 30000 constitutional constraint was meant to apply to the country as a whole and not to the individual states. Although Congress debated this interpretation, it did not resolve the specific issue.

Supporters of both the House bill and the Senate bill defended their stand with an appeal to fairness. Each had their own unique blend of fewest fractions and unrepresented people, equity of power, quota rule, and constituency considerations. In response to the claim by William Findley (PA) that a larger House would bring more wisdom, Abraham Clark (NJ) asked if this would not also bring more folly.[55] Applications of the Jelly Bean Rule were inventive, even ingenious, and sometimes entertaining.

---

[53] Ibid: 260.
[54] Annals of Congress, House of Representatives, 2nd Congress, 1st Session: 265.
[55] Ibid: 185.

Section 1.3: Resolution

Section 1.3.1   The Congressional Bill

Since Congress was deadlocked on apportionment using the basic Jefferson divisor method, Congress was open to an alternative. The gridlock led Congress to think in terms of establishing the House size first. To determine a maximum House size, h, they divided the U.S. population by 30000 yielding 120.53. So, by constitutional guidelines, the maximum House size is 120. Congress then applied the quota rule to $h = 120$ (Table 1.10).

Today, this quota rule method is known as **Hamilton's Method**. Table 1.10 presents an analysis of the Hamilton method to the 1790 census using the Balinski and Young population data set. The $h = 120$ column is blank since the first step in the process is to determine h. The Quota column then shows each state's fair share of seats in a House with 120 members. The Lower Q column is the lower quota, the smallest fair share of seats for each state. The sum of the Lower Q column is 111; hence, 9 more seats need to be distributed

Table 1.10. The apportionment bill passed by Congress.

State		Population	$h = 120$	Quota	Lower Q	Appt
CT	5	236841		7.86	7	8
DE	1	55540		1.84	1	2
GA	3	70835		2.35	2	2
KY		68705		2.28	2	2
MD	6	278514		9.24	9	9
MA	8	475327		15.77	15	16
NH	3	141822		4.71	4	5
NJ	4	179570		5.96	5	6
NY	6	331589		11.00	11	11
NC	5	353523		11.73	11	12
PA	8	432879		14.37	14	14
RI	1	68446		2.27	2	2
SC	5	206236		6.84	6	7
VT	2	85533		2.84	2	3
VA	10	630560		20.93	20	21
US	67	3615920		120	111	120

to reach the House size of 120. Hamilton's method specifically refers to a quota method where the remaining seats needed to achieve the House size are given in order to the states having the largest quota decimal fractions. Hence, the quota decimal fractions act as a priority list for the distribution of those seats. Since New Jersey has the largest quota decimal fraction, its quota is rounded up. This continues through to New Hampshire which has the ninth largest quota decimal fraction. There are pleasing results of this process. There are no quota violations. And, by a coincidence of these numbers, ordinary rounding produces the final result—in fact, all states awarded the upper quota have a quota decimal fraction greater than .7 while all states awarded the lower quota have a quota decimal fraction less than .4.

This became the first congressional apportionment bill; however, it was a close call. The Senate vote was 14-13.[56] The House receded from disagreeing with the Senate by a vote of 31-

---

[56] Annals of Congress, Senate, 2nd Congress, 1st Session: 105.

29.[57] Vice-President Adams signed the bill as presiding officer of the Senate. Then, on 26 March 1792, the bill was delivered to the Committee on Enrolled Bills to be laid before President Washington for his approval.[58]

Section 1.3.2   President Washington's Veto

After 10 days, the maximum time allowed by the Constitution, Washington vetoed the bill (Figure 1.5).[59] The veto is significant for three reasons:

- it was the first presidential veto in U. S. history;
- it was the only veto of Washington's first term as President;
- Washington vetoed the bill because of his interpretation of the Constitution.

United States [Philadelphia] April 5, 1792.

Gentlemen of the House of Representatives

I have maturely considered the Act passed by the two Houses, intitled, "An Act for an apportionment of Representatives among the several States according to the first enumeration," and I return it to your House, wherein it originated, with the following objections.

First—The Constitution has prescribed that representatives shall be apportioned among the several States according to their respective numbers: and there is no one proportion or divisor which, applied to the respective numbers of the States will yield the number and allotment of representatives proposed by the Bill.

Second—The Constitution has also provided that the number of Representatives shall not exceed one for every thirty thousand; which restriction is, by the context, and by fair and obvious construction, to be applied to the separate and respective numbers of the States: and the bill has allotted to eight of the States, more than one for thirty thousand.

George Washington

Figure 1.5. President Washington's veto letter.

Washington's second item in his veto letter is the more noteworthy. Ironically, the Constitution makes no provision for resolving disputes of interpretation. During the debates in Congress members would argue from their viewpoint of the Constitution. This veto established precedent that the President can veto using his interpretation of the Constitution. The issue at point is the 30000 constraint: does the constraint apply just to the national population, as Hamilton contended, or must it apply to each state as well, as Jefferson contended? Usually, Hamilton and Jefferson were at odds with each other. And, usually, Washington sided with Hamilton. This time, Washington sided with Jefferson.

After Congress sent the apportionment bill to President Washington for his approval, Washington called for written opinions about the constitutionality of the bill from his cabinet: Secretary of State Thomas Jefferson, Secretary of the Treasury Alexander Hamilton, Secretary

---

[57] Annals of Congress, House of Representatives, 2nd Congress, 1st Session: 482-3.
[58] Senate Journal, 2nd Congress, 1st Session, March 26, 1792: 416.
[59] http://en.wikipedia.org/wiki/Apportionment_Act

of War Henry Knox, and Attorney General John Randolph. Knox usually followed Hamilton and Randolph usually followed Jefferson. Although all four responded by letter to Washington, only Hamilton and Jefferson presented an analysis of the bill. The apportionment bill did not stipulate the method used—it merely stated that 120 seats were to be distributed as given in Table 1.10. Hamilton's letter explained the method in terms of the quota rule; hence, today's literature refers to the method as **Hamilton's Method**. Further, Jefferson explained the alternative basic divisor method in which the decimal fractions are dropped; hence, today's literature refers to this method as **Jefferson's Method**.

Jefferson's report to Washington[60] contains several manifestations of the Jelly Bean Effect. Jefferson noted that the quota decimal for eight states (Table 1.11) were rounded up (VT, NH, MA, CT, NJ, DE, NC, SC) and seven were rounded down (RI, NY, PA, MD, VA, KY, GA)—this is unfair because different states are treated differently. Also, he made the wrong placement for Virginia! Jefferson also asserts that the Constitution stipulates that apportionment must be accomplished using a single divisor. He claimed that for the states whose quota was rounded up the common divisor is 27770; but, for the states rounded down, the common divisor is 30026. The claims are correct placing Virginia correctly. But, Jefferson says, using two divisors is

Table 1.11. A spreadsheet showing congressional apportionment bill using Jefferson's census data.

State	Population	Quota 120	Lower Q	Seats
VT	85532	2.82	2	3
NH	141823	4.68	4	5
MA	475327	15.69	15	16
RI	68444	2.26	2	2
CT	235941	7.79	7	8
NY	352915	11.65	11	11
NJ	179556	5.93	5	6
PA	432880	14.29	14	14
DE	55538	1.83	1	2
MD	278513	9.19	9	9
VA	630558	20.81	20	21
KY	68705	2.27	2	2
NC	353521	11.67	11	12
SC	206236	6.81	6	7
GA	70843	2.34	2	2
US	3636332	120	111	120

unfair. The problem is that Jefferson is not clearly distinguishing between quota and divisor methods. The decimal fractions do not represent the same thing for the two methods. Jefferson did not like the idea that some numbers should be rounded up and others down. He thought it only fair that all numbers be treated the same; i.e., they all must be rounded down.

Debates in Congress also featured the opinion that the 30000 constraint had to be applied to each state. Accordingly, any apportionment giving Delaware two votes would be vetoed from this point of view. Perhaps it is surprising that advocates of the bill did not resolve this issue since it was mentioned several times in congressional debates. One could have applied

---

[60] "Opinion on Apportionment Bill, 4 April 1792," Founders Online, National Archives (http://founders.archives.gov/documents/Jefferson/01-23-02-0324, ver. 2014-05-09). Source: *The Papers of Thomas Jefferson*, vol. 23, *1 January–31 May 1792*, ed. Charles T. Cullen. Princeton: Princeton University Press, 1990, pp. 370–377. Accessed from http://founders.archives.gov/documents/Jefferson/01-23-02-0324

the Hamilton quota method to a House size that would have satisfied Washington's second objection. A quick spreadsheet analysis shows that the largest such House size is $h = 101$.

There is another nuance about this bill. Hamilton's letter to George Washington contains the following analysis.[61]

> The President desires an opinion, whether the Act intitled "An Act for an apportionment of Representatives among the several states according to the first enumeration" be constitutional, or not. It is inferred from the provisions of the Act—That the following process has been pursued.
>
> I The aggregate numbers of the United States are divided by 30000, which gives the total number of representatives, or 120.
>
> II This number is apportionned among the several states by the following rule— As the *aggregate* numbers of the *United States* are to the *total number* of representatives found as above, so are the *particular numbers of each state* to the number of representatives of such state. But
>
> III As this second process leaves a residue of Eight out of the 120 members unapportioned, these are distributed among those states which upon that second process have the largest fractions or remainders.

Step I states that the House size is set to 120. Step II indicates that then one calculates the quota for each state based on the House size of 120. Step II also implies that each state is initially apportioned its lower quota. But Step III states that this process leaves a residue of eight out of 120 members unapportioned. Table 1.10 shows nine members unapportioned. Was this just a misprint, or what happened?

"Sometimes the wrong train will get you to the right station" is a charming redemptive line in the movie *The Lunchbox*.[62] Hamilton's Step III is an example of this line. Apply a basic divisor method with divisor 30000. Rounding all the quotients down then yields the original House bill with House size 112. Now, use this as a basis to construct a House of size 120. There are now eight members unapportioned. One can then either round the quotients in the usual way or select the eight states with the largest decimal fractions in their quotients. By either train one arrives at the station of a 120-member House given in the congressional bill under consideration.

Table 1.12 (next page) displays a spreadsheet showing the calculations needed to construct a House of size 120 using the procedures described above. The Quotient column begins by dividing each state's population by 30000. The Seats column gives the number of seats obtained by Jefferson's method of rounding each quotient down. The

---

[61] National Archives, Founders Online, The Papers of Alexander Hamilton, From Alexander Hamilton to George Washington, 4 April 1792; accessed from http://founders.archives.gov/?q=Volume%3AHamilton-01-11&s=1511311112&r=195

[62] *The Lunchbox*, Sony Classic Pictures, 2013.

Table 1.12. Spreadsheet analysis showing the various ways to construct a House with 120 members based on the 1790 census. The columns Quotient/Seats/h = 120 apply to Jefferson's basic divisor method. The columns Quota/Lower/Seats apply to Hamilton's quota method.

State	Population	Quotient	Seats	h = 120	Quota	Lower	Seats
CT	236841	7.8947	7	8	7.8599	7	8
DE	55540	1.8513	1	2	1.8432	1	2
GA	70835	2.3612	2	2	2.3508	2	2
KY	68705	2.2902	2	2	2.2801	2	2
MD	278514	9.2838	9	9	9.2429	9	9
MA	475327	15.8442	15	16	15.7745	15	16
NH	141822	4.7274	4	5	4.7066	4	5
NJ	179570	5.9857	5	6	5.9593	5	6
NY	331589	11.0530	11	11	11.0043	11	11
NC	353523	11.7841	11	12	11.7322	11	12
PA	432879	14.4293	14	14	14.3658	14	14
RI	68446	2.2815	2	2	2.2715	2	2
SC	206236	6.8745	6	7	6.8443	6	7
VT	85533	2.8511	2	3	2.8385	2	3
VA	630560	21.0187	21	21	20.9261	20	21
US	3615920		112	120		111	120

h = 120 column shows the results for a House with 120 members obtained by giving eight states an additional seat to bring the House from 112 members to 120 members. Note that each state given an additional seat has a decimal fraction above 0.5. Also, these are the eight states with the eight largest decimal fractions in their quotients. It is worthwhile to note this nuance while reading the apportionment debates. For example, in the debates based on the 1830 census, there are several references to the eight additional members of the 1790 congressional apportionment bill vetoed by President Washington.

Section 1.3.3   The Apportionment Act

After Washington's veto, Congress caved and simply passed the original Senate bill. An initial attempt in the House to override President's Washington's veto failed badly. The vote did not even receive a majority (23-33)[63], let alone the two-thirds needed to override a veto. Passage of the final bill, along with Washington's signature, only took a few days in contrast to the five months of hard work that Congress put into the vetoed bill. Perhaps they just wanted it to be over. A copy of the final apportionment bill is given in Figure 1.6.[64]

---

[63] Annals of Congress, House of Representatives, 2nd Congress, 1st Session: 541.
[64] Statutes at Large, 2nd Congress, 1st Session: 253, accessed at http://memory.loc.gov/cgi-bin/ampage?collId=llsl&fileName=001/llsl001.db&recNum=376

> CHAP. XXIII.—*An Act for apportioning Representatives among the several States, according to the first enumeration.*
>
> *Be it enacted by the Senate and House of Representatives of the United States of America in Congress assembled,* That from and after the third day of March one thousand seven hundred and ninety-three, the House of Representatives shall be composed of members elected agreeably to a ratio of one member for every thirty-three thousand persons in each state, computed according to the rule prescribed by the constitution; that is to say: Within the state of New Hampshire, four; within the state of Massachussetts, fourteen; within the state of Vermont, two; within the state of Rhode Island, two; within the state of Connecticut, seven; within the state of New York, ten; within the state of New Jersey, five; within the state of Pennsylvania, thirteen; within the state of Delaware, one; within the state of Maryland, eight; within the state of Virginia, nineteen; within the state of Kentucky, two; within the state of North Carolina, ten; within the state of South Carolina, six; and within the state of Georgia, two members.
>
> APPROVED, April 14, 1792.

Figure 1.6. The first apportionment bill passed by Congress and approved into law by President Washington.

There are some interesting facets to the final apportionment bill. The apportionments are specified. The ratio, 33000, is specified. Then there is the interesting phrase "computed according to the rule prescribed by the constitution." This can only refer to the constitutional phrase "according to their respective numbers." However, that is not a rule. The fact that the fraction component of the quotients was simply dropped is not mentioned. But, finally, apportionment based on the 1790 census was done. The hard work paid off. The basic divisor method set precedent and would be used for the next five censuses.

Section 1.4: Lessons Learned

The main lesson learned is that what at first seemed like an easy problem would be exposed for what it is: a difficult problem from both mathematical and political points of view. What the 2nd Congress discovered is amazing, especially realizing that there were no computers and spreadsheet analysis had to be done by hand. It took intelligence, perception, and hard work to create the options they considered. Even today, some 225 years later, we can only admire what these people accomplished in less than six months.

Section 1.4.1   Two Approaches

There are only two appropriate approaches to apportionment given the constitutional guideline that representatives shall be "apportioned among the several states ... according to their respective numbers." Each approach is initiated by its own specific question.

- **Constituency approach**: How many people should a congressman represent?

- **House size approach**:   How many members should the House have?

Surprisingly, these two approaches lead to different solutions. Guideless for fairness for one approach can conflict with fairness guidelines from the other. The profound differences in the two approaches can be appreciated with the realization that a divisor approach *creates* seats while a House size method *distributes* seats.

The divisor approach has two variations: a basic divisor approach and a modified divisor approach. The modified approach utilizes a hybrid combination of the two questions in that it specifies in advance how many seats to create. In practice, both approaches lead to computations that produce decimal numbers having non-zero decimal fractions that must be dealt with. Thus, an approach must also adopt a criterion for converting the decimal into a whole number. An apportionment **method** involves a combination of an approach along with a decimal management criterion. Today there are three apportionment methods: basic divisor methods, modified divisor methods, and quota methods.

The three methods, basic divisor method (BDM), modified divisor method (MDM), and quota method (QM), can all be distinguished from each other by the role played by the House size, h. In a BDM h is only the result; h never figures into the calculations and appears only as a consequence of the algorithm. In an MDM h is the goal. Although h is decided first, h is then set aside as one applies a divisor method that yields h as the result. In a QM h is the resource. The designated number of House seats is proportionately distributed among the states. The House size acts not only as the goal, but directly figures into the apportionment calculations.

Section 1.4.2　　　A Mathematical Description

Let $\mathcal{U} = \{S_1, S_2, \dots, S_s\}$ be a federation of s states where $s \in \mathbb{N}_2$ ($\mathbb{N}_k = \{n \in \mathbb{N} \mid n \geq k\}$).

Let p_i be the population of state S_i; i.e., $p_i = \text{pop}(S_i)$.

The **census** is the population vector $\vec{p} = <p_1, p_2, \dots, p_s>$.

The national population, p, is the sum of the components of the census: $p = \sum_1^s p_i$.

Congressional apportionment is the process of constructing an apportionment vector, $\vec{a} = <a_1, a_2, \cdots, a_s>$, where a_i is the number of House seats awarded to state S_i. Then $h = \sum_1^s a_i$ is the House size. The vector $\vec{a}$ is subject to two constitutional constraints. The first constraint concerns the minimum House size: $a_i \geq 1$ for each i. The second constraint concerns the maximum House size and states that the number of representatives shall not exceed one per 30000 people. There are two interpretations of the maximum constraint, Washington and Hamilton.

- Washington:　$p_i/a_i \geq 30000$ for each i.
- Hamilton:　　$p/h \geq 30000$.

The Washington interpretation always satisfies the Hamilton interpretation, but not conversely. The Hamilton interpretation can be satisfied while the Washington interpretation is violated, as demonstrated by the bill that Washington vetoed.

Basic Divisor Methods

A BDM applies a 3-step algorithm:

- Step 1.　Select $d \in \mathbb{N}_{30000}$; i.e., select the divisor.
- Step 2.　Compute $q_i = p_i/d$; i.e., compute the **quotient** q_i for each state.
- Step 3.　Compute $a_i = \max(1, \text{round}(q_i))$; i.e., round q_i by some criterion.

Note that h never plays a role in the process—h is only the result. The apportionment debates based on the 1790 census presented three variations for rounding a decimal number applicable in Step 3. The Jefferson method is simply to drop the decimal fraction; i.e., $a_i = \max(1, \text{int}(q_i))$, the integer part of q_i. The usual variation is to round the decimal in the usual fashion of arithmetic; i.e., round q_i up if and only if the decimal fraction of q_i inclusively exceeds 0.5; otherwise, round down. In addition, Fisher Ames proposed rounding by closest constituency.

Jefferson's method is a BDM that uses Jefferson's variation for rounding. Since Jefferson's method was the method used for the final apportionment bill passed by Congress and signed into law by President Washington, we detail the method.

- Step 1.　Select $d \in \mathbb{N}_{30000}$.
- Step 2.　Compute $q_i = p_i/d$ for each state.
- Step 3.　Let $a_i = \max(1, \text{int}(q_i))$. The constitutional minimum must be satisfied.

Result: $\vec{a} = <a_1, a_2, \cdots, a_s>$ and $h = \sum_1^s a_i$.

Jefferson's method was used to produce the original House bill (d = 30000) and Senate bill (d = 33000). Since the final apportionment bill was based on Jefferson's method, it served as precedent and was used for the next four censuses.

Modified Divisor Methods

An MDM applies a 5-step algorithm:

- Step 1. Select $h \in \mathbb{N}_s$.
- Step 2. Select $d \in \mathbb{N}_{30000}$.
- Step 3. Compute $q_i = p_i/d$ for each state.
- Step 4. Compute $a_i = \max(1, \text{round}(q_i))$.
- Step 5. IF $\sum_1^s a_i = h$, then DONE;
  ELSE, modify d and GOTO Step 3.

In an MDM h is only the goal of a divisor process; h does not figure into the calculation of a_i. An MDM was suggested during the House debates by congressmen attracted to h = 100 and therefore supported d = 34000. An MDM should be easily recognized by any mathematics student who solved a word problem by first consulting the answer in the back of the book and then embarked on searching for a method to produce that answer. Note that an MDM is simply a BDM with a predesignated answer.

Quota Methods

A QM applies a 3-step algorithm:

- Step 1. Select $h \in \mathbb{N}_s$.
- Step 2. Calculate $Q_i = h(p_i/p)$ for each state.
- Step 3. Let $a_i = \max(1, \text{round}(Q_i))$ so that $\sum_1^s a_i = h$.

Note that h is not only initially set as the goal for the process, but also figures into the calculation of each state's quota, Q_i. In a QM, Step 3 is more involved than in a DM. One first assigns $a_i = \text{int}(Q_i)$. However, the sum of the integer parts of the quotas is smaller than the pre-set h; hence, some, but not all, quotas need to be rounded upwards. Alexander Hamilton's explanation was to award the extra seats to those states with the largest fractions in their quotas. Accordingly, in Step 3, the rounding rule is determined by the priority of largest fractions. This method of applying the Quota Rule is called **Hamilton's Method**.

Section 1.4.3   Jelly Bean Effects

A key item to notice is the pivotal number calculated by the two approaches. A divisor method computes a *quotient* for each state; a quota method computes a *quota* for each state. Although both are decimals, they are fundamentally different quantities. Intuitive rules of fairness for a quotient are different from such rules for a quota.

Recent mathematical research has proven that any divisor method can violate the quota rule regardless of what criterion is used for rounding the quotient.[65] A quota method can never violate the quota rule because it is designed using each state's quota. However, later lessons in U. S. history have shown that Hamilton's method is subject to its own violations of intuitive rules of fairness. This is summarized in the noted 1982 theorem of Balinski and Young.

> **Balinski and Young's Impossibility Theorem**: There are no perfect apportionment methods. Any divisor approach is subject to quota rule violations. Any quota rule method is subject to counter-intuitive paradoxes.[66] [67]

One Jelly Bean Effect that Congress wrestled with was least fractions and unrepresented people. Another was the simple result that a state's constituency could never exactly equal the pre-set divisor. This caused average constituency to differ from state to state. The problem could not be resolved, only dealt with. Another key lesson portrayed in the apportionment debates is that politics is always influenced by two concurrent forces: fairness and power. Further, these are not separate and distinct forces, but complementary.

For the reader comfortable with mathematical analysis, the seminal work of Balinski and Young is essential. The work also includes mathematical notions and measurements for various ideas of fairness.

Any study of apportionment, whether a detailed account of the history or an in-depth study through a mathematical lens[68] using modern day tools such as spreadsheets, can only enhance one's appreciation for the magnificent work done by those involved in the 1790 census and the subsequent work to obtain the first apportionment bill. We owe them much.

---

[65] Michael Balinski and H. Peyton Young, *Fair Representation*, Second Edition, Brookings Institution Press, 2001.
[66] http://www.cut-the-knot.org/ctk/Democracy.shtml
[67] Michael Balinski and H. Peyton Young, *The Quotient Method of Apportionment*, The American Mathematical Monthly, 82(7) 1975: 701-30.
[68] Shannon Guerrero and Charles Biles, *The History of the Congressional Apportionment Problem through a Mathematical Lens*, 2014; obtainable from http://www.nia977.wix.com/drbcap or
https://digitalcommons.humboldt.edu/cgi/viewcontent.cgi?article=1006&context=apportionment

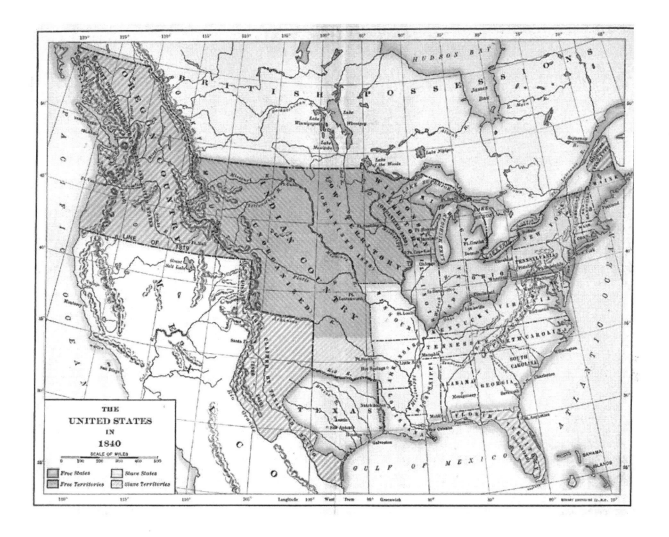

Chapter 2

Congressional Apportionment

Based on the Census

1800 – 1840

The Basic Divisor Era

Chapter 2

Table of Contents

Introduction

This chapter is devoted to the history of apportionment to the national House of Representatives based on the census years 1800 - 1840. The Constitution directs that representation in the House shall be based on an enumeration of the people as determined by a decennial census. The census years 1790 - 1840 are the basic divisor method years. The apportionment act based on the first census begun in 1790 set precedent.

A **Basic Divisor Method** is a census-based apportionment method that follows a three-step algorithm initiated by the constituency question: how many people should a congressperson represent? The answer is called the ratio, divisor, or constituency. Since the number is computationally used as a divisor, it will be denoted by d. The constitutional constraint on d is that it must be at least 30000; further, each state receives at least one representative.

The divisor is used to obtain a **quotient** for each state obtained by dividing the state's apportionment population by d. The quotient represents how many representatives a state merits based on its population and the given divisor. The quotient, for most practical purposes, is a positive non-integer decimal number. Since representatives only come as whole people, the decimal needs to be rounded to a whole number.

The simplest rounding procedure is simply to drop the decimal fraction, referred to in congressional debates simply as the **fraction**. This procedure is called Jefferson's method in today's literature. Accordingly, **Jefferson's Method** is a basic divisor method in which all quotients are rounded down. Formally, Jefferson's method is an application of the following three-step algorithm.

Step 1. How many people should a congressperson represent? Answer: d.
Step 2. Calculate each state's quotient by dividing d into each state's apportionment population.
Step 3. A state's apportionment is the quotient rounded down. However, each state must be awarded at least one seat.

Note that the House size is the sum of all the state apportionments. The House size is only a result of the method and never figures into the apportionment calculations.

Reference: The map on the Chapter 2 cover page is courtesy of the Florida Center for Instruction Technology, http://etc.usf.edu/maps.

Section 2.1: Reapportionment Based on the 1800 Census

Section 2.1.1   The 1800 Census

The 6th Congress, 1st Session, House of Representatives, met in Philadelphia, 2 December 1799 through 14 May 1800.[1] John Adams was President. During Washington's last year as President, Tennessee was admitted as the 16th state to the Union on 1 June 1796 and allocated one representative.[2] This brought the size of the House to 106 members. This Congress authorized the 1800 census with *An act providing for the second Census or Enumeration of the Inhabitants of the United States*, approved 28 February 1800.[3]

The census began on 4 August 1800. While the census was in progress, Adams lost his bid for a second term to Thomas Jefferson in one of the most contentious, bitter, and partisan elections in U.S. history.[4] President Jefferson was inaugurated on 4 March 1801. As in the 1790 census, field work was conducted by U.S. marshals, who transmitted their results to the President, who passed them to his Secretary of State, James Madison, who compiled the results as they came in. President Jefferson transmitted by letter the final results of the census in his First Annual Message to Congress (7th Congress, 1st Session, which met from 17 November 1800 through 3 March 1801) on 8 December 1801.[5] The message contained the following paragraph.

> I lay before you the result of the census lately taken of our inhabitants, to a conformity with which we are to reduce the ensuing rates of representation and taxation. You will perceive that the increase of numbers, during the last ten years, proceeding in geometrical ratio, promises a duplication in little more than twenty-two years. We contemplate this rapid growth, and the prospect it holds up to us, not with a view to the injuries it may enable us to do to others in some future day, but to the settlement of the extensive country still remaining vacant within our limits, to the multiplication of men, susceptible of happiness, educated in the love of order, habituated to self-government, and valuing its blessings above all price.[6]

A copy of the census report compiled by Madison and transmitted to Congress is displayed in Table 2.1 (next page). This report was incomplete for Tennessee and contained errors for Maryland that were later corrected. The final 1800 census figures, compiled by James Madison and transmitted to Congress by President Jefferson on 8 December 1801, showed a U. S. resident population of 5308483, including the new District of Columbia, with slaves accounting for 893602.

---

[1] Annals of Congress, House of Representatives, 6th Congress, 1st Session, accessed at http://memory.loc.gov/cgi-bin/ampage?collId=llac&fileName=010/llac010.db&recNum=90.

[2] Statutes at Large, 4th Congress, 1st Session: 491-2.

[3] Statutes at Large, 6th Congress, 1st Session: 11-14.

[4] Edward Larson, *A Magnificent Catastrophe*, Free Press, New York, 2007.

[5] Annals of Congress, 7th Congress, 1st Session: 11-16.

[6] House Journal, December 8, 1801: 9. Accessed from http://memory.loc.gov/cgi-bin/query/r?ammem/hlaw:@field%28DOCID+@lit%28hj0044%29%29

Table 2.1. The 1800 census.

ENUMERATION of Persons in the several Districts of the UNITED STATES.

Names of Districts.	FREE WHITE MALES.					FREE WHITE FEMALES.					All other free persons, except Indians not taxed.	SLAVES.	TOTAL.
	Under 10 years of age.	Of 10 and under 16.	Of 16 and under 26, including heads of families.	Of 26 and under 45, including heads of families.	Of 45 and upwards, including heads of families.	Under 10 years of age.	Of 10 and under 16.	Of 16 and under 26, including heads of families.	Of 26 and under 45, including heads of families.	Of 45 and upwards, including heads of families.			
New-Hampshire	30,694	14,581	16,379	17,569	11,715	29,871	14,193	17,153	18,361	12,147	852	8	183,858
Massachusetts	63,646	32,507	37,905	39,729	31,348	60,920	30,674	40,491	45,832	35,540	6,452	—	422,845
Maine	27,970	12,305	12,900	15,318	8,339	26,889	11,338	13,285	14,496	8,041	818	—	151,719
Connecticut	37,946	19,408	21,685	25,180	18,976	35,736	18,218	23,361	25,186	20,827	5,330	951	251,002
Vermont	29,420	12,066	13,342	16,544	8,078	28,272	11,366	12,606	15,287	7,049	557	—	134,465
Rhode-Island	9,945	5,352	5,889	5,785	4,887	9,524	5,026	6,463	6,919	5,648	3,304	380	69,122
New-York	63,161	36,953	40,045	52,454	25,497	79,154	32,822	39,086	47,710	23,161	8,575	15,602	494,065
Supplemental return for New-York state	16,936	7,320	9,230	9,149	6,358	16,319	6,649	9,050	8,761	5,460	1,801	5,011	101,985
New-Jersey	53,900	15,858	16,301	19,956	12,629	32,522	14,827	17,018	19,553	11,600	4,402	12,622	211,149
Eastern district of Pennsylvania	52,767	24,438	29,393	33,864	20,824	51,170	23,437	29,879	30,892	18,328	11,263	557	327,979
Western district of Pennsylvania	50,459	21,623	24,369	25,469	17,761	48,448	20,362	24,095	22,954	14,066	3,311	1,149	274,566
Delaware	8,250	4,437	5,121	5,012	2,813	7,628	4,277	5,563	4,981	2,390	8,268	6,153	64,273
Maryland, inclusive of Washington county, in Columbia	33,520	16,581	20,560	22,160	12,617	22,463	15,718	21,506	20,363	11,240	18,646	102,465	317,348
Additional return for Baltimore county	567	226	318	343	249	571	222	375	318	199	41	847	4,276
Eastern district of Virginia	57,837	25,998	32,444	54,584	19,087	54,597	25,469	34,307	52,641	18,823	19,194	322,199	676,682
District of Columbia, in Virginia	889	326	485	557	221	670	313	479	473	189	383	1,172	8,949
Western District of Virginia	34,601	14,502	16,284	15,674	11,134	32,726	13,366	15,923	8,632	15,169	1,930	23,597	203,518
North-Carolina	63,118	27,073	31,360	31,209	18,688	59,074	25,876	32,989	30,665	17,514	7,043	133,296	478,103
South-Carolina	37,411	16,156	17,761	19,544	10,344	34,664	15,857	18,145	17,236	9,637	3,185	146,151	345,591
Georgia	19,841	8,469	9,787	10,914	4,957	18,407	7,914	9,343	8,835	3,894	1,919	59,699	162,686
Kentucky	37,274	14,045	15,705	17,699	9,258	34,949	13,433	15,524	14,934	7,073	741	40,343	220,959
Territory N. W. river Ohio	9,562	3,647	4,356	4,832	1,955	8,644	3,553	3,861	3,542	1,395	337	—	45,365
Indiana territory	854	347	486	645	202	791	280	424	393	115	165	135	*5,641
Mississippi territory	999	356	432	780	290	955	576	352	426	165	182	3,489	8,850
												875,626	5,172,312
†Tennessee	19,227	7,194	8,282	8,332	4,125	18,450	7,042	8,554	6,995	3,491	309	13,584	105,602
‡Maryland, corrected	36,751	17,743	21,929	25,559	13,712	34,705	16,787	22,915	21,725	12,180	19,987	107,707	349,692

* Persons 766 added to the particular items of this return.
† This return has been received since the communication of the above Aggregate to Congress.
‡ This return has also been since received, and is stated by the Marshal to be a more correct return than the first, (above.)

These results must be processed into apportionment populations before legislation can be enacted. In particular, one must determine the total resident population for each state and then subtract 40% of the slave population; i.e., apply the constitutional three-fifths rule.

Section 2.1.2   The House Bill

After receiving President Jefferson's message to Congress on 8 December 1801, the House began consideration of apportionment on Monday, 14 December. William Giles (VA) moved the ratio 33000,[7] the same divisor used in the apportionment act based on the 1790 census.

On Wednesday, 16 December, discussion on the divisor included 30000, 31000, 33000, and 40000. The issue of fewest fractions was expressed as a concern. Concerns were also voiced that a ratio of 33000 would result in an increase in the House size, yielding more expenses and a more unwieldy House. Roger Griswold (CT) moved to strike "thirty-three" and substitute with a larger number. The Annals record that "On this motion a desultory debate ensued, ..."[8] Those in favor of a larger ratio argued that "a body of more than one hundred, even though it be composed of philosophers, was a mob."[9] It seems like the nastiness of the presidential election was carried over into legislative bickering.

Debate eventually settled on which divisor to use: 30000 or 33000. Most opinions were based on a Jelly Bean Rule. Some appealed to fractions in which Delaware, population 63812, was spotlighted. A ratio of 33000 would give Delaware only one seat but a ratio of 30000 would give 2 seats. Comparisons were made about which states would be adversely affected with each of the divisors.

A motion to replace 33000 by 30000 failed, 43-46.[10] Finally, a vote was taken on Mr. Giles original motion for a ratio of 33000. It passed and a committee consisting of Messrs. Van Ness (NY), Cutler (MA), and Stanton (RI), was appointed to write a bill.[11] The next day, Mr. Van Ness, on behalf of the committee, reported an apportionment bill (Table 2.2). The State column lists each state with its current number of seats. Given the 1800 census data at the moment, the House size would increase from 106 to 140. And, by now the figures for Tennessee were reported.

Friday renewed debate over 30000 vs. 33000, fairness rules, philosophies of government, and concerns for Delaware. On Monday, 4 January 1802, there was an impassioned debate over the competing divisors of 30000 vs. 33000 about the fairness issue of fractions and unrepresented populations. The exchange between Mr. Bayard (DE) and Mr. Randolph (VA) over the question of who does a congressman represent, the people of the nation as a whole or the people of his state as a sovereign entity, still occurs today with serious implications.

Table 2.2. House bill.

State	Seats
NH 4	5
MA 14	17
VT 2	4
RI 2	2
CT 7	7
NY 10	17
NJ 5	6
PA 13	18
DE 1	1
MD 8	8
VA 19	22
NC 10	12
GA 2	4
KY 2	6
TN 1	3
SC 6	8
US 106	140

---

[7] Annals of Congress, House of Representatives, 7th Congress, 1st Session: 325.
[8] Ibid, 333.
[9] Ibid, 334.
[10] Ibid, 333-5.
[11] House Journal, December 16, 1801: 19.

On Tuesday a new motion to replace 33000 by 30000 failed, 42-48.[12] Finally, on Wednesday, 6 January, after more extensive debate, the main bill passed 85-4.[13] The bill was officially named *An act for the apportionment of Representatives among the several States, according to the second enumeration* and sent to the Senate for its concurrence.[14]

Section 2.1.3   The Senate

Thursday, 7 January 1802, the Senate received the apportionment bill from the House, read it twice, and sent it to committee: George Logan (PA), Wilson Nichols (VA), Christopher Ellery (RI), James Jackson (GA), and David Stone (NC). The next day the committee reported the bill back to the Senate without amendment.[15]

Monday started with a short debate over old issues. A motion by William Wells (DE) to replace the ratio of 33000 by 30000 failed 11-15. A motion was made by Gouverneur Morris (Figure 2.1) (NY) to retain the ratio of 33000 but round the resulting quotient up if the unrepresented fraction was greater than or equal to 27000 people. The purpose of the 27000 figure was to ensure that a given state's congressional delegation did not exceed 30000 per congressman in keeping with Washington's interpretation of the 30000 constitutional constraint. This motion failed 10-15. The main motion then passed 23-5. An order was given to notify the House of the Senate's concurrence to the House apportionment bill.[16]

Figure 2.1. *Gouverneur Morris[17] (1752 - 1816) served as a U. S. senator from New York from 3 April 1800 to 3 March 1803. Mr. Morris is known as a framer and a founding father. He was a signatory to the Articles of Confederation and a delegate representing Pennsylvania to the Constitutional Convention. In this regard he is known as the "pen of the Constitution."[18] To understand the key role played by Mr. Morris in the Constitution, we recommend Ray Raphael's Constitutional Myths.[19]*

Gouverneur Morris's idea is more meritorious than the attention it received. First, only two states would be affected. Delaware and North Carolina would each get an additional representative and Washington's interpretation of the 30000 constitutional constraint would not be violated. Mr. Morris's contribution in the evolution of apportionment methodology is that perhaps a rounding criterion will help to ameliorate recognized problems, such as "fractions and unrepresented populations."

---

[12] Annals of Congress, House of Representatives, 7th Congress, 1st Session: 391.

[13] Ibid: 392-404.

[14] House Journal, Wednesday, January 6, 1802: 34.

[15] Annals of Congress, Senate, 7th Congress, 1st Session: 24-5.

[16] Ibid: 42-46.

[17] Image of Gouverneur Morris from http://commons.wikimedia.org/wiki/File:Gouverneur_Morris.jpg.

[18] http://colonialhall.com/morrisg/morrisg.php

[19] Ray Raphael, *Constitutional Myths*, The New Press, New York, 2013.

Section 2.1.4   Approval

The apportionment act approved by President Jefferson is given below in Figure 2.2.[20]

Figure 2.2. The apportionment act based on the 1800 census.

The calculations needed for the apportionment act are given in Table 2.3 (next page). The State column gives each state and the number of House members in the 7th Congress, 1st session. The Population column gives the apportionment population resulting from the final tabulations of the 1800 census. The Quotient column is computed by dividing each state's population by 33000. The Seats column is the quotient rounded down. The Fraction column is the decimal fraction part of the state quotient. The Unrepresented column is the resulting number of "unrepresented" people based on a constituency of 33000; i.e., unrepresented = (state population) – seats × 33000. The Morris column is the resulting apportionment if Gouverneur Morris's motion in the Senate were realized. The M-ratio column gives the resulting state constituency (ratio) to Mr. Morris's motion.

The reapportionment bill based on the 1800 census continued the precedent started with the 1790 census. The bill also has the distinction of being the first bill from the 7th Congress signed into law by President Jefferson (Figure 2.3, next page),[21] as he lamented in a letter to his eldest child, Martha Washington Randolph.[22] [23]

---

[20] Acts of the Seventh Congress of the United States, accessed from https://www.census.gov/history/pdf/1800_Apportionment.pdf

[21] Ibid.

[22] "From Thomas Jefferson to Martha Jefferson Randolph, 17 January 1802," Founders Online, National Archives (From Thomas Jefferson to Martha Jefferson Randolph, 17 January … (archives.gov)). Source: *The Papers of Thomas Jefferson*, vol. 36, *1 December 1801–3 March 1802*, ed. Barbara B. Oberg. Princeton: Princeton University Press, 2009, pp. 387–388.

[23] Public domain picture of Jefferson available at https://commons.wikimedia.org/wiki/File:Reproduction-of-the-1805-Rembrandt-Peale-painting-of-Thomas-Jefferson-New-York-Historical-Society_1.jpg.

Table 2.3. Spreadsheet analysis for apportionment based on the 1800 census.

State	Population	Quotient	Seats	Fraction	Unrepresented	Morris	M-Ratio
NH 4	183855	5.5714	5	0.5714	18855	5	36771
MA 14	574564	17.4110	17	0.4110	13564	17	33798
VT 2	154465	4.6808	4	0.6808	22465	4	38616
RI 2	68970	2.0900	2	0.0900	2970	2	34485
CT 7	250622	7.5946	7	0.5946	19622	7	35803
NY 10	577805	17.5092	17	0.5092	16805	17	33989
NJ 5	206181	6.2479	6	0.2479	8181	6	34364
PA 13	601863	18.2383	18	0.2383	7863	18	33437
DE 1	61812	1.8731	1	0.8731	28812	2	30906
MD 8	306610	9.2912	9	0.2912	9610	9	34068
VA 19	747362	22.6473	22	0.6473	21362	22	33971
NC 10	424785	12.8723	12	0.8723	28785	13	32676
GA 2	138807	4.2063	4	0.2063	6807	4	34702
KY 2	204822	6.2067	6	0.2067	6822	6	34137
TN 1	100169	3.0354	3	0.0354	1169	3	33390
SC 6	287131	8.7009	8	0.7009	23131	8	35891
US 106	4889823	148.1765	141	7.1765	236823	143	

Figure 2.3. Thomas Jefferson was an early key player in apportionment. Jefferson was the nation's first Secretary of State serving under President Washington. As such, as census reports came in from the field marshals and transmitted to Washington, the President passed them to Jefferson for processing. Mathematics was one of Jefferson's favorite intellectual pastimes. Of special note is the Opinion on Apportionment Bill, 4 April 1792, in which Jefferson advised President Washington to veto the first congressional apportionment bill. As a result of this Opinion, the Basic Divisor Method, in which the decimal quotients are rounded down, is now known as **Jefferson's Method**. Jefferson served as the third U.S. President (1801-1809).

Section 2.2:   Reapportionment Based on the 1810 Census

Section 2.2.1   The 1810 Census

Since the last census was taken in 1800, Ohio was recognized as a state in a law approved by President Jefferson on 19 February 1803: *An act to provide for the due execution of the laws of the United States within the state of Ohio*.[1] The topic of Ohio statehood is one of those interesting and entertaining snippets that can serve as an hors d'oeuvre for the broader topic of reapportionment based on the 1810 census.[2]

On 26 March 1810 President James Madison signed into law *An Act providing for the third census or enumeration of the inhabitants of the United States*.[3] This was by far the most extensive census authorization bill yet enacted. The act directed that the Secretary of State shall act as supervisor of the census. The census field work, as before, is to be conducted by U. S. marshals and their assistants. Results are to be reported directly to the Secretary of State. The census is to begin on the first Monday in August (6 August 1810) and end nine months later. On 13 November 1811 President Madison sent the census results to the 12th Congress, 1st session, in a report constructed under the direction of his Secretary of State, James Monroe.[4] The data reported to Congress are given in Table 2.4.[5] For convenience, the State column lists the number of representatives each state had at the start of the 12th Congress. The Apportionment column applies the three-fifths rule by subtracting 0.4 of the slave population from the resident population.

Table 2.4. The 1810 Census.

State	Resident	Slave	Apportionment
CT 7	261942	310	261818
DE 1	72674	4177	71004
GA 4	252433	105218	210346
KY 6	406511	80561	374287
MD 9	380546	111502	335946
MA 17	700745	0	700745
NH 5	214460	0	214460
NJ 6	245562	10851	241222
NY 17	959049	15017	953043
NC 12	555500	168824	487971
OH 1	230760	0	230760
PA 18	810091	795	809773
RI 2	76931	108	76888
SC 8	415115	196365	336569
TN 3	261727	44535	243913
VT 4	217895	0	217895
VA 22	974600	392516	817594
US 142	7036541	1130779	6584234

---

[1] Senate Journal, February 21, 1803.

[2] Frederick J. Blue, *The Date of Ohio Statehood*, Ohio Academy of History Newsletter, Volume XXIII, Autumn 2002; https://web.archive.org/web/20100911164131/http://www2.uakron.edu/OAH/newsletter/newsletter/Autumn2002/features.html

[3] Acts of the Eleventh Congress of the Unites States, Statute II, Chap. XVII: 564-8.

[4] http://founders.archives.gov/documents/Madison/03-04-02-0015

[5] http://www.census.gov/population/www/documentation/twps0056/twps0056.html Tables 15 through 65 in one file Excel and Excel Table A-24. See the bottom of Excel Table A-24 for GA, NC, and VA. [Unfortunately, this link from the U.S. Census Bureau is no longer available. However, the data for 1790-1820 are available at https://userpages.umbc.edu/~bouton/History407/SlaveStats.htm.]

Section 2.2.2   The House Bill

The apportionment discussion in Congress began with a new twist. Discussion began well in advance of the arrival of the census report. Just two weeks after the census bill was approved, Jonathan Fisk (NY) introduced the following resolution.

> *Resolved*, That the apportionment of Representatives amongst the several States, according to the third enumeration of the people, ought to be in the ratio of one Representative for every forty-five thousand persons in each State, and that a committee be appointed to bring in a bill accordingly.

Mr. Fisk introduced the resolution in the belief that it would be more difficult to decide on the appropriate ratio after the census is taken than before. He expressed that a divisor of 33000 would yield a House size around 218, too large for efficient conduct of the House, and "a greater number than could be accommodated within these walls."[6]

Discussion ensued around issues of power vs. fairness. Some thought that deciding the ratio now before the census data were known would prevent power struggles based on fractions and unrepresented people, a viewpoint expressed by William Burwell (VA).[7]

> Mr. BURWELL thought the present was the proper time to fix the proportion; because, after the respective numbers of each State were received, it would be in the power of the larger States to fix the ratio as they pleased, and at present none of the State jealousies could be brought into action, which would, when the returns were actually made.

Others thought that it was premature to decide on apportionment before all the facts were known; after all, how can one decide representation based on an enumeration of the people if one does not have the enumeration? Further, Congress needs to assess the fairness of the resulting apportionment, a viewpoint expressed by Josiah Quincy (MA).[8]

> The House must know the facts in order fairly to apportion representation. The apportionment ought to be made not merely in relation to the population, but to the weight of the different States in the Union—and these considerations could not have their due weight till after the relative numbers were ascertained.

Edward St. Loe Livermore (MA) noted that the issue of deciding apportionment now, before rather than after the census was reported, was a different issue than deciding what the ratio should be. He preferred that Mr. Fisk's resolution leave the ratio blank rather than specifying 45000. Accordingly, Mr. Fisk modified his motion.[9]

---

[6] Annals of Congress, House of Representatives, 11 Congress, 2nd Session: 1765.
[7] Ibid: 1766-7.
[8] Ibid.
[9] Ibid.

Nathaniel Macon (NC) made the perceptive observation that apportionment could be addressed either by fixing the House size or by fixing the ratio. Mr. Burwell also mentioned that the problem of politicizing the ratio could be solved by setting the House size instead. However, this idea was not explored, probably because congressmen were already fixed on the ratio approach. Further, it must have been difficult to focus on a single point because a jumble of issues was discussed.

- Should apportionment be decided now in advance of the census or postponed until the census report was made?
- What is the appropriate ratio (divisor)?
- What about fractions, i.e., unrepresented people?

John Smilie (PA) remarked that he was a member of Congress during the previous apportionment and he "had never seen a more difficult question."[10] Events would only reinforce this observation but resolution had to wait. The 2nd session of the House became occupied with a plethora of immediate issues: the post office, fiscal matters, commerce and foreign relations, public land issues, and reduction of the army and navy. Congress was dealing with tremors that in just over two years would erupt into the War of 1812.

The 3rd session of the 11th Congress opened on Monday, 3 December 1810. On Friday, 7 December, Mr. Fisk reintroduced his resolution but this time left the ratio as a blank line. He also stipulated that a committee be appointed to bring an apportionment bill to the House. A committee of seven was appointed.

Debate began the following Monday. Mr. Fisk, now chairman, reported that the committee did not agree on a ratio. A vote was taken on a ratio of 45000; failed, 39-56.[11] Willis Alston (NC) subsequently moved a ratio of 50000. The debate continued on Friday. Mr. Alston's motion failed, getting only 26 votes among the 95 congressmen present. After more discussion on a variety of matters, a motion to set the divisor at 40000 passed with 78 yea votes.[12]

Opponents of deciding on apportionment in advance of the census began to speak out. Timothy Pitkin (CT) expressed surprise that matters could have progressed so far in absence of the census report. He was concerned that the large divisor of 40000 will leave some states with large fractions and could even result in a loss of seats. Mr. Pitkin argued that no state should lose representatives. Josiah Quincy (MA) followed in support. He reiterated his previous argument that apportionment in advance of the census was unconstitutional because it could not be based on "respective numbers."[13] Charles Goldsborough (MD) followed in support and added that one cannot make an analysis regarding fewest fractions without the census data.[14]

---

[10] Ibid.
[11] Annals of Congress, House of Representatives, 11th Congress, 3rd Session: 397.
[12] Ibid: 401-13.
[13] Ibid: 409.
[14] Ibid: 413.

The debate continued on Monday, 17 December 1810. New issues were introduced. Jonathan Moseley (CT) introduced a Jelly Bean effect: some representatives already knew the census figures for their states.[15] After more extensive debate about fairness vs. power issues, the House decided to postpone further discussion to 11 February 1811. The forces of postponement gathered momentum as this decision passed 66-51.[16] Mr. Macon (NC) said that "When he first had a seat in this House, this was a maxim of one of the best legislators he had ever known: vote when you are in the majority, talk when you are in the minority."[17] The talk succeeded since this was the last day that the 11th Congress devoted to apportionment.

The 12th Congress opened its 1st Session on Monday, 4 November 1811. Henry Clay (KY) was elected Speaker of the House.[18] On Friday John Dawson (VA) moved that a committee be appointed to bring in an apportionment bill according to the soon expected third enumeration. The motion passed and a committee of 17 was appointed.[19]

On Wednesday, 13 November, the census report was submitted to Congress and referred to the apportionment committee. On Friday, 22 November, the House resolved itself into a Committee of the Whole to resolve the apportionment issue. Mr. Dawson, reporting on behalf of the apportionment committee, proposed a ratio of 40000. However, Mr. Dawson immediately spoke against 40000 because he felt that this ratio was too high since Rhode Island, Connecticut, and Maryland each lost a seat and Virginia lost two seats. He expressed support for 37000 because no state's delegation would decrease.[20]

Others joined the discussion which was all about the ratio. Henry Ridgely (DE) spoke in favor of 35000 because it would leave the smallest fractional numbers. Elisha Potter (RI) spoke against 40000 because it would decrease his state's delegation from 2 to 1. An apportionment bill using the ratio 35000 failed, 48-76; 40000 failed, 50-72; 38000 also failed. Finally, a bill using the ratio 37000 passed decisively, 102-18.

On Monday, 25 November, the bill was read the third time. An attempt to reconsider failed, 56-72. A vote was taken on the apportionment bill and it was approved. It was ordered that the clerk carry the bill to the Senate for concurrence.[21] Clearly, the House was on a mission! They resolved the apportionment issue in only three weeks.

Section 2.2.3   The Senate Bill

On Tuesday, 26 November 1811, the Senate received a message from the House that they had passed *An act for the apportionment of Representatives among the several States, according to*

---

[15] Ibid: 420.
[16] Ibid: 430.
[17] Ibid: 422.
[18] Annals of Congress, House of Representatives, 12th Congress, 1st Session: 329-30.
[19] Ibid: 333-4.
[20] Ibid: 363-6.
[21] House Journal, 12th Congress, 1st Session: November 25, 1811.

the third enumeration.[22] After some formal procedural moves, on Monday the Senate began debate of the apportionment bill. James Bayard (DE) moved to strike the ratio of 37000; passed, 18-16. John Taylor (SC) moved the ratio 40000; failed 13-21. Mr. Bayard moved the ratio 35000; passed, 22-12. The next day, Tuesday, 3 December, the Senate passed the main bill and sent it to the House for concurrence with amendments.[23] The House and Senate bills are displayed in Table 2.5. The House column displays the quotient using a divisor of 37000; the Senate column uses a divisor of 35000. The Seats for each is the quotient rounded down.

State	Resident	Slave	Apportionment	House	Seats	Senate	Seats
CT 7	261942	310	261818	7.0762	7	7.4805	7
DE 7	72674	4177	71004	1.9190	1	2.0287	2
GA 4	252433	105218	210346	5.6850	5	6.0099	6
KY 6	406511	80561	374287	10.1159	10	10.6939	10
MD 9	380546	111502	335946	9.0796	9	9.5985	9
MA 17	700745	0	700745	18.9391	18	20.0213	20
NH 5	214460	0	214460	5.7962	5	6.1274	6
NJ 6	245562	10851	241222	6.5195	6	6.8921	6
NY 17	959049	15017	953043	25.7579	25	27.2298	27
NC 12	555500	168824	487971	13.1884	13	13.9420	13
OH 1	230760	0	230760	6.2368	6	6.5931	6
PA 18	810091	795	809773	21.8858	21	23.1364	23
RI 2	76931	108	76888	2.0781	2	2.1968	2
SC 8	415115	196365	336569	9.0965	9	9.6163	9
TN 3	261727	44535	243913	6.5922	6	6.9689	6
VT 4	217895	0	217895	5.8891	5	6.2256	6
VA 22	974600	392516	817594	22.0971	22	23.3598	23
US 142	7036541	1130779	6584234	177.9523	170	188.1210	181

Table 2.5. The House and Senate apportionment bills.

On Thursday the House began debate. John Calhoun (SC) gave an impassioned speech declaring that he did not pay much attention to ratios and fractions, but he was deeply concerned about this power grab by the Senate. He now saw this as "a case of disagreement between the two Houses, and the contest is, which shall recede."[24] Mr. Calhoun pleaded that if the House recede to the Senate in this case, then "we must be hereafter be overpowered."[25]

The subsequent speakers did not focus on the power struggle that bothered Calhoun. They focused on Jelly Bean effects, especially losses to their state or region imposed by one bill in comparison to the other. The criterion used for evaluation was fractions in the form of unrepresented people. Table 2.6 (next page) displays a spreadsheet analysis applying the criterion of fractions using divisors of 35000 to 40000 in increments of 1000. Each divisor

---

[22] Annals of Congress, Senate, 12th Congress, 1st Session: 24.
[23] Ibid: 226.
[24] Annals of Congress, House of Representatives, 12th Congress, 1st Session: 404.
[25] Ibid: 406.

column shows first the resulting quotient (state population/divisor) and second the resulting fraction in the form of unrepresented people (decimal fraction x divisor). The bottom entry in a Fraction column shows the total number of unrepresented people for the divisor at left.

Table 2.6. Fraction analysis using divisors of 35000 to 40000 in increments of 1000.

State	Pop	35000	Fraction	36000	Fraction	37000	Fraction	38000	Fraction	39000	40000	Fraction	34800	Fraction
CT 7	261818	7.481	16818	7.273	9818	7.076	2818	6.890	33818	6.713	6.545	21818	7.524	18218
DE 7	71004	2.029	1004	1.972	35004	1.919	34004	1.869	33004	1.821	1.775	31004	2.040	1404
GA 4	210346	6.010	346	5.843	30346	5.685	25346	5.535	20346	5.393	5.259	10346	6.044	1546
KY 6	374287	10.694	24287	10.397	14287	10.116	4287	9.850	32287	9.597	9.357	14287	10.755	26287
MD 9	335946	9.598	20946	9.332	11946	9.080	2946	8.841	31946	8.614	8.399	15946	9.654	22746
MA 17	700745	20.021	745	19.465	16745	18.939	34745	18.441	16745	17.968	17.519	20745	20.136	4745
NH 5	214460	6.127	4460	5.957	34460	5.796	29460	5.644	24460	5.499	5.362	14460	6.163	5660
NJ 6	241222	6.892	31222	6.701	25222	6.520	19222	6.348	13222	6.185	6.031	1222	6.932	32422
NY 17	953043	27.230	8043	26.473	17043	25.758	28043	25.080	3043	24.437	23.826	33043	27.386	13443
NC 12	487971	13.942	32971	13.555	19971	13.188	6971	12.841	31971	12.512	12.199	7971	14.022	771
OH 1	230760	6.593	20760	6.410	14760	6.237	8760	6.073	2760	5.917	5.769	30760	6.631	21960
PA 18	809773	23.136	4773	22.494	17773	21.886	32773	21.310	11773	20.763	20.244	9773	23.269	9373
RI 2	76931	2.198	6931	2.137	4931	2.079	2931	2.025	931	1.973	1.923	36931	2.211	7331
SC 8	336569	9.616	21569	9.349	12569	9.096	3569	8.857	32569	8.630	8.414	16569	9.672	23369
TN 3	243913	6.969	33913	6.775	27913	6.592	21913	6.419	15913	6.254	6.098	3913	7.009	313
VT 4	217895	6.226	7895	6.053	1895	5.889	32895	5.734	27895	5.587	5.447	17895	6.261	9095
VA 22	817594	23.360	12594	22.711	25594	22.097	3594	21.516	19594	20.964	20.440	17594	23.494	17194
US 142	6575234	188.122	249277	182.897	320277	177.953	294277	173.270	352277	168.828	164.607	304277	189.203	215877

John Rhea (TN) gave a detailed numerical analysis about how the Senate bill with a divisor of 35000 gave a large increase in Tennessee's fraction in comparison to the House bill with a divisor of 37000. The intensity of his argument is puzzling since Tennessee gets 6 seats under either bill. Mr. Rhea argued that "If the object of the amendment [Senate bill] be to reduce great fractions, a ratio of 34800 would have done away the great fraction of Tennessee and the people of that State would then have seven representatives."[1] Mr. Rhea is correct that the problem of fractions using the divisor of 34800 would be satisfactory for Tennessee (Table 2.7); however, a worse problem would occur for New Jersey. As noted by James Fisk (VT), "No number can be fixed on as the ratio but what will leave fractions in some of the States."[2]

Robert Wright (MD) argued for accepting the Senate divisor of 35000. First, he appealed to fairness for Delaware. He noted that the problem of fractions was greater for Delaware than for Tennessee in comparing the Senate and House bills.

Table 2.7. Divisor 34800.

State	Population	34800	Fraction
CT	261818	7.524	18218
DE	71004	2.040	1404
GA	210346	6.044	1546
KY	374287	10.755	26287
MD	335946	9.654	22746
MA	700745	20.136	4745
NH	214460	6.163	5660
NJ	241222	6.932	32422
NY	953043	27.386	13443
NC	487971	14.022	771
OH	230760	6.631	21960
PA	809773	23.269	9373
RI	76888	2.209	7288
SC	336569	9.672	23369
TN	243913	7.009	313
VT	217895	6.261	9095
VA	817594	23.494	17194
US	6575234	189.202	215834

In this case, the Senate bill actually corrected the problem in awarding Delaware 2 seats instead of the 1 seat from the House bill. But the winning card for Mr. Wright was the regional comparison. Mr. Wright provided figures using fractions that the South fared worse under the House bill.[3]

Thomas Gholson (VA) argued that the House bill was constructed on principle: protection for small states, consideration of the resulting House size, and adoption of the highest ratio ensuring that no state lost representation.[4] After this introduction he expanded on the regional issue, the unfairness to the South in the Senate bill over the House bill.

After debate, a vote was taken on whether to concur with the Senate. At first, the vote seems puzzling. The vote "was determined in the negative—yeas 65, nays 64."[5] However the Speaker of the House, Henry Clay, who rarely voted, then voted nay.[6] Clay thus tied the vote; hence, a majority did not prevail and so the motion did not pass. It was then ordered that a

---

[1] Ibid: 410.
[2] Ibid: 408.
[3] Ibid: 410.
[4] Ibid.
[5] Ibid: 412.
[6] House Journal, December 5, 1811.

conference committee be appointed to meet with the Senate. The committee consisted of Lewis Condict (NJ), Abner Lacock (PA), and John Randolph (VA).[7]

On Thursday, 11 December 1811, the conference committee reported back to the House that the Senate would not compromise and rejected every alternative figure offered. Further, the House received a message from the Senate that the Senate adheres to its position.[8] A week later the House caved and voted to recede to the Senate, 72-62.[9] Other concerns loomed more important. In the voice of Richard Johnson (KY), "with Great Britain war was inevitable."[10] The War of 1812 was just over six months away. The final bill was approved into law by President Madison on 21 December 1811 (Figure 2.4).

CHAP. IX.—*An Act for the apportionment of Representatives among the several States, according to the third enumeration.(a)*

Be it enacted by the Senate and House of Representatives of the United States of America in Congress assembled, That from and after the third day of March, one thousand eight hundred and thirteen, the House of Representatives shall be composed of members elected agreeably to a ratio of one representative for every thirty-five thousand persons in each state, computed according to the rule prescribed by the constitution of the United States, that is to say: Within the state of New Hampshire, six; within the state of Massachusetts, twenty; within the state of Vermont, six; within the state of Rhode Island, two; within the state of Connecticut, seven; within the state of New York, twenty-seven; within the state of New Jersey, six; within the state of Pennsylvania, twenty-three; within the state of Delaware, two; within the state of Maryland, nine; within the state of Virginia, twenty-three; within the state of North Carolina, thirteen; within the state of South Carolina, nine; within the state of Georgia, six; within the state of Kentucky, ten; within the state of Ohio, six; within the state of Tennessee, six.

APPROVED, December 21, 1811.

Figure 2.4. The 1811 apportionment act.

---

[7] Annals of Congress, House of Representatives, 12th Congress, 1st Session: 413.
[8] Ibid: 455-6.
[9] Ibid: 558
[10] Ibid: 456

Section 2.3: Reapportionment Based on the 1820 Census

Section 2.3.1   The 1820 Census

On 14 March 1820, President James Monroe signed into law *An Act to provide for taking the fourth census or enumeration of the inhabitants of the United States, and for other purposes.* The act specified that the census be supervised by the Secretary of State and that the field work be conducted under the direction of U. S. marshals. The act also directed obtaining occupational information.[1] The act further specified that the census was to begin the first Monday in August, 7 August 1820, and be completed in 6 months. Later, a time extension was given to 1 September 1811.

The census was reported to Congress by Secretary of State John Quincy Adams on 20 December 1821.[2] A copy of the full census report is available for download from the Census Bureau.[3] The summary data reported to Congress is provided in Table 2.8 (next page).[4] The last column, Representative numbers, is the apportionment population; i.e., the three-fifths rule has been applied. The population for South Carolina is incomplete in that the returns from Kershaw District[5] are not yet reported. Further, the report from Alabama is incomplete. The final apportionment population figure for South Carolina was 439952; for Alabama, 134827.[6]

Apportionment based on the 1820 census needed to consider seven new states: Louisiana (admitted 30 April 1812), Indiana (11 December 1816), Mississippi (10 December 1817), Illinois (3 December 1818), Alabama (14 December 1819), Maine (15 March 1820), and Missouri (10 August 1821).[7]

The 17th Congress, 1st session, met from 3 December 1821 to 11 March 1822. The first business of the House was to elect Philip Barbour (VA) as Speaker of the House. He was chosen on the 12th ballot over two days of voting. He was elected with 87 votes, one more than the minimum needed for election.[8] This was perhaps a premonition of the closeness of many contentious issues faced by this Congress.

---

[1] Statutes at Large, 16th Congress, 1st Session: 548-53.

[2] House Journal, 17 Congress, 1st5 Session, December 20, 1821: 81.

[3] https://www.census.gov/prod/www/decennial.html.

[4] Ibid, Census for 1820: 18.

[5] http://www.carolana.com/SC/1800s/sc_1800s_districts_1820.html

[6] https://userpages.umbc.edu/~bouton/History407/SlaveStats.htm.

[7] http://www.50states.com/statehood.htm#.VE06WhawUQM

[8] Annals of Congress, House of Representatives, 17 Congress, 1st Session: 514-7.

Table 2.8. The 1820 census

Aggregate amount of each description of persons in the **United States** and their **Territories**, according to the Census taken in virtue of the act of Congress of the 14th of March, 1820, and the act of the 3d of March, 1821; compiled from returns received at the Department of State.

STATES AND TERRITORIES.	Total amount in each state and territory.	Representative number.
Maine	298,269	298,335
New Hampshire	244,161	244,161
Massachusetts	523,287	523,287
Rhode Island	83,059	83,038
Connecticut	275,318	275,326
Vermont	235,764	235,764
New York	1,372,812	1,368,775
New Jersey	277,575	274,551
Pennsylvania	1,049,398	1,046,313
Delaware	72,749	72,643
Maryland	407,390	364,389
Virginia	1,065,366	593,300
North Carolina	638,829	556,821
South Carolina (except Kentucky)	490,309	380,594
Georgia	340,989	281,126
Alabama	127,901	110,359
Mississippi	75,448	120,200
Louisiana	153,407	123,773
Tennessee	422,813	390,769
Kentucky	564,317	513,623
Ohio	581,434	581,434
Indiana	147,178	147,102
Illinois	55,211	54,843
Missouri	66,586	62,496
Territory of Michigan	8,896	
Territory of Arkansas	14,273	
District of Columbia	33,039	
Grand Total.	9,654,734	

51

Section 2.3.2   The House Bill

In anticipation of the census report, on 6 December 1821 John Campbell (OH) submitted "Resolved: That a committee be appointed to report a bill providing for the apportionment among the several states according to the fourth census."[9] Mr. Campbell's resolution was first read and then tabled. On 20 December the Speaker of the House announced a letter from Secretary of State John Quincy Adams submitting the report of the 1820 census. Mr. Campbell moved that his resolution be adopted and that the apportionment committee consist of one representative from each state; passed. Messrs. Campbell (OH), Harvey (NH), Dwight (MA), Durfee (RI), Tomlinson (CT), Mallary (VT), Colden (NY), Holcombe (NJ), Baldwin (PA), McLane (DE), Wright (MD), Mr. Randolph (VA), Edwards (NC), Lowndes (SC), Reid (GA), Trimble (KY), Allen (TN), Johnson (LA), Hendricks (IN), Rankin (MS), Cook (IL), Moore (AL), Whitman (ME), and Scott (MO) were appointed.[10] The census report was then referred to the committee.[11]

Discussion in the House began on Friday, 11 January 1822. First, the House resolved itself into a Committee of the Whole. Mr. Campbell, reporting on behalf of the committee, proposed a bill using Jefferson's method with a ratio of 40000. Mr. Campbell then moved to strike out 40000 and replace by 42000. James McSherry (PA) proposed that the motion be considered in two parts: first, "striking out;" then, if that passes, what figure to use for the ratio. The first part for "striking out" passed.[12] Objections were raised on deciding the ratio now since returns from South Carolina and Alabama were incomplete. Others needed time to study the issue since their attention had been recently diverted to other issues.

Debate began in earnest on Thursday, 17 January. It was unanimously agreed that the committee's proposal, "by a ratio of forty thousand," be replaced by a ratio of _____ thousand. The following numbers were proposed to fill the blank: 35 to 50, inclusively, in increments of 1, 52, 55, and 75. Starting with 75, the proposer stated his reasons and a vote was taken. The proposals from 75 down to 43 all failed. Then, Weldon Edwards (NC) proposed 42; passed, 81-73.[13]

Each proposer defended his choice by invoking a variety of Jelly Bean effects. Elias Keyes (VT) defended his choice for a ratio of 75000 because "Each member would admit that his voice was not loud enough to be heard in the various parts of this Hall."[14] John Durfee (RI) refuted by asking "Must we inquire of our Architect how many Representatives the people of the United States are entitled to?"[15] Through the give and take, congressmen were realizing that they were dealing with a difficult problem as indicated by Mr. Durfee:

---

[9] House Journal, December 6, 1821: 24.

[10] House Journal, December 20, 1821: 81.

[11] Annals of Congress, House of Representatives, 17th Congress, 1st Session: 576.

[12] Annals of Congress, House of Representatives, 17th Congress, 1st Session: 708.

[13] Ibid: 734-743.

[14] Ibid: 736.

[15] Ibid: 738.

... the question of what number of Representatives a given population is entitled to, is a question of no ordinary difficulty. I agree with gentlemen that it rests upon undefined, broad, and general principles. It opens to the view a wide and extensive field which presents no landmarks to direct the course of the traveler to a proper termination. It affords no data from which to commence our calculations in order to arrive at the proper conclusion. The rule of determining the number of Representatives by population is a rule entirely of modern invention. ... Upon this question the Constitution, it must be admitted, is but an imperfect guide.[16]

The next week brought another round of debates where fairness vs. power was a prominent issue. As noted by Romulus Saunders (NC),[17]

The power of apportioning the representation among the several States had been vested in Congress, and this, as well as all other discretionary powers, should be exercised soundly—to do so it was necessary to act on principle, and not upon any arithmetical calculation, with an eye to our own district or State, but to its operation on the whole Union.

Finally, the question was called whether the House should concur with the Committee of the Whole on the amendment for a ratio of 42000. This failed 83-88 (hence, the House voted against its own amendment).[18] This process of proposing another divisor supported by its own Jelly Bean effects and subsequently being voted down continued for several lengthy sessions. A litany of divisors joined the procession: 45000, 39000, 30000, 37000, 41000, 35000, 38000, 37500, and 38500.[19] The most successful among the defeated proposals was introduced on 5 February by Rollin Mallary (VT) who proposed the ratio of 38500. Mr. Mallary presented figures comparing the results for the ratio of 38500 against the bill's current 40000.[20] The next day a vote was taken on Mr. Mallary's motion; failed, 63-99.[21]

Finally, on 6 February, the day Mallary's proposal failed and after a few more attempts at procedural jockeying, a vote was taken on the main bill, the bill originally proposed by the select committee on 11 January using the ratio 40000. The motion passed: 100-58.[22] The bill, *An act for the apportionment of Representatives among the several states according to the fourth census*, was then sent to the Senate with a request for concurrence.[23]

---

[16] Ibid: 739.
[17] Ibid: 814
[18] Ibid: 823-4.
[19] Ibid: 832-49, 854-66, 868-75, 880-96.
[20] Ibid: 916-8.
[21] Ibid: 939.
[22] Ibid: 947.
[23] Senate Journal, 17th Congress, 1st Session, 7 February 1822.

Section 2.3.3   The Senate

On Thursday, 7 February, the day the Senate received the bill from the House, the Senate had the bill read twice. Then, by unanimous consent, the bill was referred to the Senate's Committee of the Judiciary for analysis and recommendation. On Monday, Senator Smith (MD), reported the bill out from the Committee of the Judiciary with the recommendation that the ratio of 40000 be replaced by 42000.[24]

The next day debate began in earnest. A motion was made to break the recommendation, to strike 40000 and replace by 42000, up into its two separate components. The motion to strike 40000 passed 22-16. The ratio figure was replaced by a blank. This inaugurated extensive debate about how to fill in the blank.[25] However, the discussion about the ratio became sidetracked with the concern of William King (AL) that the returns from Alabama were incomplete because of the untimely death of the U. S. marshal in Alabama.[26] An amendment to the House bill was formulated to deal with the Alabama situation.

On Tuesday, 19 February, the Senate passed the Alabama amendment, 37-8. Then came the parade of candidates to fill in the blank ratio: 47000, 38500, 37000, 41000, 46000, 47000, 45000, 43000, 41000, and 35000. All failed. The Senate then decided to reconsider the vote on the Committee of the Judiciary's recommendation to strike the House ratio figure of 40000. The vote to approve the recommendation failed, 21-25.[27] The next day the amended bill was approved, 26-19,[28] and then sent to the House for concurrence.

Section 2.3.4   Resolution

On Wednesday, 20 February, the House received the announcement that the Senate has passed the apportionment bill with an amendment. The amendment was read and then sent to the House's Committee on the Judiciary. The next day, John Sergeant (PA), reporting on behalf of the committee, recommended rejection of the Senate's amendment.[29] Almost a week later, on 28 February, Mr. Sergeant reported that from additional data Alabama seems secure for three seats given the ratio of 40000. Accordingly, the Committee on the Judiciary rescinds its previous recommendation.[30] The next day, after debate about the constitutionality of the Senate's amendment making a specific provision for Alabama, the House voted on the original recommendation to disagree to the Senate's amendment: failed, 47-98. Hence, the Senate amendment was agreed to.[31] On 7 March 1822 President James Monroe signed into law *An Act for the apportionment of representatives among the several states, according to the fourth census* (Figure 2.5, next page).[32]

---

[24] Ibid: 11 February 1822.
[25] Annals of Congress, Senate, 17 Congress, 1st Session: 205-7.
[26] Ibid: 209-12.
[27] Senate Journal, 17th Congress, 1st Session, 19 February 1822.
[28] Annals of Congress, Senate, 17 Congress, 1st Session: 223.
[29] House Journal, February 20-22, 1822.
[30] Annals of Congress, House of Representatives, 17 Congress, 1st Session: 1164-5.
[31] Ibid: 1167-72.
[32] Statutes at Large, 17th Congress, 1st Session: 651.

A spreadsheet analysis for how apportionments were computed is given in Table 2.9. The State column lists the states and the number of congressmen in the 17th Congress, 1st Session, that enacted the bill. The Population column gives the apportionment population. The Quotient column gives the quotients obtained by dividing a state population by the ratio 40000. The Seats column is the actual apportionment obtained by taking the integer part of the quotient. The apportionment bill was created by applying Jefferson's basic divisor method.

CHAP. X.—*An Act for the apportionment of representatives among the several states, according to the fourth census. (a)*

Be it enacted by the Senate and House of Representatives of the United States of America, in Congress assembled, That, from and after the third day of March, one thousand eight hundred and twenty-three, the House of Representatives shall be composed of members elected agreeably to a ratio of one representative for every forty thousand persons in each state, computed according to the rule prescribed by the constitution of the United States; that is to say: within the state of Maine, seven; within the state of New Hampshire, six; within the state of Massachusetts, thirteen; within the state of Rhode Island, two; within the state of Connecticut, six; within the state of Vermont, five; within the state of New York, thirty-four; within the state of New Jersey, six; within the state of Pennsylvania, twenty-six; within the state of Delaware, one; within the state of Maryland, nine; within the state of Virginia, twenty-two; within the state of North Carolina, thirteen; within the state of South Carolina, nine; within the state of Georgia, seven; within the state of Alabama, two; within the state of Mississippi, one; within the state of Louisiana, three; within the state of Tennessee, nine; within the state of Kentucky, twelve; within the state of Ohio, fourteen; within the state of Indiana, three; within the state of Illinois, one; and within the state of Missouri, one.

Figure 2.5. Apportionment Act of 1823.

Table 2.9. Analysis for the apportionment act of 1822.

State	Population	Quotient	Seats
Maine 7	298335	7.458	7
New Hampshire 6	244161	6.104	6
Massachusetts 13	523287	13.082	13
Rhode Island 2	83038	2.076	2
Connecticut 7	275208	6.880	6
Vermont 6	235764	5.894	5
New York 27	1368775	34.219	34
New Jersey 6	274551	6.864	6
Pennsylvania 23	1049313	26.233	26
Delaware 2	70943	1.774	1
Maryland 9	364389	9.110	9
Virginia 23	895303	22.383	22
North Carolina 13	556821	13.921	13
South Carolina 9	399351	9.984	9
Georgia 6	281126	7.028	7
Alabama 1	111147	2.779	2
Mississippi 1	62320	1.558	1
Louisiana 1	125779	3.144	3
Tennessee 6	390769	9.769	9
Kentucky 10	513623	12.841	12
Ohio 6	581434	14.536	14
Indiana 1	147102	3.678	3
Illinois 1	54843	1.371	1
Missouri 1	62496	1.562	1
USA 187	8969878	224.247	212

On 14 January 1823 President Monroe approved and signed into law *An Act concerning the apportionment of representatives in the state of Alabama*. The act specified that from 3 March 1823 Alabama shall have 3 seats in the House. This action then brought the House size for the 2nd session of the 17th Congress to 213 seats.[33]

Section 2.3.5 The Aftermath

During the lengthy debates, two proposals were interjected to deal head on with the most persistent fairness issue: fractions. The first proposal was made by William Lowndes (SC); the other was made by Ebenezer Herrick (NH). Both involved a quota method but with different mechanisms for rounding to achieve the desired House size.

On 1 February 1822 Mr. Lowndes appealed to the congressional bill first passed by Congress in 1792 but vetoed by President Washington. He recalled the method used to construct that bill and then made a proposal.[34]

[33] https://www.loc.gov/law/help/statutes-at-large/17th-congress/session-2/c17s2ch2.pdf
[34] Ibid: 871.

The plan then would be nearly this: Determining on the number of representatives, the whole general population in representative numbers should be divided by this number—thus ascertaining the ratio of representation, and the number of representatives which each State would have, and then what would be the aggregate of the whole. The complementary number—the number of members which should then be deficient of that first fixed upon, should then be divided among the States having the least representation in proportion to their respective numbers.

Mr. Lowndes did not offer a specific House size to initiate a motion incorporating his proposed plan. Instead, he closed with comments about "what ought to be the ratio of apportionment."[35]

The next few speakers presented their comments solely in terms of the ratio. Then Henry Baldwin (PA) moved to commit to the apportionment committee "with the avowed object of attempting to adopt a method of representing the fractions of the respective States in conformity to a suggestion of the gentleman from South Carolina, (Mr. Lowndes)."[36] The motion failed and Mr. Lowndes's proposal was not mentioned again in the record for this round of apportionment.

The next day Mr. Herrick proposed that the Hamilton quota method be used. He began his remarks by asserting that a basic divisor method was unconstitutional. He argued that choosing a ratio was the wrong approach to apportionment. The right course is to decide the House size first. After the House size is selected, "divide the whole population to be represented by the assumed number of representatives, and then you will have the true ratio by which to make your apportionment."[37] The rest of his proposal follows the Hamilton quota method. Mr. Herrick then followed his proposal with an illustration that used the House size 212 obtained by the proposed ratio of 40000. He also included figures by way of example using a House size of 200 because it resulted from the competing ratio of 42000.

Table 2.10 (next page) displays a spreadsheet analysis for the computations needed to form an apportionment bill using the Jefferson basic divisor method (the method used to construct the 1812 apportionment bill) along with using the Hamilton method proposed by Mr. Herrick and the Lowndes method.

---

[35] Ibid: 871-2.
[36] Ibid: 872.
[37] Ibid: 895.

Table 2.10. *Computations for apportionment using the Jefferson basic divisor method, Hamilton's method, and Lowndes's method based on the 1820 census: Jefferson (Quotient, Seats); Hamilton (Quota, Lower, Seats); Lowndes (Constituency, Seats, Constituency, Disparity).*

State	Population	Quotient	Seats	Quota	Lower	Seats	Constituency	Seats	Constituency	Disparity
ME 7	298335	7.458	7	7.0510	7	7	42619	7	37292	5327
NH 6	244161	6.104	6	5.7707	5	6	48832	6	40694	8138
MA 13	523287	13.082	13	12.3677	12	12	43607	12	40253	3354
RI 2	83038	2.076	2	1.9626	1	2	83038	2	41519	41519
CT 7	275208	6.880	6	6.5044	6	7	45868	7	39315	6553
VT 6	235764	5.894	5	5.5722	5	6	47153	6	39294	7859
NY 27	1368775	34.219	34	32.3505	32	32	42774	32	41478	1296
NJ 6	274551	6.864	6	6.4889	6	7	45759	6	39222	6537
PA 23	1049313	26.233	26	24.8002	24	25	43721	24	41973	1748
DE 2	70943	1.774	1	1.6767	1	2	70943	2	35472	35471
MD 9	364389	9.110	9	8.6122	8	9	45549	8	40488	5061
VA 23	895303	22.383	22	21.1602	21	21	42633	21	40696	1937
NC 13	556821	13.921	13	13.1603	13	13	42832	13	39773	3059
SC 9	399351	9.984	9	9.4385	9	9	44372	9	39935	4437
GA 6	281126	7.028	7	6.6443	6	7	46854	7	40161	6693
AL 1	111147	2.779	2	2.6269	2	3	55574	3	37049	18525
MS 1	62320	1.558	1	1.4729	1	1	62320	2	31160	31160
LA 1	125779	3.144	3	2.9727	2	3	62890	3	41926	20964
TN 6	390769	9.769	9	9.2357	9	9	43419	9	39077	4342
KY 10	513623	12.841	12	12.1393	12	12	42802	12	39509	3293
OH 6	581434	14.536	14	13.7420	13	14	44726	13	41531	3195
IN 1	147102	3.678	3	3.4767	3	3	49034	4	36776	12258
IL 1	54843	1.371	1	1.2962	1	1	54843	2	27422	27421
MO 1	62496	1.562	1	1.4771	1	1	62496	2	31248	31248
US 187	8969878	224.247	212	212.0000	200	212		212		

The basic divisor method uses a ratio (divisor) of 40000. The quotient for a given state is the state population divided by 40000. A seat (state apportionment) is the integer part of the quotient, i.e., the quotient rounded down.

For the Hamilton method one needs to compute the quota given the House size 212. The lower quota is the integer part of the quota; i.e., the quota rounded down. Assigning each state its lower quota distributes 200 seats. The remaining 12 seats needed to form a House of 212 are given to the 12 states with the highest decimal fractions in their quotas, from Louisiana (quota decimal fraction .9727) down to New Jersey (quota decimal fraction .4889).

The Lowndes method begins the same way as the Hamilton method by computing each state's quota and initially assigning each state its lower quota, thus distributing 200 of the 212 seats. However, the remaining 12 seats are not distributed by highest quota decimal fractions. First, compute each state's constituency (state ratio) by dividing the state's lower quota into the state's population. This yields the number of people represented by a congressman for that state, shown as the first Constituency in the Lowndes Method in Table 2.9. Lowndes then distributes the needed 12 seats to those states with the highest state constituencies. In this case, top priority goes to Rhode Island. With only one representative as a result of the lower quota, Rhode Island's congressman represents 83038 people, more than any other state. This proceeds down to Connecticut whose lower quota state constituency is 45868. The result is displayed in the Seats column to the right of the first Constituency column.

The thinking behind the Lowndes method is direct and practical. For example, consider Connecticut. Connecticut's quota is 6.5044. By the quota rule, Connecticut deserves either 6 (lower quota) or 7 (upper quota) representatives. The first Constituency column in the Lowndes Method shows the constituency with the lower quota; the second Constituency column shows the constituency with the upper quota. If Connecticut is awarded 6 representatives, then Connecticut's constituency is 45868; if awarded 7, then 39315. Clearly, awarding Connecticut 7 representatives yields a constituency much closer to the target ideal of 40000 as specified by the defining ratio for this apportionment bill. The constituency disparity between the two choices for Connecticut is 45868 – 39315 = 6553. Essentially, Lowndes method is equivalent to computing the constituency disparity for each state and then awarding the remaining 12 seats to the 12 states with the greatest constituency disparities. Hence, the Disparity column acts as a priority list for applying the Lowndes method. The disparities are displayed in the Disparity column in Table 2.9.

A comparison between the three methods illuminates the difficulty of the congressional apportionment problem. A comparison between the results from the Jefferson basic divisor method and the Hamilton quota method vividly displays flaws in the Jefferson method. First, there is a quota rule violation for New York. New York's fair share quota based on population is 32.3505; but the apportionment act awards New York 34 seats. From the viewpoint of the quota decimal fractions, the Jefferson method shows a favoritism for the larger states Massachusetts, Pennsylvania, Virginia, and New York over the smaller states Connecticut, Vermont, New Jersey, Delaware, and Alabama.

A comparison between the Jefferson basic divisor method and the Lowndes quota method shows a change in apportionment affecting 14 of the 24 states. Jefferson apportions two more seats each to New York and Louisiana than Lowndes.

A comparison between Hamilton and Lowndes shows that 8 states are affected. In comparison to Hamilton, Lowndes awards Mississippi, Indiana, Illinois, and Missouri a seat at the expense of New Jersey, Pennsylvania, Maryland, and Ohio. The most noticeable contrast between the Hamilton and Lowndes methods occurs in comparing Pennsylvania and Illinois. Pennsylvania's quotient is 24.8002, the third highest quota decimal fraction among the 24 states. Illinois's quotient is only 1.2962, which ranks 20th among the 24 states. Yet, Lowndes awards Illinois an additional seat, but not Pennsylvania. The reason for this is clear from the constituency disparities between the two states. If Pennsylvania is awarded 24 seats, the constituency is 43721; i.e., each Pennsylvania congressman would represent 43721 people. If Pennsylvania is awarded 25 seats, then the constituency is 41973. The disparity, 43721-41973, is only 1748. If Illinois is awarded 1 seat, then the constituency is 54843; 2 seats, 27422. The resulting disparity is 17421. Hence, the additional seat means much more to Illinois than to Pennsylvania in terms of the number of people that a congressman represents.

A significant detail occurs in the way both Lowndes and Herrick presented the quota method. Both started the apportionment process by first determining the House size, h, rather than deciding the ratio (divisor). Now comes the interesting detail. Both congressmen stated that after h is settled, then calculate the national divisor, D, as the national population, p, divided by the House size, i.e., $D = p/h$.[38] Then divide each state's population by this national divisor, D, to obtain each state's quotient. In the presentation of the quota method by Fisher Ames in 1791,[39] a state's quota was calculated by applying the "rule-of-three," i.e., state quota = h x (state population)/p. This idea is based on the simple premise that if a state has 10% of the population, then that state should get 10% of the seats in the House. Hence, we have the question: does the rule-of-three quota lead to the same result as the national divisor quotient? The answer is yes in that the methods are computationally equivalent.

To confirm this equivalence, we view the situation through a mathematical lens.

Let $\mathcal{U} = \{S_1, S_2, \dots, S_s\}$ where $s \in \mathbb{N}_2$ ($\mathbb{N}_k = \{n \in \mathbb{N} \mid n \geq k\}$).

Let $p_i = pop(S_i)$, $\vec{p} = <p_1, p_2, \dots, p_s>$, and $p = \sum_1^s p_i$.

Determine $\vec{a} = <a_1, a_2, \dots, a_s>$ where $a_i \in \mathbb{N}$.

$\mathcal{U}$ represents the national Union of s states ($s \geq 2$ to avoid trivial cases). The vector $\vec{p}$ is the census and $\vec{a}$ is the apportionment vector. Each state's apportionment must be a natural number. This constraint makes the apportionment problem mathematically interesting. Fractional representation has never been discussed as a serious political option for the House. The House size is $h = \sum_1^s a_i$. The only constitutional constraint on h is that $s \leq h \leq p/30000$.

Suppose that h is determined first. The **national divisor** is defined by $D = p/h$. The quota Q_i for state S_i is defined by $Q_i = h(p_i/p)$. That each state's quota is exactly the same as the state's quotient determined by using the national divisor, $q_i = p_i/D$, follows from the following equivalency chain. Let d be a divisor. Then

$$q_i = Q_i$$

$$\Leftrightarrow \quad \frac{p_i}{d} = h\left(\frac{p_i}{p}\right) \qquad \text{definition of quotient, quota}$$

$$\Leftrightarrow \quad \frac{1}{d} = h\left(\frac{1}{p}\right) \qquad \text{cancelling } p_i$$

$$\Leftrightarrow \quad d = \frac{p}{h} \qquad \text{inverting}$$

$$\Leftrightarrow \quad d = D \qquad \text{definition of } D$$

---

[38] Annals of Congress, House of Representatives, 17th Congress, 1st Session: 871, 895.
[39] Annals of Congress, House of Representatives, 2nd Congress, 1st Session: 255.

The equivalency chain verifies that a state's quota is the same as the quotient if and only if the divisor is the national divisor. We thus have established that there are two ways of presenting a quota method: (1) the rule-of-three, and (2) the national divisor. Both lead to the same set of decimal numbers for further processing.

A natural inquiry to make concerns whether the Hamilton or the Lowndes method is "fairer" or "better." Of course, this depends on one's perception of these terms. Both methods seem intuitively to have something to offer by way of fairness. In a master's thesis Margo Carr states that the Hamilton method

> is the method that appears, in common sense terms, to be the "fairest." It is the method that stays closest to the quota. Among all integer vectors in $\mathbb{R}^n$ it is the one that is closest to the quota vector in $\mathbb{R}^n$; where we define distance in $\mathbb{R}^n$ by the usual Euclidean distance.[40]

THEOREM. Given the population vector $\vec{p} = <p_1,p_2,...,p_s>$ and House size h, let $\vec{Q} = <Q_1,Q_2,...,Q_s>$ be the resulting quota vector. Then the Hamilton apportionment vector $\vec{a} = <a_1,a_2,...,a_s>$ minimizes the Euclidean distance to Q; i.e., the Hamilton apportionment solution is the unique apportionment vector closest, using the Euclidean metric, to the quota vector over all apportionment possibilities.

Carr's theorem may be understood by using a shooting range analogy. Consider the quota to be the target. Hamilton and Lowndes each take shots at the target, one shot for each state. Choose as the "better" shooter the one whose combined shots come closest to the target. In this contest Hamilton always comes closer to the target than any other rival, Lowndes included. The combined distance from the apportionment vector to the quotient vector, denoted $d(\vec{Q}, \vec{a})$, using the Euclidean metric is calculated by

$$d(\vec{Q}, \vec{a}) = \sqrt{\sum_{i=1}^{S}(Q_i - a_i)^2} \, .$$

One may also intuitively note that the Lowndes method has a built-in bias towards smaller states over larger states in that the disparity priority list in general favors the smaller states.

Section 2.3.6   Epilogue

There are several university liberal arts mathematics courses that cater to a general audience. These courses include a variety of general interest topics. Several textbooks written for these courses include a chapter on political considerations, such as voting and the ballot, power, or apportionment treated as a problem in the distribution of a fixed or known number of assets. Accordingly, these texts initiate apportionment from the contemporary point of view that the House consists of 435 members. These texts then illustrate congressional apportionment as a relevant and important modern-day example of a fixed apportionment problem.

---

[40] Margo Carr, *Numerical Analysis of Apportionment Methods*, California State University, Northridge, February 2009.

Accordingly, such texts initiate the presentation of congressional apportionment by introducing the standard divisor, called the national divisor in the previous section. Let h be the House size and p the national population. Then, the **standard divisor**, s, is the divisor $s = p/d$. This is a seductive concept because a divisor method using the standard divisor yields quotients identical to the quotas yielded by applying the rule-of-three to h.

The difficulty is that this approach is not true to the earlier part of the national historical record. It was not the approach taken by Congress in creating the apportionment acts based on the censuses from 1790 to 1840. In this respect the congressional apportionment problem is different than the fixed apportionment problem of textbooks. A fixed apportionment problem requires a fixed number of assets to be distributed. The general congressional apportionment problem, however, does not require a fixed number of seats in the House.

In the United States the congressional apportionment problem contains the following ingredients. First, we have the Union of s states: $S_1, S_2, ..., S_s$. Then, a census is conducted to determine the population of each state. Let $p_i = pop(S_i)$; i.e., p_i is the population of the ith state. The census is the population vector $<p_1, p_2, ..., p_s>$. The congressional apportionment problem is to determine an apportionment vector $<a_1, a_2, ..., a_s>$ where each a_i, the apportionment for state S_i, is a natural number (a whole number greater than or equal to 1) where the size of the House, $h = a_1 + a_2 + \cdots + a_s$, is such that $p/h \geq 30000$. One is not required to specify the House size in advance to solve a given congressional apportionment problem.

The key point here is that the congressional apportionment problem, as a problem in U. S. history, did not become a fixed apportionment problem until 1850. Although the concept of a standard divisor is useful and interesting, it is the wrong concept to initiate the congressional apportionment problem as a problem in U. S. history. A study of congressional apportionment true to the story of U. S. history must begin with the basic divisor method. In a basic divisor method h is not specified in advance; further, h plays no role in the method. The House size is not known until the end and thus is only the result of the process. Accordingly, a large part of the history of congressional apportionment as told in most mathematics textbooks contains a great deal of historical myth interspersed with the mathematical facts. One beauty of an historical approach is that it enlightens the difficult path of how a general divisor evolved into a standard divisor as a key computational component of apportionment methodology.

Section 2.4:   Reapportionment Based on the 1830 Census

Section 2.4.1   The 1830 Census

On 4 March 1829 Andrew Jackson was inaugurated as the 7th President of the United States. Andrew Jackson symbolizes a bifurcation period in American history.[1] Jackson's inauguration "made it clear that something had changed in American politics."[2] Jackson's colorful life and influence is well documented.[3] [4] Perhaps most people today recognize Jackson from his portrait on America's most popular piece of paper currency, the $20 bill. The term "Jacksonian Democracy" permeates the telling of American history.[5]

The 1st session of the 21st Congress met on this stage with its Jacksonian background. Congress passed *An Act to provide for the taking of the fifth census or enumeration of the inhabitants of the United States*, approved into law by President Jackson on 23 March 1830.[6] For the first time the act required field enumerators to use uniform printed schedules for recording data. The act specified that the 1830 census was to start on 1 June 1830 and be completed in six months with results delivered to the U. S. district marshals by 1 December 1830. The marshals were to compile and report the district results to the Secretary of State Martin Van Buren by 1 February 1831.

In the 21st Congress there was an attempt to fix the ratio of representation in advance of the publication of the census figures.[7] However, the idea never matured as Congress was occupied by a variety of hot-button issues such as Indian removal culminating in the Indian Removal Act of 28 May 1830. Other issues concerned the sale of public lands, nullification, the politics of the Eaton affair, and the organization of the Cabinet, among several others.[8]

The census figures were reported to the 22nd Congress, whose first session met from 5 December 1831 to 16 July 1832. On 7 December 1831 President Jackson sent a message to Congress with a statement from now Secretary of State Edward Livingston showing progress in taking the census.[9] Finally, on 17 January 1832, the Speaker of the House presented a letter from Secretary Livingston that was accompanied by a corrected return of the census.[10] No new states were added to the Union since the last apportionment act of 1822.

---

[1] Daniel Howe, *What Hath God Wrought: The Transformation of America, 1815-1848*, Oxford University Press, 2007.

[2] Eric Foner, *Give Me Liberty! An American Story*, W. W. Norton and Company, 2nd Edition, 2009.

[3] Robert Remini, *Andrew Jackson*, Twayne Publishers, Inc., 1969.

[4] Jon Meacham, *American Lion*, Random House, Inc., 2008.

[5] http://www.history.com/topics/jacksonian-democracy

[6] Statutes at Large, 21st Congress, 1st Session, Statute I, Chap. XI: 383-90.

[7] House Journal, 21st Congress, 1st Session, December 29, 1829: 108; January 27, 1830: 216.

[8] Robert Remini, *Andrew Jackson*, in James McPherson, *"To the Best of My Ability"* The American Presidents, DK Publishing, Revised US Edition: 56-65.

[9] House Journal, 22nd Congress, 1st Session, December 12, 1831.

[10] House Journal, 22nd Congress, 1st Session, January 4, 1832.

Section 2.4.2   The House Bill

The 1st session of the 22nd Congress opened on Monday, 5 December 1831. Andrew Stevenson (VA) was elected Speaker of the House on the first ballot.[11] On Tuesday President Jackson sent his state of the nation letter to Congress. On Wednesday Jackson sent a message with a statement from Secretary of State Livingston giving a progress report on the census. But the House was eager to move on apportionment.

The House began action on apportionment on Monday, 12 December 1831, and worked diligently until a House apportionment bill was passed on Thursday, 16 February 1832. The highlights without the intervening details of the debates and squabbles include the following.

- 12 December 1831. James K. Polk moves: "Resolved, That the message of the President of the United States, with the accompanying documents, of the 7th instant,[12] upon the subject of the fifth census of the United States, be referred to a select committee; and that said committee be instructed to report a bill fixing the ratio of representation in Congress, under the fifth census of the United States." Messrs. Polk (TN), Holland (ME), Thomson (OH), King (NY), Thomas (LA), Barstow (NY), and Bucher (PA) are appointed to the select committee.[13]

- 4 January 1832. Mr. Polk, on behalf of the select committee, submits H.R. 208, a bill for the apportionment of Representatives among the several States according to the fifth census.[14] H.R. 208 applies the Jefferson basic divisor method with the divisor 48000.

- 14 February 1832. A motion is made by Mr. Polk, "That the said bill and amendment be recommitted to a select committee, with instructions to strike out forty-four thousand three hundred as the ratio of representation, and to insert forty-seven thousand seven hundred as the ratio of representation." The motion passes 104-91.[15]

- 15 February 1832. Mr. Polk from the select committee reports H.R. 208 with the amendment that the ratio of representation be 47700. The question on whether to concur with the committee passes 119-75.[16]

- 16 February 1832. H.R. 208 was read a third time and passed, 130-58. The bill was sent to the Senate with a request for concurrence.[17]

One name clearly stands out in this summary: James Knox Polk (Figure 2.6, next page).

---

[11] House Journal, 22nd Congress, 1st Session, December 5, 1831.

[12] The term "7th instant" means the 7th day of the month.

[13] Ibid, December 12, 1831: 38.

[14] Ibid, January 4, 1832: 151.

[15] Ibid, February 14, 1832: 345, 349.

[16] Ibid, February 15, 1832: 352, 360.

[17] Ibid, February 16, 1832: 368-70.

James K. Polk (1795-1849) is a legacy person in American history. He was elected to the House from Tennessee in 1825 at the age of 29. In Jackson's second term Polk was elected Speaker of the House. He was the 11th President of the United States, 1845-1849. He is the only Speaker of the House ever to become President. He was the hardest working President in the nation's history and was totally dedicated to the public offices he held as congressman, Governor of Tennessee, and President.[18] [19] [20]

Figure 2.6.

H.R. 208 was generated by applying Jefferson's basic divisor method with a divisor of 48000 (Table 2.11). The State column lists the states in the same order as H.R. 208. The number next to each state gives its current number of representatives. The Population column gives the apportionment population for each state (the constitutional three-fifths rule has been applied). The Quotient column gives the quotient using the divisor of 48000. The Seats column gives the resulting apportionment using Jefferson's method of dropping the quotient decimal fraction.

Wrangling over the details soon began. Charles Wicliffe (KY) moved that the bill be sent to a select committee of 24, one from each state, with the 48000 divisor replaced by a blank.[21] The motion failed, 76-116. Four days later, Mr. Wicliffe moved that the 48000 divisor be replaced by a blank.[22] The next day a vote was taken on Mr. Wicliffe's motion; failed, 94-99.[23] Henry Hubbard (NH) then moved that 48000 be replaced by 44000. The next day a vote was taken and Mr. Hubbard's motion passed, 98-96.[24]

Table 2.11. Apportionment calculations based on the 1830 census.

State	Population	Quotient	Seats
Maine 7	399454	8.3220	8
New Hampshire 6	269326	5.6110	5
Massachusetts 13	610408	12.7168	12
Rhode Island 2	97194	2.0249	2
Connecticut 6	297665	6.2014	6
Vermont 5	280657	5.8470	5
New York 34	1918578	39.9704	39
New Jersey 6	319922	6.6650	6
Pennsylvania 26	1348072	28.0848	28
Delaware 1	75432	1.5715	1
Maryland 9	405843	8.4551	8
Virginia 22	1023503	21.3230	21
North Carolina 13	639747	13.3281	13
South Carolina 9	455025	9.4797	9
Georgia 7	429811	8.9544	8
Kentucky 12	621832	12.9548	12
Tennessee 9	625263	13.0263	13
Ohio 14	937901	19.5396	19
Indiana 3	343031	7.1465	7
Mississippi 1	110358	2.2991	2
Illinois 1	157147	3.2739	3
Louisiana 3	171904	3.5813	3
Missouri 1	130419	2.7171	2
Alabama 3	262508	5.4689	5
USA 213	11931000	248.5625	237

---

[18] Robert Merry, *A Country of Vast Designs*, Simon and Schuster Paperbacks, 2009.

[19] Walter Borneman, *Polk: The Man Who Transformed the Presidency and America*, 2009 Random House Trade Paperback Edition.

[20] Image from *http://www.history.com/topics/us-presidents/james-polk*

[21] House Journal, 22nd Congress, 1st Session, January 26, 1832: 245.

[22] Ibid, January 30, 1832: 268.

[23] Ibid, January 31, 1832: 273.

[24] Ibid, February 1, 1832: 276.

On 2 February Thomas McKennan (PA) moved to reconsider the vote replacing 48000 by 44000. Heman Allan (KY) interjected to move that H.R. 208 be sent back to the select committee to construct a bill so that the House size would be 200; failed, 32-161. Subsequently, the vote to reconsider passed 100-94.[25] On Thursday, 7 February, a vote on McKennan's motion to reconsider the vote replacing 48000 by 44000 was taken; failed, 88-102. Clement Clay (AL) moved to replace 48000 by 47000; failed, 65-127. Then, John Kerr moved to replace 48000 by 45000.[26]

The next day a vote was taken on Kerr's motion; failed, 68-118.[27] Philip Doddridge (VA) moved to replace 48000 by 46000; failed, 71-117. Joseph Vance (OH) moved to replace 48000 by 44400. The vote tied, 97-97. Speaker of the House Andrew Stevenson (VA) voted aye; hence, the motion passed. John Taylor (NY) followed with a motion to replace 44400 by 53000; failed 66-123.[28]

The next day, Thursday, 9 February, George Evans (ME) moved to replace the 44400 divisor by 44300. Amendments to replace 44300 by 43300, 47300, and 42300 all failed.[29]

The House resumed debate on H.R. 208 the following Tuesday, 14 February. A vote was taken on the previous motion by George Evans; passed 108-87. Then James K. Polk (TN) moved to recommit H.R. 208 to the select committee with 44300 replaced by 47700. Proposed amendments to Mr. Polk's motion all failed. The Polk motion then passed, 104-91.[30]

The next day Mr. Polk reported H.R. 208 out of the select committee with adjustments for using the divisor 47700. Ten different motions to replace the 47700 divisor all failed. A vote was taken to concur with the select committee's report; passed, 119-75.[31]

Finally, the next day, Thursday, 16 February 1832, H.R. 208 was read the third time and a vote was taken; passed, 130-58.[32] Table 2.12 (next page) presents a spreadsheet showing the calculations for constructing the amended H.R. 208 using the divisor 47700. The resulting House bill constructs a House with 240 members. In particular, three states benefitted by gaining a seat from replacing the original divisor of 48000 by 47700: New York, Georgia, and Kentucky. The divisor of 47700 reduced the "unrepresented" decimal fraction from 11.5625 to 10.1258. The bill, *An act for the apportionment of representatives among the several states, according to the fifth census*, was sent to the Senate for concurrence.

---

[25] Ibid, February 2, 1838: 278-82.
[26] Ibid, February 2, 1832: 276-82.
[27] Ibid, February 8, 1832: 309.
[28] Ibid: 309-17.
[29] Ibid, February 9, 1832: 322-25.
[30] Ibid, February 14, 1832: 344-50.
[31] Ibid, February 15, 1832: 352-61.
[32] Ibid, February 16, 1832: 368-70.

Table 2.12. The House bill comparing the results of using a divisor of 48000 with 47700.

State	Population	d = 48000	Seats	d = 47700	Seats
Maine 7	399454	8.3220	8	8.3743	8
New Hampshire 6	269326	5.6110	5	5.6462	5
Massachusetts 13	610408	12.7168	12	12.7968	12
Rhode Island 2	97194	2.0249	2	2.0376	2
Connecticut 6	297665	6.2014	6	6.2404	6
Vermont 5	280657	5.8470	5	5.8838	5
New York 34	1918578	39.9704	39	40.2218	40
New Jersey 6	319922	6.6650	6	6.7070	6
Pennsylvania 26	1348072	28.0848	28	28.2615	28
Delaware 1	75432	1.5715	1	1.5814	1
Maryland 9	405843	8.4551	8	8.5082	8
Virginia 22	1023503	21.3230	21	21.4571	21
North Carolina 13	639747	13.3281	13	13.4119	13
South Carolina 9	455025	9.4797	9	9.5393	9
Georgia 7	429811	8.9544	8	9.0107	9
Kentucky12	621832	12.9548	12	13.0363	13
Tennessee 9	625263	13.0263	13	13.1082	13
Ohio 14	937901	19.5396	19	19.6625	19
Indiana 3	343031	7.1465	7	7.1914	7
Mississippi 1	110358	2.2991	2	2.3136	2
Illinois 1	157147	3.2739	3	3.2945	3
Louisiana 3	171904	3.5813	3	3.6039	3
Missouri 1	130419	2.7171	2	2.7342	2
Alabama 3	262508	5.4689	5	5.5033	5
USA 213	11931000	248.5625	237	250.1258	240

Section 2.4.3   The Senate Bill

The Senate received the bill the same day, Thursday, 16 February 1832. It was read and agreed to pass to a second reading.[33] The next day Daniel Webster (MA) successfully moved that the bill be referred to a select committee of seven. Messrs. Webster, Buckner (MO), Hayne (SC), Marcy (NY), Tipton (IN), Dallas (PA), and Forsyth (GA) were appointed.

On 1 March 1832 Mr. Webster proposed an amendment to the House bill to change the methodology of apportionment. He proposed that first a divisor of 47000 be applied. Then each state would be awarded the quotient rounded down. However, if a state has a remainder fraction greater than 25000, then the state will be awarded an additional seat.   Hence, instead of all state quotients being rounded down, Webster is proposing a criterion for which a state's quotient is rounded up.

---

[33] Senate Journal, February 16, 1832: 139.

Mr. Webster then launched into a rationale for his amendment that was based on fractions. Webster first noted that the House bill could be generated using a divisor of 47700 or 47000. The only effect that increasing 47000 to 47700 had was to decrease the fractions but the final apportionment was exactly the same. The calculations relevant to Webster's amendment and argument on fractions are presented in Table 2.13. Webster's amendment proposal increases the House size from 240 to 255. Webster argued that the House bill would reduce the seats for four states (NH, MA, MD, VA). He felt that no state should experience a decrease in its number of seats. Finally, Webster noted a quota rule violation in the House bill for New York (see Table 2.14, next page, Quota/Seats columns). However, Webster at this time merely noted the flaw and did not exploit it.[34]

Table 2.13. A comparison of Webster's proposal with the House bill.

State	Population	$d = 48000$	Seats	$d = 47700$	Seats	$d = 47000$	Seats	Webster	Seats
Maine 7	399454	8.3220	8	8.3743	8	8.4990	8	23454	8
New Hampshire 6	269326	5.6110	5	5.6462	5	5.7303	5	34326	6
Massachusetts 13	610408	12.7168	12	12.7968	12	12.9874	12	46408	13
Rhode Island 2	97194	2.0249	2	2.0376	2	2.0680	2	3194	2
Connecticut 6	297665	6.2014	6	6.2404	6	6.3333	6	15665	6
Vermont 5	280657	5.8470	5	5.8838	5	5.9714	5	45657	6
New York 34	1918578	39.9704	39	40.2218	40	40.8208	40	38578	41
New Jersey 6	319922	6.6650	6	6.7070	6	6.8069	6	37922	7
Pennsylvania 26	1348072	28.0848	28	28.2615	28	28.6824	28	32072	29
Delaware 1	75432	1.5715	1	1.5814	1	1.6049	1	28432	2
Maryland 9	405843	8.4551	8	8.5082	8	8.6350	8	29843	9
Virginia 22	1023503	21.3230	21	21.4571	21	21.7767	21	36503	22
North Carolina 13	639747	13.3281	13	13.4119	13	13.6116	13	28747	14
South Carolina 9	455025	9.4797	9	9.5393	9	9.6814	9	32025	10
Georgia 7	429811	8.9544	8	9.0107	9	9.1449	9	6811	9
Kentucky 12	621832	12.9548	12	13.0363	13	13.2305	13	10832	13
Tennessee 9	625263	13.0263	13	13.1082	13	13.3035	13	14263	13
Ohio 14	937901	19.5396	19	19.6625	19	19.9553	19	44901	20
Indiana 3	343031	7.1465	7	7.1914	7	7.2985	7	14031	7
Mississippi 1	110358	2.2991	2	2.3136	2	2.3480	2	16358	2
Illinois 1	157147	3.2739	3	3.2945	3	3.3436	3	16147	3
Louisiana 3	171904	3.5813	3	3.6039	3	3.6575	3	30904	4
Missouri 1	130419	2.7171	2	2.7342	2	2.7749	2	36419	3
Alabama 3	262508	5.4689	5	5.5033	5	5.5853	5	27508	6
USA 213	11931000	248.5625	237	250.1258	240	253.8511	240		255

---

[34] Register of Debates, Senate, 22nd Congress, 1st Session: 487-490.

Figure 2.14. A comparison between the House Bill with divisors 47700 and 47000, Webster #1, and Hamilton.

State	Population	d=47700	Seats	d=47000	Seats	Webster	Quota	Lower	Seats
Maine 7	399454	8.3743	8	8.4990	8	8	8.0353	8	8
New Hampshire 6	269326	5.6462	5	5.7303	5	6	5.4177	5	5
Massachusetts 13	610408	12.7968	12	12.9874	12	13	12.2788	12	12
Rhode Island 2	97194	2.0376	2	2.0680	2	2	1.9551	1	2
Connecticut 6	297665	6.2404	6	6.3333	6	6	5.9877	5	6
Vermont 5	280657	5.8838	5	5.9714	5	6	5.6456	5	6
New York 34	1918578	40.2218	40	40.8208	40	41	38.5935	38	39
New Jersey 6	319922	6.7070	6	6.8069	6	7	6.4354	6	6
Pennsylvania 26	1348072	28.2615	28	28.6824	28	29	27.1174	27	27
Delaware 1	75432	1.5814	1	1.6049	1	2	1.5174	1	2
Maryland 9	405843	8.5082	8	8.6350	8	9	8.1638	8	8
Virginia 22	1023503	21.4571	21	21.7767	21	22	20.5884	20	21
North Carolina 13	639747	13.4119	13	13.6116	13	14	12.8689	12	13
South Carolina 9	455025	9.5393	9	9.6814	9	10	9.1531	9	9
Georgia 7	429811	9.0107	9	9.1449	9	9	8.6459	8	9
Kentucky 12	621832	13.0363	13	13.2305	13	13	12.5086	12	12
Tennessee 9	625263	13.1082	13	13.3035	13	13	12.5776	12	13
Ohio 14	937901	19.6625	19	19.9553	19	20	18.8665	18	19
Indiana 3	343031	7.1914	7	7.2985	7	7	6.9003	6	7
Mississippi 1	110358	2.3136	2	2.3480	2	2	2.2199	2	2
Illinois 1	157147	3.2945	3	3.3436	3	3	3.1611	3	3
Louisiana 3	171904	3.6039	3	3.6575	3	4	3.4580	3	3
Missouri 1	130419	2.7342	2	2.7749	2	3	2.6235	2	3
Alabama 3	262508	5.5033	5	5.5853	5	6	5.2805	5	5
USA 213	11931000	250.1258	240	253.8511	240	255	240	228	240

Following Webster's proposal, on 5 March William Marcy (NY) gave an extensive rebuttal. Mr. Marcy summarized Webster's opposition to the House bill into two points: inequality and constitutionality. Marcy proceeded to give cogent arguments that the House bill constructed using a divisor method was constitutional and that it was Webster's proposal based on a Hamilton style method that was unconstitutional. He summarized that the "inequality" arguments were all based on "fractions." Marcy argued that the problem with fractions can never be eliminated; further, an apportionment methodology driven by fractions was unconstitutional. Marcy even turned a key Webster argument against him. Webster noted that using a divisor of 47000 or 47700 produced the same House bill. The only difference between the two divisors was their resulting fractions, not the seats awarded. So, any method adjusting for fractions would yield different adjustments on the same apportionment bill![35]

---

[35] Ibid: 503-9.

Clearly, Webster was thinking intensely about methods of apportionment. The next day, 6 March, Webster switched gears and offered a new amendment: apportion by distributing 256 seats using Hamilton's method. Webster articulated the fraction rule for quotas by stating that a state receives an additional seat from the lower quota if the decimal part of the quota "will bring its number of representatives nearer to its exact proportion than the omission of such additional member." This occurs precisely "where a fraction exceeds a moiety of the common representative number." This expression is an archaic way of saying that one should round the decimal in the usual way; i.e., round the decimal up if the fraction part is at least 0.5.[36] Perhaps Webster chose the House size 256 because of the feature that a quota would be rounded up if and only if its decimal fraction was greater than 0.5.

The fraction issue bothered several senators. For example, Nathaniel Silsbee (MA) argued as follows: the national population divided by the House divisor, 47700, yields a House of 250+; but the House bill distributes only 240 seats. Where have the other 10+ representatives gone? This leaves 480,731 people unrepresented, 4% of the entire population.[37]

Earlier, William Marcy presented his argument that a round up criterion was a rob Peter to pay Paul scenario. A state was rounded up, he accused, by taking a smaller fraction from one state and giving it to a state with a larger fraction so that the state could be allocated an additional seat. He saw such as a virtual redistribution of the population of one state into the boundaries of another.[38] Hugh White (TN) put the argument in basic terms. Webster's new proposal "was not an equal rule, applicable to each State, and operating in like manner upon each State. The rule gives an additional member to each of the twelve major fractions and withholds it from the twelve minor fractions. … It was the same old plan, presented in a new shape, which, forty years ago, was repudiated as unconstitutional."[39]

John Forsyth (GA) moved that the Senate strike that part of Webster's amendment that would provide for a representation of fractions (i.e., give an additional seat if some rounding criterion is met). On 12 March a vote was taken on Forsyth's motion; passed, 24-23. Webster then withdrew his proposal indicating that his amendment was no longer of any consequence. Instantly, the divisor game began. Isaac Hill (NH) moved to strike 47700 from the House bill and replace by 44000. Then Littleton Tazewell (VA) requested the motion be divided into its component parts: the strike out and the replacement number. The component to strike out was defeated. So, the divisor game ended as soon as it started. This cleared the way for the House bill. A vote was taken to proceed to a third reading of the House bill; passed, 27-20.[40]

What appeared settled on 12 March became unsettled on 27 March. A motion to reconsider passed 26-20. The House bill was committed to a select committee of five senators: Messrs. Webster (MA), Clayton (DE), Mangum (NC), Forsyth (GA), and Hayne (SC). On 5 April,

---

[36] Ibid, 513-4.
[37] Ibid, 518.
[38] Ibid, 516-7.
[39] Ibid, 521.
[40] Ibid, 530.

on behalf of the select committee, Webster presented an extensive report to the Senate.[41] The committee recommended another amendment to the House bill. The plan was Hamilton's method with House size a blank to be determined by the Senate acting as a Committee of the Whole. However, the rule for rounding a state's quota was stated in a nebulous fashion, "there shall be chosen within each State that number of representatives which is the nearest to its exact proportion of representation in a House of — members, as aforesaid, according to its population compared with the whole population of the United States, both being computed agreeably to the rule of the constitution … ."[42] A later remark made it clear that the rounding rule is that specified by Hamilton's method.

However, Webster confuses the message, ending the report by introducing a basic divisor method in which rounding of a decimal number is achieved by a method recommended in a recent letter from James Dean, a mathematics professor at the University of Vermont. The report includes the following extract from Professor Dean's letter.[43]

> I cannot express my rule so densely and perspicuously as I could wish, but its meaning is, that each State shall have such a number of representatives, that the population for each shall be the nearest possible, whether over or under, to [—]. The number for each State may be ascertained thus: divide the representative number by the number assumed to fill the blank, disregarding the remainder; the quotient, or the next greater number, will be the number of representatives. In order to determine which is the proper one, divide the representative number of the State by the two numbers separately, then subtract the least quotient from the assumed number, and the assumed number from the quotient; and that from which results the least remainder, is the number of representatives for the State.

Webster's purpose in introducing Dean's method was to exploit it to substantiate his claim that in the House bill "its ratio is arbitrary, and its proposed number of the House is arbitrary; that is, the number is not to be found by any process; the necessary consequence is, that no State's share of the House is found by any rule of proportion."[44] This argument was probably advanced as the flip side to the point in Washington's veto message that the original congressional bill in 1792 could not be constructed on the basis of a single divisor.

Webster then provided a table illustrating Dean's method using a divisor of 49496. This cryptic divisor is the national divisor based on a House size of 241; i.e., national population divided by 241. Although Dean's method is an engaging, out-of-the box way of thinking, it has nothing to do with the committee's recommendation. Even the Register's recorder added a note following the Dean table, "The principle laid down by Professor Dean appears to be this: each State should have that share of representation which bears the nearest possible

---

[41] Appendix to Gales and Seaton's Register of Debates, 22nd Congress, 1st Session: 92-99.
[42] Ibid, 98.
[43] Ibid.
[44] Ibid, 99.

proportion to the ratio assumed."[45] Dean's independent proposal is exactly the same as a forgotten proposal made by Fisher Ames during the debates based on the 1790 census.

The report took a while to digest as the Senate did not resume the debate until 25 April. Webster reported that "he was instructed by the committee to move to fill the blank with 241." Webster then referred the senators to printed tables and explained the method.[46]

After Webster's remarks, a cogent rebuttal was given by George Dallas (PA).

> I have come to the conclusion that the question of preference between the bill, as sent to us by the House of Representatives, and the projet of the Senator from Massachusetts, cannot be satisfactorily determined by a comparison of minute calculations, but must be governed by broad and general principles. The unequal results of the two plans may be strongly and variously illustrated by an endless series of estimates. ... it is impossible, as I apprehend, to attain any firm conviction by balancing one set of arithmetical details against another.[47]

Mr. Dallas continued that the House should have priority in deciding its own makeup. Then he made a strong appeal to tradition, noting how the first apportionment act was based on the Jefferson basic divisor method and that this method has been used in enacting all subsequent apportionment acts. These comments were flavored by spiced appeals to the constitutionality of dismissing fractions. It is notable how Dallas's comments were a polished echo of sentiments expressed by James K. Polk in the House. It is thus interesting that James K. Polk selected George Dallas as his vice-president twelve years later.[48]

John Clayton (DE) then spoke on behalf of the select committee to defend the report and recommendation. He gave an extensive, detailed lecture on the history of congressional apportionment up to this point. His motivation was to support dealing with fractions through an appropriate round-up criterion.[49] Isaac Hill (NH) followed by stating that although the committee's amendment would be advantageous to his state, he was still opposed to adjusting for fractions. Regarding Hill's statements, the Register of Debates records, "In three lines, Washington has presented a more conclusive argument against the amendment, than has been furnished in the whole course of a long and protracted debate on the other side; and his foundation has not been shaken even by the elaborate, and ingenious, and plausible report of the committee." Hill argued that an hour's discussion in a jury of intelligent New Hampshire farmers would rule against adjusting for fractions.[50]

---

[45] Ibid.
[46] Register of Debates, 22nd Congress, 1st Session: 835.
[47] Ibid, 835.
[48] Ibid, 835-841.
[49] Ibid, 841-863.
[50] Ibid, 863-4.

A vote was then taken on the amendment of the special committee: 22-22. Vice-President John C. Calhoun, as President of the Senate, broke the tie voting aye; hence, the motion passed. The business now was to fill in the blank to decide the size of the House. A motion for 256 was defeated, 19-21. Then, a motion for 251 passed, 27-14. The resulting bill then passed, 23-20.[51]

Table 2.15 (next page) presents the spreadsheet calculations needed for the apportionment debate thus far. The State column lists each state with its current number of seats in Congress. The Population column gives the apportionment populations for each state. The Quotient column shows the quotients resulting from the 47700 divisor where quotient = (state population)/47700. The Lower column shows the number of seats awarded by Jefferson's method of assigning the lower (integer) part of the quotient. The Webster column shows the number of seats by rounding the quotient in the usual way. Note that in using the basic divisor of 47700, Jefferson's method creates a House with 240 seats; Webster's method, 251 seats. The Quota, Lower, and Seats columns show the results of apportioning 251 seats using Hamilton's method. Finally, on Thursday, 26 April 1822, the Senate apportionment bill was read the third time and passed 20-18.[52] The bill was then sent to the House for concurrence.

Easily, Daniel Webster was the leading figure in the Senate over apportionment. Today, an important method of apportionment is called Webster's Method. It is named for Webster, like so many items, not because he originated it, but because he was a key leader in articulating and advocating it. Daniel Webster is an important person in American History (Figure 2.7 [53] [54]).

Daniel Webster was arguably the best orator ever to serve in Congress. He was a representative for New Hampshire from 1813-17; then, Massachusetts from 1845-50. He was a Whig leader in the Senate, serving from 1827-41 and 1845-50. In Congress he was a staunch supporter of American nationalism and a strong Federal government. He served twice as Secretary of State, 1841-3 and 1850-2. He is noted for his role in the Webster-Ashburton Treaty (1842) that settled the boundary of Maine avoiding another war with Great Britain.

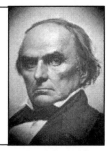

Figure 2.7. Daniel Webster.

Why did the Senate so easily decide on a House size of 251? An easy explanation is the convergence of methodologies. Reform senators led by Daniel Webster intensely wanted to correct the perceived injustice due to fractions. The method recommended by the report of the select committee was to abandon the basic divisor method in favor of the quota method. In an arithmetical twist of good fate for Webster, rounding the quotients in the basic divisor method by moiety (round up if the fraction part of the decimal quotient is greater than 0.5)

---

[51] Ibid, 865-6.

[52] Ibid, 866.

[53] Wikimedia Commons contributors, "File:DanielWebster ca1847 Whipple 2403624668-crop.jpg," https://commons.wikimedia.org/w/index.php?title=File:DanielWebster_ca1847_Whipple_2403624668-crop.jpg&oldid=219254111 (accessed October 18, 2017).

[54] Robert Remini, *Daniel Webster: The Man and His Time*, W. W. Norton, 1997.

Table 2.15. The Senate bill.

State	Population	Quotient	Lower	Webster	Quota	Lower	Seats
Maine 7	399454	8.3743	8	8	8.4036	8	8
New Hampshire 6	269326	5.6462	5	6	5.6660	5	6
Massachusetts 13	610408	12.7968	12	13	12.8415	12	13
Rhode Island 2	97194	2.0376	2	2	2.0447	2	2
Connecticut 6	297665	6.2404	6	6	6.2622	6	6
Vermont 5	280657	5.8838	5	6	5.9044	5	6
New York 34	1918578	40.2218	40	40	40.3623	40	40
New Jersey 6	319922	6.7070	6	7	6.7304	6	7
Pennsylvania 26	1348072	28.2615	28	28	28.3602	28	28
Delaware 1	75432	1.5814	1	2	1.5869	1	2
Maryland 9	405843	8.5082	8	9	8.5380	8	9
Virginia 22	1023503	21.4571	21	21	21.5321	21	21
North Carolina 13	639747	13.4119	13	13	13.4588	13	13
South Carolina 9	455025	9.5393	9	10	9.5726	9	10
Georgia 7	429811	9.0107	9	9	9.0422	9	9
Kentucky 12	621832	13.0363	13	13	13.0819	13	13
Tennessee 9	625263	13.1082	13	13	13.1541	13	13
Ohio 14	937901	19.6625	19	20	19.7312	19	20
Indiana 3	343031	7.1914	7	7	7.2166	7	7
Mississippi 1	110358	2.3136	2	2	2.3217	2	2
Illinois 1	157147	3.2945	3	3	3.3060	3	3
Louisiana 3	171904	3.6039	3	4	3.6165	3	4
Missouri 1	130419	2.7342	2	3	2.7437	2	3
Alabama 3	262508	5.5033	5	6	5.5225	5	6
USA 213	11931000	250.1258	240	251	251.0000	240	251

created a House of size 251 and the resulting apportionment coincided perfectly with that produced by Hamilton's method.

Section 2.4.4   Resolution

On Thursday, 26 April 1832, the House received the message that the Senate passed H.R. 208 with an amendment, asking concurrence.[55] The next day Mr. Polk moved to suspend the order of business to act on the Senate amendment; passed. Polk then moved to refer the bill to a select committee; passed. Messrs. Polk (TN), Everett (MA), Hoffman (NY), Vance (OH), Muhlenberg (PA), Gordon (VA), and Jarvis (ME) were appointed to the select committee.[56]

A week later, on 3 May, Polk, on behalf of the select committee, recommended that the House disagree with the Senate amendment. Also, Polk submitted a Report of the Majority.[57]

---

[55] House Journal, April 26, 1832: 663.
[56] House Journal, April 27, 1832: 664.
[57] Appendix, Gales and Seaton's Register of Debates, 22nd Congress, 1st Session: 99-105.

It was brilliant. Polk meets Webster's arguments head on. Polk's skills as an analyst, debater, and politician are manifest in the report. On 7 May Edward Everett (MA) from the select committee filed A Report of the Minority.[58] [59] The report comes across as wonkish rather than enlightening in comparison to Polk's Report of the Majority.

On Monday, 14 May, Mr. Everett moved to amend the House bill by having it read

> from and after the third day of March, Anno Domini one thousand eight hundred and thirty-three, the House of Representatives shall consist of two hundred and fifty-six members; and, in order that the said representatives may be apportioned among the several States as near as may be according to their respective numbers, they shall be chosen in the following manner; that is to say: there shall be chosen within each State that number of representatives which is nearest to its exact proportion of representatives in a House of two hundred and fifty six members, as aforesaid, according to its population compared with the whole population of the United States,[60]

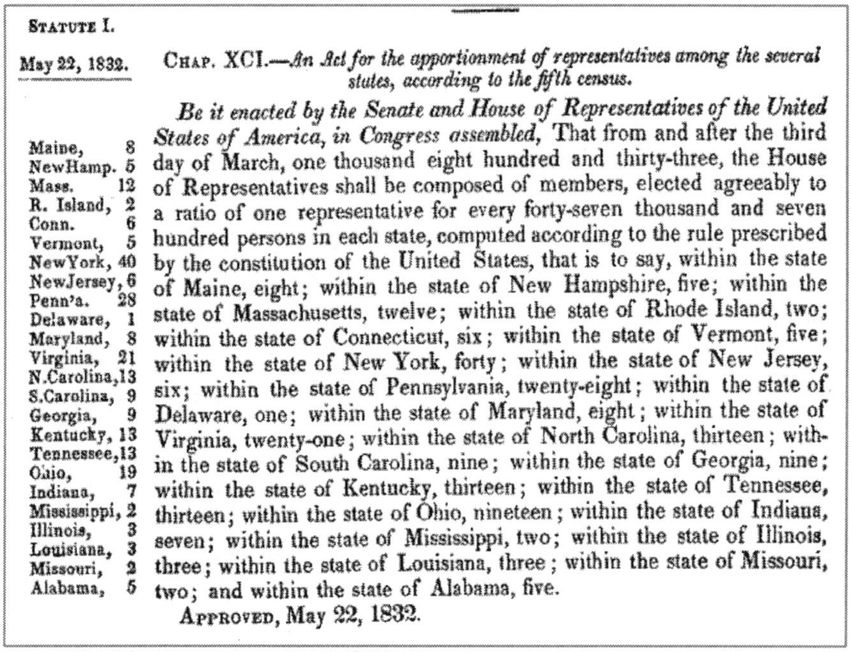
STATUTE I.

May 22, 1832.

CHAP. XCI.—*An Act for the apportionment of representatives among the several states, according to the fifth census.*

Maine,	8
NewHamp.	5
Mass.	12
R. Island,	2
Conn.	6
Vermont,	5
NewYork,	40
NewJersey,	6
Penn'a.	28
Delaware,	1
Maryland,	8
Virginia,	21
N.Carolina,	13
S.Carolina,	9
Georgia,	9
Kentucky,	13
Tennessee,	13
Ohio,	19
Indiana,	7
Mississippi,	2
Illinois,	3
Louisiana,	3
Missouri,	2
Alabama,	5

Be it enacted by the Senate and House of Representatives of the United States of America, in Congress assembled, That from and after the third day of March, one thousand eight hundred and thirty-three, the House of Representatives shall be composed of members, elected agreeably to a ratio of one representative for every forty-seven thousand and seven hundred persons in each state, computed according to the rule prescribed by the constitution of the United States, that is to say, within the state of Maine, eight; within the state of New Hampshire, five; within the state of Massachusetts, twelve; within the state of Rhode Island, two; within the state of Connecticut, six; within the state of Vermont, five; within the state of New York, forty; within the state of New Jersey, six; within the state of Pennsylvania, twenty-eight; within the state of Delaware, one; within the state of Maryland, eight; within the state of Virginia, twenty-one; within the state of North Carolina, thirteen; within the state of South Carolina, nine; within the state of Georgia, nine; within the state of Kentucky, thirteen; within the state of Tennessee, thirteen; within the state of Ohio, nineteen; within the state of Indiana, seven; within the state of Mississippi, two; within the state of Illinois, three; within the state of Louisiana, three; within the state of Missouri, two; and within the state of Alabama, five.

APPROVED, May 22, 1832.

Figure 2.8. The apportionment act of 1832.

It is unclear what method of apportionment Mr. Everett had in mind. It sounds like some hybrid of Hamilton's quota method with Webster's method of rounding; however, those two components are not always compatible. The problem is moot since the motion failed, 30-152. A vote to disagree with the Senate amendment passed, 134-57.[61]

The Senate caved to this action by the House on Saturday, 19 May. Hugh White (TN) moved that the Senate recede from their amendment; passed, 26-19.[62] The bill then passed to President Jackson who approved and signed *An Act for the apportionment of representatives among the several states, according to the fifth census* on 22 May 1832 (Figure 2.8).[63]

---

[58] House Journal, May 3, 1832: 712.

[59] Ibid, 105-11.

[60] House Journal, May 14, 1832: 744.

[61] House Journal, May 17, 1832: 749.

[62] Senate Journal, May 19, 1832: 287-8.

[63] Statutes at Large, 22nd Congress, STAT 1, Chap XCI: 516. Accessed from American Memory.

Section 2.4.5   The Aftermath

The debate over reapportionment based on the 1830 census added several ingredients to the apportionment stew and it began to simmer. Based on the 1790 census, the Jefferson basic divisor method was only challenged by a congressional bill based on Hamilton's method. But Washington's veto chilled that method. The Jefferson basic divisor method, although not unchallenged, was the method used to construct the apportionment acts based on the first five censuses from 1790-1830. But historical experience was exposing nagging problems formulated in the language of fractions.

The Jefferson basic divisor method had simplicity in its favor. It was an easy to understand, easy to apply 3-step algorithm.

1. How many people should a congressman represent? Answer, d.
2. Calculate each state's quotient based on d.
3. A state's apportionment is its quotient rounded down.

Even fairness seemed simple enough. If a state's quotient was 6.237 or 6.836, the state clearly merited 6 seats, but the state did not have enough for a 7th seat.

However, there was another simple rule of fairness that was easily acknowledged: the quota rule. If a state has 10% of the national population, then it should have 10% of the seats in the House. The original House bill based on the 1790 census had a quota rule violation that doomed it in competition with the Senate bill which had no quote rule violation. None of the first three apportionment acts had a quota rule violation. When a proposed bill had a quota violation, opponents exploited the fact to argue unfairness. The first act to display a quota rule violation was the apportionment act based on the 1820 census. However, in general, quota rule violations were few and perhaps were tolerated by advocates of the basic divisor method as by-products of a difficult process that had to deal with fractions.

The debate based on the 1830 census brought new proposals to the table. In particular, after steps 1 and 2 of a basic divisor method were completed, alternate techniques were offered for how to deal with the decimal quotient. The traditional Jefferson method was simply to discard the fraction part of the decimal quotient, i.e., round all decimal quotients down. Alternatively, Webster proposed to round by moiety, i.e., round in the usual way in that an additional seat should be added to a state if its decimal fraction exceeded 0.5. Additionally, there was the proposal of Dean that offered a different rounding criterion: round the quotient up or down according to which option yields a state constituency closer to the divisor.

In addition to these three decimal rounding criteria, Webster had another card which he did not play. After the House bill passed, John Quincy Adams (MA) was upset over the effects on New England. Adams wrote a letter to his colleague, Daniel Webster, chair of the Senate apportionment committee, proposing that quotients be rounded up rather than down.[64]

---

[64] Michel Balinski and H. Peyton Young, *Fair Representation: Meeting the Ideal of One Man, One Vote*, Brookings Institution Press, Second Edition, 2001: 26-8.

Hence, Webster had four schemes on his table for rounding the quotient decimal: Jefferson (down), Webster (usual), Dean (constituency), and Adams (up). How can one contrast and compare all these methods? There are two reasonable comparison methods based on the two approaches to the congressional apportionment problem: the constituency approach and the House size approach. The constituency approach starts with the question: how many people should a congressman represent? The House size approach begins with the question: how many seats should the House have?

One compares methods from the constituency approach by applying the first two steps of the basic divisor method and then comparing the results by using the different procedures for rounding the decimal in step 3. The results based on the 1790 census are given in Table 2.16.

Clearly Jefferson gives the minimum House size and Adams the maximum. Any method using a rounding criterion where some entries are rounded down and others rounded up, such as Webster or Dean, must yield an intermediate House size. Based on the 1790 census, the methods of Dean and Webster produce the same result. A bill formulated on the results produced by using Webster, Dean, or Adams would have been vetoed by President Washington based on his interpretation of the constitutional constraint that "the number of representatives shall not exceed one for every thirty thousand"[65] since Delaware's population was under 60000.

Table 2.16. Apportionment based on the 1790 census using the quotient rounding methods of Jefferson, Webster, Dean, and Adams.

State	Population	Quotient	Jefferson	Webster	Dean	Adams
Connecticut 5	236841	7.1770	7	7	7	8
Delaware 1	55540	1.6830	1	2	2	2
Georgia 3	70835	2.1465	2	2	2	3
Kentucky	68705	2.0820	2	2	2	3
Maryland 6	278514	8.4398	8	8	8	9
Massachusetts 8	475327	14.4038	14	14	14	15
New Hampshire 3	141822	4.2976	4	4	4	5
New Jersey 4	179570	5.4415	5	5	5	6
New York 6	331589	10.0482	10	10	10	11
North Carolina 5	353523	10.7128	10	11	11	11
Pennsylvania 8	432879	13.1175	13	13	13	14
Rhode Island 1	68446	2.0741	2	2	2	3
South Carolina 5	206236	6.2496	6	6	6	7
Vermont 2	85533	2.5919	2	3	3	3
Virginia 10	630560	19.1079	19	19	19	20
US 67	3615920	109.5733	105	108	108	120

---

[65] United States Constitution, Article I, Section 2, Paragraph 3.

Table 2.17 displays a similar spreadsheet analysis based on the 1830 census. The Quotient column uses a divisor of 47700; i.e., quotient = (state population)/47700. The four columns to the right round the quotient decimal by the methods of Jefferson (round down), Webster (moiety, usual rounding), Dean (closest constituency), and Adams (round up). Again, the Dean and Webster methods agree. This explains why Webster sometimes described the rounding by moiety and other times by constituency nearest the divisor. Also, as noted earlier, Jefferson has a quota rule violation for New York. Adams also has a quota rule violation for New York. With a House of size 264, New York's quota is 42.45 but Adams apportions New York only 41 seats. Webster and Dean have no quota rule violations for House size 251.

Table 2.17. *Apportionment results based on the 1830 census using the quotient rounding methods of Jefferson, Webster, Dean, and Adams.*

State	Population	Quotient	Jefferson	Webster	Dean	Adams
Maine 7	399454	8.3743	8	8	8	9
New Hampshire 6	269326	5.6462	5	6	6	6
Massachusetts 13	610408	12.7968	12	13	13	13
Rhode Island 2	97194	2.0376	2	2	2	3
Connecticut 6	297665	6.2404	6	6	6	7
Vermont 5	280657	5.8838	5	6	6	6
New York 34	1918578	40.2218	40	40	40	41
New Jersey 6	319922	6.7070	6	7	7	7
Pennsylvania 26	1348072	28.2615	28	28	28	29
Delaware 1	75432	1.5814	1	2	2	2
Maryland 9	405843	8.5082	8	9	9	9
Virginia 22	1023503	21.4571	21	21	21	22
North Carolina 13	639747	13.4119	13	13	13	14
South Carolina 9	455025	9.5393	9	10	10	10
Georgia 7	429811	9.0107	9	9	9	10
Kentucky 12	621832	13.0363	13	13	13	14
Tennessee 9	625263	13.1082	13	13	13	14
Ohio 14	937901	19.6625	19	20	20	20
Indiana 3	343031	7.1914	7	7	7	8
Mississippi 1	110358	2.3136	2	2	2	3
Illinois 1	157147	3.2945	3	3	3	4
Louisiana 3	171904	3.6039	3	4	4	4
Missouri 1	130419	2.7342	2	3	3	3
Alabama 3	262508	5.5033	5	6	6	6
USA 213	11931000	250.1258	240	251	251	264

At this point one might conjecture that Webster's and Dean's method are equivalent. An analysis based on the 1810 census negates that conjecture (Table 2.18). The 1812 apportionment act was fabricated using a divisor of 35000. Using this divisor, Webster yields a House with 188 members: Dean, 189. Dean assigns an additional seat to Connecticut where Webster does not. Connecticut's quotient is 7.4805. Both Jefferson and Webster award Connecticut 7 seats; Adams, 8 seats. To determine how many seats Dean awards Connecticut, we need the corresponding constituencies. If Connecticut is awarded 7 seats, then its constituency is 261818/7 = 37403; if 8, then 261818/8 = 32727. Since 32727 is closer to the divisor 35000 than 37403, then Dean awards Connecticut 8 seats. Hence, Dean can award a state an additional seat even though its quotient decimal fraction is under 0.5.

State	Population	Quotient	Jefferson	Webster	Dean	Adams
Connecticut 7	261818	7.4805	7	7	8	8
Delaware 1	71004	2.0287	2	2	2	3
Georgia 4	210346	6.0099	6	6	6	7
Kentucky 6	374287	10.6939	10	11	11	11
Maryland 9	335946	9.5985	9	10	10	10
Massachusetts 17	700745	20.0213	20	20	20	21
New Hampshire 5	214460	6.1274	6	6	6	7
New Jersey y	241222	6.8921	6	7	7	7
New York 17	953043	27.2298	27	27	27	28
North Carolina 12	487971	13.9420	13	14	14	14
Ohio 1	230760	6.5931	6	7	7	7
Pennsylvania 18	809773	23.1364	23	23	23	24
Rhode Island 2	76888	2.1968	2	2	2	3
South Carolina 8	336569	9.6163	9	10	10	10
Tennessee 3	243913	6.9689	6	7	7	7
Vermont 4	217895	6.2256	6	6	6	7
Virginia 22	817594	23.3598	23	23	23	24
USA 142	6575234	188.1210	181	188	189	198

Table 2.18. Apportionment results based on the 1810 census using the quotient rounding methods of Jefferson, Webster, Dean, and Adams.

Thus far we have compared the methods of Jefferson, Webster, Dean, and Adams by comparing them as basic divisor methods. The only way the methods differ is how they round the decimal quotient. Accordingly, they yield different results for the size of the House.

Another way to compare methods is to use the House size approach. This is relevant today since now the size of the House is frozen by law at 435. Hence, to compare methods, we want to compare them in a way where the methods yield the same House size. To do this we must modify the divisor. This is the flip side of comparing using the constituency approach where one keeps the divisor constant, but the resulting House size will vary. Here, the House size is kept constant, but the needed divisor will vary. To make comparisons in this manner, we must apply a 5-step **modified divisor method**.

Step 1. Select the House size, *h*.
Step 2. Select a divisor, *d*.
Step 3. Calculate each state's quotient.
Step 4. Obtain each state's apportionment by rounding the quotient.
Step 5. If the state apportionments add up to *h*, then done;
else, modify *d* and go to step 3.

One can save considerable computation time by starting with a smart choice for Step 2. Today's textbooks usually start with the **standard divisor**, *s* = (national population)/*h*. Further, one needs a rounding criterion to apply in Step 4. The Jefferson criterion rounds the quotient down; Adams rounds the quotient up; Webster rounds by moiety (the usual way); and Dean rounds by constituency closest to the divisor.

CAUTION. All apportionment acts signed into law based on a census from 1790 to 1840 were created using a basic divisor method. A modified divisor method is useful here only for purposes of evaluation and comparison, not for purposes of describing the historical record.

We now illustrate this method of evaluation using the 1790 census (Table 2.19). The apportionment act of 1792 created a House with 105 members. How would these 105 seats be distributed if Webster's, Dean's, or Adam's method had been used to distribute the same sized House? To answer this question, we have a pre-set selection for Step 1, *h* = 105. For Step 2 the following divisors work: Jefferson, 33000; Webster 34500, Dean, 35000, and Adams 36500.

Surprisingly, Dean and Adams yield the same distribution of seats. But the methods of Jefferson, Webster, and Dean all yield different apportionments.

State	Population	Jefferson	Webster	Dean	Adams
Connecticut 5	236841	7	7	7	7
Delaware 1	55540	1	2	2	2
Georgia 3	70835	2	2	2	2
Kentucky	68705	2	2	2	2
Maryland 6	278514	8	8	8	8
Massachusetts 8	475327	14	14	14	14
New Hampshire 3	141822	4	4	4	4
New Jersey 4	179570	5	5	5	5
New York 6	331589	10	10	10	10
North Carolina 5	353523	10	10	10	10
Pennsylvania 8	432879	13	13	12	12
Rhode Island 1	68446	2	2	2	2
South Carolina 5	206236	6	6	6	6
Vermont 2	85533	2	2	3	3
Virginia 10	630560	19	18	18	18
USA 67	3615920	105	105	105	105

Table 2.19. Apportionment results based on the 1790 census using the quotient rounding methods of Jefferson, Webster, Dean, and Adams.

Table 2.20 displays a spreadsheet analysis for apportionment based on the 1830 census for House size 240 using the four methods of rounding a decimal. The following divisors work: Jefferson, 47700; Webster, 49800; Dean, 49900; and Adams, 52300. In Table 2.20 the Jefferson column shows the quotients by using the divisor 47700. The Seats column to the right of the Jefferson column are obtained by rounding those quotients by the Jefferson method of rounding, round down. The Webster column shows the quotients by using the divisor of 49800. The adjacent Seats column then rounds those quotients by the Webster method of rounding, moiety (usual rounding). The Dean column shows the quotients by using the divisor of 49900. The adjacent Seats column then rounds those quotients by the Dean method of rounding, closest constituency. Finally, the Adams column shows the quotients by using the divisor of 52300. The adjacent Seats column then rounds those quotients by the Adams method of rounding, round up. The four methods all apportion a 240 seat House differently. Webster and Dean come close in that apportionments differ for only two states, New York and Louisiana.

Table 2.20. Apportionment results based on the 1830 census using the House size 240 and applying the quotient rounding methods of Jefferson, Webster, Dean, and Adams.

State	Population	Jefferson	Seats	Webster	Seats	Dean	Seats	Adams	Seats
Maine 7	399454	8.3743	8	8.0212	8	8.0051	8	7.6377	8
New Hampshire 6	269326	5.6462	5	5.4082	5	5.3973	5	5.1496	6
Massachusetts 13	610408	12.7968	12	12.2572	12	12.2326	12	11.6713	12
RI 2	97194	2.0376	2	1.9517	2	1.9478	2	1.8584	2
Connecticut 6	297665	6.2404	6	5.9772	6	5.9652	6	5.6915	6
Vermont 5	280657	5.8838	5	5.6357	6	5.6244	6	5.3663	6
New York 34	1918578	40.2218	40	38.5257	39	38.4485	38	36.6841	37
New jersey 6	319922	6.7070	6	6.4241	6	6.4113	6	6.1171	7
Pennsylvania 26	1348072	28.2615	28	27.0697	27	27.0155	27	25.7758	26
Delaware 1	75432	1.5814	1	1.5147	2	1.5117	2	1.4423	2
Maryland 9	405843	8.5082	8	8.1495	8	8.1331	8	7.7599	8
Virginia 22	1023503	21.4571	21	20.5523	21	20.5111	21	19.5698	20
North Carolina 13	639747	13.4119	13	12.8463	13	12.8206	13	12.2323	13
South Carolina 9	455025	9.5393	9	9.1370	9	9.1187	9	8.7003	9
Georgia 7	429811	9.0107	9	8.6307	9	8.6134	9	8.2182	9
Kentucky 12	621832	13.0363	13	12.4866	12	12.4616	12	11.8897	12
Tennessee 9	625263	13.1082	13	12.5555	13	12.5303	13	11.9553	12
Ohio 14	937901	19.6625	19	18.8334	19	18.7956	19	17.9331	18
Indiana 3	343031	7.1914	7	6.8882	7	6.8744	7	6.5589	7
Mississippi 1	110358	2.3136	2	2.2160	2	2.2116	2	2.1101	3
Illinois 1	157147	3.2945	3	3.1556	3	3.1492	3	3.0047	4
Louisiana 3	171904	3.6039	3	3.4519	3	3.4450	4	3.2869	4
Missouri 1	130419	2.7342	2	2.6189	3	2.6136	3	2.4937	3
Alabama 3	262508	5.5033	5	5.2712	5	5.2607	5	5.0193	6
USA 213	11931000	250.1258	240		240		240		240

Section 2.4.6   Webster and Dean through a Mathematical Lens[66]

Recall the presentation of the congressional apportionment problem using mathematical notation.

Let $\mathcal{U} = \{S_1, S_2, \ldots, S_s\}$ where $s \in \mathbb{N}_2$ ($\mathbb{N}_k = \{n \in \mathbb{N} \mid n \geq k\}$).   The states.

Let $p_i = \text{pop}(S_i)$, $\vec{p} = <p_1, p_2, \ldots, p_s>$, and $p = \sum_1^s p_i$.   The census.

Determine $\vec{a} = <a_1, a_2, \ldots, a_s>$ where $a_i \in \mathbb{N}$.   The apportionment.

$\mathcal{U}$ represents the union of s states ($s \geq 2$ to avoid trivial cases). The vector $\vec{p}$ is the census and $\vec{a}$ is the apportionment vector. Each state's apportionment must be a natural number. The House size is given by $h = \sum_1^s a_i$. The only constitutional constraint on h is that $s \leq h \leq p/30000$.

The Webster and Dean methods are variations of a 3-step basic divisor method.

Step 1. Select $d \in \mathbb{N}_{30000}$.

Step 2. Calculate $q_i = p_i/d$. Let $n_i = \text{int}(q_i)$.

Step 3. Select $a_i \in \{n_i, n_i + 1\}$ where $a_i = n_i + 1$ if and only if

Dean: $p_i/(n_i + 1)$ is closer to d than p_i/n_i.

Webster: $q_i \geq n_i + 0.5$.

Think of d as the constituency target (Figure 2.9). Now n_i is the largest natural number such that $p_i/n_i \geq d$ and $n_i + 1$ is the smallest such that $p_i/(n_i+1) < d$. This is verified as follows.

$$n_i \leq q_i < n_i + 1$$

$$\Leftrightarrow \quad n_i \leq \frac{p_i}{d} < n_i + 1 \qquad \text{definition } q_i$$

$$\Leftrightarrow \quad \frac{n_i}{p_i} \leq \frac{1}{d} < \frac{n_i+1}{p_i} \qquad \text{divide through by } p_i$$

$$\Leftrightarrow \quad \frac{p_i}{n_i+1} < d \leq \frac{p_i}{n_i} \qquad \text{reciprocal inequality}$$

With d as the target and apportionment as a natural number, then p_i/n_i and $p_i/(n_i + 1)$ are the best shots that a basic divisor method can take at d. Dean merely asks, which shot comes closer to the target?

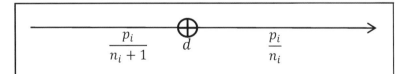

Figure 2.9. A geometric view of Dean's Method.

Hence, Dean's criterion for rounding is: $a_i = n_i+1$ iff $d - \frac{p_i}{n_i+1} \leq \frac{p_i}{n_i} - d$.

[66] Charles M. Biles, "Congressional Apportionment: A Liberal Arts Perspective" (2016). *Congressional Apportionment*. 24. http://digitalcommons.humboldt.edu/apportionment/24.

Applying some precalculus algebra yields

$$a_i = n_i + 1 \iff d - \frac{p_i}{n_i+1} \le \frac{p_i}{n_i} - d$$

$$\iff 2d \le \frac{p_i}{n_i} + \frac{p_i}{n_i+1}$$

$$\iff 2d \le p_i \left(\frac{1}{n_i} + \frac{1}{n_{i+1}} \right)$$

$$\iff \frac{2}{\frac{1}{n_i}+\frac{1}{n_i+1}} \le \frac{p_i}{d}$$

$$\iff HM(n_i, n_i + 1) \le q_i \qquad \text{Harmonic Mean}$$

Dean's criterion for rounding is mathematically equivalent to round up if and only if the quotient is greater than or equal to the harmonic mean (HM) of the options n_i and $n_i + 1$.

Webster's method is a remodel of Dean's method. Recall the view of Dean's method (see Figure 2.9). Now remodel the target range by considering

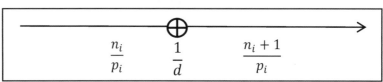

Figure 2.10. A geometric view of Webster's Method.

the reciprocal view of Dean's target range to obtain Webster's target range (Figure 2.10).

Where Dean puts the focus on the representative (congressman, how many people do you represent?), Webster puts the focus on the individual (sir/madam, how many representatives do you have?). This can be seen from the units of the target:

- Dean: d people/representative (constituency)
- Webster: $1/d$ representatives/person

Again, measuring distances (Figure 2.10), we obtain the rounding criterion

$$a_i = n_i + 1 \text{ if and only if } d - \frac{n_i+1}{p_i} \le \frac{n_i}{p_i} - d.$$

Applying some precalculus algebra yields

$$a_i = n_i + 1 \iff \frac{n_i+1}{p_i} - \frac{1}{d} \le \frac{1}{d} - \frac{n_i}{p_i}$$

$$\iff \frac{n_i}{p_i} + \frac{n_i+1}{p_i} \le \frac{2}{d}$$

$$\iff \frac{n_i+(n_i+1)}{2} \le \frac{p_i}{d}$$

$$\iff AM(n_i, n_i + 1) \le q_i \qquad \text{Arithmetic Mean}$$

The enlightening point here is that Webster's arithmetical rounding criterion is mathematically equivalent to rounding according to which option, n_i or $n_i + 1$, is closer to the targeted individual representation $1/d$, in contrast to Dean's targeted constituency d. Note that the half-way point between n_i and $n_i + 1$ is the arithmetic mean (AM) of the two options.

There is an ironic twist to this event in history. Dean, a mathematics professor, gave his proposal in practical political language. He was probably unaware of the mathematical equivalence of rounding the quotient up if and only if the quotient is greater than or equal to the harmonic mean of the round-down, round-up options. And Webster, the consummate politician, gave his proposal in simple mathematical language. He was probably unaware of the political equivalence of rounding the quotient up if and only if individual representation using the round-up option was closer to the representation target than the individual representation using the round-down option. Hence, the mathematician was unaware of the mathematical equivalency of his political proposal and the politician was unaware of the political equivalency of his arithmetical proposal.

Computations supporting the apportionment debate based on the 1830 census were extensive. Ebenezer Cummins prepared tables for a variety of possible divisors, a tedious chore that had to be done by hand. In the cover letter presenting his tables, Mr. Cummins wrote, "Whosoever may undertake to travel over the same field of numbers, without this chart to assist him, will find the journey long and intricate."[67] First, Cummins tabulated figures based on divisors from 48000 to 55000 in increments of 1000.[68] Later he presented tables for divisors 45000 to 47000.[69] For this he was paid $150,[70] equivalent to about $4203 in today's dollars.[71]

Using spreadsheets, we now calculate in a few minutes what took days in the 1830s. Noting Webster's observation that divisors of 47000 and 47700 both produced a House with 240 seats, we inquire, what range of values produce this House size? In a short time on a spreadsheet one gets the interval [46955,47756]. Since fractions were such a major concern, it behooved one to propose a divisor that would minimize fractions, i.e., minimize the number of "unrepresented people." This is done by minimizing the quantity $\sum_1^s (p_i - a_i d)$ for a fixed h, accomplished by maximizing the value of d that will yield h. For $h = 240$, this is accomplished with $d = 47756$. Hence, to the nearest hundred, 47700 is a best value for d for the purpose of minimizing fractions, making Polk's motion for $d = 47700$ look even more remarkable.

Americans can feel indebted to the in-depth work and reports issued by James K. Polk and Daniel Webster. These reports set the stage for evolutionary forces that would change the focus of congressional actions on reapportionment based on the 1840 census and end the Jefferson method as the basis for creating the apportionment act.

---

[67] Journal of the House of Delegates of the Commonwealth of Virginia, Printed by Thomas Ritchie, Printer to the Commonwealth, 1831, Doc. No. 16. Accessed 13 August 2019 from https://books.google.com/books?id=_WJNAAAAYAAJ&pg=RA1-PA162&lpg=RA1-PA162&dq=Cummins=bl&ots=rUivOz0vDC&sig=5K1beJpwms9gUIiJB6eIKfZyR_M&hl=en&sa=X&ei=V75fVPqkDMz8yQT484HQBw#v=onepage&q=Cummins&f=false; https://babel.hathitrust.org/cgi/pt?id=uc1.b3983198&view=1up&seq=449.

[68] Senate Journal, 22nd Congress, 1st Session, December 23, 1832: 38.

[69] Senate Journal, 22nd Congress, 1st Session, January 4, 1832: 56-7.

[70] Senate Journal, 22nd Congress, 1st Session, July 14, 1832: 474.

[71] https://www.officialdata.org/us/inflation/1830?amount=150.

Section 2.5: Reapportionment Based on the 1840 Census

Section 2.5.1   The 1840 Census

An act to provide for taking the sixth census or enumeration of the inhabitants of the United States was approved into law by President Martin Van Buren (1837-1841) on 3 March 1839.[1] Along with some amendments, the act specified that the sixth census should start 1 June 1840 and be completed four months later with results reported to the U. S. marshals by 1 November and delivered to the Secretary of State by 1 December.

The 1840 census accommodated two new states: Arkansas, admitted 15 June 1836,[2] and Michigan, admitted 26 January 1837,[3] bringing the nation to 26 states. At the time of the sixth census there were powerful political, social, and cultural forces at work. President Jackson's vendetta against the U. S. Bank and his Specie Circular of 1836 brought economic ruin, leading to the Panic of 1837 and contributing to the Panic of 1839. Martin Van Buren, inaugurated 4 March 1837, was unable to cope with the economic crisis and the President became known as Martin Van Ruin. This depression lasted until 1843 and its economic effects were exceeded only by the Great Depression.[4]

Van Buren served only one term, defeated in large part by the economy. Voter turnout was an astonishing 80.2% of all qualified voters.[5] William Henry Harrison was elected to succeed Van Buren. Harrison's presidency is the shortest on record, 4 March 1841 to 4 April 1841, the first president to die in office.[6] Vice-President John Tyler then succeeded to the presidency, the first Vice-President to do so. Tyler's detractors thus referred to him as "His Accidency."[7]

Critical forces were at work creating a cultural and political rift between the North and the South. Especially in the North, tremendous effects of fruition were being felt as a result of religious fervor and activity known as the Second Great Awakening. The Awakening was a major contributor to northern advances and "Yankee ingenuity." In contrast, the South grew, but did not progress. In the North there was so much excitement and individual initiative that a major part became known as "the burnt over region." This achievement was fueled with major contributions from the Americanization of Calvinism under the leadership of Roxanne and Lyman Beecher, and Charles Finney. Two forces emerging from the Second Great Awakening were the sobering temperance movement and the abolition movement. The South became conservative, and power was entrenched in the planter aristocracy. The preservation of slavery became synonymous with the preservation of the Southern way of life. In 1838 the

---

[1] Statutes at Large, 26th Congress, Stat I, Chap LXXX: 331-37.
[2] Statutes at Large, 24th Congress, Stat I, Chap C: 50-52.
[3] Statutes at Large, 24th Congress, Stat II, Chap VI: 144.
[4] Daniel Howe, *What Hath God Wrought: The Transformation of America, 1815-1848*, Oxford University Press, 2009: 483-508.
[5] Ibid, 576.
[6] http://www.whitehouse.gov/about/presidents/williamhenryharrison.
[7] http://www.whitehouse.gov/about/presidents/johntyler.

Presbyterian General Assembly split into a New School Assembly and an Old School Assembly. This rift was a preview of the horrible rift of the Civil War. The New School was engaged in progress and problem solving. The Old School was mired in tradition in discipline, struggling to maintain a lifestyle that was subsequently described as *Gone with the Wind*.[8]

Section 2.5.2   The House Bill

The results of the sixth census were presented to Congress on 23 December 1841. In anticipation, on Friday, 10 December, Millard Fillmore (NY) moved to appoint a select committee on the apportionment of representatives; passed.[9] The committee was appointed the following Monday, 13 December: Horace Everett (VT), Timothy Childs (NY), Robert L. Caruthers (TN), George W. Summers (VA), James A. Pearce (MD), John T. Stuart (IL), Benjamin A. Bidlack (PA), Edward Cross (AR), and John B. Weller (OH).[10] Items concerning apportionment were referred to this select committee.[11]

On Saturday, 22 January, Mr. Everett, on behalf of the select committee, reported H.R. 73, a bill for the apportionment of representatives among the several states according to the sixth census. The bill was based on the Jefferson basic divisor method using a divisor of 68000. It was accompanied by a report and read twice. Then, John Stuart (IL) moved that the bill be committed to the Committee of the Whole on the State of the Union.[12]

Mr. Everett was eager to get moving on H.R. 73. On 9 February he moved the resolution that 10000 copies of the census report be printed for use by the House.[13] On 14 February he moved a procedural change to get things going; defeated, 58-124.[14] Despite Mr. Everett's efforts, it would be more than a month before the House began considerations.

The House began considerations of H.R. 73 on Wednesday, 20 April, with the game of divisor. And 21 April was the super bowl of the divisor game which saw 84 congressmen sponsoring 59 different motions for establishing a divisor (Figure 2.11).[15] Behavior such as this was often cited by the majority Whig party as

Figure 2.11. *Excerpt from the Congressional Globe displaying the 59 proposed divisors.*

---

[8] Howe, 164-195.

[9] House Journal, December 10, 1841: 33-6.

[10] House Journal, December 13, 1841: 40.

[11] House Journal, 27th Congress, 2nd Session: 86, 107-8, 126-7, 221, 234.

[12] House Journal, January 22, 1842: 263-4.

[13] House Journal, February 9, 1842: 350.

[14] House Journal, February 14, 1842: 366-7.

[15] Congressional Globe, 27th Congress, 2nd Session, April 21, 1842: 435.

evidence for the need for reform in the House of Representatives. Politicians and the press often referred to the House as the "bear garden."[16]

The debates concerning the Apportionment Act of 1842 formed a complex web featuring four separate components:[17]

- The divisor, 20 April to 17 June;
- Congressional districts, 26 April to 17 June;
- President Tyler's signing message, 25 June to 16 July;
- Enforcement, 22 January 1844 to 14 February 1844.

We restrict our discussion only to the apportionment issue. The other issues were based on a variety of concerns, including federal vs. state power, and merit a study on their own.

The main steps in the debate can be followed via the various printings related to H.R. 73.[18]

- 22 January. Mr. Everett (VT) submits the original proposal based on the Jefferson basic divisor method with divisor 68000.
- 14 February. James Pearce (MD) proposed an amendment with divisor 53999.
- 7 March. Mr. Everett proposes to strike out 68000 and replace by 50391, yielding a House of 305 in which no state will have a decrease in its number of representatives. As an alternative, he would amend the amendment to have a divisor of 70680 yielding a House with 217 members.
- 27 April. Mr. Everett proposes an amendment with divisor 70680.
- 4 May. H.R. 73 now has the divisor 50179. The bill is read twice and sent to the Judiciary Committee.

The divisor game continued until 3 May 1842 when an amendment to use 50179 passed, 101-99. A motion to reconsider failed. The motion on the main bill passed, 113-87. The bill was sent to the Judiciary committee for final writing and then passed to the Senate for concurrence.[19]

The House bill, H.R. 73, had two sections. Section 1 simply dealt with apportionment by applying the Jefferson basic divisor method with divisor 50179. Section 2 read:[20]

> *And be it further enacted*, That in every case where a State is entitled to more than one Representative, the number to which each State shall be entitled under this

---

[16] Johanna Shields, Whigs Reform the "Bear Garden": Representation and the Apportionment Act of 1842, *Journal of the Early Republic*, 5(3), Autumn, 1985: 355-82.

[17] Martin Quitt, The Apportionment Act Debates of 1842 and 1844, *Journal of the Early Republic*, 28(4), Winter 2008: 627-51.

[18] Bills and Resolutions, House of Representatives, 27th Congress, 2nd Session, Bill 73: January 22, 1842; February 14, 1842; March 7, 1842; April 27, 1842; May 4, 1842; May 13, 1842.

[19] Ibid, May 3, 1842: 471-2.

[20] Congressional Globe, 27th Congress, 2nd Session, April 21, 1842: 472.

apportionment shall be elected by districts, composed of contiguous territory, equal in number to the number of Representatives to which said State may be entitled, no one district electing more than one Representative.

Hence, the apportionment bill began to incorporate other issues of representation beyond apportionment; in particular, the nature of congressional districts. The apportionment section of the bill was dealt with in committee by the select committee; the district section, by the Judiciary Committee, a standing committee of the House.

Table 2.21 displays a spreadsheet analysis for the House bill. The apportionment populations were obtained from an amendment to H.R. 73 proposed on 27 April 1842 by Mr. Everett.[21] The State column displays the states in the same order as Mr. Everett's amendment. The number next to each state gives the number of representatives the state has in the 27th Congress. The Population column gives the apportionment population; i.e., the constitutional three-fifths rule has been applied. The Quotient column is obtained by dividing 50179 into a state's population. The Seats column is the integer part of the quotient.

Table 2.21. House bill H.R. 73 based on the census of 1840.

State	Population	Quotient	Seats
Maine 8	501793	10.0001	10
New Hampshire 5	284574	5.6712	5
Massachusetts 12	737699	14.7013	14
Rhode Island 2	108828	2.1688	2
Connecticut 6	310008	6.1780	6
Vermont 5	291948	5.8181	5
New York 40	2428919	48.4051	48
New Jersey 6	373036	7.4341	7
Pennsylvania 28	1724007	34.3571	34
Delaware 1	77043	1.5354	1
Maryland 8	434124	8.6515	8
Virginia 21	1060202	21.1284	21
North Carolina 13	655092	13.0551	13
South Carolina 9	463583	9.2386	9
Georgia 9	579014	11.5390	11
Alabama 5	489343	9.7519	9
Mississippi 2	297567	5.9301	5
Louisiana 3	285030	5.6803	5
Tennessee 13	755986	15.0658	15
Kentucky 13	706925	14.0881	14
Ohio 19	1519466	30.2809	30
Indiana 7	685865	13.6684	13
Illinois 3	476051	9.4871	9
Missouri 2	360406	7.1824	7
Arkansas 1	89600	1.7856	1
Michigan 1	212267	4.2302	4
USA 242	15908376	317.0325	306

Section 2.5.3   The Senate Bill

On Wednesday, 4 May 1842, the Senate received a message from Mr. Clarke, clerk of the House of Representatives, that the House had passed H.R. 73, a bill for the apportionment of representatives among the several states, according to the sixth census, and requests the concurrence of the Senate. On motion of Robert Walker (MS), the bill was referred to the Senate's standing Committee on the Judiciary.[22]

---

[21] Bills and Resolutions, House of Representatives, 27th Congress, 2nd Session, Bill 73, April 27, 1842.
[22] Senate Journal, 27th Congress, 2nd Session, May 4, 1842: 326-7.

On Friday, 13 May, John Berrien (GA), on behalf of the Committee on the Judiciary, reported *AN ACT for the apportionment of Representatives among the several States, according to the sixth census.* This proposal amended Section 1 of H.R. 73 by replacing 50179 with 50000, and adding "one additional Representative for each State having a fraction greater than one moiety of the said ratio;" i.e., to use Webster's method of rounding the quotient decimal. The Committee also reported an amendment to Section 2 by adding clarifying language about congressional districts.[23]

Debate on the committee's amendments to the House bill began the following Tuesday, 24 May. On Wednesday, a vote was taken whether to agree with the committee's amendment to round by moiety; passed, 25-22. Then the Senate discussed the question to replace 50179 by 50000. Richard Bayard (DE) moved to strike 50179; passed, 25-23. By this action, the ratio was replaced by a blank.[24]

The next day the Senate began its game of divisor. To fill the blank ratio, 27 motions were made proposing divisors from 49594 to 92000. Of the 27 nominated divisors, 3 were less than 50179, the House figure in H.R. 73, and 24 were greater, with 19 of the proposed divisors larger than 60000. The main reference to the divisor was the resulting House size.[25] It was becoming clear that the sentiment of the Senate was to decrease the size of the House.

Decision time on the divisor began on Friday, 27 March. Voting began on the various proposals: 92000 failed, 10-36; 77000 failed, 12-34; 76000 failed, 16-30; 74000 failed, 21-24; 74391 failed, 22-23; 72354 failed, 22-24; 71257 passed, 25-21. Then Robert Walker (MS) moved to reconsider; passed. The bill was then tabled, 24-22.

On Monday the voting continued. A motion by Alexander Barrow (LA) to use 71257 was made and withdrawn. A motion to reconsider the divisor 74607 failed, 20-26. Then, Mr. Barrow moved the 70680 divisor proposed earlier by James Buchanan (PA); passed, 28-18. This completed the apportionment component, Section 1, of the Senate bill. Apportionment was to be accomplished using the Webster basic divisor method.

From 1 June to through 9 June the Senate debated the nuances of regulating congressional districts. On Friday, 10 June, the Senate completed debate and voting on Section 2 regarding congressional districts. A vote was taken to approve the bill as amended; passed, 25-19. Ironically, Senator Buchanan voted "nay." The bill with amendments was then sent back to the House for concurrence.[26]

---

[23] Congressional Globe, 27th Congress, 2nd Session, May 13, 1842: 496.
[24] Senate Journal, 27th Congress, 2nd Session, May 24, 1842: 356-7.
[25] Congressional Globe, 27th Congress, 2nd Session, May 13, 1842: 537-40.
[26] Senate Journal, 27th Congress, 2nd Session, June 10, 1842: 390-3.

Section 2.5.4   Resolution

The House was notified on Saturday, 11 June, of the Senate's passing of the apportionment bill with amendments, asking for the concurrence of the House.[27] On Monday the House voted to agree to the Senate amendment to Section 1; failed, 95-114.[28] On Tuesday the House rejected the Senate amendment to Section 2, 50-161.[29] The House then notified the Senate that the House did not concur with the Senate amendments.

On Wednesday, 15 June, the Senate resolved to insist on its amendments. In particular, the vote to strike the House divisor 50179 and replace with 70680 passed 30-14. It was ordered to so notify the House.[30] Upon receipt of the Senate notification, the House proceeded to take up the issue. After initially deciding to insist on their version,[31] on Friday the House voted to concur with the Senate's amendments. In particular, the vote to replace the divisor of 50179 by 70780 passed 113-104. The vote to round the quotient by moiety passed 110-102.[32] The resulting bill was then enrolled and sent to President Tyler for his approval. President Tyler signed the bill on Saturday, 25 June 1842 (Figure 2.12, next page).

The apportionment act of 1842 had four interesting features. First, the bill resulted in a House size of 223, the only time in U. S. history when the size of the House decreased by a reapportionment act based on the decennial census. Second, it is the first time that the Webster (moiety) method was used to round the quotients resulting from the specified divisor. This terminated the application of the Jefferson basic divisor method for fabricating an apportionment bill based on the census. Third, President Tyler's letter to the House:

> To the House of Representatives:
>
> I have this day approved and signed an act, which originated in the House of Representatives, entitled "An act for an apportionment of Representatives among the several States according to the sixth census," and have caused the same to be deposited in the office of the Secretary of State, accompanied by an exposition of my reasons for giving to it my sanction.
>
> JOHN TYLER. Washington, June 25, 1842.

The letter initiated a constitutional controversy initiated by John Quincy Adams.[33] [34] Fourth, the bill launched a full-scale debate about the design and implementation of congressional districts, an issue still unresolved to this day.[35]

---

[27] House Journal, 27th Congress, 2nd Session, June 11, 1842: 946.

[28] Ibid, June 13, 1842: 956-61.

[29] Ibid, June 14, 1842: 961-66.

[30] Senate Journal, June 15, 1842: 399-400.

[31] House Journal, June 15, 1842: 970, 975-8; June 16, 1842: 982-4.

[32] Ibid, June 17, 1842: 986-994.

[33] Congressional Globe, 27th Congress, 2nd Session, June 27, 1842: 689-90.

[34] Martin Quitt, Congressional (Partisan) Constitutionalism: The Apportionment Act Debates of 1842 and 1844, *Journal of the Early Republic*, 28(4), Winter 2008: 643-6.

[35] https://history.house.gov/Blog/2019/April/4-16-Apportionment-1/.

CHAP. XLVII.—*An Act for the apportionment of Representatives among the several States according to the sixth census. (a)*

Be it enacted by the Senate and House of Representatives of the United States of America in Congress assembled, That from and after the third day of March, one thousand eight hundred and forty-three, the House of Representatives shall be composed of members elected agreeably to a ratio of one Representative for every seventy thousand six hundred and eighty persons in each State, and of one additional representative for each State having a fraction greater than one moiety of the said ratio, computed according to the rule prescribed by the Constitution of the United States; that is to say: Within the State of Maine, seven; within the State of New Hampshire, four; within the State of Massachusetts, ten; within the State of Rhode Island, two; within the State of Connecticut, four; within the State of Vermont, four; within the State of New York, thirty-four; within the State of New Jersey, five; within the State of Pennsylvania, twenty-four; within the State of Delaware, one; within the State of Maryland, six; within the State of Virginia, fifteen; within the State of North Carolina, nine; within the State of South Carolina, seven; within the State of Georgia, eight; within the State of Alabama, seven; within the State of Louisiana, four; within the State of Mississippi, four; within the State of Tennessee, eleven; within the State of Kentucky, ten; within the State of Ohio, twenty-one; within the State of Indiana, ten; within the State of Illinois, seven; within the State of Missouri, five; within the State of Arkansas, one; and within the State of Michigan, three.

SEC. 2. *And be it further enacted,* That in every case where a State is entitled to more than one Representative, the number to which each State shall be entitled under this apportionment shall be elected by districts composed of contiguous territory equal in number to the number of Representatives to which said State may be entitled, no one district electing more than one Representative.

APPROVED, June 25, 1842.

Figure 2.12. The 1842 apportionment act signed by President Tyler.

Section 2.5.5   The Aftermath

In this section we apply our contrast and compare tests to the 1842 apportionment act. First, we apply the divisor approach in which we consider the effect of the various apportionment methods using the divisor 70680. Second, we apply the House size approach by considering the various results to distribute a House with 223 seats.

Table 2.22 (next page) displays the comparison of the Jefferson, Webster, Dean, and Adams basic divisor methods using the divisor 70680. The number next to each state is its current number of representatives in the 27th Congress. The Quotient column is computed by dividing each state's population by 70680. The four methods all yield different results. Notice the close call for Ohio in comparing Dean's and Webster's methods. Ohio's quotient is 21.4978, not enough to satisfy the criterion for getting an additional seat by Webster's moiety method. But Dean's method awards Ohio an additional seat if the quotient is greater than the harmonic mean of the round-down, round-up options. Here, HM(21,22) = 21.488+. Since Ohio's quotient is greater than the harmonic mean of 21 and 22, Dean awards Ohio an additional seat. All the methods except Adams result in a decrease in the House size.

State	Population	Quotient	Jefferson	Webster	Dean	Adams
Maine 8	501793	7.0995	7	7	7	8
New Hampshire 5	284574	4.0262	4	4	4	5
Massachusetts 12	737699	10.4372	10	10	10	11
Rhode Island 2	108828	1.5397	1	2	2	2
Connecticut 6	310008	4.3861	4	4	4	5
Vermont 5	291948	4.1306	4	4	4	5
New York 40	2428919	34.3650	34	34	34	35
New Jersey 6	373036	5.2778	5	5	5	6
Pennsylvania 28	1724007	24.3917	24	24	24	25
Delaware 1	77043	1.0900	1	1	1	2
Maryland 8	434124	6.1421	6	6	6	7
Virginia 21	1060202	15.0000	15	15	15	16
North Carolina 13	655092	9.2684	9	9	9	10
South Carolina 9	463583	6.5589	6	7	7	7
Georgia 9	579014	8.1920	8	8	8	9
Alabama 5	489343	6.9234	6	7	7	7
Mississippi 2	297567	4.2101	4	4	4	5
Louisiana 3	285030	4.0327	4	4	4	5
Tennessee 13	755986	10.6959	10	11	11	11
Kentucky 13	706925	10.0018	10	10	10	11
Ohio 19	1519466	21.4978	21	21	22	22
Indiana 7	685865	9.7038	9	10	10	10
Illinois 3	476051	6.7353	6	7	7	7
Missouri 2	360406	5.0991	5	5	5	6
Arkansas 1	89600	1.2677	1	1	1	2
Michigan 1	212267	3.0032	3	3	3	4
USA 242	15908376		217	223	224	243

Table 2.22. Spreadsheet analysis comparing basic divisor methods using divisor 70860.

Table 2.23 (next page) displays the comparison of the Hamilton quota method (Columns Quota/Lower/Seats) with the modified divisor methods of Jefferson, Webster, Dean, and Adams. The methods of Jefferson, Webster, Dean, and Adams need a modified divisor to achieve the result of House size 223. To this end the following divisors work: Jefferson, 68500; Webster, 70680; Dean 70750; and Adams, 75600. Hamilton, Dean, and Webster all yield the same distribution of 223 seats. The methods of Jefferson and Adams show quota rule anomalies. Jefferson has no direct quota rule violations; however, there is obvious favorable treatment given to New York, Pennsylvania, and Ohio from the viewpoint of the quota. In particular, New York's quota of 223 seats is 34.048; yet Jefferson distributes 35 seats to New York. All three of Jefferson's quota rule anomalies favor large states.

The flaws in the Adams distribution are even greater. There are quota rule violations for New York and Pennsylvania. New York's quota is 34.048; yet Adams distributes only 33 seats to New York. Pennsylvania's quota is 24.1667; yet Adams distributes only 23 seats to Pennsylvania. Further, with respect to the quota, Adams displays anomalies towards Connecticut, Delaware, Georgia, Tennessee, and Arkansas.

It was becoming quite clear that "divisor games" was no longer some amusement or trivial matter. The games were elevating into the realm of the warfare of power politics. The foundation for a search for a meaningful alternative was now well-established. An alternative was established by the Vinton Act of 1850.

Table 2.23. Spreadsheet analysis comparing basic divisor methods using divisor 70860.

State	Population	Quota	Lower	Seats	Jefferson	Webster	Dean	Adams
Maine 8	501793	7.0340	7	7	7	7	7	7
New Hampshire 5	284574	3.9891	3	4	4	4	4	4
Massachusetts 12	737699	10.3409	10	10	10	10	10	10
Rhode Island 2	108828	1.5255	1	2	1	2	2	2
Connecticut 6	310008	4.3456	4	4	4	4	4	5
Vermont 5	291948	4.0925	4	4	4	4	4	4
New York 40	2428919	34.0480	34	34	35	34	34	33
New Jersey 6	373036	5.2291	5	5	5	5	5	5
Pennsylvania 28	1724007	24.1667	24	24	25	24	24	23
Delaware 1	77043	1.0800	1	1	1	1	1	2
Maryland 8	434124	6.0855	6	6	6	6	6	6
Virginia 21	1060202	14.8617	14	15	15	15	15	15
North Carolina 13	655092	9.1829	9	9	9	9	9	9
South Carolina 9	463583	6.4984	6	7	6	7	7	7
Georgia 9	579014	8.1165	8	8	8	8	8	8
Alabama 5	489343	6.8595	6	7	7	7	7	7
Mississippi 2	297567	4.1712	4	4	4	4	4	4
Louisiana 3	285030	3.9955	3	4	4	4	4	4
Tennessee 13	755986	10.5972	10	11	11	11	11	10
Kentucky 13	706925	9.9095	9	10	10	10	10	10
Ohio 19	1519466	21.2995	21	21	22	21	21	21
Indiana 7	685865	9.6143	9	10	10	10	10	10
Illinois 3	476051	6.6732	6	7	6	7	7	7
Missouri 2	360406	5.0521	5	5	5	5	5	5
Arkansas 1	89600	1.2560	1	1	1	1	1	2
Michigan 1	212267	2.9755	2	3	3	3	3	3
USA 242	15908376	223.0000	212	223	223	223	223	223

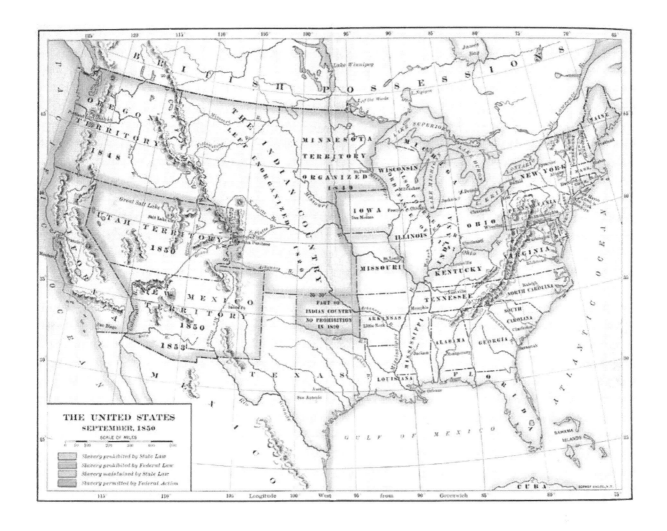

Chapter 3

Congressional Apportionment

Based on the Census

1850 – 1890

The Quota Method Era

Chapter 3
Congressional Apportionment Based on the Census: 1850-1890
The Quota Method Era

Table of Contents

Reference: The map on the cover page is courtesy of the Florida Center for Instruction Technology, http://etc.usf.edu/maps/pages/2900/2906/2906.htm.

Introduction

This chapter is devoted to the history of congressional apportionment to the national House of Representatives based on the census years 1850 – 1890. The Constitution directs that representation in the House shall be based on an enumeration of the people as determined by a decennial census. The census years 1850 – 1890 are based on the Hamilton-Vinton quota method for congressional apportionment.

Previously, the seats in the U. S. House of Representatives were created using a basic divisor method. The apportionment acts based on the census 1790-1830 were fabricated using the Jefferson basic divisor method. The 1840 apportionment act was written applying the Webster basic divisor method.

A Basic Divisor Method is a census-based method that is initiated by the constituency approach to congressional apportionment: how many people should a congressman represent? The answer is called the ratio, divisor, or constituency. Experience taught that there are political effects to the choice of divisor. In one day in the House during the apportionment debates based on the 1840 census, 84 congressmen sponsored 59 different divisors ranging from 30000 to 141000. During another day in the Senate there were 27 different proposed divisors ranging from 49594 to 92000. It became evident that local and regional power interests were dominating national fairness concerns.

Forces emerged to change the approach to apportionment from a constituency approach to a House size approach. The constituency initiating question, how many people should a congressman represent, was replaced by, what should be the size of the House? This leads to a different methodology that legislators hoped would take the politics out of a census-based reapportionment of the House. This time, however, it was not unacceptable political consequences that doomed the method but unexpected mathematical consequences that were revealed over the next fifty years.

---

[1] Congressional Globe, 32nd Congress, 1st Session, 7 April 1852: 994.

Section 3.1:   Reapportionment Based on the 1850 Census

Section 3.1.1   Background

The decade leading up to 1850 saw Manifest Destiny in full force. Primarily by settling the Oregon Territory problem with Great Britain and engineering the Mexican American war, President Polk succeeded in increasing the territorial size of the United States around 50 per cent. Five new states were considered for the 1850 census: Florida (admitted 3 March 1845), Texas (29 December 1845), Iowa (28 December 1846), Wisconsin (26 December 1848), and California (9 September 1850).[1]

The 30th Congress, 1st Session, House of Representatives, met in Washington, D. C., during its term from 4 March 1847 through 4 March 1849.[2] This took place during the last two years of the Polk administration. Polk was no lame-duck president. He campaigned on a pledge to serve only one term stating that he wanted to work full-time as president and avoid re-election politics. His administration worked diligently to streamline the federal government. In response Congress passed *An Act to establish the home Department, and to provide for the Treasury Department an Assistant Secretary of the Treasury, and a Commissioner of the Customs*, approved and signed into law by President Polk on 3 March 1849. The act created the Department of the Interior.[3]

Also approved on 3 March 1849 was *An Act to make Arrangements for taking the seventh Census*. Congress was establishing the machinery for conducting the census. The act created a Census Board to be occupied by the Secretary of State, the Attorney-General, and the Postmaster-General. The board was to prepare and print the necessary forms to be completed during the census.[4]

The 31st Congress, 1st session, opened at noon on Monday, 3 December 1849, with a contentious start. The first order of business was to select a Speaker. Finally, after 63 ballots, the most for Speaker in U. S. history, Howell Cobb (GA) was elected Speaker of the House.[5] The Speaker was sworn in on Saturday, 22 December. The contentiousness was a premonition. Ten years later, Howell Cobb became one of the founders of the Confederate States of America. He was the President of the Provincial Confederate Congress and served as CSA President in the two-week interim which elected Jefferson Davis.[6]

Zachary Taylor, succeeding James K. Polk, was inaugurated President on 4 March 1849 with Millard Fillmore as Vice-President. On 24 December 1849, after Congress was sworn in and

---

[1] http://www.50states.com/statehood.htm#.VG5gtsnN5r8.

[2] Annals of Congress, House of Representatives, 6th Congress, 1st Session, accessed at http://memory.loc.gov/cgi-bin/ampage?collId=llac&fileName=010/llac010.db&recNum=90

[3] Statutes at Large, 30th Congress, 2nd Session, Chap. CVIII: 395-7.

[4] Ibid, Chap. CXV: 402-3.

[5] House Journal, 31st Congress, 1st Session, 22 December 1850: 161-5.

[6] http://www.georgiaencyclopedia.org/articles/government-politics/howell-cobb-1815-1868.

seated, President Taylor delivered his State of the Union letter to Congress. The President's letter directed the attention of Congress to a buffet of issues. The letter was accompanied by reports from the Secretaries of the Interior, Treasury, War, Navy, and the Postmaster General appealing for congressional action. Attention was especially directed to growing pain issues resulting from the additional territory to the United States obtained as a result of the Mexican American War. President Taylor also asked Congress for legislation regulating an individual American citizen's activity in foreign affairs, and for amendments to existing laws of the African slave trade, "with a view to the effectual suppression of that barbarous traffic." A number of domestic issues were also cited that needed congressional attention.[7]

In this letter, President Taylor stated that the Executive is ready for action by Congress to authorize the 1850 census.[8]

> By the act of the 3d of March, 1849, a board was constituted to make arrangements for taking the seventh census, composed of the Secretary of State, the Attorney General, and the Postmaster General; and it was made the duty of this board "to prepare, and cause to be printed, such forms and schedules as might be necessary for the full enumeration of the inhabitants of the United States; and also proper forms and schedules for collecting, in statistical tables, under proper heads, such information as to mines, agriculture, commerce, manufactures, education, and other topics, as would exhibit a full view of the pursuits, industry, education, and resources of the country." The duties enjoined upon the census board thus established having been performed, it now rests with Congress to enact a law for carrying into effect the provision of the constitution which requires an actual enumeration of the people of the United States within the ensuing year.

Thus, President Taylor announced that the business of the Executive was in place and it was now up to Congress to act.

Section 3.1.2   The Congressional Bill

On 7 March 1850 the House referred consideration of the seventh census to the Committee on the Judiciary.[9] A month later James Thompson (MS), on behalf of the committee, reported bill No. 216, to provide for the taking of the seventh census, to the House.[10] But, three days later the House was notified that the Senate passed S. 76, *An act providing for the taking of the seventh census*, and asked for concurrence from the House. This was the first time in U. S. history that the Senate was first to submit a census bill. The bill concerned itself with the mechanics and authorization of the census; in particular, the census should be conducted by U. S. marshals and their assistants under the direction of the Secretary of the Interior. House bill

---

[7] House Journal, 31st Congress, 1st Session, 24 December 1849: 169-182.
[8] Ibid: 181.
[9] Ibid, 7 March 1850: 642
[10] Ibid, 8 April 1850: 758.

No. 216 was discharged from any further consideration and the Senate bill was referred to the House Committee on the Judiciary.[11]

The Committee reported S. 76 with many amendments on Monday, 11 April. The House decided to begin discussion on the bill and amendments on Wednesday and each subsequent day until the issue was resolved.[12] Debate proceeded for two weeks, mostly centered on the constitutionality of the bill. Was Congress constitutionally allowed to collect statistical data about people and occupations? Or was Congress constitutionally restricted to *only* making an enumeration? The strict view was passionately advanced by Daniel Miller (IA).[13]

> The language of the Constitution is clear, it is plain, there is no misunderstanding it. It requires an enumeration of the inhabitants to be made every ten years. There it stops; and I care not what may be the value of the information sought to be obtained; it is enough for me to know that the Constitution limits the duty that is to be performed, and we have no right to go beyond that limit.

This sentiment was supported by Alexander Stephens (GA) who felt that it may be the desire of States to collect the statistics asked in S. 76, but Congress had no constitutional authority to do so. Along with bickering about the constitutionality of gathering statistics, fears were raised about whether the data requested was really for information purposes or for tax purposes. The Constitution states that House apportionment and *direct taxes* are to be based on population. Some congressmen saw the data gathering as some plot to raise taxes.[14]

Then on Thursday Samuel Vinton (OH) rose to announce his intention of introducing two amendments. The first sought to establish a permanent mechanism for taking the census and apportioning the House. The second offered a particular mechanism for apportioning the House: set the House size and then distribute the seats using Hamilton's method. Mr. Vinton first noted that the current process demanded two separate acts of Congress: a census authorization act followed by an apportionment act. He argued that this established the government only on a temporary basis, 10 years at a time. Hence, if Congress failed to act by not passing a census authorization act or failed to apportion the House based on the census, then the government was in danger of collapse since it had no authorization to legislate.[15]

Mr. Vinton argued that his plan had five important benefits. The first is that "it completes the organization of the Government, and puts it beyond the reach of accident or faction from this cause." Second, "it obviates the necessity of future legislation in respect to the organization of the House." Third, fixing the size of the House will be made for reasons of national interest. Fourth, it eliminates the need of passing a decennial apportionment law and "thus save Congress from the waste of much time and from a disreputable contest about the

---

[11] Ibid, 11 April 1850: 771.
[12] Ibid, 22 April 1850: 792.
[13] Ibid, 24 April 1850: 811.
[14] Ibid: 809-14; 25 April 1850: 820-3.
[15] Ibid, 30 April 1850: 862.

unrepresented fractions." Fifth, it would save every state "much expense and inconvenience" because the state legislatures will not have to call a special session for the purpose of re-districting based on the new census-based apportionment act.[16]

Mr. Vinton's proposal contained three paragraphs. The first paragraph would make the 1850 census act permanent. Its provisions would become the decennial mechanism for the census and for apportionment until altered by Congress. If Congress failed to take any action, then the provisions of the act would go into effect automatically on 1 January xxx1. The second paragraph fixed the size of the House at 200. The third paragraph stipulated that as soon as the census is completed, then the Secretary of the Interior shall determine the apportionment population for each state and then determine the distribution of the House seats by Hamilton's method. The paragraph also contained a provision that the number of seats allocated to a new state is a temporary addition to the House until the next reapportionment.[17]

From 24 April through 6 May, the House considered Senate Bill S. 76 with amendments recommended by the Committee on the Judiciary. Consideration proceeded one section at a time through all 23 sections of the bill. On Monday, 6 May, Mr. Vinton introduced his amendments. The first amendment concerned the census bill; the second, apportionment. Mr. Vinton withdrew the second amendment for the time being so that the House could consider his proposals one at a time. The first amendment read, *Be it enacted*,

> That this act shall continue in force until altered or repealed; and if no other law be passed providing for the taking of any subsequent census of the United States, on or before the first day of January of any year when, by the Constitution of the United States, any future enumeration of the inhabitants thereof is required to be taken such census shall, in all things, be taken and completed according to the provisions of this act.[18]

James Thompson (PA) spoke strongly to endorse the amendment. It then passed with no further discussion. There was no dissent. Mr. Vinton then renewed his second amendment to apportion a House of 200 by Hamilton's method. John Crowell (OH) rose to amend by replacing 200 with 300; rejected. A House size frenzy, similar to the divisor frenzy based on the 1840 census, erupted in earnest. Orin Fowler (MA) moved to amend by replacing 200 with 260; rejected. George Jones (TN) moved to strike the figure 200; failed 44-73. Samuel Calvin (PA) moved to replace 200 by 230; rejected, 58-67. David Kaufmann (TX) moved to replace 200 by 150; rejected. Motions to replace 200 by 500, 225, 275, 240, and 231 all failed. Then Richard Bowie (MD) moved to replace the House size of 200 by a divisor of 100000; failed. Motions to replace 200 by 240, 251, 235, 234, 270, 180, 209, 234, and 233 either failed or were withdrawn. Finally, a vote was taken on Mr. Vinton's second amendment; passed, 72-63.[19]

---

[16] Ibid: 863.
[17] Ibid.
[18] Ibid, 7 May 1850: 923.
[19] Ibid, 7 May 1850: 929.

The House then took a critical vote on an amendment of Mr. Miller (OH) that would authorize the census only to enumerate the inhabitants and not take any statistics. The Miller amendment decisively failed, 50-92.[20]

James Thompson (PA) moved that the Committee of the Whole on the state of the Union rise and report the bill S. 76 as amended to the entire House; passed. He then moved to strike 200 and insert 233. After some procedural jostling, the House adjourned. The next day the House began by voting on amendments proposed by the Committee on the Judiciary but not decided by the Committee of the Whole on the state of the Union. Two technical amendments were quickly approved. A vote was taken on Mr. Vinton's first amendment which passed without further discussion. A vote was taken on Mr. Thompson's motion of the previous day; passed, 93-78. Hence, the House size now reads as 233. Mr. Vinton's second amendment then passed, 115-62. A vote was then taken on the complete, amended bill; passed, 109-61.[21]

Mr. Thompson's motion for a title of the bill passed. The official name thus became *An act providing for the taking of the seventh and subsequent censuses of the United States, fixing the number of representatives and providing for their future apportionment among the several States*.[22] The result was sent to the Senate for its concurrence. The Senate received the bill on Thursday, 9 May 1850, and referred it to a select committee on the census to recommend action on the House amendments. Messrs. John Davis (MA), Andrew Butler (SC), Joseph Underwood (KY). Daniel Sturgeon (PA), and James Shields (IL) were appointed to the select committee.[23]

Mr. Davis, on behalf of the select committee, reported back to the Senate on Monday. It was agreed to begin deliberations on the specifics the next day.[24] On Tuesday, discussion began in earnest to consider all 33 amendments offered by the House for the 24 sections of S. 76. Each section of the bill was read and the amendments to each section were considered in order.

The first of the Vinton amendments was immediately agreed to. The second Vinton amendment fixing the size of the House was then discussed. The select committee recommended replacing 233 by 200; failed, 17-27. Salmon Chase (OH) moved to replace 233 by 300; failed, 9-38. John Hale (NH) moved to replace 233 by 250; failed. Subsequently, the Senate voted to concur with the House amendment. At the end of the day, the Senate concurred with twenty-five of the House amendments, did not concur with six amendments, and agreed to two others with amendments. All of the Vinton proposals were agreed to. Disagreement only existed now with some details of the management and conduct of the census. The Senate also accepted the House title for the bill.[25]

---

[20] Ibid: 930.

[21] Ibid, 8 May 1850: 939-40.

[22] Ibid: 940.

[23] Senate Journal, 31st Congress, 1st Session, 9 May 1850: 328-9.

[24] The Congressional Globe, 31st Congress, 1st Session, 13 May 1850: 984-5.

[25] Ibid, 14 May 1850: 989-4; Senate Journal, 14 May 1850: 334-5.

On Wednesday the House was notified of the Senate's actions. On Thursday the House considered those actions. The two Senate amendments were agreed to. Of the six amendments that the Senate did not concur, the House decided to insist on three and recede on three. The House then resolved to appoint a conference committee to iron out the final details with the Senate. Messrs. Richard Meade (VA), Robert Schenck (OH), and Charles Morehead (KY) were appointed to represent the House in the conference committee.[26]

The Senate was notified the same day of the House desire to have a conference regarding S. 76. The Senate quickly agreed and Messrs. John Davis (MA), Joseph Underwood (KY), and Jesse Bright (IN) were appointed to represent the Senate. The joint conference committee quickly met and amicably came to agreement. The conference committee report was submitted on Monday and both chambers approved the report. The bill was then sent to President Taylor on Thursday, 23 May. President Taylor approved and signed the bill on the same day. The final combined census and apportionment act contains 27 sections.[27]

Shortly after passage of the census/apportionment bill the political scene was interrupted by the untimely death of President Zachary Taylor on 9 July 1850 in Washington, D.C. Vice-President Millard Fillmore then became the second vice-president to assume the presidency as a result of the death of the President. Millard Fillmore served the remaining three years of Zachary Taylor's term as President.[28]

Section 3.1.3   Apportionment

The census act of 1850 contained several mutations in the apportionment process. The most significant mutation was that the encompassing view of seating the House of Representatives was transformed from a representation problem into a formal apportionment problem. In a representation problem one transforms the census into a seating; i.e., a state population is transformed into a state constituency. This was accomplished by applying a basic divisor method. With the new view, along with the census, the House size is fixed. One then apportions (i.e., distributes) the given number of seats according to the population as determined by the census. This distribution was based on a quota method. The specific mechanics are referred to as the Hamilton method or Hamilton-Vinton method.[29]

The key congressman in providing this mutation was Representative Samuel Vinton, a Whig from Ohio (Figure 3.1, next page).[30] Mr. Vinton inaugurated the House size view in apportioning the House. Another key mutation proposed by Mr. Vinton and enacted in the 1850 census act was that apportionment was made an "automatic" process placed in the

---

[26] House Journal, 16 May 1850: 931-2.
[27] https://www.census.gov/history/pdf/1850_Census_Act.pdf.
[28] https://www.whitehouse.gov/about-the-white-house/presidents/millard-fillmore/.
[29] https://www.census.gov/history/www/reference/apportionment/methods_of_apportionment.html.
[30] Public domain portrait of Samuel Finley Vinton obtained from
http://en.wikipedia.org/wiki/Samuel_Finley_Vinton#mediaviewer/File:Samuel_Finley_Vinton_by_howe.png.

Department of the Interior. After the census was completed, the Secretary of the Interior was to make the apportionment calculations and subsequently notify Congress. This removed the decennial debate politicized by "fractions."

Figure 3.1. Samuel Vinton.

The first Report of the Superintendent of the Census was submitted on 1 December 1851. The report contained a table with the apportionment calculations showing the distribution of 233 seats in the House for the next congressional election (Table 3.1, next page).[31] The returns from California were incomplete because "a portion of the California returns was destroyed by the conflagration in San Francisco—."[32]

Table 3.2 (following Table 3.1) displays a spreadsheet that shows the calculations needed to obtain the apportionment results shown in Table 3.1. The States column shows the 31 states in the Union. The Population column shows their respective apportionment populations which incorporates the 3/5ths rule for slaves. The law set the House size at 233 with apportionment calculated by the Hamilton-Vinton quota method. Calculations needed for the Hamilton method of apportionment are displayed in the Quota/Lower/Seats columns.

For comparison the results of using a modified divisor method using the rounding methods of Jefferson, Dean, Webster, and Adams is also given in Table 2.16. To obtain a House with 233 members, the following divisors work: Jefferson 89000, Dean 94340, Webster 93400, and Adams 99450.

It is noteworthy that the Hamilton result is consistent with the modified Webster method of apportioning the House in that all 14 states awarded an additional seat had a quota whose decimal component was greater than 0.5. Louisiana got a tough break with a quota of 4.4939.

However, these apportionment calculations were only preliminary and based on a guesstimate from the incomplete returns from California. A series of devastating fires in San Francisco destroyed several of the census records. On 16 February 1852 the Senate received a message from President Fillmore in which he transmitted a report from the Secretary of the Interior describing his inability to make the final apportionment calculation as required by the law of 23 March 1850 as a consequence of incomplete returns from California. The President suggested that remedial legislation is necessary. The Senate then referred the President's letter to the Committee on the Judiciary.[33]

Table 3.1. *The apportionment population and apportionment of the House based on the 1850 census.*

---

[31] Report of the Superintendent of the Census, 1 December 1851; downloaded from http://www2.census.gov/prod2/decennial/documents/1850d-04.pdf.
[32] Ibid.
[33] Congressional Globe, 32nd Congress, 1st Session: 569.

160

Population of the United States, and representation in Thirty-third Congress.

STATES.	Whites.	Free colored.	Total free population.	Slaves.	Total population.	Representative population.	Number of representatives.	Fractions.	Present number of representatives.
Maine	581,813	1,356	563,169		563,169	563,169	6	2,631	7
New Hampshire	317,456	520	317,976		317,976	317,976	3	37,707	4
Vermont	313,402	718	314,120		314,120	314,120	3	33,851	4
Massachusetts	985,450	9,064	994,514		994,514	994,514	11	*60,284	10
Rhode Island	143,875	3,670	147,545		147,545	147,545	2	*54,122	2
Connecticut	363,099	7,693	370,792		370,792	370,792	4	*90,523	4
New York	3,048,325	49,069	3,097,394		3,097,394	3,097,394	33	14,435	34
Pennsylvania	2,258,463	53,383	2,311,786		2,311,786	2,311,786	25	*69,634	24
Ohio	1,955,108	25,319	1,980,427		1,980,427	1,980,427	21	18,544	21
Indiana	977,628	10,788	988,416		988,416	988,416	11	*54,186	10
Illinois	846,035	5,435	851,470		851,470	851,470	9	10,663	7
Michigan	395,097	2,557	397,654		397,654	397,654	4	23,962	3
Wisconsin	304,756	633	305,391		305,391	305,391	3	25,122	3
Iowa	191,879	335	192,214		192,214	192,214	2	5,368	2
California	91,632	965	92,597		92,597	92,597	2	92,351	
New Jersey	465,513	23,820	489,333	†922	489,555	489,466	5	*79,771	5
Delaware	71,169	18,073	89,242	2,290	91,532	90,616	1	18,150	1
Maryland	417,943	74,723	492,666	90,368	583,034	546,886	6	6,235	6
Virginia	894,800	54,333	949,133	472,528	1,421,661	1,232,649	13	*47,398	15
North Carolina	553,028	27,463	580,491	288,548	869,039	753,619	8	6,198	9
South Carolina	274,567	8,956	283,523	384,984	668,507	514,513	6	*73,976	7
Georgia	521,572	2,931	524,503	381,682	906,185	753,512	8	15,495	8
Alabama	426,486	2,293	428,779	342,892	771,671	634,514	7	46,146	7
Mississippi	295,718	930	296,648	309,878	606,526	482,574	5	*66,023	4
Louisiana	255,491	17,462	272,953	244,809	517,762	419,838	4	15,495	4
Tennessee	756,753	6,401	763,154	239,460	1,002,614	906,830	10	*66,023	11
Kentucky	761,417	10,007	771,424	210,981	982,405	898,012	10	*57,205	10
Missouri	592,004	2,618	594,622	87,422	682,044	647,075	7	*86,537	5
Arkansas	162,189	608	162,797	47,100	209,897	191,057	2	4,211	1
Florida	47,211	924	48,135	39,309	87,444	71,720	1		1
Texas	154,034	397	154,491	58,161	212,592	189,327	2	2,481	2
District of Columbia	38,027	9,973	48,000	3,687	51,687				
Utah Territory	11,330	24	11,354	26	11,380				
Minnesota Territory	6,038	39	6,077		6,077				
New Mexico Territory	61,520	17	61,547		61,547				
Oregon Territory	13,088	206	13,294		13,294				
Aggregate	19,553,928	433,643	19,987,573	3,204,347	23,191,918	21,767,673	234		233

* Have the addition of a member on account of the fractions.

† "Apprentices" by the "act to abolish slavery," passed April 18, 1846.

Table 3.2. *Spreadsheet analysis for the apportionment of the 233 seats in the House of Representatives among the 31 states as specified by the census act of 1850 and based on the 1850 census. Computations for the Hamilton method are displayed in the Quota/Lower/Seats columns.*

State	Population	Quota	Lower	Seats	Jefferson	Dean	Webster	Adams
ME	583169	6.2422	6	6	6	6	6	6
NH	317976	3.4036	3	3	3	3	3	4
VT	314120	3.3623	3	3	3	3	3	4
MA	994514	10.6452	10	11	11	11	11	11
RI	147545	1.5793	1	2	1	2	2	2
CT	370792	3.9689	3	4	4	4	4	4
NY	3097394	33.1543	33	33	34	33	33	32
PA	2311786	24.7452	24	25	25	25	25	24
OH	1980427	21.1984	21	21	22	21	21	20
IN	988416	10.5800	10	11	11	11	11	10
IL	851470	9.1141	9	9	9	9	9	9
MI	397654	4.2565	4	4	4	4	4	4
WI	305391	3.2689	3	3	3	3	3	4
IA	192214	2.0574	2	2	2	2	2	2
CA	92597	0.9912	0	1	1	1	1	1
NJ	489466	5.2392	5	5	5	5	5	5
DE	90616	0.9699	0	1	1	1	1	1
MD	546886	5.8538	5	6	6	6	6	6
VA	1232649	13.1942	13	13	13	13	13	13
NC	753619	8.0667	8	8	8	8	8	8
SC	514513	5.5073	5	6	5	5	6	6
GA	753512	8.0656	8	8	8	8	8	8
AL	634514	6.7918	6	7	7	7	7	7
MS	482574	5.1654	5	5	5	5	5	5
LA	419838	4.4939	4	4	4	5	4	5
TN	906830	9.7067	9	10	10	10	10	10
KY	898012	9.6123	9	10	10	10	10	10
MO	647075	6.9263	6	7	7	7	7	7
AR	191057	2.0451	2	2	2	2	2	2
FL	71720	0.7677	0	1	1	1	1	1
TX	189327	2.0265	2	2	2	2	2	2
	21767673	233.0000	219	233	233	233	233	233

At this juncture history featured the other important result of congressional apportionment: The Electoral College. The President is not elected directly by popular vote but by the Electoral College. In the College the states vote. The number of votes each state may cast equals its number of congresspersons: representatives plus two senators. Hence, congressional apportionment determines the number of votes each state casts in the Electoral College.

On 24 February Solon Borland (AR) introduced a joint resolution which was agreed to by the Senate.[34]

> That the number of electoral votes to which each State shall be entitled in the election of President and Vice-President of the United States in 1852, shall be equal to the number of Senators and Representatives to which each of said States will be found entitled by the apportionment under the enumeration of 1850, as provided by the act for "taking the Seventh, and subsequent Censuses," approved May 25, 1850.

On 10 March 1852 Solomon Downs (LA), on behalf of the Senate Committee on the Judiciary, reported on the resolution. John Davis (MA) noted the dilemma that "The College of Electors would act under the census of 1850, and the House of Representatives would be elected under the census of 1840." Mr. Downs responded that the Committee on the Judiciary considered this matter. However, that is the way things have always been done because "when the votes are counted, the Constitution requires that Congress shall be in session. It must, therefore, necessarily be the old Congress under the old apportionment, for the new Congress under the new apportionment cannot meet until the 3[d] of March next." The Judiciary Committee felt that the issue was so obvious that a joint resolution (Senate and House) was unnecessary and that a Senate resolution only was simpler and would suffice. The recommendation was adopted. [35]

Downs also submitted a report about the latest census results with a bill, S. 281, An Act supplementary to *An Act providing for the taking of the seventh and subsequent Censuses of the United States, and to fix the number of the Members of the House of Representatives, and provide for their future Apportionment among the several States*, approved 23 May 1850. The bill instructs the Secretary of the Interior to forthwith make the apportionment calculations based on the returns thus far submitted to the census office.[36] [37]

On 5 April 1852 debate began in earnest on the proposed bill.[38] The debate was interesting and driven by important issues and circumstances. George Badger (NC) said "there is no bill on the Senate calendar which ought to be taken up and disposed of sooner." Legislation was

---

[34] Ibid: 619.
[35] Ibid: 709.
[36] Senate Journal, 32nd Congress, 1st Session, 10 March 1850: 266.
[37] Bills and Resolutions, 32nd Congress, 1st Session S. 281, 10 March 1852; accessed from http://memory.loc.gov/cgi-bin/ampage?collId=llsb&fileName=032/llsb032.db&recNum=706.
[38] Congressional Globe, 32nd Congress, 1st Session, 5 April 1852:968-76.

needed because the Secretary of the Interior was unable to carry out the apportionment calculations required by the 1850 law because of difficulties with the census returns from California. The urgency was supported by Senator Davis (MA). Then, James Bradbury (VT) rose to move an amendment to the bill by adding the following section.[39]

> *And be it further enacted*, That the State of California shall be entitled to the same number of Representatives in Congress that said State now has; and that for this purpose the act of May 23d, 1850, providing for the apportionment of Representatives among the several States, be so amended that the whole number shall be two hundred and thirty-four instead of two hundred and twenty-three, until an apportionment under a new census.

Mr. Downs offered five reasons against the amendment. First, by the Constitution, reapportionment must be based on an enumeration of the population as determined by the census. Second, there were official returns from California. One cannot base apportionment calculations on mere estimates of the population. Mr. Downs, a member of the Committee on the Judiciary, claimed that there were enough official returns from California on which to determine apportionment and that as a result California merits one seat in the House. Third, the 1850 census act fixed the House size at 233. Since the method of apportionment applies to all states equally, no state can complain of the results. California currently held two seats based on population estimates when admitted as a state in 1850. Fourth, California's official census returns show a population of 117821. This entitles California to one seat based on a national divisor of 93420. In order to give California two seats in a House of 233, South Carolina would lose a seat even though South Carolina's fraction exceeded California's fraction. This is clearly unfair! Fifth, California has had ample time to make needed corrections to the official reports but nothing significant has been done in the past year. Mr. Downs concluded by stating that if this amendment passes, then he will insist that his state, Louisiana, be given an additional seat also (Louisiana's quota was 4.4939).[40]

Mr. Bradbury gave a determined rebuttal to Mr. Downs's arguments. He first acknowledged the importance of this topic. Then he phrased the key issue: "Shall a State be deprived of her just representation on account of the imperfection, or want of an accurate census of her population?" Mr. Bradbury noted that the census is the responsibility of the federal, not the state, government. He then offered cogent arguments that the returns from California were grossly inaccurate; in particular, the marshal who had charge of the census in California impeached the results. The State of California needed population figures to apportion the state legislature. The State used a population estimate of 300000 in April, 1851, for the purposes of state government. Mr. Bradbury argued

> In cases where the returns approximate to accuracy, we ought not to depart from them; but when they are shown to be so grossly incorrect as to afford no accurate

---

[39] Ibid: 968.
[40] Ibid: 978-9.

basis for an apportionment, and no approximation to the actual population, it would be unjust to the State to be governed by them.

Mr. Bradbury concluded that his amendment increases the size of the House from 233 to 234 so that South Carolina will not have to lose a seat to accommodate an additional seat for California.

William Gwin (CA) continued the argument. By law, the Secretary of the Interior cannot make the apportionment calculations until the census is complete. The census from California is not complete. The Downs supplementary act was offered because of a report from the Secretary of the Interior testifying that the returns from California are incomplete and remedial legislative action is needed. Mr. Gwin noted that the census for California was further complicated by Section 2 of a supplement to the census act that was approved on 30 August 1850 that directed that the census for California must include anyone who left any state or territory prior to 1 June 1850 and subsequently settled in California. This time period includes the noted gold rush (1848-1858).[41] Many of these people included miners who settled in remote regions and were transient, moving from one mine field to another. Accordingly, census work was expensive. Congress allocated only $5000 for the census in California; the marshal said he needed more like $50000. For example, one deputy was allotted $200 to complete his census job; yet his expenses exceeded $700. The deputy worked a while in the gold mines to earn the extra $500+ he needed just to do his job. Hence, the census reports were incomplete and inaccurate due to several complicating conditions: untimely fires, rapid migration, transience, and lack of funds.

The main proponents in the debate were Senator Downs vs. Senators Bradbury and Gwin. Downs argued for immediate apportionment using the returns that had been made for California (population 117821). Mr. Bradbury and Gwin argued this is unfair because the census figure is a gross undercount. Since the census is a federal responsibility, Congress needs to correct the resulting injustices.

William Seward (NY) rose as an interested spectator to the debate. Mr. Seward said at first his inclination was to side with Mr. Downs, but he had become persuaded by the arguments on behalf of California. He further noted that the amount in federal taxes paid by California proves that the official census returns for California are in error.

John Hale (NH) rose to speak his concern that the 1850 census act sets the House size at 233. Given the current census returns, California is awarded one seat and South Carolina six seats. If the enumeration for California is corrected and thereby California is awarded two seats, then, South Carolina's delegation must be reduced to five to keep the House size at 233. But the amendment increases the House size to 234 to restore the lost seat to South Carolina. Hence, Mr. Hale claimed, the effect of the amendment is to award South Carolina a seat it does not deserve based on the census.

---

[41] http://ocp.hul.harvard.edu/immigration/goldrush.html.

Henry Geyer (MO) rose to make the perceptive point that the 1850 census act fixes the size of the House at 233. With a fixed House size one then computes the national divisor: (national population)/233. So, to apportion, one must know the national population. Hence, without knowing the population of California apportionment cannot be done. The current situation has its embarrassments and difficulties. The problem can be solved if the population of California were known. But, the enumeration from California is faulty. It is important that apportionment be done soon. However, there is not enough time to census California. Further, it would be impossible to determine the population for California in June 1850, almost two years ago. Hence, the Bradbury amendment is simply the best compromise that can be done given the unfortunate circumstances.

The debate now turned to the question whether an apportionment for a state can be made on the basis of an estimate, rather than an enumeration. But this focus ended as the Senate adjourned for the day. The debate resumed on 7 April with the various points centered on the main theme: was an enumeration conducted in California?[42]

Robert Barnwell Rhett (SC) opened by noting that Congress passed the 1850 act with a pre-set House size (233) to avoid the controversy of fractions. Further, the act admitting California into the Union awarded the state two representatives until the next enumeration. However, in this census California has not been enumerated, leading to the current difficulty faced by Congress. It is too late to enumerate California now; so, what can Congress do? Senator Rhett recommended California retain two representatives under the state's admission act. He also advocated that South Carolina be awarded 6 seats. Although he did not specify, this would be consistent with $h = 234$. Thomas Rush (TX) then spoke to support the position that no enumeration has taken place in California.

Senator Bradbury then offered a rewording of his amendment to reflect that California be awarded two representatives by the act admitting the state to the Union. There was no objection to the rewording. Hence, the Bradbury amendment to the Downs motion is that "California shall be entitled to the number of Representatives prescribed by the act admitting said State into the Union" and that the House size be reset from 233 to 234.[43]

Mr. Downs then argued that 234 is an even number. It is better to have an odd number. Mr. Downs vigorously contended that there are returns from California. But, given the circumstances, it would be better to have a House of 235 in which California is given two seats and then the remaining 233 apportioned without California involved in the calculations, giving both South Carolina and Louisiana an additional seat. Note that Downs is from Louisiana.

John Davis (MA) noted that Congress is wrestling with an embarrassment from an unanticipated source: is there an enumeration for California? If Congress sticks to the 1850 census act, then, the problem to solve is: who gets the 233rd seat, South Carolina or California?

---

[42] Congressional Globe, 32nd Congress, 1st Session, 7 April 1852: 992-1001.
[43] Ibid: 993.

Mr. Davis then asked, what is the evidence that the quota fraction for California is greater than the quota fraction for South Carolina?

Mr. Gwin (CA) reiterated his assertion that no enumeration for California has ever been completed; hence, a comparison between South Carolina and California is impossible. William Dawson (GA) argued that an enumeration of California has been made. The original figure was 92579. Later, returns from three more counties (Santa Clara, Contra Costa, and San Francisco) were submitted, bringing the population of California to 117829. Based on this enumeration, California is entitled to only one representative. An extensive exchange then ensued between John Weller (CA) and Mr. Dawson as to whether this actually constituted an enumeration.

The discussion was settling on solving the California problem by basically denying that an enumeration had occurred and reverting to the act of admission to statehood granting California two seats until an enumeration takes place. The key now is the size of the House: 233, 234, or 235.

Debate continued the next day.[44] Mr. Badger put the problem in context. The census act of 1850 did not specify a census deadline, but did specify that that the Secretary of the Interior was to make and announce apportionment upon completion of the census. The Secretary of the Interior sent a message to Congress that the census for California was not complete and so, by law, he could not make the apportionment. Hence, remedial legislation is needed.

Mr. Downs repeated his case that there are official returns from California and referred to several documents yielding a population figure of 117821 for California.[45] A spreadsheet analysis using this population for California shows no change from the previous apportionment (see Table 3.3, next page). However, there was little support for Downs's position that the census figures returned for California formed an acceptable enumeration. The simple fact was that this whole process was initiated by a letter from President Fillmore transmitting a report from the Secretary of the Interior that he could not make the apportionment directed by the act of 1850 because of incomplete returns from California. Further, the Secretary of the Interior had asked the Attorney General to file suit against the census agent for California against his bond for failure to complete the census there. And there was a letter from the census agent in California stating that the census was not complete.

A way out of this embarrassment emerged. The census act of 1850 was passed in July. California was admitted into the Union in September with the proviso that California would have two representatives until an enumeration of the population. Since the enumeration of the population for California was not complete, then California should maintain two representatives under the state's admission act. The apportionment can then be made for the other states on the basis of their completed returns.

---

[44] Ibid, 8 April 1852: 1007-15.
[45] Ibid: 1012.

Salmon Chase (OH) moved to amend the amendment to retain the House size at 233 rather than increasing it to 234; failed, 14-24. The Bradbury amendment then passed in the Senate acting as a Committee of the Whole. The bill was referred to the full Senate for action. An amendment proposed by Mr. Geyser to reword the Bradbury amendment to reflect the use of California's admission act to justify two representatives passed. Joseph Underwood (KY) inquired whether the House size of 234 was a permanent amendment to the 1850 census act or was it to be in effect only until the next reapportionment. He was assured that the 234 House size applied only to the apportionment based on the 1850 census. A motion by Mr. Downs to replace the House size 234 by 235 failed badly, 5-26. However, the President of the Senate noted that a quorum was not present and the Senate adjourned.

The matter rested for two weeks. On 22 April the Senate took up the apportionment bill again. The Downs motion failed and the Bradbury amendment to the bill passed the full Senate. On 26 April the Senate sent the bill to the House for concurrence. This bill was part of a package with thirteen other bills passed by the Senate. On 23 July the bill passed the House. President Fillmore approved and signed the supplementary act on 30 July 1852.[46] The supplementary act completed apportionment legislation based on the 1850 census.

Table 3.3. Apportionment based on the 1850 census.

State	Population	Quota	Lower	Seats
ME	583169	6.2420	6	6
NH	317976	3.4035	3	3
VT	314120	3.3622	3	3
MA	994514	10.6448	10	11
RI	147545	1.5793	1	2
CT	370792	3.9688	3	4
NY	3097394	33.1531	33	33
PA	2311786	24.7443	24	25
OH	1980427	21.1976	21	21
IN	988416	10.5795	10	11
IL	851470	9.1137	9	9
MI	397654	4.2563	4	4
WI	305391	3.2688	3	3
IA	192214	2.0574	2	2
NJ	489466	5.2390	5	5
DE	90616	0.9699	0	1
MD	546886	5.8536	5	6
VA	1232649	13.1937	13	13
NC	753619	8.0664	8	8
SC	514513	5.5071	5	6
GA	753512	8.0652	8	8
AL	634514	6.7915	6	7
MS	482574	5.1652	5	5
LA	419838	4.4938	4	4
TN	906830	9.7063	9	10
KY	898012	9.6119	9	10
MO	647075	6.9260	6	7
AR	191057	2.0450	2	2
FL	71720	0.7677	0	1
TX	189327	2.0265	2	2
	21675076	232.0000	219	232

Hence, the apportionment took place as follows. First, two seats were awarded to California based on the state's admission act. Then, 232 seats were apportioned to the other thirty states using the census returns by applying Hamilton's method. Returns from California did not figure into the apportionment calculations. The spreadsheet computations are displayed in Figure 3.3. This brought the House size to 234.

---

[46] Statutes at Large, 32nd Congress, 1st Session, 1852, Chap. LXXIV: 25.

The final census report was submitted on 1 December 1852. The Seventh Census of the United States: 1850, by James Debow, superintendent of the U. S. Census, and published in 1853, is available as a free ebook from Google Books.[47]

The debate highlighted a practical distinction between a divisor method and a quota method of apportionment: how to proceed in the event of a census malfunction for a given state. In a quota method one cannot proceed until one knows the total population. It is precisely this situation that led to the impasse necessitating the supplementary act and taking an extra year and a half to resolve reapportionment based on the census of 1850.

In addition to apportionment, Congress had severe issues to deal with. The Compromise of 1850, a series of five bills passed in September 1850, was meant to head off a civil war. The components only added fuel to the firestorm building in the decade of the fifties. It is thus not surprising that so much time and debate was spent over a single seat and who should get it. Much like the Compromise of 1850, the award of the second seat to California, a free state, was balanced with the additional seat to South Carolina, a slave state.

The apportionment debates ended just in time. The nation was becoming fixated on a weekly series that ran in the *National Era*, a weekly newspaper, from 5 June 1851 to 1 April 1852. The series was published as a book that became a runaway best seller and would affect the national psyche in a way not seen since Thomas Paine's *Common Sense*. The work was a mature product of the Second Great Awakening, Harriet Beecher Stowe's *Uncle Tom's Cabin*.[48]

---

[47]http://books.google.com/books?id=25TicJOdU0AC&printsec=frontcover&source=gbs_ge_summary_r&cad=0#v=onepage&q&f=false.

[48] https://www.harrietbeecherstowecenter.org/; http://www.ushistory.org/us/28d.asp.

Section 3.2: Reapportionment Based on the 1860 Census

Section 3.2.1   Background

In the decade of the 1860's secession and the Civil War dominated everything. Virtually every other issue, including apportionment, was affected. The census of 1860 included three new states: Minnesota, admitted 11 May 1858 with two representatives[1]; Oregon, admitted 14 February 1859 with one representative[2]; and Kansas, admitted 29 January 1861 with one representative[3]. Hence, the 1860 census encompassed 34 states.

South Carolina declared its secession from the Union on 20 December 1860. Six more states followed before the acknowledged start of the Civil War with the firing on Fort Sumter, South Carolina, 12 April 1861. Four more states seceded to form the 11-state Confederate States of America. For the most part these states did not send representatives to Congress.

Section 3.2.2   Apportionment

The census and apportionment were conducted using the mechanism of the act of 1850. Officially, the Secretary of the Interior supervised the census. The field work was performed by U. S. marshals and their sworn assistants. The official returns were submitted to the Department of the Interior. The statistics were organized and presented by the superintendent of the census and his staff. Based on the completed returns, the Secretary of the Interior was to compute the apportionment based on the census using Hamilton's method. Hence, the act of 1850 formulated a mechanism for which the combined census and apportionment procedure bypassed Congress in the initial apportionment.

On 5 July 1861, Caleb Smith, Secretary of the Interior, announced the apportionment of the House of Representatives of the several states under the eighth census.[4] The results were presented to Congress on Monday, 8 July.[5] The population of the states and territories is displayed in Table 3.4 (next page).[6] This time there was no census malfunction; however, novel issues presented themselves during the decade. Table 3.5 (following Table 3.5) displays a spreadsheet for analyzing the apportionment results. Calculations for the Hamilton-Vinton method are shown in the Quota/Lower/Seats column. To achieve the House size of 233, the Jefferson, Dean, Webster, and Adams methods use the following divisors: Jefferson 121200, Dean 120200, Webster 127000, Adams 135500. Jefferson, Dean, Webster, and Adams are divisor methods; hence, to reach the same House size, different divisors must be used due to the different procedures for rounding their decimal quotients.

---

[1] Statutes at Large, 35th Congress, 1st Session, Chap. XXXI: 285.

[2] Ibid, 35th Congress, 2nd Session, Chap. XXXIII: 383-4.

[3] Ibid, 36th Congress, 1st Session, Ch. 20: 126-7.

[4] Jos. C. G. Kennedy, Preliminary Report on the Eighth Census, Washington, Government Printing Office, 1862: 20.

[5] Congressional Globe, 37th Congress, 1st Session, 8 July 1861: 26.

[6] Jos. C. G. Kennedy, Preliminary Report on the Eighth Census, Washington, Government Printing Office, 1862: 131.

Table 3.4. Population data from the 1860 census.

TABLE No. 1.—*Population of the States and Territories, &c.—1860.*

STATES.	CENSUS OF 1860.				RATIO OF INCREASE FROM 1850 TO 1860.			
	White.	Free colored.	Slave.	Total.	White.	Free colored	Slave.	Total.
Alabama	526,431	2,690	435,080	964,201	23.43	18.76	27.18	24.96
Arkansas.............	324,191	144	111,115	435,450	99.88	81.25*l*	135.91	107.46
California	361,353	4,086	...........,	[*14,555] 365,439	294.34	324.74	.........,	310.37
Connecticut	451,520	8,627	....	460,147	31.35	12.14	....	42.10
Delaware.............	90,589	19,829	1,798	112,216	27.28	9.72	21.48*l*	22.60
Florida	77,748	932	61,745	140,425	64.70	....	57.07	60.59
Georgia	591,588	3,500	462,198	1,057,286	13.42	19.41	21.10	16.67
Illinois	1,704,323	7,628	....	1,711,951	101.45	40.33	....	101.06
Indiana	1,339,000	11,428	....	1,350,428	37.03	1.47	....	36.63
Iowa.................	673,844	1,069	....	674,913	251.18	231.53	....	251.14
Kansas...............	106,579	625	2	107,206	....	....	....	....
Kentucky	919,517	10,684	225,483	1,155,684	20.76	6.72	6.87	17.64
Louisiana	357,629	18,647	331,726	708,002	39.98	6.78	35.50	36.74
Maine	626,952	1,327	....	628,279	7.76	2.14*l*	....	7.74
Maryland............	515,918	83,942	87,189	687,049	23.14	12.35	3.52*l*	17.84
Massachusetts	1,221,464	9,602	....	1,231,066	23.95	5.93	....	23 79
Michigan	742,314	6,799	....	749,113	87.89	163.22	....	88.38
Minnesota...........	171,864	259	....	172,123	2,775.06	769.38	....	2,760.87
Mississippi	353,901	773	436,631	791,305	19.68	16.88*l*	40.90	30.47
Missouri.............	1,063,509	3,572	114,931	1,182,012	79.64	28.44	31.47	73.30
New Hampshire	325,579	494	....	326,073	2.56	5.00*l*	....	2.55
New Jersey...........	646,699	25,318	18	672,035	38.92	6.33	92.37*l*	37.27
New York............	3,831,730	49,005	....	3,880,735	25.70	0.13*l*	....	25.29
North Carolina........	631,100	30,463	331,059	992,622	14.12	10.92	14.73	14.20
Ohio	2,302,838	36,673	....	2,339,511	17.79	41.12	....	18.14
Oregon	52,337	128	....	52,465	299.92	38.16*l*	....	294.65
Pennsylvania	2,849,266	56,849	....	2,906,115	26.18	6.01	....	25.71
Rhode Island	170,668	3,952	....	174,620	18.63	7.68	....	18.35
South Carolina..	291,388	9,914	402,406	703,708	6.13	10.65	4.53	5.27
Tennessee............	826,783	7,300	275,719	1,109,801	9.24	13.67	15.14	10.68
Texas...............	421,294	355	182,566	604,215	173.51	10.58*l*	213.89	184.22
Vermont.............	314,389	709	....	315,098	0.31	1.25*l*	....	0.31
Virginia	1,047,411	58,042	490,865	1,596,318	17.06	6.83	3.88	12.29
Wisconsin............	774,710	1,171	....	775,881	154.20	8.44	....	154.06
	26,706,425	476,536	3,950,531	31,148,047	37.37	12.30	23.44	35.04
TERRITORIES.								
Colorado	34,231	46	....	34,277 *a*2,261	....	....	....	....
Dakota..............	2,576	....	....	2,576	....	....	....	....
Nebraska............	28,759	67	15	28,841	....	....	....	....
Nevada	6,812	45	....	6,857 *a*10,507	....	....	....	....
New Mexico..........	82,924	85	....	83,009	34.73	....	....	51.94
Utah	40,214	30	29	40,273 *a*426	254.18	....	11.53	253.89
Washington	11,138	30	....	11,168	....	....	....	....
District of Columbia	60,764	11,131	3,185	75,080	60.15	10.66	13.62*l*	45.26
	26,973,843	487,970	3,953,760	31,443,322	37.97	12.33	23.39	35.59

a Indians.

113

Table 3.5. *Spreadsheet computations for apportionment based on the 1860 census.*

State	Population	Quota	Lower	Seats	Jefferson	Dean	Webster	Adams
AL	790169	6.2297	6	6	6	6	6	6
AR	391004	3.0827	3	3	3	3	3	3
CA	365439	2.8811	2	3	3	3	3	3
CT	460147	3.6278	3	4	3	4	4	4
DE	111496	0.8790	0	1	1	1	1	1
FL	115726	0.9124	0	1	1	1	1	1
GA	872406	6.8781	6	7	7	7	7	7
IL	1711951	13.4971	13	13	14	13	13	13
IN	1350428	10.6468	10	11	11	10	11	10
IA	674913	5.3210	5	5	5	5	5	5
KS	107206	0.8452	0	1	1	1	1	1
KY	1065491	8.4004	8	8	8	8	8	8
LA	575311	4.5358	4	5	4	5	5	5
ME	628279	4.9534	4	5	5	5	5	5
MD	652173	5.1418	5	5	5	5	5	5
MA	1231066	9.7058	9	10	10	10	10	10
MI	749113	5.9060	5	6	6	6	6	6
MN	172123	1.3570	1	1	1	1	1	2
MS	616652	4.8617	4	5	5	5	5	5
MO	1136040	8.9566	8	9	9	9	9	9
NH	326073	2.5708	2	3	2	3	3	3
NJ	672035	5.2983	5	5	5	5	5	5
NY	3880735	30.5959	30	31	32	30	31	29
NC	860198	6.7818	6	7	7	7	7	7
OH	2339511	18.4448	18	18	19	18	18	18
OR	52465	0.4136	0	1	1	1	1	1
PA	2906215	22.9127	22	23	23	23	23	22
RI	174620	1.3767	1	1	1	2	1	2
SC	542745	4.2790	4	4	4	4	4	5
TN	999513	7.8802	7	8	8	8	8	8
TX	531188	4.1879	4	4	4	4	4	4
VT	315098	2.4842	2	2	2	3	2	3
VA	1399972	11.0374	11	11	11	11	11	11
WI	775881	6.1171	6	6	6	6	6	6
US	29553382	233.0000	214	233	233	233	233	233

A novel result is that the Hamilton-Vinton award of one seat for Oregon is obtained by invoking the constitutional requirement that each state must receive at least one seat. Note that the quota fraction for Oregon is smaller than the quota fraction for Vermont; yet, by the constitutional minimum rule, Oregon is given a seat over Vermont. This is the first time that the constitutional minimum rule for congressional apportionment was applied.

A similar thing happens in applying the Jefferson and Webster methods. In the Jefferson method the constitutional minimum rule comes into play for four states. The divisor 121000 produces 229 seats; but, Delaware, Florida, Kansas, and Oregon all have quotients less than one. Thus, the Jefferson rounding procedure allocates no seats for these states. The constitutional minimum rule provides each state with a seat to bring the House size to 233. The minimum rule is automatic for the Dean and Adams methods since they round up any quotient between zero and one.

The minimum rule comes into play for the Webster method for Oregon. Hence, a complete statement of the Webster method must include the constitutional minimum case.

- If a state's quotient is less than 0.5, then the state's apportionment is one seat.
- Suppose a state's quotient is greater than or equal to 0.5. Then the state's apportionment is the integer part of the quotient if the quotient fraction is less than 0.5; otherwise, the state's apportionment is one more than the integer part of the quotient.

Thus, Webster's method directs that the quotient decimal is rounded normally, but allocate the state one seat if the quotient rounded normally is 0.

Note that the methods of Hamilton and Webster agree for apportionment based on the 1860 census. Both Jefferson and Adams display a quota rule violation for New York. Another interesting anomaly is that although Jefferson rounds the quotient down and Adams rounds the quotient up, Jefferson awards New York 32 seats in contrast to Adams 29. This is due to the fact that the Adams divisor, 135500, is much larger than the Jefferson divisor, 121200. With Adams's larger divisor the resulting quotient is smaller.

Section 3.2.3   The Supplement

Apportionment for the 38th Congress, as announced by Secretary of the Interior Caleb Smith on 5 July 1860, went smoothly without any congressional intervention. This was about to change. On 5 August 1861 Representative William Kellogg (IL) rose to report from the House Committee on the Judiciary. He introduced a resolution which was read twice, engrossed as H.R. 104, read a third time, and passed with no discussion. A voice vote was taken with no request for the ayes and nays.[7] H.R. 104 was titled *An Act Fixing the number of members of the House of Representatives from and after the third March, eighteen hundred and sixty-one*. This act would increase the size of the House from 233 as specified by the act of 1850 to 239 to be apportioned by the method specified in the act of 1850, the Hamilton-Vinton method (see Table 3.6, next page, *h*=239/Lower/Seats columns).[8] The same day H.R. 104 was sent to the Senate asking for concurrence.[9]

---

[7] Congressional Globe, 37th Congress, 1st Session, 5 August 1861: 447.
[8] Bills and Resolutions, House of Representatives, 37th Congress, 1st Session.
[9] Congressional Globe, 37th Congress, 1st Session, 5 August 1861: 442.

The Senate did not consider H.R. 104 until 13 February 1862. Jacob Collamer (VT) (Figure 3.2[10]) proposed an amendment that would allocate the six additional seats to the six states with the next largest fractions in the quota calculations for House size 233 (Table 3.6, next page, Collamer column). Accordingly, the six seats would be awarded to Illinois, Vermont, Ohio, Kentucky, Rhode Island, and Minnesota.[11] Mr. Collamer argued that his amendment was the intention of H.R. 104; "but, a certain process of arithmetic, if you do not amend it as I propose, makes it quite a different thing."[12] This certain process of arithmetic happens because changing the House size changes the national divisor. Accordingly, the apportionment quotas are different for House size 233 than 239. This affects four states. Applying the Hamilton-Vinton method gives an

Figure 3.2. Senator Jacob Collamer (VT).

additional seat to Iowa and Pennsylvania whereas Collamer's amendment gives these seats to Rhode Island and Minnesota (see Table 3.6, next page, for details). Mr. Collamer gave his rationale as follows:

> The States should have their representation apportioned to them in such a manner that a Representative will, many State, have a constituency equal or almost equal, to the constituency of a Representative in any other State. [13]

This criterion as stated by Mr. Collamer is an equivalent criterion for Dean's method.

Lyman Trumball (IL) spoke about the discrepancy in the Hamilton-Vinton calculations for House size 233 and 239. In particular, he noted that using the quota method, Pennsylvania and Iowa deserve the seats, not Rhode Island and Minnesota as awarded by Mr. Collamer's amendment. Mr. Trumball asserted that "it is a troublesome and a difficult question at best. I question very much whether it is advisable for us to interfere with the present law."[14]

The exchange of ideas continued on 26 February. Mr. Collamer opened by withdrawing his previous amendment and replacing it with another specifying a House of 241 in which the additional seats from 233 would be awarded to Pennsylvania, Ohio, Kentucky, Illinois, Iowa, Minnesota, Vermont, and Rhode Island (see Table 3.7, Collamer column).[15]

---

[10] The University of Vermont Libraries, Center for Digital Initiatives; accessed at https://cdi.uvm.edu/image/uvmcdi-195.

[11] Ibid, 37th Congress, 2nd Session, 13 February 1862: 786-7.

[12] Ibid: 786.

[13] Ibid.

[14] Ibid: 787.

[15] Ibid, 26 February 1862: 962.

Table 3.6. *Spreadsheet calculations for H.R. 104. The h = 233 column gives the quotas for House size 233. Similarly, the h = 239 column gives the quotas for House size 239.*

State	Population	h = 233	Lower	Seats	h = 239	Lower	Seats	Collamer
AL	790169	6.2297	6	6	6.3901	6	6	6
AR	391004	3.0827	3	3	3.1621	3	3	3
CA	365439	2.8811	2	3	2.9553	2	3	3
CT	460147	3.6278	3	4	3.7212	3	4	4
DE	111496	0.8790	0	1	0.9017	0	1	1
FL	115726	0.9124	0	1	0.9359	0	1	1
GA	872406	6.8781	6	7	7.0552	7	7	7
IL	1711951	13.4971	13	13	13.8447	13	14	14
IN	1350428	10.6468	10	11	10.9210	10	11	11
IA	674913	5.3210	5	5	5.4581	5	6	5
KS	107206	0.8452	0	1	0.8670	0	1	1
KY	1065491	8.4004	8	8	8.6167	8	9	9
LA	575311	4.5358	4	5	4.6526	4	5	5
ME	628279	4.9534	4	5	5.0809	5	5	5
MD	652173	5.1418	5	5	5.2742	5	5	5
MA	1231066	9.7058	9	10	9.9557	9	10	10
MI	749113	5.9060	5	6	6.0581	6	6	6
MN	172123	1.3570	1	1	1.3920	1	1	2
MS	616652	4.8617	4	5	4.9869	4	5	5
MO	1136040	8.9566	8	9	9.1872	9	9	9
NH	326073	2.5708	2	3	2.6370	2	3	3
NJ	672035	5.2983	5	5	5.4348	5	5	5
NY	3880735	30.5959	30	31	31.3837	31	31	31
NC	860198	6.7818	6	7	6.9565	6	7	7
OH	2339511	18.4448	18	18	18.9198	18	19	19
OR	52465	0.4136	0	1	0.4243	0	1	1
PA	2906215	22.9127	22	23	23.5027	23	24	23
RI	174620	1.3767	1	1	1.4122	1	1	2
SC	542745	4.2790	4	4	4.3892	4	4	4
TN	999513	7.8802	7	8	8.0831	8	8	8
TX	531188	4.1879	4	4	4.2957	4	4	4
VT	315098	2.4842	2	2	2.5482	2	3	3
VA	1399972	11.0374	11	11	11.3217	11	11	11
WI	775881	6.1171	6	6	6.2746	6	6	6
US	29553382	233.0000	214	233	239.0000	221	239	239

Table 3.7. *Spreadsheet calculations for analysis of Collamer's proposal for House size 241. The Quota/Lower/Seats columns display the Hamilton-Vinton results. To obtain h=241, Jefferson uses a divisor of 115000, Dean 123500, Webster 122000, and Adams 131600.*

State	Population	Quota	Lower	Seats	Jefferson	Dean	Webster	Adams	Collamer
AL	790169	6.4436	6	6	6	6	6	7	6
AR	391004	3.1885	3	3	3	3	3	3	3
CA	365439	2.9801	2	3	3	3	3	3	3
CT	460147	3.7524	3	4	4	4	4	4	4
DE	111496	0.9092	0	1	1	1	1	1	1
FL	115726	0.9437	0	1	1	1	1	1	1
GA	872406	7.1142	7	7	7	7	7	7	7
IL	1711951	13.9605	13	14	14	14	14	13	14
IN	1350428	11.0124	11	11	11	11	11	11	11
IA	674913	5.5037	5	6	5	6	6	6	6
KS	107206	0.8742	0	1	1	1	1	1	1
KY	1065491	8.6888	8	9	9	9	9	9	9
LA	575311	4.6915	4	5	5	5	5	5	5
ME	628279	5.1234	5	5	5	5	5	5	5
MD	652173	5.3183	5	5	5	5	5	5	5
MA	1231066	10.0390	10	10	10	10	10	10	10
MI	749113	6.1088	6	6	6	6	6	6	6
MN	172123	1.4036	1	1	1	2	1	2	2
MS	616652	5.0286	5	5	5	5	5	5	5
MO	1136040	9.2641	9	9	9	9	9	9	9
NH	326073	2.6590	2	3	2	3	3	3	3
NJ	672035	5.4803	5	6	5	5	6	6	5
NY	3880735	31.6464	31	32	33	31	32	30	31
NC	860198	7.0147	7	7	7	7	7	7	7
OH	2339511	19.0781	19	19	20	19	19	18	19
OR	52465	0.4278	0	1	1	1	1	1	1
PA	2906215	23.6994	23	24	25	24	24	23	24
RI	174620	1.4240	1	1	1	2	1	2	2
SC	542745	4.4259	4	4	4	4	4	5	4
TN	999513	8.1508	8	8	8	8	8	8	8
TX	531188	4.3317	4	4	4	4	4	5	4
VT	315098	2.5695	2	3	2	3	3	3	3
VA	1399972	11.4164	11	11	12	11	11	11	11
WI	775881	6.3271	6	6	6	6	6	6	6
US	29553382	241.0000	226	241	241	241	241	241	241

Mr. Collamer noted that the results of apportionment affect not only representation in the House but also the Electoral College, the number of cadets admitted to West Point, and the midshipmen admitted to the Naval School.[16] He noted that apportionment for direct taxes can be made "with arithmetical certainty." Calculations can be made to the nearest penny; outside of that, nobody cares. Although dollars can be apportioned to the nearest fraction of 0.01, congressmen cannot come in "fractions" like dollars. He then gave a rationale that is precisely the description of Dean's method.

Mr. Collamer then spoke specifically to advance his new amendment. Bringing the House size to 241 means that 15 states will need an additional seat after awarding each state its lower quota, which distributes 226 seats (see Table 3.7, Lower column, for details). However, the Hamilton-Vinton quota method leads to Dean-criterion violations yielding underrepresentation for Minnesota and Rhode Island. H.R. 104 with Mr. Collamer's new amendment yields an apportionment for House size 241 in perfect agreement with Dean's method. For comparison the results for House size 241 using the methods of Hamilton-Vinton (Quota/Lower/Seats columns), Jefferson (divisor 115000), Dean (divisor 123500), Webster (divisor 122000), and Adams (divisor 131690) are also provided. The Adams method is particularly sensitive to the divisor; i.e., to achieve a House size of 241, the Adams divisor must be between 131689 and 131694 inclusively.

At the conclusion of Mr. Collamer's arguments, the new amendment passed. Then, H.R. 104 as amended passed. Subsequently, it was smooth sailing as the House agreed with the Senate amendment. President Lincoln signed the bill on 4 March 1862.[17] Accordingly, during the eight censuses of the nation's history at this point, the nation has used the basic divisor methods of Jefferson and Webster, the Hamilton quota method, and now the Dean modified divisor method to achieve apportionment of the House of Representatives.

Did Congress actually use the Dean method to apportion based on the 1860 census? This is one of those questions that can be answered yes and no. The initial apportionment of 233 seats was based on the Hamilton-Vinton method. The supplement allocation specifying 241 seats was not distributed by Hamilton's method. It started out by applying Hamilton's method to apportion 233 seats, but then modified the results in a way not consistent with Hamilton's method. Dean's method was not specifically named in the supplement act nor was it identified by name in the debates. However, the justification for the final apportionment of the supplement act is exactly the criterion defining Dean's method. In particular, Mr. Collamer argued the following in advancing his amendment:[18]

> Mr. President, by what power and right and principle is it that you give Representatives to fractions at all? I take it, it is because in giving them to the fractions you approximate nearer to the representative ratio. Then you ought to give representation to each State so long as by giving it they will be nearer to the

---

[16] Ibid.

[17] Statutes at Large, 37th Congress, 2nd Session, Chap. XXXVI: 353.

[18] Congressional Globe, 37th Congress, 2nd Session, 26 February 1862: 963.

representative ratio than they will be by withholding it. That is the great point—great in my estimation—which I wish to make; that when you go to give it to a fraction, you have no right to stop short of their role; that is, you will give it to every State when by giving it to her she will come nearer to the representative ratio than she will by withholding it. I think no other just rule can be found. This law of 1850 does not give her that.

It can be reasonably argued that Mr. Collamer knew full well that his amendment led to an apportionment that completely satisfied the stated criterion. Although the calculations were not originally made using Dean's rule, the result satisfied Dean's method and did not conform to any other method as Table 3.7 verifies.

Section 3.2.4   California

California was formally admitted to the Union on 9 September 1850. The admission act admitted California with two representatives until the next enumeration. However, there was a census malfunction for California in the 1850 census. The apportionment supplement act of 30 July 1852 distributed 232 seats using the Hamilton-Vinton method for all states except California. California was to "retain the number of representatives prescribed by the act of admission thereof into the Union until a new apportionment."[19]

On the first day of the 2nd session of the 37th Congress, 2 December 1861, Representative Timothy Phelps of California rose to address the House.[20]

I desire to present the credentials of Hon. F. F. Lowe, elected as a third member from the State of California, and move that they be referred to the Committee of Elections. I desire to present these papers and have them referred for the purpose of bringing up and having settled the question whether California is entitled to two or three members upon this floor.

Earlier in the day, Aaron Sargent and Timothy Phelps without objection were sworn in as representatives from California. Certainly, California was entitled to two representatives. The Secretary of the Interior on 5 July 1861 announced the apportionment results based on the 1860 census and effective for the 38th Congress whose term began 4 March 1863 (see Table 3.6, $h=233$/Lower/Seats columns). Was California entitled to a third representative now? On 6 December the case was referred to the Committee on Elections.[21]

California believed that the state was an exception for apportionment based on the act of 1852. California was to have two representatives "until a new apportionment." Since the "new apportionment" was announced on 5 July 1861, California held an at-large election for the House of Representatives on 5 September 1860. The three with the most votes, in order, were

---

[19] Statutes at Large, 32nd Congress, 1st Session, Chap. LXXIV: 25.
[20] Congressional Globe, 37th Congress, 2nd Session, 2 December 1861: 4.
[21] Ibid, 6 December 1861: 76.

Aaron Sargent, Timothy Phelps, and Frederick Ferdinand Low (the congressional records sometimes misspell the name as Lowe or referred to him as R. L. Lowe). On 14 April 1862 on behalf of the Committee on Elections, Mr. Henry Dawes (MA) presented a committee report and a resolution that Mr. F. F. Low should not be seated.[22]

The majority of the Committee on Elections decided that California's claim was based on a too strict and narrow interpretation of the supplement law of 1852. The committee noted that the Secretary of Interior, in releasing his apportionment report, specified that the results were to be effective with the 38th Congress. Hence California was only entitled to two seats in the 37th Congress; but is entitled to three seats in the 38th Congress. The Committee further argued that the apportionment rules should be the same for all states. Further, the supplement act just passed on 4 March 1862 specified that the new apportionment will go into effect for the 38th Congress, "from and after the third day of March, eighteen hundred and sixty-three."[23] The Committee argued that congressional apportionment should be uniform, based on a decennial census with results applicable to the Congress beginning from and after the 3rd of March 1863 and every subsequent ten years.[24]

The committee report concerning the case of F. F. Low was finally considered on 6 May 1862. After an extensive debate Mr. Sargent moved to amend the resolution by striking "not." The amendment failed, 49-69. The resolution of the committee that Mr. Low not be seated was then agreed to.[25]

Mr. Phelps immediately moved to rectify the situation by introducing H.R. 459. The bill was read twice and referred to the House Committee on the Judiciary.[26] H.R. 459, as introduced by Mr. Phelps on 6 May, contained two sections. The first section ordered that the census for 1870 for the purposes of congressional apportionment take effect from and after 3 March 1873 and the pattern repeated every subsequent ten years. The second section specified that California was immediately allowed three representatives.[27]

On 29 May H.R. 459 was reported out of the Committee on the Judiciary with amendments. The first amendment was to strike the first section; passed 74-37. Three amendments that offered minor grammatical changes passed. An adjusting title change also passed. The bill was sent to the Senate for concurrence.[28] The same day the Senate read the bill twice and sent it to the Committee on the Judiciary.[29] Two days later the Committee on the Judiciary reported the

---

[22] Ibid, 14 April 1862: 1656.

[23] Statutes at Large, 37th Congress, 2nd Session, Chap. XXXVL: 353.

[24] Ascher C. Hinds, Hinds' Precedents of the House of Representatives of the United States, Vol. 1, 1907: 182-5; https://www.govinfo.gov/content/pkg/GPO-HPREC-HINDS-V1/pdf/GPO-HPREC-HINDS-V1.pdf (accessed 13 August 2019).

[25] Congressional Globe, 37th Congress, 2nd Session, 6 May 1862: 1967-71.

[26] Ibid: 1971.

[27] Bills and Resolutions, 37th Congress, 2nd Session, 6 May 1862: H.R. 459.

[28] Congressional Globe, 37th Congress, 2nd Session, 29 May 1862: 2432-3.

[29] Senate Journal, 37th Congress, 2nd Session, 29 May 1862: 540-1.

bill without amendment. The Senate subsequently passed the bill on 2 June 1862.[30] President Lincoln approved and signed the bill, *An Act to allow the State of California an additional Representative in the thirty-seventh Congress.*[31]

So, why did Congress change its mind? The winning argument for California can be summarized by the patriotic call "no taxation without representation." On 5 April 1861 President Lincoln signed into law *An Act to provide increased Revenue from Imports, to pay Interest on the Public Debt, and for other Purposes.*[32] The act assessed some direct taxes to each of the states based on reapportionment from the 1860 census. The act assessed California $254538⅔. California exploited this fact to claim that in reference to the state's admission act, the "next enumeration" already had taken place. Since California's 1850-based apportionment was an isolated case in the law, it won enough sympathy to win the day. The arguments were reflected in the law.[33]

> *Be it enacted by the Senate and House of Representatives of the United States of America in Congress assembled*, That as the census has never been reliably taken in the State of California until the year eighteen hundred and sixty, and as it appears that the said State had sufficient population to entitle her to three representatives in the thirty-seventh Congress, and as three representatives have been duly elected to the thirty-seventh Congress under the supposition that the said State was entitled to the same, as appears by the certificate of the Governor thereof, and as direct taxes have been apportioned to and paid by said State under the census of eighteen hundred and sixty, therefore the said State shall be allowed three representatives in the thirty-seventh Congress, and for that purpose the whole number of representatives is hereby increased one, until the beginning of the thirty-eighth Congress.
> APPROVED, June 2, 1862.

This law is significant for two reasons. First, it is another example of the perceived importance of a single congressional seat. Second, it is the only case in the history of apportionment where a state was awarded a seat by special circumstance other than statehood admission or a supplement adjustment to an already computed apportionment. It is impressive how Congress has given regular and significant attention to this subject.

---

[30] Ibid, 31 May 1862: 549.
[31] Statutes at Large, 37th Congress, 2nd Session, Chap. XCL: 411.
[32] Ibid, 37th Congress, 1st Session, Chap. XLV: 292-313.
[33] Statutes at Large, 37th Congress, 2nd Session, Chap. XCL: 411.

Section 3.3:   Reapportionment Based on the 1870 Census

Section 3.3.1   Background

Early in the decade of 1860 the United States dealt with the worst tragedy in the nation's history: The Civil War. The remainder of the decade and the greater part of the 1870s found the nation immersed in Reconstruction. To start the decade of 1860, the nation also had to deal with a crisis of leadership. President Lincoln, arguably the best of all Presidents in American history, was sandwiched between James Buchanan and Andrew Johnson, arguably the worst Presidents in American history.[1]

The census of 1870 encompassed three new states: West Virginia (admitted 20 June 1863, three representatives)[2], Nevada (31 October 1864, one representative)[3], and Nebraska (1 March 1867, one representative)[4]. Each of these state admissions has an interesting story that could justify a separate essay. For example, Nebraska was the first state to be admitted with a congressional override of a presidential veto. Congress overrode 15 of President Johnson's vetoes,[5] more than any other President in American history.[6]

The passage of the thirteenth and fourteenth amendments to the U. S. Constitution dramatically affected apportionment. The thirteenth amendment outlawed slavery "within the United States, or any place subject to their jurisdiction." Section 2 of the fourteenth amendment rid apportionment of the infamous three-fifths rule: "Representatives shall be apportioned among the several States according to their respective numbers, counting the whole number of persons in each State, excluding Indians not taxed."

Section 3.3.2   Apportionment

The 1870 census and subsequent reapportionment was covered under the act of 1850. The only significant change was that Congress increased the size of the House from 233, as specified in the act of 1850, to 241 as specified by the act of 4 March 1862. As a result, the census and resulting apportionment were on automatic pilot. The Hon. C. Delano, Secretary of the Interior, released the complete report of the 1870 census, supervised by Francis A. Walker, Superintendent of the Census, on 24 August 1872.[7] The component featuring apportionment was released earlier on 20 June 1871 (Table 3.8, next page).

---

[1] http://www.americanpresidents.org/survey/historians/.
[2] Statutes at Large, 37 Congress, 3rd Session: 633-4; President Lincoln's Proclamation: 731.
[3] Ibid, 38th Congress, 1st Session, Chap. XXXVI: 31-2; President Lincoln's Proclamation: 749-50.
[4] Ibid, 39th Congress, 2nd Session, Chap. XXXVI: 391-2.
[5] Gregory Harness, Presidential Vetoes, 1789-1988, S. Pub. 102-12, U.S. Government Printing Office, 1992: 10.
[6] http://en.wikipedia.org/wiki/List_of_United_States_presidential_vetoes.
[7] Francis A. Walker, Ninth Census, Vol. I, Government Printing Office, 1872; available from the Census Bureau's web site, https://www.census.gov/programs-surveys/decennial-census/decade/decennial-publications.1870.html; especially Part I, pages xiv-xv.

Table 3.8. *Population and apportionment result from the Superintendent of the 1870 census.*

STATES.	Representative population.	241. Ratio: 1 to 158,156.			250. Ratio: 1 to 152,463.			260. Ratio: 1 to 146,599.			270. Ratio: 1 to 141,169.			283. Ratio: 1 to 134,684.			292. Ratio: 1 to 130,533.			300. Ratio: 1 to 127,052.		
		No. of Representatives on even division.	Fractions.	Total number of Representatives.	No. of Representatives on even division.	Fractions.	Total number of Representatives.	No. of Representatives on even division.	Fractions.	Total number of Representatives.	No. of Representatives on even division.	Fractions.	Total number of Representatives.	No. of Representatives on even division.	Fractions.	Total number of Representatives.	No. of Representatives on even division.	Fractions.	Total number of Representatives.	No. of Representatives on even division.	Fractions.	Total number of Representatives.
The United States.	38,115,641	226	2,623,587	241	236	2,302,803	250	247	2,110,662	260	254	2,441,969	270	266	2,447,011	283	278	1,968,177	292	283	2,286,711	300
1 Alabama	996,992	6	48,056	6	6	89,214	6	6	117,308	7	7	8,809	7	7	54,204	7	7	83,261	8	7	107,628	8
2 Arkansas	484,471	3	10,003	3	3	27,082	3	3	44,674	3	3	60,964	3	3	80,419	4	3	92,872	4	3	103,315	4
3 California	560,247	3	85,779	4	3	102,858	4	3	120,450	4	3	136,740	4	4	21,511	4	4	38,115	4	4	52,039	4
4 Connecticut	537,454	3	62,986	3	3	80,065	3	3	97,657	4	3	113,947	4	3	133,402	4	4	15,322	4	4	29,246	4
5 Delaware	125,015	*1	....	1	*1	....	1	*1	....	1	*1	....	1	*1	....	1	*1	....	1	*1	....	1
6 Florida	187,748	1	29,592	1	1	35,285	1	1	41,149	1	1	46,579	1	1	53,064	1	1	57,215	1	1	60,696	1
7 Georgia	1,184,109	7	77,017	7	7	116,868	8	8	11,317	8	8	54,757	8	8	106,637	9	9	9,312	9	9	40,641	9
8 Illinois	2,539,891	16	9,395	16	16	100,483	17	17	47,708	17	17	140,018	18	18	115,579	19	19	59,764	20	19	125,903	20
9 Indiana	1,680,637	10	99,077	11	11	3,544	11	11	68,048	11	11	127,778	12	12	64,429	12	12	114,241	13	13	28,961	13
10 Iowa	1,194,020	7	86,928	7	7	126,779	8	8	21,228	8	8	64,668	8	8	116,548	9	9	19,223	9	9	50,552	9
11 Kansas	364,399	2	48,087	2	2	59,473	2	2	71,201	3	2	82,061	3	2	95,031	3	2	103,333	3	2	110,295	3
12 Kentucky	1,321,011	8	55,763	8	8	101,307	9	9	1,620	9	9	50,490	9	9	108,855	10	10	15,681	10	10	59,491	10
13 Louisiana	726,915	4	94,291	5	4	117,063	5	4	140,519	5	5	21,070	5	5	53,495	5	5	74,250	6	5	91,655	6
14 Maine	626,915	3	152,447	4	4	17,063	4	4	40,519	4	4	62,239	4	4	88,179	5	4	104,783	5	4	118,707	5
15 Maryland	780,894	4	148,270	5	5	18,570	5	5	47,899	5	5	75,049	6	5	107,474	6	5	128,229	6	6	18,582	6
16 Massachusetts	1,457,351	9	33,947	9	9	85,184	10	9	137,960	10	10	45,661	10	10	110,511	11	11	21,488	11	11	59,779	11
17 Michigan	1,184,059	7	76,967	7	7	116,818	8	8	11,267	8	8	54,707	8	8	106,587	9	9	9,262	9	9	40,591	9
18 Minnesota	439,706	2	123,394	3	2	134,780	3	2	146,508	3	3	16,199	3	3	35,654	3	3	48,107	3	3	58,550	3
19 Mississippi	827,922	5	37,142	5	5	65,667	5	5	94,927	6	5	122,077	6	6	19,818	6	6	44,724	6	6	65,610	7
20 Missouri	1,721,295	10	139,735	11	11	44,202	11	11	108,706	12	12	27,267	12	12	105,087	13	13	24,366	13	13	69,619	14
21 Nebraska	122,993	*1	....	1	*1	....	1	*1	....	1	*1	....	1	*1	....	1	*1	....	1	*1	....	1
22 Nevada	42,491	*1	....	1	*1	....	1	*1	....	1	*1	....	1	*1	....	1	*1	....	1	*1	....	1
23 New Hampshire	318,300	2	1,988	2	2	13,374	2	2	25,102	2	2	35,962	2	2	48,932	2	2	57,234	2	2	64,196	3
24 New Jersey	906,096	5	115,316	6	5	143,781	6	6	26,502	6	6	59,082	6	6	97,992	7	6	122,898	7	7	16,732	7
25 New York	4,382,759	27	112,547	28	28	113,795	29	29	131,388	30	31	6,520	31	32	72,871	32	33	75,170	34	34	62,991	35
26 North Carolina	1,071,361	6	122,425	7	7	4,120	7	7	45,168	7	7	83,178	8	7	123,573	8	8	27,097	8	8	54,945	8
27 Ohio	2,665,260	16	134,764	17	17	73,380	17	18	26,478	18	18	124,218	19	19	106,264	20	20	54,600	20	20	124,220	21
28 Oregon	90,923	*1	....	1	*1	....	1	*1	....	1	*1	....	1	*1	....	1	*1	....	1	*1	....	1
29 Pennsylvania	3,521,951	22	42,519	22	23	15,302	23	24	3,575	24	24	133,895	25	26	20,107	26	26	128,093	27	27	91,547	28
30 Rhode Island	217,353	1	59,197	1	1	64,890	1	1	70,754	1	1	76,184	2	1	82,669	2	1	86,820	2	1	90,301	2
31 South Carolina	705,606	4	72,982	4	4	95,754	5	4	119,210	5	4	140,930	5	5	32,186	5	5	52,941	5	5	70,346	6
32 Tennessee	1,258,520	7	151,428	8	8	33,810	8	8	85,728	9	8	129,108	9	9	46,364	9	9	83,723	10	9	115,052	10
33 Texas	818,579	5	27,799	5	5	56,264	5	5	85,584	6	5	112,734	6	6	10,475	6	6	35,381	6	6	56,267	6
34 Vermont	330,551	2	14,239	2	2	25,625	2	2	37,353	2	2	48,213	2	2	61,183	2	2	69,485	3	2	76,447	3
35 Virginia	1,225,163	7	118,071	8	8	5,450	8	8	52,371	8	8	95,811	9	9	13,007	9	9	50,366	9	9	81,695	10
36 West Virginia	442,014	2	125,702	3	2	137,088	3	3	2,217	3	3	18,507	3	3	37,962	3	3	50,415	3	3	60,858	3
37 Wisconsin	1,054,670	6	105,734	7	6	139,892	7	7	28,477	7	7	66,487	8	7	111,882	8	8	10,406	8	8	38,254	8

*Subject to constitutional provision assigning at least one Representative to each State, whatever its population.

For the convenience of Congress, the Census Bureau computed apportionments for House size 241, 250, 260, 270, 283, 292, and 300. In the 241 main column the table provides the national divisor. The three sub-columns provide the lower quota, the resulting fraction, and the final apportionment. The "Fractions" are the remainders when the states' populations are divided by the national divisor. The convenience calculations were made in the event that Congress wanted to pursue enlarging the size of the House.

Of course, Congress could not leave well-enough alone. Perhaps the demands of California from eight years previous still echoed through the House chambers. The apportionment information based on the 1870 census was released by the Department of the Interior on 20 June 1871. Hence, it was possible that the results could be instituted for the 3rd session of the 42nd Congress. And there was time to adjust the size of the House.

In anticipation the 2nd session of the 41st Congress went to work. On 16 December 1869 William Allison (IA) introduced H.R. 604 that would reset the House size to 300 members. This was echoed on 10 January 1870 by William Paine (GA) who introduced a competing bill, H.R. 766, which also set the House size at 300. Another bill, H.R. 1823 reported out of the House Committee on the Judiciary, also specified a House size of 300. Variations in the different bills included reforms to correct errors of procedure in order to obtain a more accurate and timelier census. The bills also made the effort to have the new apportionments become effective at the start of the 3rd session of the 41st Congress.

However, the House was in a combative mood over the details. On 23 June 1870 Jesse Moore (IL) gave a speech venting his frustrations. Mr. Moore complained that he was "painfully surprised at the fierce opposition … to the measure now under consideration." The measure was H.R. 1823 that would make apportionment based on the 1870 census effective at the next session of Congress and set the House size at 300. Mr. Moore lamented regional conflicts, "I am sorry, sir, to see high-tariff and low-tariff considerations coming in here to settle a question of such vital importance." Some objected that the Secretary of the Interior and not Congress was making the apportionment calculations. Others objected to the increased House size. Another issue raised by Mr. Moore appeared as a premonition to today's concerns.[8]

> I am sorry to see the fluttering anxiety which shows itself here among some in reference to the unprecedented growth of the great West, the great producing sections of this country. The great monopolies in the manufacturing regions and their representatives in this House are uneasy. They begin to fear that we shall not much longer bear the yoke which we have worn too long already. They see that we shall soon be able to take care of our own interests, and emancipate ourselves from the tyranny which has been put upon our people and their labor by legislation suggested and consummated in the interests of wealthy corporations and privileged monopolies.

With the timing of implementation of apportionment based on the 1870 census now a lost cause, the 3rd session of the 41st Congress focused its apportionment attention on the House size. On 9 January 1871 Julius Strong (CT) introduced H.R. 2682 which would set the House size

---

[8] Appendix to the Congressional Globe, 41st Congress, 2nd Session, 23 June 1870: 547-8.

at 275. On 10 January 1871 Ulysses Mercur (PA) introduced H.R. 2687[9] that would set the House size at 280.[10] But, the 3rd session resolved neither bill.

The term of the 42nd Congress went from 4 March 1871 to 4 March 1873. The 1st session was short and met from 4 March to 20 April 1871. The session was inundated with a myriad of bills. Among them were three apportionment bills. On 9 March Mr. Mercur introduced H.R. 8 which was read twice and referred to the House Committee on the Judiciary.[11] The bill proposed a House size of 280. On 20 March Burton Cook (IL) introduced H.R. 243 which was referred to the House Committee of the Whole on the State of the Union.[12] The bill proposed a House size of 281, adding an additional seat to Ohio based on the Hamilton-Vinton method (Table 3.9, next page). Finally, on 5 April Mr. Mercur introduced H.R. 328, which was referred to the Committee on the Judiciary.[13] Mercur's second bill retained his proposed House size of 280. None of the apportionment bills made it out of committee during this session of Congress.

The 2nd session began on 6 December 1871. Two days later in the House, John Farnsworth (IL) initiated consideration of H.R. 243. Mr. Mercur rose to present a substitute bill which set the House size at 280 to be apportioned using the modified Webster method. Mr. Mercur recounted how the House in the previous Congress passed a bill setting the House size at 275. The Senate amended the bill to House size 300. However, the House failed to act on the Senate amendment and the bill subsequently died. Mr. Mercur was a member of the Committee on the Judiciary and said that apportionment was extensively discussed in committee and they "fixed upon two hundred and eighty as the proper number which we would recommend to this House."[14] Table 3.9 (next page) displays a spreadsheet of calculations.

An "elaborate table"[15] of apportionments was prepared and a copy was placed on each representative's desk to aid in following the discussion. Referring to the tables, Mr. Mercur noted that the national divisor with House size 280 is 136119; whereas the divisor applied to create his substitute bill is 137800. Mr. Mercur explained that "the object was to keep the whole number as low as two hundred and eighty and yet give each State that has a moiety an additional member for that fraction."[16] Congressmen then noted that although the two methods produced a House size of 280, the resulting apportionments were different; in particular, Mr. Mercur's bill gave Arkansas and Rhode Island a seat at the expense of Illinois and Missouri (see Table 3.9, next page).

---

[9] Bills and Resolutions, 41st Congress, 3rd Session, H.R. 2687.

[10] House Journal, 41st Congress, 3rd Session, 10 January 1871: 131.

[11] Bills and Resolutions, 42nd Congress, 1st Session, H.R. 8.

[12] Ibid, H.R. 243.

[13] Ibid, H.R. 328.

[14] Congressional Globe, 42nd Congress, 2nd Session, 6 December 1871: 32-35.

[15] Ibid: 33.

[16] Ibid: 34; also, moiety here means decimal fraction greater than .5.

Table 3.9. A spreadsheet showing apportionments for House size 280 in contrast to H. R. 243.

State	Population	HR243	Quota280	Lower	Seats	137800	quotient
Alabama	996,992	7	7.3240	7	7	7	7.2351
Arkansas	484,471	4	3.5590	3	3	4	3.5158
California	560,247	4	4.1156	4	4	4	4.0657
Connecticut	537,454	4	3.9482	3	4	4	3.9002
Delaware	125,015	1	0.9184	0	1	1	0.9072
Florida	187,748	1	1.3792	1	1	1	1.3625
Georgia	1,184,109	9	8.6985	8	9	9	8.5930
Illinois	2,539,891	19	18.6582	18	19	18	18.4317
Indiana	1,680,637	12	12.3461	12	12	12	12.1962
Iowa	1,194,020	9	8.7713	8	9	9	8.6649
Kansas	364,399	3	2.6769	2	3	3	2.6444
Kentucky	1,321,011	10	9.7042	9	10	10	9.5864
Louisiana	726,915	5	5.3400	5	5	5	5.2751
Maine	626,915	5	4.6054	4	5	5	4.5495
Maryland	780,894	6	5.7365	5	6	6	5.6669
Massachusetts	1,457,351	11	10.7058	10	11	11	10.5758
Michigan	1,184,059	9	8.6982	8	9	9	8.5926
Minnesota	439,706	3	3.2301	3	3	3	3.1909
Mississippi	827,922	6	6.0820	6	6	6	6.0081
Missouri	1,721,295	12	12.6447	12	13	12	12.4913
Nebraska	122,993	1	0.9035	0	1	1	0.8925
Nevada	42,491	1	0.3121	0	1	1	0.3084
New Hampshire	318,300	2	2.3383	2	2	2	2.3099
New Jersey	906,096	7	6.6562	6	7	7	6.5754
New York	4,382,759	32	32.1960	32	32	32	31.8052
North Carolina	1,071,361	8	7.8703	7	8	8	7.7748
Ohio	2,665,260	19	19.5792	19	19	19	19.3415
Oregon	90,923	1	0.6679	0	1	1	0.6598
Pennsylvania	3,521,951	26	25.8725	25	26	26	25.5584
Rhode Island	217,353	2	1.5967	1	1	2	1.5773
South Carolina	705,606	5	5.1834	5	5	5	5.1205
Tennessee	1,258,520	9	9.2452	9	9	9	9.1329
Texas	818,579	6	6.0133	6	6	6	5.9403
Vermont	330,551	2	2.4282	2	2	2	2.3988
Virginia	1,225,163	9	9.0001	9	9	9	8.8909
West Virginia	442,014	3	3.2471	3	3	3	3.2076
Wisconsin	1,054,670	8	7.7477	7	8	8	7.6536
U. S.	38,115,641	281	280.0000	261	280	280	276.6012

The discussion was confused at times because there were several different sets of comparison. H.R. 243 specified a House size of 281 and gave the seats for each state but did not specify a method of apportionment. The bill was consistent with neither the Hamilton-Vinton method nor a Webster method (Table 3.10, next page). In contrast Mercur's bill specified a House size of 280 apportioned by a modified Webster method. So, in addition to contrasting House sizes, 280 vs. 281, there were contrasting methods of apportionment, Hamilton-Vinton vs. modified Webster, which used different divisors, 136127 for Hamilton-Vinton (although Mercur quoted 136119) and 137000 for modified Webster.

Table 3.10. A contrast of H. R. 243 with apportionment of 281 seats by Hamilton-Vinton (Quota/Lower/Seats columns) and Websters method with divisor 137300 (137300/Quotient columns).

State	Population	HR243	Quota	Lower	Seats	137300	Quotient
Alabama	996,992	7	7.3501	7	7	7	7.2614
Arkansas	484,471	4	3.5717	3	3	4	3.5286
California	560,247	4	4.1303	4	4	4	4.0805
Connecticut	537,454	4	3.9623	3	4	4	3.9145
Delaware	125,015	1	0.9216	0	1	1	0.9105
Florida	187,748	1	1.3841	1	1	1	1.3674
Georgia	1,184,109	9	8.7296	8	9	9	8.6242
Illinois	2,539,891	19	18.7248	18	19	18	18.4988
Indiana	1,680,637	12	12.3902	12	12	12	12.2406
Iowa	1,194,020	9	8.8027	8	9	9	8.6964
Kansas	364,399	3	2.6865	2	3	3	2.6540
Kentucky	1,321,011	10	9.7389	9	10	10	9.6213
Louisiana	726,915	5	5.3590	5	5	5	5.2944
Maine	626,915	5	4.6218	4	5	5	4.5660
Maryland	780,894	6	5.7570	5	6	6	5.6875
Massachusetts	1,457,351	11	10.7440	10	11	11	10.6144
Michigan	1,184,059	9	8.7292	8	9	9	8.6239
Minnesota	439,706	3	3.2416	3	3	3	3.2025
Mississippi	827,922	6	6.1037	6	6	6	6.0300
Missouri	1,721,295	12	12.6899	12	13	13	12.5367
Nebraska	122,993	1	0.9067	0	1	1	0.8958
Nevada	42,491	1	0.3133	0	1	1	0.3095
New Hampshire	318,300	2	2.3466	2	2	2	2.3183
New Jersey	906,096	7	6.6800	6	7	7	6.5994
New York	4,382,759	32	32.3110	32	32	32	31.9210
North Carolina	1,071,361	8	7.8984	7	8	8	7.8031
Ohio	2,665,260	19	19.6491	19	20	19	19.4119
Oregon	90,923	1	0.6703	0	1	1	0.6622
Pennsylvania	3,521,951	26	25.9649	25	26	26	25.6515
Rhode Island	217,353	2	1.6024	1	1	2	1.5831
South Carolina	705,606	5	5.2019	5	5	5	5.1392
Tennessee	1,258,520	9	9.2782	9	9	9	9.1662
Texas	818,579	6	6.0348	6	6	6	5.9620
Vermont	330,551	2	2.4369	2	2	2	2.4075
Virginia	1,225,163	9	9.0323	9	9	9	8.9233
West Virginia	442,014	3	3.2587	3	3	3	3.2193
Wisconsin	1,054,670	8	7.7753	7	8	8	7.6815
U. S.	38,115,641	281	281.0000	261	281	281	277.6085

An example of confusion arose in considering Missouri. For House size 280 Missouri's quota is 12.6447 while the quotient for Webster's method using the divisor of 137800 is 12.4913 (see Table 3.9). Missouri's quota justifies an additional seat but not the quotient. Mr. Farnsworth argued "Missouri, like Illinois, has a fraction larger than moiety of the number entitling it to a member."[17] It was difficult for congressmen to place a fraction in its appropriate context. Farnsworth noted that "by simply amending Mr. Cook's bill so as to give the State of Missouri thirteen members instead of twelve, you have it mathematically correct."[18] Farnsworth subsequently moved to amend by adding a seat to Missouri. This brings the House size to 282, yielding a result consistent with Webster's method (the method Mr. Farnsworth objected to), but inconsistent with the Hamilton-Vinton method (the method he supported) by adding a seat to Arkansas at the expense of Ohio (Table 3.11, next page).

Mr. Mercur noted that the only difference between his substitute bill and H.R. 243 was that Illinois received one less seat under his bill. If the House size is set at 280, then four states are affected between Hamilton-Vinton vs. Webster; in particular, using Webster, Arkansas and Rhode Island gain at the expense of Missouri and Illinois. If the House size is set at 281, then Ohio gains the additional seat using Hamilton-Vinton while Missouri gains the additional seat using Webster. In comparison with Webster, H.R. 243 adds a seat for Illinois at the expense of Missouri. In comparison with Hamilton-Vinton, H.R. 243 adds seats to Arkansas and Rhode Island at the expense of Missouri and Ohio. Hence, at House size 281 the competing methods of H.R. 243, Hamilton-Vinton and Webster, affect the apportionments of five states: Arkansas, Illinois, Missouri, Ohio, and Rhode Island. That was a lot to keep straight.

Attempts to amend the House size to 243, 291, 250, or 283 all failed. On 14 December James Garfield (OH) (Figure 3.3[19] [20]) moved to amend Mercur's substitution by setting the House size at 283; passed, 93-89. The debate between methods, Webster vs. Hamilton-Vinton, became moot because at House size 283 the two methods agreed (Table 3.12. Finally, Mercur's amended substitute bill passed on 14 December. An additional amendment, which passed 86-48, stipulated that no new state can be admitted without a population justifying at least one representative by ratio of the current apportionment bill.[21]

James Garfield served nine consecutive terms from 1863 to 1881 as a representative from Ohio. In 1880 the Ohio state legislature elected him to the U. S. Senate. He became the compromise Republican presidential candidate and won the 1880 election. He is the only sitting representative to be elected President. His term was short, 4 March 1881 to 19 September 1881, a victim as the second President to be assassinated in office. James Garfield was good at mathematics. You can watch a video of Garfield's proof of the Pythagorean Theorem on the Khan Academy's website.

Figure 3.3. James Garfield.

---

[17] Ibid.

[18] Ibid: 35.

[19] http://en.wikipedia.org/wiki/James_A._Garfield.

[20] https://www.khanacademy.org/math/basic-geo/basic-geo-pythagorean-topic/basic-geo-pythagorean-proofs/v/garfield-s-proof-of-the-pythagorean-theorem.

[21] Ibid, 14 December 1871: 137-146.

Table 3.11. Spreadsheet analysis for House size 282 based on the 1870 census. The Quota/Lower/Seats columns show the Hamilton-Vinton method. The 137000/quotient columns show the Webster method using a divisor of 137000.

State	Population	Quota	Lower	Seats	137000	quotient	HR243
Alabama	996,992	7.3763	7	7	7	7.2773	7
Arkansas	484,471	3.5844	3	3	4	3.5363	4
California	560,247	4.1450	4	4	4	4.0894	4
Connecticut	537,454	3.9764	3	4	4	3.9230	4
Delaware	125,015	0.9249	0	1	1	0.9125	1
Florida	187,748	1.3891	1	1	1	1.3704	1
Georgia	1,184,109	8.7607	8	9	9	8.6431	9
Illinois	2,539,891	18.7915	18	19	19	18.5394	19
Indiana	1,680,637	12.4343	12	12	12	12.2674	12
Iowa	1,194,020	8.8340	8	9	9	8.7155	9
Kansas	364,399	2.6960	2	3	3	2.6598	3
Kentucky	1,321,011	9.7735	9	10	10	9.6424	10
Louisiana	726,915	5.3781	5	5	5	5.3059	5
Maine	626,915	4.6383	4	5	5	4.5760	5
Maryland	780,894	5.7775	5	6	6	5.7000	6
Massachusetts	1,457,351	10.7823	10	11	11	10.6376	11
Michigan	1,184,059	8.7603	8	9	9	8.6428	9
Minnesota	439,706	3.2532	3	3	3	3.2095	3
Mississippi	827,922	6.1254	6	6	6	6.0432	6
Missouri	1,721,295	12.7351	12	13	13	12.5642	13
Nebraska	122,993	0.9100	0	1	1	0.8978	1
Nevada	42,491	0.3144	0	1	1	0.3102	1
New Hampshire	318,300	2.3550	2	2	2	2.3234	2
New Jersey	906,096	6.7038	6	7	7	6.6138	7
New York	4,382,759	32.4260	32	32	32	31.9909	32
North Carolina	1,071,361	7.9265	7	8	8	7.8202	8
Ohio	2,665,260	19.7190	19	20	19	19.4545	19
Oregon	90,923	0.6727	0	1	1	0.6637	1
Pennsylvania	3,521,951	26.0573	26	26	26	25.7077	26
Rhode Island	217,353	1.6081	1	2	2	1.5865	2
South Carolina	705,606	5.2205	5	5	5	5.1504	5
Tennessee	1,258,520	9.3112	9	9	9	9.1863	9
Texas	818,579	6.0563	6	6	6	5.9750	6
Vermont	330,551	2.4456	2	2	2	2.4128	2
Virginia	1,225,163	9.0644	9	9	9	8.9428	9
West Virginia	442,014	3.2703	3	3	3	3.2264	3
Wisconsin	1,054,670	7.8030	7	8	8	7.6983	8
U. S.	38,115,641	282.0000	262	282	282	278.2164	282

Table 3.12. Spreadsheet for House size 283 comparing the Hamilton-Vinton and Webster methods of apportionment based on the 1870 census. The Quota/Lower/Seats columns provide the calculations for the Hamilton-Vinton method. For the Webster method, the quotient is obtained by applying the divisor 136500 to achieve the House size 283.

State	Population	Quota	Lower	Seats	136500	quotient
Alabama	996,992	7.4024	7	7	7	7.3040
Arkansas	484,471	3.5971	3	4	4	3.5492
California	560,247	4.1597	4	4	4	4.1044
Connecticut	537,454	3.9905	3	4	4	3.9374
Delaware	125,015	0.9282	0	1	1	0.9159
Florida	187,748	1.3940	1	1	1	1.3754
Georgia	1,184,109	8.7917	8	9	9	8.6748
Illinois	2,539,891	18.8581	18	19	19	18.6073
Indiana	1,680,637	12.4783	12	12	12	12.3124
Iowa	1,194,020	8.8653	8	9	9	8.7474
Kansas	364,399	2.7056	2	3	3	2.6696
Kentucky	1,321,011	9.8082	9	10	10	9.6777
Louisiana	726,915	5.3972	5	5	5	5.3254
Maine	626,915	4.6547	4	5	5	4.5928
Maryland	780,894	5.7980	5	6	6	5.7208
Massachusetts	1,457,351	10.8205	10	11	11	10.6766
Michigan	1,184,059	8.7914	8	9	9	8.6744
Minnesota	439,706	3.2647	3	3	3	3.2213
Mississippi	827,922	6.1471	6	6	6	6.0654
Missouri	1,721,295	12.7802	12	13	13	12.6102
Nebraska	122,993	0.9132	0	1	1	0.9010
Nevada	42,491	0.3155	0	1	1	0.3113
New Hampshire	318,300	2.3633	2	2	2	2.3319
New Jersey	906,096	6.7276	6	7	7	6.6381
New York	4,382,759	32.5410	32	32	32	32.1081
North Carolina	1,071,361	7.9546	7	8	8	7.8488
Ohio	2,665,260	19.7890	19	20	20	19.5257
Oregon	90,923	0.6751	0	1	1	0.6661
Pennsylvania	3,521,951	26.1497	26	26	26	25.8018
Rhode Island	217,353	1.6138	1	2	2	1.5923
South Carolina	705,606	5.2390	5	5	5	5.1693
Tennessee	1,258,520	9.3442	9	9	9	9.2199
Texas	818,579	6.0778	6	6	6	5.9969
Vermont	330,551	2.4543	2	2	2	2.4216
Virginia	1,225,163	9.0966	9	9	9	8.9756
West Virginia	442,014	3.2819	3	3	3	3.2382
Wisconsin	1,054,670	7.8307	7	8	8	7.7265
U. S.	38,115,641	283.0000	262	283	283	279.2355

H.R. 243 then finally read that the House size would be 283. The specified distribution of seats was consistent with the Hamilton-Vinton method specified in the act of 1850. It was sent to the Senate for concurrence. After a minor adjustment, concurrence was reached between the two chambers of Congress. President Ulysses Grant approved *An Act for the Apportionment of Representatives to Congress among the several States according to the ninth Census* on 2 February 1872.[22]

Section 3.3.3   The Supplement

On 30 May 1872 President Grant signed *An Act supplemental to an Act entitled "An Act for the Apportionment of Representatives to Congress among the several States according to the ninth Census."* The act read as follows.[23]

> *Be it enacted by the Senate and House of Representatives of the United States of America in Congress assembled,* That from and after the third day of March, eighteen hundred and seventy-three, the following States shall be entitled to one representative each in the Congress of the United States in addition to the number apportioned to such States by the act entitled "An act for the apportionment of representatives to Congress among the several States according to the ninth census," approved February second, eighteen hundred and seventy-two, to wit: New Hampshire, Vermont, New York, Pennsylvania, Indiana, Tennessee, Louisiana, Alabama, and Florida, and be elected by separate districts, as in said act directed: *Provided,* That in the election of representatives to the forty-third Congress only, in any State which by this law is given an increased number of representatives, the additional representatives allowed to such State may be elected by the State at large, unless the legislature of said State shall otherwise provide before the time fixed by law for the election of representatives therein.
> APPROVED, May 30, 1872.

To help understand the rationale of Congress for this supplement, see Table 3.13 (next page). The first set of Quota/Lower/Seats columns shows the computations needed to apply the Hamilton-Vinton method given the House size 292. The Webster and Dean columns show the figures needed for those methods to achieve the same House size. A divisor of 130200 works to produce a House of size 292 using Webster's method, 132000 using Dean's method.

The result of the supplement bill increased the House size from 283 to 292. Did Congress distribute 292 seats according to some apportionment method? Or, did Congress adjust the 283 apportionment by giving an additional seat to nine states to adjust their seats for some reason; or, something else? The debate was sparse and, in the Senate, centered mostly on the *Provided* component of the supplement bill. At the time Congress was concerned about having an election of representatives take place by congressional districts rather than at-large.[24]

---

[22] Statutes at Large, 42nd Congress, 2nd Session, Chap. XI, 2 February 1872: 28-9.
[23] Statutes at Large, 42nd Congress, 2nd Session, Chap. CCXXXIX: 192.
[24] Congressional Globe, 42nd Congress, 2nd Session: 3637-8, 3698-700, 3763-66, 3798, 3842, 3848.

Table 3.13. Spreadsheet analysis to accompany the 1872 supplement apportionment bill. The first Quota/Lower/Seats columns represent the Hamilton-Vinton method for House size 292. The Quotient/130200 columns represent Webster's method while the Quotient/132000 columns represent Dean's method. The final Quota/Lower/Seats columns represent the Hamilton-Vinton method for House size 290.

State	Population	Quota	Lower	Seats	Quotient	130200	Quotient	132000	Quota	Lower	Seats
Alabama	996,992	7.6379	7	8	7.6574	8	7.5530	8	7.5855	7	8
Arkansas	484,471	3.7115	3	4	3.7210	4	3.6702	4	3.6861	3	4
California	560,247	4.2920	4	4	4.3030	4	4.2443	4	4.2626	4	4
Connecticut	537,454	4.1174	4	4	4.1279	4	4.0716	4	4.0892	4	4
Delaware	125,015	0.9577	0	1	0.9602	1	0.9471	1	0.9512	0	1
Florida	187,748	1.4383	1	1	1.4420	1	1.4223	2	1.4285	1	1
Georgia	1,184,109	9.0713	9	9	9.0945	9	8.9705	9	9.0092	9	9
Illinois	2,539,891	19.4578	19	20	19.5076	20	19.2416	19	19.3246	19	19
Indiana	1,680,637	12.8752	12	13	12.9081	13	12.7321	13	12.7870	12	13
Iowa	1,194,020	9.1473	9	9	9.1707	9	9.0456	9	9.0846	9	9
Kansas	364,399	2.7916	2	3	2.7988	3	2.7606	3	2.7725	2	3
Kentucky	1,321,011	10.1201	10	10	10.1460	10	10.0077	10	10.0508	10	10
Louisiana	726,915	5.5688	5	6	5.5831	6	5.5069	6	5.5307	5	6
Maine	626,915	4.8027	4	5	4.8150	5	4.7494	5	4.7698	4	5
Maryland	780,894	5.9823	5	6	5.9976	6	5.9159	6	5.9414	5	6
Massachusetts	1,457,351	11.1646	11	11	11.1932	11	11.0405	11	11.0881	11	11
Michigan	1,184,059	9.0710	9	9	9.0942	9	8.9701	9	9.0088	9	9
Minnesota	439,706	3.3685	3	3	3.3772	3	3.3311	3	3.3455	3	3
Mississippi	827,922	6.3426	6	6	6.3588	6	6.2721	6	6.2992	6	6
Missouri	1,721,295	13.1867	13	13	13.2204	13	13.0401	13	13.0963	13	13
Nebraska	122,993	0.9422	0	1	0.9446	1	0.9318	1	0.9358	0	1
Nevada	42,491	0.3255	0	1	0.3264	1	0.3219	1	0.3233	0	1
New Hampshire	318,300	2.4385	2	2	2.4447	2	2.4114	3	2.4218	2	2
New Jersey	906,096	6.9415	6	7	6.9593	7	6.8644	7	6.8940	6	7
New York	4,382,759	33.5759	33	34	33.6617	34	33.2027	33	33.3459	33	33
North Carolina	1,071,361	8.2076	8	8	8.2286	8	8.1164	8	8.1514	8	8
Ohio	2,665,260	20.4183	20	20	20.4705	20	20.1914	20	20.2784	20	20
Oregon	90,923	0.6966	0	1	0.6983	1	0.6888	1	0.6918	0	1
Pennsylvania	3,521,951	26.9813	26	27	27.0503	27	26.6814	27	26.7965	26	27
Rhode Island	217,353	1.6651	1	2	1.6694	2	1.6466	2	1.6537	1	2
South Carolina	705,606	5.4056	5	5	5.4194	5	5.3455	5	5.3686	5	5
Tennessee	1,258,520	9.6414	9	10	9.6661	10	9.5342	10	9.5754	9	10
Texas	818,579	6.2710	6	6	6.2871	6	6.2014	6	6.2281	6	6
Vermont	330,551	2.5323	2	3	2.5388	3	2.5042	3	2.5150	2	3
Virginia	1,225,163	9.3858	9	9	9.4099	9	9.2815	9	9.3216	9	9
West Virginia	442,014	3.3862	3	3	3.3949	3	3.3486	3	3.3630	3	3
Wisconsin	1,054,670	8.0797	8	8	8.1004	8	7.9899	8	8.0244	8	8
U. S.	38,115,641	292.0000	274	292	292.7469	292	288.7549	292	290.0000	274	290

Did Congress distribute seats according to some apportionment method? The answer is yes and no because a hybrid process was used. The main spokesman in the House for the supplement was Representative Ulysses Mercur (PA). In justifying the supplement Mr. Mercur said, "The only two States whose representation the existing law proposes to decrease are Vermont and New Hampshire. This bill, if it becomes a law, will allow to these States their present representation, three members each."[25] The motivation for the supplement came from the House Committee on the Judiciary with the purpose of augmenting the apportionment act of 2 February 1872 so that no state's congressional delegation decreased. Hence a justification was needed to give an additional seat to New Hampshire and Vermont.

Increasing the House size from 283 to 290 almost did the job. First, at House size 290 the Hamilton-Vinton and Webster methods agreed. It was important to Mr. Mercur that every state with a "fraction greater than moiety" receive an additional seat. House size 290 accomplishes this but New Hampshire does not get an additional seat. Mr. Mercur's solution was to supplement the seven additional seats with an additional seat to New Hampshire. But, at $h = 290$ New Hampshire's quota decimal fraction is 0.4218 and Florida's is 0.4285. Hence, an additional seat to New Hampshire required an additional seat to Florida. New Hampshire and Florida were the only two states with a decimal fraction between .4 and moiety. James Garfield asked what would happen if the quota method were applied to House size 292. Unfortunately, he did not follow up on this point since Samuel Cox (NY) changed the direction of the discussion by inquiring how these supplemental representatives would be elected: at-large or district. After Mr. Mercur assured Mr. Cox that immediate redistricting was not required for the supplements, the House passed H.R. 1343.[26]

Mr. Garfield's concern raises interesting points. First, if the Hamilton-Vinton method would have been applied for House size 292, then the two additional supplement seats would not have gone to New Hampshire and Florida but to Illinois and New York (see Table 3.13, previous page). Mr. Mercur's aim was to provide a supplement so that no state's apportionment would decrease. The smallest House size that would accomplish this using the Hamilton-Vinton method is 293 (Table 3.14, next page). But at House size 293 the Hamilton-Vinton and Webster methods are not equivalent. Mr. Mercur could have achieved his objective that New Hampshire's delegation retains three members without New Hampshire's fraction having moiety, but this would have been inconsistent with his previous arguments based on moiety.

If the Hamilton-Vinton method as specified by the act of 1850 had been followed, the supplement should have increased the House size by ten members (so that New Hampshire would not lose a seat) with the additional seats going to New York (two additional seats), Vermont, New Hampshire, Pennsylvania, Illinois, Indiana, Alabama, Louisiana, and Tennessee. But, instead, the supplement increased the House size by nine members with the additional seats going to New Hampshire, Florida, New York, Vermont, Pennsylvania, Indiana, Alabama, Louisiana, and Tennessee.

---

[25] Ibid, 8 May 1872: 3198.
[26] Ibid, 3198-9.

Table 3.14. Spreadsheet for House size 293 using the Hamilton-Vinton, Webster, and Dean methods. The Hamilton-Vinton calculations are shown in the Quota/Lower/Seats columns. The Webster method uses a divisor of 130000. The Dean method uses a divisor of 130500.

State	Population	Quota	Lower	Seats	Webster	Seats	Dean	Seats
Alabama	996,992	7.6640	7	8	7.6692	8	7.6398	8
Arkansas	484,471	3.7242	3	4	3.7267	4	3.7124	4
California	560,247	4.3067	4	4	4.3096	4	4.2931	4
Connecticut	537,454	4.1315	4	4	4.1343	4	4.1184	4
Delaware	125,015	0.9610	0	1	0.9617	1	0.9580	1
Florida	187,748	1.4432	1	1	1.4442	1	1.4387	2
Georgia	1,184,109	9.1024	9	9	9.1085	9	9.0736	9
Illinois	2,539,891	19.5245	19	20	19.5376	20	19.4628	19
Indiana	1,680,637	12.9193	12	13	12.9280	13	12.8784	13
Iowa	1,194,020	9.1786	9	9	9.1848	9	9.1496	9
Kansas	364,399	2.8012	2	3	2.8031	3	2.7923	3
Kentucky	1,321,011	10.1548	10	10	10.1616	10	10.1227	10
Louisiana	726,915	5.5879	5	6	5.5917	6	5.5702	6
Maine	626,915	4.8192	4	5	4.8224	5	4.8039	5
Maryland	780,894	6.0028	6	6	6.0069	6	5.9839	6
Massachusetts	1,457,351	11.2029	11	11	11.2104	11	11.1674	11
Michigan	1,184,059	9.1020	9	9	9.1081	9	9.0732	9
Minnesota	439,706	3.3801	3	3	3.3824	3	3.3694	3
Mississippi	827,922	6.3643	6	6	6.3686	6	6.3442	6
Missouri	1,721,295	13.2318	13	13	13.2407	13	13.1900	13
Nebraska	122,993	0.9455	0	1	0.9461	1	0.9425	1
Nevada	42,491	0.3266	0	1	0.3269	1	0.3256	1
New Hampshire	318,300	2.4468	2	3	2.4485	2	2.4391	3
New Jersey	906,096	6.9653	6	7	6.9700	7	6.9433	7
New York	4,382,759	33.6909	33	34	33.7135	34	33.5844	34
North Carolina	1,071,361	8.2357	8	8	8.2412	8	8.2097	8
Ohio	2,665,260	20.4882	20	20	20.5020	21	20.4234	20
Oregon	90,923	0.6989	0	1	0.6994	1	0.6967	1
Pennsylvania	3,521,951	27.0737	27	27	27.0919	27	26.9881	27
Rhode Island	217,353	1.6708	1	2	1.6719	2	1.6655	2
South Carolina	705,606	5.4241	5	5	5.4277	5	5.4069	5
Tennessee	1,258,520	9.6744	9	10	9.6809	10	9.6438	10
Texas	818,579	6.2925	6	6	6.2968	6	6.2726	6
Vermont	330,551	2.5410	2	3	2.5427	3	2.5330	3
Virginia	1,225,163	9.4180	9	9	9.4243	9	9.3882	9
West Virginia	442,014	3.3978	3	3	3.4001	3	3.3871	3
Wisconsin	1,054,670	8.1074	8	8	8.1128	8	8.0818	8
U. S.	38,115,641	293.0000	276	293	219.5480	293	292.0739	293

Hence, there are three reasonable scenarios to explore on the table of possibilities:

1. House size 292 with the supplements awarded to New Hampshire, Vermont, New York, Pennsylvania, Indiana, Alabama, Florida, Louisiana, and Tennessee.

2. House size 292 with the supplements awarded to Vermont, New York (2), Pennsylvania, Illinois, Indiana, Alabama, Louisiana, and Tennessee.

3. House size 293 with the supplements awarded to New York (2), Vermont, New Hampshire, Pennsylvania, Illinois, Indiana, Alabama, Louisiana, and Tennessee.

The choice was soon to have presidential consequences.

Section 3.3.4   The 1876 Presidential Election

Figure 3.4. Campaign posters featured in the presidential election of 1876.

The presidential election of 1876 primarily featured Republican Rutherford B. Hayes, governor of Ohio, against Democratic contender Samuel J. Tilden, governor of New York (Figure 3.4). Volumes have already been written about this subject; accordingly, we refer the reader to other sources for details about the election. Tilden won a majority of the popular vote: 4284020 (51%), Hayes 4036572 (48%), and Cooper 81737 (1%). However, presidential elections are not decided by the popular vote. They are decided by a vote in the Electoral College where

Hayes won over Tilden, 185-184. This is the only presidential election in U. S. history where a candidate won a majority of the popular vote but lost the election.

Our concern is, did congressional apportionment affect the outcome of the election? Several, such as Balinski and Young, claim: "Had Hamilton's method been followed as required by law, Tilden would have won instead."[27] There are two issues involved in this statement. First, had Hamilton's method been followed *as required by law*; second, Tilden would have won instead.

The first issue is a legal one. Hamilton's method was required by the act of 23 May 1850; but the act applied to the Secretary of the Interior. Immediately after a census is completed, the Secretary of the Interior is to make a computation of apportionment based on Hamilton's method and send the results to Congress and the States. This was done. However, Congress has the right, under the constraint of constitutional guidelines, to modify those results. Modification was done with reapportionment based on the 1850 census on two occasions, the supplementary acts of 30 August 1850 and 30 July 1852. A similar thing happened with the 1860 census. The Department of the Interior made its initial apportionment of 233 seats using Hamilton's method followed by the supplementary act of 4 March 1862. None of these supplements conformed to Hamilton's method. There is no legal requirement that a supplement must follow Hamilton's method.

The second issue concerns whether Tilden would have won the Electoral College vote, and hence the presidency, if Hamilton's method of apportionment had been specified in the supplement act of 1872 which increased the House size to 292. By applying the apportionment results specified by the supplement act, Hayes won over Tilden in the Electoral College, 185-184. If the Hamilton-Vinton method were followed, then the results would have been reversed. The cause of the reversal is that Florida would not have had an additional seat in the House (Florida's electoral votes went to Hayes); hence, Florida would have had three electoral votes instead of four. That additional vote would have gone to New York, which Tilden won.

Although Tilden would have won from this point of view, it is an improbable point of view. Congress most likely would not have passed the supplement based on Hamilton's method. The announced purpose of Mr. Mercur, the leading spokesman for the supplement bill in the House, was to provide an additional seat to both Vermont and New Hampshire so that no state would lose representation in the new Congress. House size 292 under the Hamilton-Vinton method does not accomplish this goal. One would have to increase the House to 293 to accomplish this objective with the Hamilton-Vinton method (see Tables 3.13 and 3.14).

Colorado was admitted as a new state on 1 August 1876 under a proclamation of President Grant.[28] The enabling act for Colorado's admission, approved 3 March 1875, prescribed one

---

[27] Michel L. Balinski and H. Peyton Young, *Fair Representation: Meeting the Ideal of One Man, One Vote*, Second Edition, Brookings Institution Press, 2001: 37; endnote 3: 184.
[28] http://www.presidency.ucsb.edu/ws/index.php?pid=70540.

representative until the next census.[29] This gave Colorado three electoral votes. If Congress had passed an apportionment bill with House size 293 using Hamilton's method, along with Colorado's admission, then the Electoral College would have 372 votes which would have resulted in a Hayes-Tilden tie at 186 votes each. Accordingly, the election would have been turned over to the House of Representatives where each state would have one vote. Assuming that states would vote along party lines, Tilden would have won at least 23-12 among the 38 states. Three states had split delegations: Florida, Massachusetts, and New York.[30] Factoring in the popular vote giving New York to Tilden and Massachusetts to Hayes, the final House vote would probably have been Tilden 24, Hayes 13, with Florida undecided.

Hence, it is reasonable to conclude that the supplement bill of 1872 did affect the presidential outcome. However, this is not a surprising conclusion. If a candidate wins the Electoral College by one vote, then of course, the method of apportionment, in hindsight, matters in the event that the methods of Hamilton, Webster, and Dean are not equivalent.

Although apportionment played a decisive role in the presidential election of 1876, there were also other important factors such as the extensive voter suppression, dirty tricks, and power politics. Rutherford Hayes knew he was a compromise candidate and upon nomination pledged to serve only one term if elected. The Hayes administration was honest and basic. The first lady, Lucy Hayes, was known as "Lemonade Lucy." She was a complete teetotaler and alcohol was banned from the White House. Critics complained that the White House was a place where "water flowed like wine" and referred to the President as "Rutherfraud Hayes."[31]

The inauguration of President Hayes signaled the end of Reconstruction and the beginning of a period in American history known as The Gilded Age.[32] In less than 20 years the American economy would double. Further, the presidential election of 1876 would serve as a background to events that would lead to a paradoxical demise of the Hamilton method of apportionment.

Section 3.3.5   A Paradox

On 11 December 1871 Mr. Mercur rose to make a personal explanation "based upon a dispatch in the New York Times of the 8th instant."[33] The article accused Mr. Mercur of making apportionment miscalculations by abusing the House size. Mr. Mercur defended his positions criticized in the article and, criticizing the reporter's inaccuracy, he noted that the article said the House size was 240 when it was really 243. Then Mr. Mercur interjected:[34]

> If I had seen proper to go further and criticize the illogical conclusion to which this statement leads I might have done so. It appears, by reference to this statement, that allowing two hundred and seventy members to this House, the

[29] Statutes at Large, 43rd Congress, 2nd Session: 474.

[30] http://en.wikipedia.org/wiki/44th_United_States_Congress.

[31] Carter Smith, *Presidents: All You Need To Know*, Hylas Publishing, Revised Edition, 2008: 124-7.

[32] http://www.ushistory.org/us/36.asp.

[33] Congressional Globe, 42nd Congress, 2nd Session, 11 December 1871: 59.

[34] Ibid: 60.

State of Rhode Island will have two members, but when the aggregate number of members of the House is increased to two hundred and eighty Rhode Island has by this statement but one member. Whether it is in pursuance of law matters not. We are not expounding the old law; we are seeking to establish a new law more in accordance with justice, with reason, and with wisdom.

Mr. Mercur seemed so intent on defending himself that the impact of the computational oddity appeared to escape him as he dismissed the anomaly by simply moving to alternatives based on "justice, reason, and wisdom." The anomaly that he mentioned may be described as an *increased size paradox: increased resources may result in a decreased share.* This seems totally counter-intuitive: if a given amount of resource leads to a fair share for a member, how can an increase in resources lead to a decrease in a proportional share?

The numbers for Rhode Island for House size 270 and 280 are presented in Table 3.15 (next page). It is surprising that Rhode Island's proportional fair share in a House of 270 is two seats; whereas, in a House of 280 seats Rhode Island's proportional fair share is only one seat. This paradox would eventually lead to the demise of the Hamilton-Vinton method.

Table 3.15. Spreadsheet analysis for House size 270 and 280 using the Hamilton-Vinton method.
The h=270 and h=280 columns display the respective quotas.

State	Population	h = 270	Lower	Seats	h = 280	Lower	Seats
Alabama	996,992	7.0624	7	7	7.3240	7	7
Arkansas	484,471	3.4319	3	3	3.5590	3	3
California	560,247	3.9686	3	4	4.1156	4	4
Connecticut	537,454	3.8072	3	4	3.9482	3	4
Delaware	125,015	0.8856	0	1	0.9184	0	1
Florida	187,748	1.3300	1	1	1.3792	1	1
Georgia	1,184,109	8.3879	8	8	8.6985	8	9
Illinois	2,539,891	17.9918	17	18	18.6582	18	19
Indiana	1,680,637	11.9051	11	12	12.3461	12	12
Iowa	1,194,020	8.4581	8	8	8.7713	8	9
Kansas	364,399	2.5813	2	3	2.6769	2	3
Kentucky	1,321,011	9.3577	9	9	9.7042	9	10
Louisiana	726,915	5.1493	5	5	5.3400	5	5
Maine	626,915	4.4409	4	4	4.6054	4	5
Maryland	780,894	5.5316	5	6	5.7365	5	6
Massachusetts	1,457,351	10.3234	10	10	10.7058	10	11
Michigan	1,184,059	8.3875	8	8	8.6982	8	9
Minnesota	439,706	3.1147	3	3	3.2301	3	3
Mississippi	827,922	5.8648	5	6	6.0820	6	6
Missouri	1,721,295	12.1931	12	12	12.6447	12	13
Nebraska	122,993	0.8712	0	1	0.9035	0	1
Nevada	42,491	0.3010	0	1	0.3121	0	1
New Hampshire	318,300	2.2547	2	2	2.3383	2	2
New Jersey	906,096	6.4185	6	6	6.6562	6	7
New York	4,382,759	31.0462	31	31	32.1960	32	32
North Carolina	1,071,361	7.5892	7	8	7.8703	7	8
Ohio	2,665,260	18.8799	18	19	19.5792	19	19
Oregon	90,923	0.6441	0	1	0.6679	0	1
Pennsylvania	3,521,951	24.9485	24	25	25.8725	25	26
Rhode Island	217,353	1.5397	1	2	1.5967	1	1
South Carolina	705,606	4.9983	4	5	5.1834	5	5
Tennessee	1,258,520	8.9150	8	9	9.2452	9	9
Texas	818,579	5.7986	5	6	6.0133	6	6
Vermont	330,551	2.3415	2	2	2.4282	2	2
Virginia	1,225,163	8.6787	8	9	9.0001	9	9
West Virginia	442,014	3.1311	3	3	3.2471	3	3
Wisconsin	1,054,670	7.4710	7	8	7.7477	7	8
U. S.	38,115,641	270.0000	250	270	280.0000	261	280

Section 3.4:   Reapportionment Based on the 1880 Census

Section 3.4.1   Francis Amasa Walker

The census of 1880 would see only one additional state after the 1870 census, Colorado, bringing the number of states to 38. The tenth census was covered under the guidelines of *An act to provide for taking the tenth and subsequent censuses*[1] signed into law by President Hayes on 3 March 1879 along with an amendment[2] approved on 20 April 1880. The new law featured several innovations. The regional census would no longer be under the supervision of U. S. marshals, but under the direction of appointed supervisors under the direct control of the Census Office within the Department of the Interior.[3]

Figure 3.5. Francis Walker.

The legislation called for a new position within the Department of the Interior, the Superintendent of the Census, appointed by the President. The first superintendent under the new law was Francis Amasa Walker (Figure 3.5[4]). The United States was most fortunate in this capable choice. In the 1950s Paul J. FitzPatrick began a project of writing the history of the field of statistics in the United States. The project included an article presenting the seven leading American statisticians of the nineteenth century.[5] Francis Walker was one of them.

Earlier, Walker was supervisor for the 1870 census. In December 1872 he resigned to accept a position becoming the first professor of economics at Yale. In accepting the superintendent position for the 1880 census under the new law, he was allowed to appoint the census enumerators. It is noteworthy that the 1880 census was the first census in which women were allowed to be enumerators. Walker is known for reorganizing the Bureau of Statistics on a scientific basis.

On 17 January 1881 the Speaker of the House presented a communication from Mr. Carl Schurz, Secretary of the Interior, which transmitted a report from Francis Walker, Superintendent of the Census. The report contained the revised returns from the 1880 census. Based on these returns, Samuel Cox (NY), chair of the House Committee on the Census, moved to have the report and additional tables printed "as they bear upon the most important and interesting duty of Congress—apportionment."[6]

---

[1] Statutes at Large, 45th Congress, 3rd Session, Chap. 195: 473-81.

[2] Statutes at Large, 46th Congress, 2nd Session, Chap. 57: 75-6.

[3] Diana L. Magnuson, History of Enumeration Procedures, 1790-1940, accessed from https://usa.ipums.org/usa/voliii/enumproc1.shtml 9 February 2015.

[4] http://en.wikipedia.org/wiki/Francis_Amasa_Walker#mediaviewer/File:Francis_A_Walker_MIT_2.jpg.

[5] Paul J. FitzPatrick, Leading American Statisticians in the Nineteenth Century, *Journal of the American Statistical Association*, 52(279) September 1957: 301-21.

[6] Congressional Record, 46th Congress, 3rd Session, 17 January 1881: 686.

The additional tables calculated apportionment based on revised population returns for House size 293-307 using the Hamilton-Vinton method as specified by the law of 1850. The tables, produced at the request of Mr. Cox, were accompanied by the following letter.[7]

DEPARTMENT OF THE INTERIOR, CENSUS OFFICE,
Washington, D. C., January 17, 1881.

SIR: I have the honor, in compliance with your request, to send you with this a table which exhibits the apportionment of Representatives among the several States, according to their respective populations as ascertained at the tenth census of the United States, upon certain successive assumptions as to the total number of Representatives.

The numbers taken for the purpose range from 293 to 307, both inclusive. It appears that by the increase from 293 to 294, Massachusetts gains 1; by the increase to 295, Louisiana gains 1; by the increase to 296, Pennsylvania gains 1; by the increase to 297, Maryland gains 1; by the increase to 298, New York gains 1; by the increase to 299, Alabama gains 1. When the total number of Representatives is increased to 300, one of the most striking features of the table appears, Alabama loses the Representative she gained at 299, and Texas and Illinois gain 1 each. At 301, Alabama regains the representative so lost; by the increase to 302, Florida gains 1; by the increase to 303, Ohio gains 1; by the increase to 304, North Carolina gains 1; by the increase to 305, Tennessee gains 1; by the increase to 306 Pennsylvania gains 1.

I have not carried the computation further, as this was the limit indicated in your request for the preparation of this table. The table exhibits in full the arithmetical process by which the number in each case is reached. The smaller table accompanying (marked Table B) exhibits simply the number of Representatives to be assigned to each State according to the total number taken.

Respectfully, your obedient servant,

FRANCIS A. WALKER,
Superintendent of Census

Mr. Cox subsequently sent a note to Mr. Walker asking for an explanation of the Alabama situation. Mr. Walker responded with a detailed letter titled, THE ALABAMA PARADOX.[8] The name stuck, and subsequently the increased resources paradox, when applied to congressional apportionment, is referred to as the Alabama paradox. In describing this scenario to the House, Mr. Cox said, "It is a curious eccentricity of mathematics—a paradox, the explication of which upon pure arithmetical logic, may be found in one of the communications which accompanies the tables."[9] Table 3.16 (next page) displays the Alabama Paradox.

---

[7] Ibid: 687.
[8] Ibid: 689.
[9] Ibid: 686.

To circumvent the Alabama paradox, Mr. Cox introduced a bill, H.R. No. 6958, which would set the House size at 301 members to be distributed by the Hamilton-Vinton method. Spreadsheet calculations for House size 293, 299, 300, and 301 are displayed in Table 3.16.

Table 3.16. Spreadsheet analysis for House size 299-301 based on the 1880 census.

State	Pop	h = 293	Lower	Seats	h = 299	Lower	Seats	h = 300	Lower	Seats	h = 301	Lower	Seats
AL	1262794	7.4945	7	7	7.6479	7	8	7.6735	7	7	7.6991	7	8
AR	802564	4.7631	4	5	4.8606	4	5	4.8769	4	5	4.8931	4	5
CA	864686	5.1318	5	5	5.2368	5	5	5.2544	5	5	5.2719	5	5
CO	194649	1.1552	1	1	1.1789	1	1	1.1828	1	1	1.1867	1	1
CT	622683	3.6955	3	4	3.7712	3	4	3.7838	3	4	3.7964	3	4
DE	146654	0.8704	0	1	0.8882	0	1	0.8912	0	1	0.8941	0	1
FL	267351	1.5867	1	1	1.6192	1	1	1.6246	1	1	1.6300	1	1
GA	1539048	9.1340	9	9	9.3210	9	9	9.3522	9	9	9.3834	9	9
IL	3078769	18.2720	18	18	18.6461	18	18	18.7085	18	19	18.7709	18	19
IN	1978362	11.7412	11	12	11.9817	11	12	12.0217	12	12	12.0618	12	12
IA	1624620	9.6418	9	10	9.8393	9	10	9.8722	9	10	9.9051	9	10
KS	995966	5.9109	5	6	6.0319	6	6	6.0521	6	6	6.0723	6	6
KY	1648708	9.7848	9	10	9.9852	9	10	10.0186	10	10	10.0520	10	10
LA	940103	5.5793	5	5	5.6936	5	6	5.7126	5	6	5.7317	5	6
ME	648945	3.8514	3	4	3.9302	3	4	3.9434	3	4	3.9565	3	4
MD	934632	5.5469	5	5	5.6605	5	6	5.6794	5	6	5.6983	5	6
MA	1783012	10.5819	10	10	10.7986	10	11	10.8347	10	11	10.8708	10	11
MI	1636331	9.7113	9	10	9.9102	9	10	9.9434	9	10	9.9765	9	10
MN	780806	4.6339	4	5	4.7288	4	5	4.7447	4	5	4.7605	4	5
MS	1131592	6.7158	6	7	6.8533	6	7	6.8762	6	7	6.8992	6	7
MO	2168804	12.8715	12	13	13.1351	13	13	13.1790	13	13	13.2229	13	13
NE	452433	2.6851	2	3	2.7401	2	3	2.7493	2	3	2.7584	2	3
NV	62265	0.3695	0	1	0.3771	0	1	0.3784	0	1	0.3796	0	1
NH	346984	2.0593	2	2	2.1015	2	2	2.1085	2	2	2.1155	2	2
NJ	1130983	6.7122	6	7	6.8496	6	7	6.8725	6	7	6.8955	6	7
NY	5083810	30.1715	30	30	30.7894	30	31	30.8924	30	31	30.9953	30	31
NC	1400047	8.3090	8	8	8.4792	8	8	8.5075	8	8	8.5359	8	8
OH	3198239	18.9810	18	19	19.3697	19	19	19.4345	19	19	19.4992	19	19
OR	174767	1.0372	1	1	1.0585	1	1	1.0620	1	1	1.0655	1	1
PA	4282786	25.4176	25	25	25.9381	25	26	26.0248	26	26	26.1116	26	26
RI	276528	1.6411	1	2	1.6748	1	2	1.6804	1	2	1.6860	1	2
SC	995622	5.9088	5	6	6.0298	6	6	6.0500	6	6	6.0702	6	6
TN	1542463	9.1543	9	9	9.3417	9	9	9.3730	9	9	9.4042	9	9
TX	1592574	9.4517	9	9	9.6452	9	9	9.6775	9	10	9.7097	9	10
VT	332286	1.9721	1	2	2.0124	2	2	2.0192	2	2	2.0259	2	2
VA	1512806	8.9782	8	9	9.1621	9	9	9.1927	9	9	9.2234	9	9
WV	618443	3.6704	3	4	3.7455	3	4	3.7580	3	4	3.7706	3	4
WI	1315480	7.8071	7	8	7.9670	7	8	7.9937	7	8	8.0203	8	8
US	49369595	293.0000	271	293	299.0000	277	299	300.0000	280	300	301.0000	281	301

The Alabama paradox has become revered in the literature as the pivotal example of anomalies that illustrate the mathematical difficulty of the congressional apportionment problem. However, the name itself is an example of Martin's Law[10]:

> Mathematical formulas and theorems are usually not named after their original discoverers.

---

[10] http://www.santarosa.edu/~jomartin/PythThm/PShowPDF.pdf (slide 18).

Martin's Law, named after John Martin (Figure 3.6), has applicability far beyond mathematics. Items are often named not after their origins but after someone or something whose contribution to the subject came at a later significant time. This is true throughout the naming of concepts in apportionment. As noted earlier, the Alabama paradox was articulated a decade earlier by Ulysses Mercur as applied to Rhode Island. The methods of Hamilton, Jefferson, Webster, and Dean were not initially introduced by either of these men. For example, Dean's method was articulated earlier by Fisher Ames in the apportionment debates based on the 1790 census.

John Martin is an emeritus professor of Mathematics at Santa Rosa Junior College. In 2011 he garnished a George Pólya Award for The Helen of Geometry about the cycloid published in the College Mathematics Journal.[11] Professor Martin is famous for his T-shirt designs for the annual Northern California Mathematics Conference at Asilomar. He also is known as a superb presenter of engaging mathematical topics. Professor Martin's main application of Martin's Law is Martin's Law itself!

Figure 3.6. John Martin.

Resolution of the Alabama paradox would have to wait. The term of the 46th Congress would soon end, concluding on 3 March 1881. Soon after, the nation had to adjust to the tragedy of the assassination of President Garfield. Vice-President Chester A. Arthur assumed the presidency on 19 September 1881. Discussion on apportionment would not resume for a year. In the meantime Francis Walker resigned his position as Superintendent of the Census to accept the position as President of M.I.T.[12]

Section 3.4.2 Charles Williams Seaton

The first session of the 47th Congress opened on 5 December 1881. Cyrus Prescott (NY) was the new chair of the House Committee on the Census. Mr. Prescott opened the apportionment discussion on 7 February 1882 by summarizing the importance of the problem, its history, key issues, and noting that each decade had its own unique circumstances. He then addressed the Alabama paradox by introducing a letter from C. W. Seaton (Figure 3.6, next page). The letter was accompanied by tables showing the Hamilton-Vinton apportionment for House size 275-350 inclusive and using the final population figures for the 1880 census. Commenting on the Alabama paradox, Mr. Seaton wrote:[13]

> Such a result as this is to me conclusive proof that the process employed in obtaining it is defective, and that it does not in fact "apportion representatives among the several States according to their respective numbers."

---

[11] http://www.maa.org/programs/maa-awards/writing-awards/the-helen-of-geometry

[12] Paul. J. FitzPatrick, Leading American Statisticians of the Nineteenth Century II, *Journal of the American Statistical Association*, 53(283) September 1958: 695.

[13] Congressional Record—House, 47th Congress, 1st Session, 7 February 1882: 967.

This conclusion has been confirmed by the discovery of other anomalies, and the result of my study of this question is the strong conviction that an entirely different process should be employed.

Charles Seaton[14] succeeded Francis Walker as Superintendent of the Census on 4 November 1881. Like Walker, Seaton was honest, dedicated, professional, and hard-working. Seaton applied his inventiveness to tackling the mountains of data that the census office had to process. He developed a tallying machine, first used in 1872, the first machine used for tabulating census data. Seaton's machine was the precursor to the electrical tabulation machine of Herman Hollarith, the beginning of electronic data processing.[15] [16]

Figure 3.6. Charles Seaton

To Mr. Seaton's credit, he did not just criticize the Hamilton-Vinton method but offered an alternative method. Mr. Seaton wrote,[17]

It is the mode of determining to which of the States the additional Representatives shall be assigned which I believe to be erroneous, and it is at this point that the variance between the process heretofore employed and the one which I now propose begins. (For the sake of convenience the two processes will hereafter be characterized respectively as the old and the new method.)

The old method compares the remainders left after the divisions above described, and assigns an additional Representative, first, to that State where the remainder after division was greatest; next, to the State where the remainder was next in size; and so on in order of rank of the remainders until the difference is made up. It is my opinion that it is not these remainders but rather the quotients which result from dividing the populations of the States by the increased number of Representatives which should govern the allotment, and that the additional Representatives should be so assigned that the population of the districts formed in the State to which additional Representatives are allotted shall fall as little below the average number for the United States as possible; in other words, that the districts ultimately formed from the States so increased shall approximate as closely as possible in population to that of a district which should be formed by dividing the total population of the United States exactly by the proposed total number of Representatives. … But the practice and, so far as I know, the law has uniformly aimed to divide the States finally after the number of Representatives for each State has been determined, in such manner that in each State the districts shall be as nearly equal to each other in population.

---

[14] http://www.census.gov/history/www/census_then_now/director_biographies/directors_1865_-_1893.html.

[15] Ibid.

[16] http://history-computer.com/ModernComputer/Basis/TabulatingMachine_Hollerith.html.

[17] Ibid.

The apportionment bill under consideration, H.R. 3550, contained a section specifying that congressmen "shall be elected by Districts composed of contiguous territory, and containing, as nearly as practicable, an equal number of inhabitants, and equal in number to the Representatives to which such State may be entitled in Congress, no one District electing more than one Representative."[18] Hence, Seaton felt that the practical guideline of district size should be employed rather than simply using an abstract fraction. This district size thinking is reminiscent of the thinking behind Dean's method and also the method of Lowndes.

A reading of Seaton's letter leads one to believe that he is merely proposing a quota method with a different method of deciding which states get an additional representative. Seaton's criterion is to first give each state its lower quota. To determine whether to give a state an additional seat, compute the state's constituency with the additional seat. This constituency will be less than the modulus, the national divisor. Give additional seats using the priority list of constituencies closest to the modulus. This can be seen by subtracting a state's constituency from the modulus. The state with the smallest difference gets an additional seat. Continue in this fashion until the House size is met. Using this method, in comparison to the Hamilton-Vinton method, Missouri, Texas, and Wisconsin each pick up an additional seat at the expense of California, Florida, and Rhode Island (Table 3.17, next page).

In Table 3.17 the State/Pop columns lists the 38 states in the Union and their respective apportionment populations based on the 1880 census. The Old/Lower/Seats columns give the calculations needed for a Hamilton-Vinton apportionment of a House with 320 members. The New/Lower/Seats columns show the apportionment for a House of 320 members using the description in Seaton's letter. Note how Seaton's method begins the same as the Hamilton-Vinton method. First, compute the Quota, then assign each state the lower quota. This distributes 302 seats; hence, an additional 18 seats need to be distributed to bring the total to 320 seats. Hamilton-Vinton distributes according to the decimal fraction of the quota, distributing an additional seat first to Tennessee (quota decimal fraction .9968), then finally to Iowa (.5300) which has the eighteenth largest quota decimal fraction.

To see how the basic Seaton method works, look at the Lower/+1/+2 column set. The modulus, or ideal district size, for a House of size 320 is obtained by (national population)/320 = 154285. The Lower column gives the difference between the district size and the modulus using the lower quota. The + 1 column gives the difference between the modulus and the district size using the upper quota (i.e., giving the state an additional seat). Seaton's basic method then works as follows: should I give a state an additional seat? If I give Tennessee an additional seat, then Tennessee's average district size will deviate from the modulus by only 49 people. Tennessee's deviation of 49 puts Tennessee closest to the modulus; hence, Tennessee is first in line to be awarded an additional seat; second, Georgia (67); third, New York (259), and finally, eighteenth, Iowa (6593).

---

[18] Ibid: 963-4.

Table 3.17. Spreadsheet analysis for House size 320 using Seaton's method.

State	Pop	Old	Lower	Seats	New	Lower	Seats	Lower	+1	+2	Exp	Lower	Seats
AL	1,262,505	8.1829	8	8	8.1829	8	8	3528	14007	28035	8.1829	8	8
AR	802,525	5.2016	5	5	5.2016	5	5	6220	20531	39639	5.2016	5	5
CA	864,694	5.6045	5	6	5.6045	5	5	18654	10169	30757	5.6045	5	5
CO	194,327	1.2595	1	1	1.2595	1	1	40042	57122	89509	1.2595	1	1
CT	622,700	4.0360	4	4	4.0360	4	4	1390	29745	50502	4.0360	4	4
DE	146,608	0.9502	0	1	0.9502	0	1		7677	80981	0.9502	0	1
FL	269,493	1.7467	1	2	1.7467	1	1	115208	19539	64454	1.7467	1	1
GA	1,542,180	9.9957	9	10	9.9957	9	10	17068	67	14087	9.9957	9	10
IL	3,077,871	19.9493	19	20	19.9493	19	20	7708	391	7720	19.9493	19	21
IN	1,978,301	12.8224	12	13	12.8224	12	13	10573	2108	12978	12.8224	12	13
IA	1,624,615	10.5300	10	11	10.5300	10	11	8177	6593	18900	10.5300	10	11
KS	996,096	6.4562	6	6	6.4562	6	6	11731	11986	29773	6.4562	6	6
KY	1,648,690	10.6860	10	11	10.6860	10	11	10584	4404	16894	10.6860	10	11
LA	939,946	6.0923	6	6	6.0923	6	6	2373	20007	36792	6.0923	6	6
ME	648,936	4.2061	4	4	4.2061	4	4	7949	24498	46129	4.2061	4	4
MD	934,943	6.0598	6	6	6.0598	6	6	1539	20722	37417	6.0598	6	6
MA	1,783,085	11.5571	11	12	11.5571	11	12	7814	5695	17125	11.5571	11	12
MI	1,636,937	10.6098	10	11	10.6098	10	11	9409	5473	17874	10.6098	10	11
MN	780,773	5.0606	5	5	5.0606	5	5	1870	24156	42746	5.0606	5	5
MS	1,131,597	7.3345	7	7	7.3345	7	7	7372	12835	28552	7.3345	7	7
MO	2,168,380	14.0544	14	14	14.0544	14	15	599	9726	18761	14.0544	14	14
NE	452,402	2.9322	2	3	2.9322	2	3	71916	3484	41185	2.9322	2	3
NV	62,266	0.4036	0	1	0.4036	0	1		92019	123152	0.4036	0	1
NH	346,991	2.2490	2	2	2.2490	2	2	19211	38621	67537	2.2490	2	2
NJ	1,131,116	7.3313	7	7	7.3313	7	7	7303	12896	28605	7.3313	7	7
NY	5,082,871	32.9447	32	33	32.9447	32	33	4555	259	4789	32.9447	32	34
NC	1,399,750	9.0725	9	9	9.0725	9	9	1243	14310	27035	9.0725	9	9
OH	3,198,062	20.7283	20	21	20.7283	20	21	5618	1996	8919	20.7283	20	21
OR	174,768	1.1328	1	1	1.1328	1	1	20483	66901	96029	1.1328	1	1
PA	4,282,891	27.7596	27	28	27.7596	27	28	4341	1325	6599	27.7596	27	29
RI	276,531	1.7923	1	2	1.7923	1	1	122246	16020	62108	1.7923	1	1
SC	995,577	6.4528	6	6	6.4528	6	6	11645	12060	29838	6.4528	6	6
TN	1,542,359	9.9968	9	10	9.9968	9	10	17088	49	14071	9.9968	9	10
TX	1,591,749	10.3169	10	10	10.3169	10	11	4890	9581	21639	10.3169	10	10
VT	332,286	2.1537	2	2	2.1537	2	2	11858	43523	71214	2.1537	2	2
VA	1,512,565	9.8037	9	10	9.8037	9	10	13778	3029	16779	9.8037	9	10
WV	618,457	4.0085	4	4	4.0085	4	4	329	30594	51209	4.0085	4	4
WI	1,315,497	8.5264	8	8	8.5264	8	9	10152	8119	22735	8.5264	8	8
US	49,371,340	320.0009	302	320	320.0009	302	320				320.0009	302	320

However, Seaton expanded this thinking and carried it a step further. Focusing on the notion of district size, he inquired if awarding a state yet another seat would do even a better job of equalizing average district sizes. The +2 column gives the results awarding two additional seats beyond the lower quota. Consider that the +1/+2 column set consists of a duo-column super list of priority numbers. The lowest number in the expanded list is 49; hence, Tennessee is the first state to be awarded an additional seat. Previously, the last three priority numbers (for the 16th, 17th, and 18th additional seats) were 9726 (Missouri), 9581 (Texas), and 8119 (Wisconsin). However, in the expanded list, the 16th, 17th, and 18th priority numbers are 4789, 6599, and 7720 which belong to New York, Pennsylvania, and Illinois, respectively.

Accordingly, Seaton's expanded method agreed with the Hamilton-Vinton method except for six states. This time, Illinois, New York, and Pennsylvania gain a seat at the expense of

California, Florida, and Rhode Island, as shown in Table 3.17, Exp/Lower/Seats column set. The notation "Exp" stands for the expanded Seaton method.

It is unfortunate for Seaton that he focused so strongly on district size that he entered the expanded arena. Seaton recommended that his new method, based on the expanded thinking, should replace the Hamilton-Vinton method. Congressmen jumped on and ridiculed the expanded Seaton method for its quota rule violations. These violations became the new paradoxes in comments by detractors of Seaton's method.[19]

Shortly after the presentation of Seaton's proposed alternative, George Robinson (MA) spoke against it. First, he acknowledged that they were looking at two methods, an old method and a new method. He offered, "Take the new method if it is better. What is the result? I submit … that it is always a fair test of any question to stop and look back at your result after you get there; for somehow or other there comes a conviction if your result … does not look right, that there must be something wrong in the argument, something the matter with the process." He argued that although the old method contains the Alabama paradox, the new method has paradoxes of its own. In particular, under the old method, each Florida district would average 19869 less than the modulus; under the new method, 105208 more than the modulus. The new method made a greater disparity among the average district sizes. He gave analogous figures for the other five states involved in the old vs. new methods.[20] [George Robinson is better known today as one of the three-attorney defense team responsible for the acquittal of Lizzie Borden.[21]]

Roger Mills (TX) then spoke against the proposal by zeroing in on the quota rule violations, although he did not use that terminology. He also was a bit overwhelmed by the fifty-plus page report submitted by Seaton containing the tables for apportionment from House size 275 to 350 using both the old and new methods. Mr. Mills said,[22]

> Whenever, therefore, any new-fangled system is suggested to the American Congress as fit to be adopted it is necessary to see whether the mathematics of that system reach the object intended by the framers of the Constitution.
> Now let us see this new method which we have here as a sort of new revelation in mathematics. I thought, Mr. Speaker, that mathematics was a divine science.
> But here is a new system of mathematics that demonstrates the truth to be false. … Let me state, before going further, how much I dislike to go into these lengthy and elaborate mathematical computations. [Laughter.] … If there is any one thing for which these men are noted it is their ability to cover an ordinary man all up with figures—just simply bury him. [Great laughter.]

---

[19] Congressional Record—House, 47th Congress, 1st Session, 7 February 1882: 968-72.
[20] Ibid: 969.
[21] http://en.wikipedia.org/wiki/George_D._Robinson; also
    http://law2.umkc.edu/faculty/projects/ftrials/LizzieBorden/bordenaccount.html.
[22] Ibid: 970-1.

Roswell Horr (MI) joined the levity. He noted that[23]

> under the old plan, New York was entitled to 32 members and eighty-nine
> hundredths of an additional member." [Laughter.]
>
> Now, for the sake of argument I am willing to admit that they might perhaps be
> able to find in the State of New York somebody small enough to represent this
> eighty-nine hundredths of a man. [Laughter.] But, Mr. Speaker, this bill goes even
> further and gives another man, another Representative, for no population at all.
> Where is your man, even in that large State, small enough to properly fill this bill?
> [Renewed laughter and applause.]

It became evident that quota rule violations were a deal breaker for the expanded Seaton
method. Debate continued the next three days. Some, especially Thomas Bayne (PA),
defended Seaton's expanded method. Bayne argued that Seaton's method was fairer because
it was focused on equalizing congressional district size.[24] However, Bayne's pleas to look at the
results only called attention to quota rule violations that for most congressmen trumped any
theoretical arguments about other fairness concerns.

Section 3.4.3   Resolution

On 15 February Hilary Herbert (AL) began, "I had expected to discuss the Seaton plan of
apportionment, but the injustice of that new mathematical invention has already been
exposed. It is already dead."[25] The funeral was held the next day. Mr. Bayne introduced a
futile resolution to adopt the Seaton method; it failed decisively, 9-148.[26] Mr. Prescott
introduced a resolution to adopt the old method; it passed. Shortly afterwards a vote was
taken on an amendment by John Anderson (KS) to set the House size at 325 apportioned by the
Hamilton-Vinton method; passed, 162-104 with 26 not voting.

After the Seaton method decisively failed, the House quickly passed its apportionment bill
because most of the issues had been defined, clarified, and decided during that debate. For
example, on 26 January 1882 Richard Warner (TN) tried to set the course for legislative action.
He began with a historical survey of congressional apportionment. He distinguished the two
approaches: constituency (how many people should a congressman represent?) and the House
size (how many members should the House have?). He also discussed the problem of dealing
with fractions. Then he argued that on constitutional grounds the base for creating legislation
is the state; i.e., representatives are to be allocated to the states, not to the nation or to
districts. He concluded that the House size approach was unconstitutional and that Congress
must return to the basic divisor method used in the first five censuses. Further, allocating an
additional seat based on a state's fraction was also unconstitutional.[27] However, nobody
followed this pied piper. His arguments meant that the previous four apportionments were

---

[23] Ibid: 971.
[24] Ibid: 991-6.
[25] Ibid: 1168.
[26] Ibid: 1228.
[27] Ibid: 665-669.

unconstitutional—few supported this thinking. The basic divisor method was as dead as Seaton's new method.

On 7 February Mr. Prescott from the Committee on the Census, set the course.[28]

> The only problems now presented to us for solution are: First, what is the proper number to constitute a representative body for these United States? Second, having determined such number, how shall we the most justly distribute them among the States?

On 13 February Olin Wellborn (TX) gave an elegant summary of the sense of Congress about apportionment. He started by noting that the prime directives came from the Constitution: representatives shall be apportioned among the several States according to their respective numbers, and those numbers are determined by a decennial census. He then stated that the end result of these two directives "ought to be the result of three processes."[29] In logical sequence, they are:

- First, fix the House size.
- Second, determine the ratio of Representatives (i.e., divisor or constituency).
- Third, distribute the number of representatives based on the ratio.

Mr. Wellborn noted that there are only two options for an initial step: either fix the House size or fix the ratio of representation. He argued that if one fixes the ratio first and then divides it into each state's population to obtain the number of representatives, then "it makes the size of the House a pure mathematical result, when it ought to be a fact determined independently of all calculations based on numbers." To support this viewpoint, he quoted James Garfield in the Senate ten years before.

> I desire to say to the House in regard to the whole matter of representation that there are just two ways in which the Government has settled the question. For the first fifty years of the Government it was settled by fixing, not the number of members of the House, but the number of population which should be entitled to a Representative; and when that was fixed dividing the total population by that number and letting the size of the House be the result of that division. For fifty years the size of the House of Representatives was so determined. In 1840 a change was made in that respect, after a long and most searching debate. The result of that debate was that they fixed the number of members of the House and finding the total population, divided that by the number of members and got the basis for each Representative.

---

[28] Ibid: 966-8.
[29] Ibid: 1097.

Mr. Wellborn's summary argued that experience taught that the House size approach to apportionment was preferable to the constituency approach. The only matter of substance was to decide the House size. Once decided, the act of 1850 made the rest automatic.

This same thinking was emphasized two days later by John Anderson (KS) who argued that there are only two steps in making an apportionment bill. The first step is to determine the House size and the second is to distribute the seats. The first is a matter of choice and the second is a matter of arithmetic. During this time the House got down to the business of determining the House size. The bill reported out of committee, H.R. 3550, used House size 320. There were amendments and substitutes for House size 294, 307, 316, 319, 320, 321, 322, 324, 325, and 365. John Sherwin (IL) noted an Alabama paradox for Georgia which was awarded ten seats in a House of 306 but only nine seats in a House of 307. Such anomalies were deal breakers for a proposed House size, just like quota rule violations were a deal breaker for Seaton's method. [30]

With debate now defining and focusing the issue to House size, the House quickly decided on 325 and sent the bill to the Senate for concurrence on 16 February. The Senate referred the bill to the Select Committee on the Census. Four days later, on behalf of the Committee, Eugene Hale (ME) reported that the Committee on the Census unanimously recommends the bill pass without amendment.[31] The Senate passed the bill the next day.[32] On 25 February 1882 President Chester Arthur approved and signed into law *An act making an apportionment of Representatives in Congress among the several States under the tenth census.*[33]

The spreadsheet displayed in Table 3.18 shows apportionment of 325 seats using the methods of Hamilton-Vinton (columns Quota/Lower/Seats), expanded Seaton (columns S1/S2/Seats), Webster (columns Webster/Seats), and Dean (columns Dean/Seats). Webster's method can use a divisor of 151000 and Dean's method a divisor of 151700 to achieve the goal of 325 seats. Note that the methods of Hamilton, Webster, and Dean all agree.

The S1 and S2 columns lists the Seaton priority numbers given to each state if awarded 1 or 2 additional seats beyond the lower quota. The priority number is the difference between the modulus (national divisor), 151911, and the resulting state constituency if awarded 1 or 2 additional seats. The lower this difference the higher the Seaton priority. First, each state is given its lower quota. This distributes 309 seats; hence, there are an additional 16 seats to be distributed. The 310th seat goes to Virginia (priority number 654); 311th seat to Nebraska (priority 1110), ..., 320th Pennsylvania (4225), 321st Illinois (5345), 322nd Ohio (6544), 323rd New York (6686 for a second additional seat), 324th Texas (7206), and 325th Missouri (7352). Hence, in comparison with the Hamilton-Vinton method, the Seaton method affected ten states—

---

[30] Ibid: 1168-1193.
[31] Ibid, 20 February 1882: 1283.
[32] Ibid, 21 February 1882: 1334.
[33] Statutes at Large, 47th Congress, 1st Session, Chap. 20: 5-6.

Illinois, Missouri, New York, Ohio, and Pennsylvania each gain a seat at the expense of California, Florida, Kansas, Rhode Island, and South Carolina.

Table 3.18. Spreadsheet analysis for House size 350 based on the 1880 census.

State	Pop	Quota	Lower	Seats	S1	S2	Seats	Webster	Seats	Dean	Seats
Alabama	1,262,505	8.3108	8	8	11632	25660	8	8.3610	8	8.3224	8
Arkansas	802,525	5.2828	5	5	18156	37264	5	5.3147	5	5.2902	5
California	864,694	5.6921	5	6	7795	28383	5	5.7265	6	5.7000	6
Colorado	194,327	1.2792	1	1	54747	87135	1	1.2869	1	1.2810	1
Connecticut	622,700	4.0991	4	4	27371	48127	4	4.1238	4	4.1048	4
Delaware	146,608	0.9651	0	1	5303	78607	1	0.9709	1	0.9664	1
Florida	269,493	1.7740	1	2	17164	62080	1	1.7847	2	1.7765	2
Georgia	1,542,180	10.1518	10	10	11712	23396	10	10.2131	10	10.1660	10
Illinois	3,077,871	20.2609	20	20	5345	12007	21	20.3833	20	20.2892	20
Indiana	1,978,301	13.0227	13	13	10603	20024	13	13.1013	13	13.0409	13
Iowa	1,624,615	10.6945	10	11	4218	16526	11	10.7590	11	10.7094	11
Kansas	996,096	6.5571	6	7	9611	27399	6	6.5967	7	6.5662	7
Kentucky	1,648,690	10.8529	10	11	2030	14520	11	10.9185	11	10.8681	11
Louisiana	939,946	6.1874	6	6	17633	34417	6	6.2248	6	6.1961	6
Maine	648,936	4.2718	4	4	22123	43755	4	4.2976	4	4.2778	4
Maryland	934,943	6.1545	6	6	18347	35043	6	6.1917	6	6.1631	6
Massachusetts	1,783,085	11.7376	11	12	3320	14750	12	11.8085	12	11.7540	12
Michigan	1,636,937	10.7756	10	11	3098	15499	11	10.8406	11	10.7906	11
Minnesota	780,773	5.1396	5	5	21782	40372	5	5.1707	5	5.1468	5
Mississippi	1,131,597	7.4490	7	7	10461	26178	7	7.4940	7	7.4594	7
Missouri	2,168,380	14.2739	14	14	7352	16387	15	14.3601	14	14.2939	14
Nebraska	452,402	2.9781	2	3	1110	38810	3	2.9960	3	2.9822	3
Nevada	62,266	0.4099	0	1	89645	120778	1	0.4124	1	0.4105	1
New Hampshire	346,991	2.2842	2	2	36247	65163	2	2.2980	2	2.2874	2
New Jersey	1,131,116	7.4459	7	7	10521	26231	7	7.4908	7	7.4563	7
New York	5,082,871	33.4594	33	34	2414	6686	35	33.6614	34	33.5061	34
North Carolina	1,399,750	9.2142	9	9	11936	24661	9	9.2699	9	9.2271	9
Ohio	3,198,062	21.0521	21	21	6544	12864	22	21.1792	21	21.0815	21
Oregon	174,768	1.1505	1	1	64527	93655	1	1.1574	1	1.1521	1
Pennsylvania	4,282,891	28.1933	28	28	4225	9147	29	28.3635	28	28.2326	28
Rhode Island	276,531	1.8203	1	2	13645	59734	1	1.8313	2	1.8229	2
South Carolina	995,577	6.5537	6	7	9685	27463	6	6.5932	7	6.5628	7
Tennessee	1,542,359	10.1530	10	10	11696	23381	10	10.2143	10	10.1672	10
Texas	1,591,749	10.4781	10	11	7206	19265	11	10.5414	11	10.4927	11
Vermont	332,286	2.1874	2	2	41149	68839	2	2.2006	2	2.1904	2
Virginia	1,512,565	9.9569	9	10	654	14405	10	10.0170	10	9.9708	10
West Virginia	618,457	4.0712	4	4	28219	48834	4	4.0957	4	4.0768	4
Wisconsin	1,315,497	8.6596	8	9	5744	20361	9	8.7119	9	8.6717	9
U. S.	49,371,340	325.0000	309	325			325	326.9625	325	325.4538	325

In the basic Seaton method, only the priority numbers for the 1 additional seat would be used. In comparison with the Hamilton-Vinton method, the basic Seaton method affected eight states with Illinois, Missouri, Ohio, and Pennsylvania gaining at the expense of Florida, Kansas, Rhode Island, and South Carolina. The basic Seaton plan has the advantage of not violating the quota rule. However, the Seaton method was never viewed in the basic context, only in the expanded context throughout the congressional debates since Seaton submitted tables only in reference to the expanded method.

Section 3.4.4   The Aftermath

The debate in the House clarified that Congress now approached the congressional apportionment problem from the House size viewpoint. The process became simple as presented by John Anderson (KA). There are only two steps in making an apportionment bill. First determine the House size; second distribute the seats. Mr. Anderson explained that the first is a matter of choice and the second is a matter of arithmetic.

Merely deciding the House size focused on an easily understood question. After the House size was determined, the rest was put on automatic pilot. The ratio of representation (how many people does a congressman represent?) is now easy to determine: divide the House size into the total population. Seaton called this national constituency the modulus. The modulus was then divided into each state's population to obtain each state's quota. At this juncture each state was awarded its lower quota, unanimously recognized as each state's minimum fair share. However, the sum of these lower quotas was always less than the pre-set House size. Hence, additional seats had to be given to some states to distribute all the seats of the House. Based on the act of 1850, Mr. Anderson saw this as an automatic process. Seaton's alternative proposal showed that the methodology was not intrinsically automatic.

In 1850 Congress turned to the Hamilton-Vinton quota method because of the increasing problem of quota rule violations incurred by the basic divisor methods used in reapportionments based on the censuses of 1790-1840. Now, Walker and Seaton exposed the downside of the quota method: the Alabama paradox.

However, Congress had an easy and workable solution to the Alabama paradox: simply avoid those House sizes which displayed the paradox. In his effort to avoid the paradox Seaton perhaps overanalyzed and overthought the situation to propose his new method. Congress quickly noted the quota rule violations of Seaton's expanded method and quickly killed the proposal. It is also perhaps unfortunate that Seaton did not use the premise for his new method to propose the basic method where he stayed within quota. Congress would then have had to wrestle with the problem that things were not simply conceptually automatic after the House size was decided.

Seaton's tables carried a brilliant innovation that was sixty years ahead of its time: the use of priority numbers to illustrate apportionment based on House size (Table 3.19, next page). Seaton's table only took one page in the Congressional Record.[34] First, one seat is given to each state as prescribed by the Constitution. This distributed 38 seats since there were 38 states. Who should get the 39th seat? Seaton's table shows that, based on constituency, New York merits that seat. The table proceeds in this fashion up to House size 350.

---

[34] Ibid: 777.

Table 3.19. Seaton's priority tables for House size up to 350.

State	Seats	Constituency	Rank
Alabama	1	1,262,505	1
Arkansas	1	802,525	2
California	1	864,694	3
Colorado	1	194,327	4
Connecticut	1	622,700	5
Delaware	1	146,608	6
Florida	1	269,493	7
Georgia	1	1,542,180	8
Illinois	1	3,077,871	9
Indiana	1	1,978,301	10
Iowa	1	1,624,615	11
Kansas	1	996,096	12
Kentucky	1	1,648,690	13
Louisiana	1	939,946	14
Maine	1	648,936	15
Maryland	1	934,943	16
Massachusetts	1	1,783,085	17
Michigan	1	1,636,937	18
Minnesota	1	780,773	19
Mississippi	1	1,131,597	20
Missouri	1	2,168,380	21
Nebraska	1	452,402	22
Nevada	1	62,266	23
New Hampshire	1	346,991	24
New Jersey	1	1,131,116	25
New York	1	5,082,871	26
North Carolina	1	1,399,750	27
Ohio	1	3,198,062	28
Oregon	1	174,768	29
Pennsylvania	1	4,282,891	30
Rhode Island	1	276,531	31
South Carolina	1	995,577	32
Tennessee	1	1,542,359	33
Texas	1	1,591,749	34
Vermont	1	332,286	35
Virginia	1	1,512,565	36
West Virginia	1	618,457	37
Wisconsin	1	1,315,497	38
New York	2	2,541,436	39
Pennsylvania	2	2,141,446	40
New York	3	1,694,290	41
Ohio	2	1,599,031	42
Illinois	2	1,538,936	43
Pennsylvania	3	1,427,630	44
New York	4	1,270,718	45
Missouri	2	1,084,190	46
Pennsylvania	4	1,070,723	47
Ohio	3	1,066,021	48
Illinois	3	1,025,957	49
New York	5	1,016,574	50
Indiana	2	989,151	51
Massachusetts	2	891,543	52
Pennsylvania	5	856,578	53
New York	6	847,145	54
Kentucky	2	824,345	55

State	Seats	Constituency	Rank
Michigan	2	818,469	56
Iowa	2	812,308	57
Ohio	4	799,516	58
Texas	2	795,875	59
Tennessee	2	771,180	60
Georgia	2	771,090	61
Illinois	4	769,468	62
Virginia	2	756,283	63
New York	7	726,124	64
Missouri	3	722,793	65
Pennsylvania	6	713,815	66
North Carolina	2	699,875	67
Indiana	3	659,434	68
Wisconsin	2	657,749	69
Ohio	5	639,612	70
New York	8	635,359	71
Alabama	2	631,253	72
Illinois	5	615,574	73
Pennsylvania	7	611,842	74
Massachusetts	3	594,362	75
Mississippi	2	565,799	76
New Jersey	2	565,558	77
New York	9	564,763	78
Kentucky	3	549,563	79
Michigan	3	545,646	80
Missouri	4	542,095	81
Iowa	3	541,538	82
Pennsylvania	8	535,361	83
Ohio	6	533,010	84
Texas	3	530,583	85
Tennessee	3	514,120	86
Georgia	3	514,060	87
Illinois	6	512,979	88
New York	10	508,287	89
Virginia	3	504,188	90
Kansas	2	498,048	91
South Carolina	2	497,789	92
Indiana	4	494,575	93
Pennsylvania	9	475,877	94
Louisiana	2	469,973	95
Maryland	2	467,472	96
North Carolina	3	466,583	97
New York	11	462,079	98
Ohio	7	456,866	99
Massachusetts	4	445,771	100
Illinois	7	439,696	101
Wisconsin	3	438,499	102
Missouri	5	433,676	103
California	2	432,347	104
Pennsylvania	10	428,289	105
New York	12	423,573	106
Alabama	3	420,835	107
Kentucky	4	412,173	108
Michigan	4	409,234	109
Iowa	4	406,154	110

State	Seats	Constituency	Rank
Arkansas	2	401,263	111
Ohio	8	399,758	112
Texas	4	397,937	113
Indiana	5	395,660	114
New York	13	390,990	115
Minnesota	2	390,387	116
Pennsylvania	11	389,354	117
Tennessee	4	385,590	118
Georgia	4	385,545	119
Illinois	8	384,734	120
Virginia	4	378,141	121
Mississippi	3	377,199	122
New Jersey	3	377,039	123
New York	14	363,062	124
Missouri	6	361,397	125
Pennsylvania	12	356,908	126
Massachusetts	5	356,617	127
Ohio	9	355,340	128
North Carolina	4	349,938	129
Illinois	9	341,986	130
New York	15	338,858	131
Kansas	3	332,032	132
South Carolina	3	331,859	133
Kentucky	5	329,738	134
Indiana	6	329,717	135
Pennsylvania	13	329,453	136
Wisconsin	4	328,874	137
Michigan	5	327,387	138
Iowa	5	324,923	139
Maine	2	324,468	140
Ohio	10	319,806	141
Texas	5	318,350	142
New York	16	317,679	143
Alabama	4	315,626	144
Louisiana	3	313,315	145
Maryland	3	311,648	146
Connecticut	2	311,350	147
Missouri	7	309,769	148
West Virginia	2	309,229	149
Tennessee	5	308,472	150
Georgia	5	308,436	151
Illinois	10	307,787	152
Pennsylvania	14	305,921	153
Virginia	5	302,513	154
New York	17	298,992	155
Massachusetts	6	297,181	156
Ohio	11	290,733	157
California	3	288,231	158
Pennsylvania	15	285,526	159
Mississippi	4	282,899	160
New Jersey	4	282,779	161
Indiana	7	282,614	162
New York	18	282,382	163
North Carolina	5	279,950	164
Illinois	11	279,806	165

State	Seats	Constituency	Rank
Kentucky	6	274,782	166
Michigan	6	272,823	167
Missouri	8	271,048	168
Iowa	6	270,769	169
Pennsylvania	16	267,681	170
New York	19	267,520	171
Arkansas	3	267,508	172
Ohio	12	266,505	173
Texas	6	265,292	174
Wisconsin	5	263,099	175
Minnesota	3	260,258	176
Tennessee	6	257,060	177
Georgia	6	257,030	178
Illinois	12	256,489	179
Massachusetts	7	254,726	180
New York	20	254,144	181
Alabama	5	252,501	182
Virginia	6	252,094	183
Pennsylvania	17	251,935	184
Kansas	4	249,024	185
South Carolina	4	248,894	186
Indiana	8	247,288	187
Ohio	13	246,005	188
New York	21	242,041	189
Missouri	9	240,931	190
Pennsylvania	18	237,938	191
Illinois	13	236,759	192
Kentucky	7	235,527	193
Louisiana	4	234,987	194
Michigan	7	233,848	195
Maryland	4	233,736	196
North Carolina	6	233,292	197
Iowa	7	232,088	198
New York	22	231,040	199
Ohio	14	228,433	200
Texas	7	227,393	201
Mississippi	5	226,319	202
New Jersey	5	226,223	203
Nebraska	2	226,201	204
Pennsylvania	19	225,415	205
Massachusetts	8	222,886	206
New York	23	220,994	207
Tennessee	7	220,337	208
Georgia	7	220,311	209
Illinois	14	219,848	210
Indiana	9	219,811	211
Wisconsin	6	219,250	212
Missouri	10	216,838	213
Maine	3	216,312	214
California	4	216,174	215
Virginia	7	216,081	216
Pennsylvania	20	214,145	217
Ohio	15	213,204	218
New York	24	211,786	219
Alabama	6	210,418	220

State	Seats	Constituency	Rank
Connecticut	3	207,567	221
West Virginia	3	206,152	222
Kentucky	8	206,086	223
Illinois	15	205,191	224
Michigan	8	204,617	225
Pennsylvania	21	203,947	226
New York	25	203,315	227
Iowa	8	203,077	228
Arkansas	4	200,631	229
North Carolina	7	199,964	230
Ohio	16	199,879	231
Kansas	5	199,219	232
South Carolina	5	199,115	233
Texas	8	198,969	234
Massachusetts	9	198,121	235
Indiana	10	197,830	236
Missouri	11	197,125	237
New York	26	195,495	238
Minnesota	4	195,193	239
Pennsylvania	22	194,677	240
Tennessee	8	192,795	241
Georgia	8	192,773	242
Illinois	16	192,367	243
Virginia	8	189,071	244
Mississippi	6	188,600	245
New Jersey	6	188,519	246
New York	27	188,254	247
Ohio	17	188,121	248
Louisiana	5	187,989	249
Wisconsin	7	187,928	250
Maryland	5	186,989	251
Pennsylvania	23	186,213	252
Kentucky	9	183,188	253
Michigan	9	181,882	254
New York	28	181,531	255
Illinois	17	181,051	256
Missouri	12	180,698	257
Iowa	9	180,513	258
Alabama	7	180,358	259
Indiana	11	179,846	260
Pennsylvania	24	178,454	261
Massachusetts	10	178,309	262
Ohio	18	177,670	263
Texas	9	176,861	264
New York	29	175,271	265
North Carolina	8	174,969	266
New Hampshire	2	173,496	267
California	5	172,939	268
Tennessee	9	171,373	269
Georgia	9	171,353	270
Pennsylvania	25	171,316	271
Illinois	18	170,993	272
New York	30	169,429	273
Ohio	19	168,319	274
Virginia	9	168,063	275

State	Seats	Constituency	Rank
Missouri	13	166,798	276
Vermont	2	166,143	277
Kansas	6	166,016	278
South Carolina	6	165,930	279
Kentucky	10	164,869	280
Indiana	12	164,858	281
Pennsylvania	26	164,727	282
Wisconsin	8	164,437	283
New York	31	163,964	284
Michigan	10	163,694	285
Iowa	10	162,462	286
Maine	4	162,234	287
Massachusetts	11	162,099	288
Illinois	19	161,993	289
Mississippi	7	161,657	290
New Jersey	7	161,588	291
Arkansas	5	160,505	292
Ohio	20	159,903	293
Texas	10	159,175	294
New York	32	158,840	295
Pennsylvania	27	158,626	296
Alabama	8	157,813	297
Louisiana	6	156,658	298
Minnesota	5	156,155	299
Maryland	6	155,824	300
Connecticut	4	155,675	301
North Carolina	9	155,528	302
Missouri	14	154,884	303
West Virginia	4	154,614	304
Tennessee	10	154,236	305
Georgia	10	154,218	306
New York	33	154,026	307
Illinois	20	153,894	308
Pennsylvania	28	152,960	309
Ohio	21	152,289	310
Indiana	13	152,177	311
Virginia	10	151,257	312
Nebraska	3	150,801	313
Kentucky	11	149,881	314
New York	34	149,496	315
Michigan	11	148,812	316
Massachusetts	12	148,590	317
Iowa	11	147,692	318
Pennsylvania	29	147,686	319
Illinois	21	146,565	320
Wisconsin	9	146,166	321
Ohio	22	145,366	322
New York	35	145,225	323
Texas	11	144,704	324
Missouri	15	144,559	325
California	6	144,116	326
Pennsylvania	30	142,763	327
Kansas	7	142,299	328
South Carolina	7	142,225	329
Mississippi	8	141,450	330

State	Seats	Constituency	Rank
New Jersey	8	141,390	331
Indiana	14	141,307	332
New York	36	141,191	333
Alabama	9	140,278	334
Tennessee	11	140,214	335
Georgia	11	140,198	336
North Carolina	10	139,975	337
Illinois	22	139,903	338
Ohio	23	139,046	339
Rhode Island	2	138,266	340
Pennsylvania	31	138,158	341
Virginia	11	137,506	342
Kentucky	12	137,391	343
New York	37	137,375	344
Massachusetts	13	137,160	345
Michigan	12	136,411	346
Missouri	16	135,524	347
Iowa	12	135,385	348
Florida	2	134,747	349
Louisiana	7	134,278	350

Seaton's priority numbers for a given state are computed by dividing the state's population by a successive number of representatives: 1, 2, 3, 4, etc. For example, Minnesota's population was 780773. Hence, Minnesota's priority number for a second seat is 780773/2 = 390385; for a third seat, 780773/3 = 260257; for a fourth seat, 280773/4 =195193; etc. So, given any House size, the next seat would go to the state with the highest unused priority number.

Priority was based on constituency in Seaton's list. The state with the highest unused constituency was next in line to receive the next House seat. The priority list gives a new way of computing apportionment. Using a priority list one does not need to re-compute everything for a new House size.

Previously, the method of Dean and the method of Lowndes utilized a constituency criterion for determining how states merited an additional seat. Seaton's methods show that a congressional apportionment is a complex and even mystifying problem. It comes as a surprise that Seaton's new (expanded) method is mathematically equivalent to the modified Jefferson divisor method. Applying the basic Jefferson method with a divisor of 144000 creates the same 325 member House as Seaton's method. Seaton, and the entire Congress as well, had no idea.

Section 3.5:   Reapportionment Based on the 1890 Census

Section 3.5.1   Background

The 1890 census saw the nation experience a growth spurt with the addition of six new states: North and South Dakota (admitted 2 November 1889), Montana (8 November 1889), Washington (11 November 1889), Idaho (3 July 1890) and Wyoming (10 July 1890). South Dakota was awarded two representatives upon admission; the others, one each. This brought the number of states to 44. The specifications for admission for North Dakota, South Dakota, Montana, and Washington were provided in the Enabling Act of 1889, approved by President Grover Cleveland on 22 February 1889.[1] Actual admission to the Union was declared by proclamation from President Benjamin Harrison.[2] Separate admission bills were passed for Idaho[3] and Wyoming[4]. These actions brought the size of the House to 332 members.

These new states initiated new ideas and visions onto the American landscape. Wyoming serves as a good example. Wyoming's nickname is *The Equality State* and the state motto is *Equal Rights*. Wyoming earned this distinction by being the first state to grant the right to vote to women, in addition to allowing women to serve on juries and hold public office. Such a liberal viewpoint was almost a deal breaker for Wyoming statehood. The Wyoming statehood bill passed the House by the close vote of 139-127 with most no votes reflecting opposition to extending political rights to women.[5] Wyoming is the proud holder of several national firsts: first national monument, Devils Tower (1906); first state to have a county library system (1886); first national park, Yellowstone (1872); and first national forest, Shoshone (1891).

This period surrounding the census of 1890 featured some presidential anomalies. Washington is the only state to be named after a president. Grover Cleveland is the only president to be counted twice among American presidents, the 22nd and 24th, due to the fact that he is the only president to serve two non-successive terms, 4 March 1885 to 4 March 1889 and 4 March 1893 to 4 March 1897. President Cleveland's two terms were interrupted by the presidency of Benjamin Harrison, 4 March 1889 to 4 March 1893. Benjamin Harrison is the grandson of William Henry Harrison, the only grandfather-grandson presidential pair in American history.[6]

On 1 March 1889 President Cleveland approved into law *An act to provide for taking the eleventh and subsequent censuses* that specified the operations and conduct of the census.[7] Although the law specified that the census start on 1 June 1890, this day fell on a Sunday; so, 2 June 1890 was the operative census day. The census featured electronic data processing using

---

[1] 25 Stat 676

[2] 26 Stat, Presidential Proclamations 6, 7, 8: 1549-53.

[3] 26 Stat 215

[4] 26 Stat 664

[5] http://www.wyo.gov/about-wyoming/wyoming-history;

[6] Carter Smith, *Presidents*, Hylas Publishing, 2008: 136-147.

[7] 25 Stat 319

the Hollerith punched card system which reduced data processing time from 8 years for the 1880 census to 1 year for the 1890 census. This feature even made the cover of the 30 August 1890 issue of Scientific American. The work was conducted under the supervision of Robert Porter, Superintendent of the Census from 17 April 1889 to 31 July 1893. It is unfortunate that most of the data was destroyed by fire in 1921.[8]

The ordinary press even took notice of the eleventh census.[9]

> WASHINGTON, December 31st.—The Superintendent of the Census has submitted to the Secretary of the Interior a report of the operations of the Bureau for the six months ended to-day. On the subject of the apportionment of Representatives in Congress, Porter says: "The apportionment of Representatives in Congress was not delayed a moment by the failure of the census office to have the official returns of the population ready on the convening of Congress. If the Apportionment bill which passed the House should pass the Senate and become a law the apportionment under the Eleventh Census would be about two years earlier than any heretofore made."

The amount of information processed was prolific and was considerably greater than that of all the previous ten censuses combined.[10] The final report that Superintendent Porter sent to Congress clearly reflected his pride in the achievements of his office.[11]

> The count was pushed with such energy that the Census Office had had the official returns of the population ready on the convening of Congress in 1890, causing no delay in the apportionment of national representatives. The passage of the apportionment bill, for the first time in the history of the country, in the next session of Congress following the census, makes it worthwhile briefly to review the apportionment legislation.
>
> The ninth and tenth apportionments were made by Congress; hence it may be assumed that the power conferred on the Secretary of the Interior by the act of May 23, 1850, was repealed by implication. Heretofore all apportionments have been made at the long sessions of Congress, being the second session after each census year, but early enough for the election of representatives to the next ensuing Congress.
>
> The apportionment under the Eleventh Census was relatively about two years earlier than any before made.

---

[8] https://www.census.gov/history/www/through_the_decades/overview/1890.html.

[9] Daily Alta California 84(1), 1 January 1891 (from http://cdnc.ucr.edu/cgi-bin/cdnc?a=d&d=DAC18910101.2.5#).

[10] Robert L. Dorman, The creation and Destruction of the 1890 Federal Census, *The American Archivist*, 71(2) Fall-Winter, 2008: 350-383.

[11] Robert P. Porter, Compendium of the Eleventh Census: 1890, Government Printing Office, Washington D.C., 1892: x-xi. Downloaded from https://www.census.gov/prod/www/decennial.html.

Section 3.5.2   Apportionment

Congressional apportionment based on the 1890 census was the easiest process thus far. Controversy and opposition were minor in comparison to previous years. Initially the House referred a few apportionment proposals to the Select Committee on the Eleventh Census chaired by Mark Dunnell (MN). On 12 December 1890 the committee issued House Report No. 3280 from the 51st Congress, 2nd Session.[12] The select committee recommended the passage of the apportionment bill H.R. 12500. The bill would distribute 356 seats using the Vinton plan.

Debate on the bill began on 16 December. The next day the House passed the bill 187-82, 62 not voting. Subsequently the Senate referred the bill to its Committee on the Census. On 22 January 1891 the Senate committee recommended passage of the House bill. After a short debate on 29 January the Senate passed the bill 37-24, 27 absent. On 7 February 1891 President Benjamin Harrison approved *An act making an apportionment of Representatives in Congress among the several States under the Eleventh Census.*[13]

There were several factors that facilitated relatively easy passage of the apportionment bill. First, House Report No. 3280 was thorough and efficient. The current House size was 332. The report displayed tables showing apportionment for House sizes from 332 to 375 based on the Vinton plan. The House size 356 met three satisfying criteria.

- It was the smallest House size in which no state lost a representative.
- It was the only size that satisfied moiety; i.e., The Vinton plan agreed with Webster's method of rounding.
- It did not involve an Alabama paradox.

Compared to previous decades, there was little debate on House size. There were some congressmen that did not like the idea of increasing the House size since they felt that it was already too difficult to always hear in the House chamber. However, keeping the current House size of 332 meant that 10 states would lose a representative. Loss of representatives was a deal breaker for most congressmen.

The only efforts to change the House size came from congressmen supporting an additional seat for Arkansas, Minnesota, New York, or Missouri. The national population was 61908906. With House size 356, the ratio (national divisor) was 173901. Thus moiety, the half-way point, is 86950. The remainder fraction for New York was 85291; Arkansas, 84773; Minnesota, 84519; Missouri, 70669. Much of the argument for an additional seat came across as whining because the fraction was a bit under moiety. The moiety argument was also severely compromised in that the chairman of the Select Committee on the Census was also the author of H.R. 12500 and was from Minnesota. The most extensive argument was launched by New York claiming the census undercounted New York City by around 200000; hence, New York deserved an

---

[12] Reports of the Committees of the Senate of the United States for the Second Session of the Fifty-First Congress, 1890-91, Government Printing Office, Washington, D.C., 1891 (accessed from Google Books).
[13] Statutes at Large, 51st Congress, 2nd Session, Chap. 116: 735-6.

additional representative. As several other localities complained about a census undercount, these arguments also became perceived as whining.

An amendment by Thomas McRae (AR) to change the House size from 356 to 359 failed 113-145, 73 not voting. Roswell Flower (NY) proposed an amendment to replace 356 with 357, thereby giving New York an additional seat. The proposal lost favor when it was pointed out that with House size 357 Arkansas would be denied an additional seat even though Arkansas satisfied moiety. To compromise, Joseph Washington (TN), also a member of Select Committee on the Eleventh Census, proposed a substitute amendment that New York would be awarded an additional seat if a census recount of New York City showed that New York would then have a fraction greater than moiety. Mr. Flowers accepted the substitute. But the substitute failed, 123-148, 60 not voting. Subsequently a vote was taken on the unamended apportionment bill which passed decisively, 187-82, 62 not voting.[14]

Of course, there were the usual us vs. them purely partisan viewpoints, illustrated by Richard Vaux (PA) who stated that he was not voting for the bill because the census and this apportionment bill was nothing but a Republican plot to get Republicans more power than they deserve. Needless to say, Representative Vaux was a partisan Democrat.

After the House passed H.R. 12500 the bill was sent to the Senate for concurrence. The Senate read the bill twice and then referred it to the Senate Committee on the Census chaired by Eugene Hale (ME). Four days later the Senate committee issued its own Senate Report No. 1962 recommending that the Senate concur and attached the House report.[15]

The Senate report also attached a minority report submitted by Cushman Davis (MN) and also signed by James Berry (AR) and Rufus Blodgett (NJ). Their objection to H.R. 12500 appears that they were appalled that apportionment should be a mathematical process that trumps the decision-making ability of Congress.

> This is the first attempt, so far as the undersigned are advised, to make the mere production of an equation the desideratum of an apportionment bill.
> No such estoppal of justice by a mere mathematical process has ever before been proposed so far as our researches inform us. It means simply that it is the duty of Congress in making an apportionment to compute on the basis of different numbers of membership (from 332 to 375 in the present case) and to take that number of which the excess after an even division will be just the number, no more, no less, that will be equal to and be absorbed by the States having a moiety or more of the ratio.

The minority report further sneers at the mathematical process by referring to the House size 332-375 tables and the occurrence of an Alabama paradox for Tennessee at House size 336

---

[14] Congressional Record, 51st Congress, 2nd Session: 530-55, 589-610.
[15] https://babel.hathitrust.org/cgi/pt?id=uc1.b3987170&view=1up&seq=661.

where Tennessee has 10 seats; then, 9 seats at House size 337; then 10 seats at House size 338. A similar Alabama paradox occurs for Arkansas which has 7, then 6, then 7 seats again for House sizes 359, 360, and 361. However, in general, Congress dealt with the infrequent Alabama paradoxes by simply avoiding those House sizes where the paradox occurred.

The minority report recommends a House size of 360 obtained by modifying the apportionment given in the H.R. 12500 with House size 356 based on the Vinton plan by giving an additional seat to New York, Arkansas, Minnesota, and Missouri. However, this proposal is inconsistent with House size 360 apportioned by the Vinton plan. Accordingly, Mr. Davis proposed an amendment to H.R. 12500 to make the House size 360 with an additional seat for Arkansas, Minnesota, Missouri, and New York.

Despite the anomalies of the recommendation in the minority report, the Senate vote was close on Mr. Davis's amendment. The Senate decided to vote on the items one at a time. First, the proposal to award Arkansas an additional seat failed 32-33, 23 absent. Second, the proposal to award Minnesota an addition seat failed 31-32, 25 absent. Third, the proposal to award Missouri an additional seat failed 30-38, 20 absent. Fourth, the proposal to award New York an additional seat failed 29-38, 21 absent. At this point, Mr. Davis withdrew his amendment.[16]

George Vest (MO), echoing the sentiments of the minority report, lamented that "the bill now presented to the Senate—and I do not attach its fairness—is intended simply to comply with certain arithmetical rules." Despite such lamentations, the Senate then concurred with the House, 37-24, 27 absent.[17]

Section 3.5.3   Aftermath

Table 3.20 (next page) displays the spreadsheet computations needed to distribute 356-360 seats using the Hamilton-Vinton method. The Qh/Lower/Seats column sets provide the numbers for the indicated House size. The apportionment act of 1891 specified the House size of 356. The Lower column reflects the integer part of the quota; however, if the lower quota is 0; then the zero is replaced by 1 to reflect the Constitution's requirement that each state must have at least one representative. Note that the apportionment is consistent with both the methods of Hamilton-Vinton and Webster. Also, the Alabama paradox for Arkansas at House size 359 to 360 is evident.

During the second day of debate in the House, on 17 December 1890, Charles Buckalew (PA) made an interesting point. He noted that the populations for Delaware, Idaho, Montana, Nevada, and Wyoming were all below the ratio (national divisor) of 173901. Hence, by constitutional guidelines, these five states were to be given the minimum of one seat each. This would distribute 5 of the 356 seats; hence, these states should then be removed from the data sheet and the remaining 351 seats distributed among the remaining 39 states. He did not

---

[16] Congressional Record, 51st Congress, 2nd Session, 29 January 1891: 1951-2.
[17] Ibid: 1953-5.

Table 3.20. Spreadsheet for computing apportionment based on the 1890 census for House sizes 356-360 using the Hamilton-Vinton method. The notation Quota 365 stands for the Quota computed for House size 365, etc.

State	Population	Quota 356	Lower	Seats	Quota 357	Lower	Seats	Quota 358	Lower	Seats	Quota 359	Lower	Seats	Quota 360	Lower	Seats
AL	1513017	8.700	8	9	8.725	8	9	8.749	8	9	8.749	8	9	8.749	8	9
AR	1128179	6.487	6	6	6.506	6	6	8.749	6	6	6.524	6	7	6.524	6	6
CA	1208130	6.947	6	7	6.967	6	7	8.749	6	7	6.986	6	7	6.986	6	7
CO	412198	2.370	2	2	2.377	2	2	8.749	2	2	2.384	2	2	2.384	2	2
CT	746258	4.291	4	4	4.303	4	4	8.749	4	4	4.315	4	4	4.315	4	4
DE	168493	0.969	1	1	0.972	0	1	8.749	0	1	0.974	0	1	0.974	0	1
FL	391422	2.251	2	2	2.257	2	2	8.749	2	2	2.263	2	2	2.263	2	2
GA	1837353	10.565	10	11	10.595	10	11	8.749	10	11	10.625	10	11	10.625	10	11
ID	84385	0.485	1	1	0.487	0	1	8.749	0	1	0.488	0	1	0.488	0	1
IL	3826351	22.003	22	22	22.065	22	22	8.749	22	22	22.127	22	22	22.127	22	23
IN	2192404	12.607	12	13	12.643	12	13	8.749	12	13	12.678	12	13	12.678	12	13
IA	1911896	10.994	10	11	11.025	11	11	8.749	11	11	11.056	11	11	11.056	11	11
KS	1427096	8.206	8	8	8.229	8	8	8.749	8	8	8.252	8	8	8.252	8	8
KY	1858635	10.688	10	11	10.718	10	11	8.749	10	11	10.748	10	11	10.748	10	11
LA	1118587	6.432	6	6	6.450	6	6	8.749	6	6	6.468	6	6	6.468	6	6
ME	661086	3.801	3	4	3.812	3	4	8.749	3	4	3.823	3	4	3.823	3	4
MD	1042390	5.994	5	6	6.011	6	6	8.749	6	6	6.028	6	6	6.028	6	6
MA	2238943	12.875	12	13	12.911	12	13	8.749	12	13	12.947	12	13	12.947	12	13
MI	2093889	12.041	12	12	12.074	12	12	8.749	12	12	12.108	12	12	12.108	12	12
MN	1301826	7.486	7	7	7.507	7	7	8.749	7	8	7.528	7	8	7.528	7	8
MS	1289600	7.416	7	7	7.437	7	7	8.749	7	7	7.457	7	7	7.457	7	7
MO	2679184	15.406	15	15	15.450	15	15	8.749	15	15	15.493	15	15	15.493	15	16
MT	132159	0.760	1	1	0.762	0	1	8.749	0	1	0.764	0	1	0.764	0	1
NE	1058910	6.089	6	6	6.106	6	6	8.749	6	6	6.123	6	6	6.123	6	6
NV	45761	0.263	1	1	0.264	0	1	8.749	0	1	0.265	0	1	0.265	0	1
NH	376530	2.165	2	2	2.171	2	2	8.749	2	2	2.177	2	2	2.177	2	2
NJ	1444933	8.309	8	8	8.332	8	8	8.749	8	8	8.356	8	8	8.356	8	8
NY	5997853	34.490	34	34	34.587	34	35	8.749	34	35	34.684	34	35	34.684	34	35
NC	1617947	9.304	9	9	9.330	9	9	8.749	9	9	9.356	9	9	9.356	9	9
ND	182719	1.051	1	1	1.054	1	1	8.749	1	1	1.057	1	1	1.057	1	1
OH	3672316	21.117	21	21	21.177	21	21	8.749	21	21	21.236	21	21	21.236	21	21
OR	313767	1.804	1	2	1.809	1	2	8.749	1	2	1.814	1	2	1.814	1	2
PA	5258014	30.236	30	30	30.321	30	30	8.749	30	30	30.405	30	30	30.405	30	30
RI	345506	1.987	1	2	1.992	1	2	8.749	1	2	1.998	1	2	1.998	1	2
SC	1151149	6.620	6	7	6.638	6	7	8.749	6	7	6.657	6	7	6.657	6	7
SD	328808	1.891	1	2	1.896	1	2	8.749	1	2	1.901	1	2	1.901	1	2
TN	1767518	10.164	10	10	10.192	10	10	8.749	10	10	10.221	10	10	10.221	10	10
TX	2235523	12.855	12	13	12.891	12	13	8.749	12	13	12.927	12	13	12.927	12	13
VT	332422	1.912	1	2	1.917	1	2	8.749	1	2	1.922	1	2	1.922	1	2
VA	1655980	9.523	9	10	9.549	9	10	8.749	9	10	9.576	9	10	9.576	9	10
WA	349390	2.009	2	2	2.015	2	2	8.749	2	2	2.020	2	2	2.020	2	2
WV	762794	4.386	4	4	4.399	4	4	8.749	4	4	4.411	4	4	4.411	4	4
WI	1686880	9.700	9	10	9.727	9	10	8.749	9	10	9.755	9	10	9.755	9	10
WY	60705	0.349	1	1	0.350	0	1	8.749	0	1	0.351	0	1	0.351	0	1
US	61908906	356.000	339	356	357.000	327	357	8.749	336	358	358.000	336	359	358.000	336	360

push his point; neither did he supply any resulting computations.[18] If he had done so, then results may have been interesting. By eliminating the five small states from the spreadsheet after allocating them one seat each, and then apportioning the remaining 351 seats using the

---

[18] Ibid: 594.

Hamilton-Vinton method, one gets the results displayed in Table 3.21 (next page). The first notable consequence is that moiety is no longer satisfied; in particular, four states with a resulting quota having a decimal part between .5 and .6 do not get an additional seat. These states are Arkansas, Minnesota, Missouri, and Virginia. Satisfying moiety was a big selling point for H.R. 12500.

Even worse, New York is awarded an additional seat at the expense of Virginia, resulting in 35 seats for New York and 9 seats for Virginia. However, the top selling point for H.R. 12500 was that no state would lose a seat. Virginia in 1890 had 10 seats and this method of calculating apportionment for 356 seats would have resulted in the loss of a seat for Virginia.

Without realizing it Mr. Buckalew raised a computational issue based on the constitutional requirement that each state must get at least one seat. Should a small state be retained in the computations after being awarded its seat? The question remained unaddressed and hence unresolved.

Accordingly, there are two options regarding the Constitution's requirement that each state have at least one representative: should the requirement be imposed at the start of the computations or at the end?

Table 3.21. Spreadsheet for Buckalew's proposal.

State	Population	Quota	Lower	Seats
Alabama	1513017	8.7701	8	9
Arkansas	1128179	6.5394	6	6
California	1208130	7.0028	7	7
Colorado	412198	2.3893	2	2
Connecticut	746258	4.3256	4	4
Florida	391422	2.2688	2	2
Georgia	1837353	10.6500	10	11
Illinois	3826351	22.1791	22	22
Indiana	2192404	12.7081	12	13
Iowa	1911896	11.0821	11	11
Kansas	1427096	8.2720	8	8
Kentucky	1858635	10.7734	10	11
Louisiana	1118587	6.4838	6	6
Maine	661086	3.8319	3	4
Maryland	1042390	6.0421	6	6
Massachusetts	2238943	12.9778	12	13
Michigan	2093889	12.1370	12	12
Minnesota	1301826	7.5459	7	7
Mississippi	1289600	7.4750	7	7
Missouri	2679184	15.5296	15	15
Nebraska	1058910	6.1379	6	6
New Hampshire	376530	2.1825	2	2
New Jersey	1444933	8.3754	8	8
New York	5997853	34.7660	34	35
North Carolina	1617947	9.3783	9	9
North Dakota	182719	1.0591	1	1
Ohio	3672316	21.2862	21	21
Oregon	313767	1.8187	1	2
Pennsylvania	5258014	30.4776	30	30
Rhode Island	345506	2.0027	2	2
South Carolina	1151149	6.6725	6	7
South Dakota	328808	1.9059	1	2
Tennessee	1767518	10.2452	10	10
Texas	2235523	12.9580	12	13
Vermont	332422	1.9269	1	2
Virginia	1655980	9.5987	9	9
Washington	349390	2.0252	2	2
West Virginia	762794	4.4215	4	4
Wisconsin	1686880	9.7778	9	10
United States	61417403	356.0000	338	351

If imposed at the end, then one gets H.R. 125000 as reflected in Table 3.20, Seats column with Q356. The computations work in this case as follows. When the requirement is imposed at the end, the Lower column would contain a 0 for Delaware, Montana, Nevada, Oregon, and Wyoming. This distributes 334 of the 356 seats, leaving 22 more seats to be distributed. Giving an additional seat to each state with a quota decimal fraction greater than .5 distributes 19 more seats, bringing the House size to 353. The next three states in order of quota decimal fraction size are New York (.4900), Minnesota (.4860), and Idaho (.4852), bringing the total to 356. However, Wyoming (.3491) and Nevada (.2631) would be unrepresented. Hence, Wyoming and Nevada need to be assigned a seat at the expense of Minnesota and New York.

Mr. Buckalew's point then leads to the question, when should the constitutional minimum requirement be imposed in the computational process? How should one determine which states are involved? Mr. Buckalew proposed that any state whose population is below ratio (national divisor) should be awarded their seat and then their statistics eliminated from the Vinton plan for distributing the remaining House seats. The previous paragraph shows that three of the five states would be correctly accommodated; however, a final adjustment needs to be made for Wyoming and Nevada.

What if one merely dealt with Wyoming and Nevada at the start by awarding them one seat each and them eliminating them from the calculations to distribute 354 seats? The results would then be the same as H.R. 12500 except that giving an additional seat by moiety would have distributed only 352 seats. The next two states in line would be Virginia (.4853) and Idaho (.4852). The complicating issue would be that the final result was no longer consistent with moiety, one of the selling points of H.R. 12500.

The touchy technical feature of which states to eliminate at the beginning by assigning them a seat and then dropping them from any additional calculations would probably have been a deal breaker for serious consideration of this computational option.

Another way to deal with the constitutional minimum requirement is to first give each state one seat; then, distribute the remaining seats using the Vinton plan. This would have really changed things! The hanging point left by Mr. Buckalew is that when and how to invoke the Constitution's minimum requirement can dramatically affect the apportionment result.

Chapter 4

Congressional Apportionment

Based on the Census

1900 - 1930

The Modified Divisor Method Era

Chapter 4
Congressional Apportionment Based on the Census 1900-1930
The Modified Divisor Method Era

Table of Contents

Reference:

The map on the cover page is courtesy of the Florida Center for Instruction Technology, Albert Bushnell Hart, L.L.D., The American Nation Vol. 25 (New York, NY: Harper and Brothers, 1919), map #02798; downloaded from http://etc.usf.edu/maps/pages/2700/2798/2798.pdf

If there is anything that is sacred in this country, it should be an apportionment bill.[1]

Representative Albert Hopkins, Illinois
Chair, House Committee on the Census

Introduction

This chapter is devoted to the history of apportionment of the national House of Representatives based on the census years 1900-1930. The Constitution directs that representation in the House shall be based on an enumeration of the people as determined by a decennial census. The census years 1900-1930 are the transition years for congressional apportionment.

During the first six census decades, 1790-1840, Congress applied a basic divisor method, a census-based method initiated by the constituency approach to congressional apportionment: how many people should a congressman represent? The answer is called the ratio, divisor, or constituency. The ratio is divided into a state's population to calculate the state's quotient. During the first five censuses, 1790-1830, the fractional remainder was dropped to obtain a state's apportionment. In 1840 the first mutation in apportionment methodology occurred when Webster's rounding criterion was applied to the quotients. The quotient was rounded normally to obtain a state's apportionment. Experience taught that there are political effects to the choice of divisor.

In 1850 forces emerged to change the approach to apportionment from a constituency approach to a House size approach. The constituency initiating question, how many people should a congressman represent, was replaced by, what should be the size of the House? The resulting seats in the House were then distributed by Hamilton's method, also referred to as the Vinton plan. This led to a different methodology that legislators hoped would take the politics out of reapportionment of the House. This time, however, it was not unacceptable political consequences that doomed the method but unexpected mathematical consequences. Over the next fifty years unintuitive paradoxes began to reveal themselves.

Quota rule violations doomed the basic divisor method. Paradoxes, led by the Alabama paradox, doomed the Hamilton-Vinton method. Congress scrambled to invent an alternative. The eventual result was a modified divisor method where the House size was first established and then set aside as a goal for a divisor method. A new method of rounding the quotient decimal also came to the forefront during this transition period from the basic method to a modified divisor method.

---

[1] Congressional Record—House, 53rd Congress, 3rd Session, 4 January 1901: 566.

Section 4.1: Reapportionment Based on the 1900 Census

Section 4.1.1   Background

Only one new state entered the Union since the 1890 census. The enabling act of 16 July 1894 set the stage for Utah's admission.[1] The act allowed Utah one representative upon admission. President Grover Cleveland formally declared admission for Utah on 4 January 1896.[2] This brought the number of states in the Union to 45 and the House size to 357.

On 3 March 1899 President William McKinley approved *An act To provide for taking the Twelfth and subsequent censuses*.[3] The act had 33 sections containing the specific details for taking and managing the census and established the Census Office under the direction of the secretary of the Department of the Interior. The director of the Census Office was to be appointed by the President. The act specified that the Census Office utilize five chief statisticians for analyzing the census data. The census was to commence on 1 June 1900.

There were two major-ticket issues dominating the American political landscape at the time. The two remain today, still basically unresolved.

1. An equitable distribution of wealth and resources.
2. Equal protection and opportunity under the law.

The severe underlying problems associated with these two issues make reading the historical record at times difficult and disturbing using today's standards.

During the 1890s issues associated with wealth and resources led to the formation of a populist movement and the formation of the Populist Party. A key motivation for the movement and party was to obtain relief for small farmers being unmercifully gouged by banking interests, railroads, and silo managers. For example, annual loan rates for farm equipment ranged from 40 to 350 per cent.[4] Populists attracted and associated themselves with the labor movement, women's suffrage, and free silver.[5] In the 56th Congress, 2nd Session, there were 7 senators and 6 representatives from the Populist Party. Populists had notable political success in Colorado, Idaho, Kansas, and Nebraska.

Were the leaders of American industrialization "captains of industry" or "robber barons?" They were both—captain and robber were two sides of the same coin. While many people prospered, many others were brutally exploited. Populists aligned themselves with the

---

[1] 28 Stat. 138

[2] Grover Cleveland: "Proclamation 382 - Admitting Utah to the Union," January 4, 1896. Online by Gerhard Peters and John T. Woolley, *The American Presidency Project*.
https://www.presidency.ucsb.edu/documents/proclamation-382-admitting-utah-the-union.

[3] 30 Stat. 419

[4] http://www.digitalhistory.uh.edu/disp_textbook.cfm?smtID=2&psid=3127.

[5] Eric Foner, *Give Me Liberty: An American History*, W. W. Norton & Company, New York, Second Seagull Edition, 2009: 599-608.

Democrats in the presidential election of 1896, won handily by Republican William McKinley. The silver-tongued orator William Jennings Bryan passionately articulated many of the causes supported by populists. Critics, however, used the term "populism" in the same sneering fashion that today's opponents of government services use the term "socialism." And, perhaps unfortunately, rather than being remembered for support of programs that would resonate with today's progressives, most remember Bryant for his 1925 role as the prosecutor in the infamous Scopes Monkey Trial.[6]

A major social issue centered on renewed emergence of white supremacy, especially in the South. The Thirteenth Amendment, ratified 6 December 1865, abolished slavery. On 9 July 1868 the Fourteenth Amendment was ratified. The Fifteenth Amendment, ratified 3 February 1870, asserted that the right to vote shall "not be denied or abridged by the United States or by any State on account of race, color, or previous condition of servitude." Section 2 of the Fourteenth Amendment eliminated the infamous 3/5[ths] rule. The section further declared,

> But when the right to vote at any election for the choice of electors for President and Vice President of the United States, Representatives in Congress, the Executive and Judicial officers of a State, or the members of the Legislature thereof, is denied to any of the male inhabitants of such State, being twenty-one years of age, and citizens of the United States, or in any was abridged, except for participation in rebellion, or other crime, the basis of representation therein shall be reduced in the proportion which the number of such male citizens shall bear to the whole number of male citizens twenty-one years of age in such State.

The old Confederacy was not about to sign on to Negro equality. Through a concerted plan of segregation and voter suppression enforced by fear through domestic terrorism, especially lynching, white supremacy became the established norm in the old South. The effort was effective and had a lasting effect. As the historian Eric Foner notes, "As late as 1940, only 3 percent of adult black southerners were registered to vote."[7] Add to the domestic issues the imperialistic approaches to foreign policy emanating from the Spanish-American War, one has enough material for several volumes in a Howard Zinn American history series.

Against this background President McKinley wrote his letter to Congress for the start of the 56th Congress, 2nd Session, on 3 December 1900. After several lengthy remarks concerning foreign affairs, he addressed some domestic concerns. Among them he noted that the Director of the Census reports that work in connection with the Twelfth Census was progressing favorably and showed that the American economy was forging ahead at a healthy pace. He included, "I recommend that the Congress at its present session apportion representation among the several States as provided by the Constitution."[8]

---

[6] http://www.ushistory.org/us/47b.asp.

[7] Ibid: 612-3.

[8] Congressional Record, 56th Congress, 2nd Session, 3 December 1900: 12.

Section 4.1.2   The Congressional Bill

Shortly after President McKinley's letter was read to the House, Edgar Crumpacker (D-IN) introduced H.R. 12222, *An Act making an apportionment of Representatives in Congress under the Twelfth Census*.[9] The proposal was referred to the Committee on the Census.

On 7 December William R. Merriam, Director the Census, sent a letter of transmission to the House submitting a report of the state populations from the twelfth census.[10] The letter also attached two sets of apportionment tables. One set displayed apportionments for House size 350-400 using Hamilton's method. The other displayed apportionments using a divisor from 213000 to 186500 in decreasing order of increments of 500 applying the Jefferson and Webster basic divisor methods. On 13 December Edwin Burleigh (R-ME) introduced H.R. 12664, an apportionment bill also referred to the Committee on the Census.[11] The next day Albert Hopkins (R-IL) introduced H.R. 12740, a third and final apportionment bill, also referred to the Committee on the Census.[12] These were the only apportionment bills submitted in the House.

Just a week later Albert Hopkins, as chair of the House Committee on the Census, rose to say that he was directed by the Committee to report back H.R. 12740 with a favorable recommendation. The recommendation was accompanied by House Report No. 2130 which contained the report of the majority along with the minority reports of Mr. Crumpacker and Mr. Burleigh.[13] The 149-page report also contained the letter and attachments from Mr. Merriam, Director of the Census.

H.R. 12222, the Crumpacker bill, was a bill that incorporated the spirit of Section 2 of the Fourteenth Amendment. The bill did not make it out of committee. So, at the end of his report Mr. Crumpacker included a copy of his adjusted bill that was the same as the Hopkins bill except it used a House size of 386 and then subtracted 3 seats each for Louisiana, Mississippi, North Carolina, and South Carolina.

H.R. 12664, the Burleigh bill, was based on the table supplied by the Census Bureau for House size 384. However, Burleigh made an adjustment allocating an additional seat to Nebraska and Virginia for major fractions (i.e., the decimal fraction for the quota was greater than 0.5). This brought the proposed House size to 386. Further, this was the smallest House size where no state lost representation using this adjusted Hamilton method.

---

[9] Ibid: 18.

[10] Catalogue of the Public Documents of the Fifty-Sixth Congress and of other departments of the Government of the United States for the Period from July 1, 1899 to June 30, 1901: 149; accessed from https://books.google.com/books?id=imQhAQAAMAAJ&pg=PA149&lpg=PA149&dq=apportionment+twelfth+censu s+House+Report+No.+2130&source=bl&ots=fwh1fjX-7m&sig=H0eFnnrzHhW3Yuj98iB0Ms-hOik&hl=en&sa=X&ei=siU9VaW9DsjYggTxqoD4DA&ved=0CDMQ6AEwBw#v=onepage&q=apportionment%20twelf th%20census%20House%20Report%20No.%202130&f=false.

[11] Congressional Record, 56th Congress, 2nd Session, 13 December 1900: 298.

[12] Ibid, 14 December 1900: 331.

[13] Ibid, 20 December 1990: 486-88.

H.R. 12740, the Hopkins bill, was based on the apportionment table supplied by the Census Bureau for House size 357, the current House size. Since the Hopkins bill was recommended by the Committee on the Census, it became the reference point for debate in the House. The bill contained five sections.

- Section 1 set the House size at 357 with distribution of seats determined by Hamilton's method.
- Section 2 stipulated that representation for any new states admitted to the Union would be in addition to the 357 seats apportioned by Section 1.
- Section 3 stipulated that congressional districts should be composed of contiguous territory and be of equal size as nearly as practicable with one congressman per district.
- Section 4 stipulated that if a state gained in representatives, then additional congressmen may be elected at-large until the state redistricted.
- Section 5 stipulated that any previously enacted items inconsistent with this law are repealed.

The committee also recommended an amendment to Section 3 of the Hopkins proposal to change "contiguous" to "contiguous and compact." Hence, for all practical purposes there were only two competing apportionment bills on the table, the Hopkins and Burleigh bills. It is worthwhile to note that the Hopkins bill became the recommended bill by a 7-6 vote in the Select Committee on the Census. Six congressmen signed the minority report supporting the Burleigh bill. Crumpacker was the only signer of his minority report.

The first day of debate exposed three deal-breaking anomalies for Section 1 of the Hopkins bill (see Table 4.1, next page, for the spreadsheet figures in order to follow the debate). First, eight states would lose a seat: Indiana, Kansas, Kentucky, Maine, Nebraska, Ohio, South Carolina, and Virginia. Loss of representation does not garner support for an apportionment proposal. Second, three states (Colorado, Florida, and North Dakota) had major fractions but did not get an additional seat beyond the lower quota. In recent apportionments no loss of representation and additional seats by moiety had become accepted guidelines for fairness. Third, the Alabama paradox was glaring.

At House size 357 the Alabama paradox shined a spotlight on Colorado. Colorado received two seats at House size 357 but three seats for all other House sizes between 350 and 400. Previously Congress avoided House sizes where the Alabama paradox came into play. Here the Hopkins bill walked right into the paradox. The Alabama paradox also spotlighted West Virginia who received 5 seats at House size 351 but only four seats at House size 352 and 353. The paradox was so vivid for Maine that several congressmen became convinced that the Hamilton method was flawed. Maine received three seats for House sizes 350-382, 386, and 389-390 but four seats for House sizes 383-385, 387-388, and 391-400.

Table 4.1. Spreadsheet figures for House size 357, 384, and 386 using the Hamilton method. House size 357 is the basis for the Hopkins bill. House size 384 is the basis for the Burleigh bill which added an additional seat to Nebraska and Virginia, creating a House of size 386.

State	Population	Quota 357	Lower	Fraction	Seats	Quota 384	Lower	Fraction	Seats	Burleigh	Quota 386	Lower	Fraction	Seats
Alabama 9	1828697	8.755	8	157753	9	9.417	9	81059	9	9	9.466	9	90113	9
Arkansas 6	1311564	6.279	6	58356	6	6.754	6	146472	7	7	6.789	6	152508	7
California 7	1483504	7.103	7	21428	7	7.640	7	124230	8	8	7.680	7	131272	8
Colorado 2	539103	2.581	2	121367	2	2.776	2	150739	3	3	2.791	2	152751	3
Connecticut 4	908355	4.349	4	72883	4	4.678	4	131627	5	5	4.702	4	135651	5
Delaware 1	184735	0.884	0	184735	1	0.951	0	184735	1	1	0.956	0	184735	1
Florida 2	528542	2.531	2	110806	2	2.722	2	140178	3	3	2.736	2	142190	3
Georgia 11	2216331	10.611	10	127651	11	11.414	11	80329	11	11	11.473	11	91395	11
Idaho 1	159475	0.764	0	159475	1	0.821	0	159475	1	1	0.826	0	159475	1
Illinois 22	4821550	23.084	23	17586	23	24.830	24	161182	25	25	24.959	24	185326	25
Indiana 13	2516462	12.048	12	10046	12	12.959	12	186278	13	13	13.027	13	5174	13
Iowa 11	2231853	10.685	10	143173	11	11.494	11	95851	11	11	11.553	11	106917	11
Kansas 8	1470495	7.040	7	8419	7	7.573	7	111221	8	8	7.612	7	118263	8
Kentucky 11	2147174	10.280	10	58494	10	11.058	11	11172	11	11	11.115	11	22238	11
Louisiana 6	1381625	6.615	6	128417	7	7.115	7	22351	7	7	7.152	7	29393	7
Maine 4	694466	3.325	3	67862	3	3.576	3	111920	4	4	3.595	3	114938	4
Maryland 6	1190050	5.698	5	145710	6	6.129	6	24958	6	6	6.160	6	30994	6
Massachusetts 13	2805346	13.431	13	90062	13	14.447	14	86798	14	14	14.522	14	100882	14
Michigan 12	2420982	11.591	11	123434	12	12.468	12	90798	12	12	12.533	12	102870	12
Minnesota 7	1749626	8.377	8	78682	8	9.010	9	1988	9	9	9.057	9	11042	9
Mississippi 7	1551270	7.427	7	89194	7	7.989	7	191996	8	8	8.030	8	5862	8
Missouri 15	3106665	14.874	14	182513	15	15.999	15	193935	16	16	16.082	16	15849	16
Montana 1	232583	1.114	1	23715	1	1.198	1	38401	1	1	1.204	1	39407	1
Nebraska6	1068539	5.116	5	24199	5	5.503	5	97629	5	6	5.531	5	102659	5
Nevada 1	40670	0.195	0	40670	1	0.209	0	40670	1	1	0.211	0	40670	1
New Hampshire 2	411588	1.971	1	202720	2	2.120	2	23224	2	2	2.131	2	25236	2
New Jersey 8	1883669	9.018	9	3857	9	9.701	9	136031	10	10	9.751	9	145085	10
New York 34	7263301	34.775	34	161789	35	37.405	37	78567	37	37	37.599	37	115789	38
North Carolina 9	1893810	9.067	9	13998	9	9.753	9	146172	10	10	9.804	9	155226	10
North Dakota 1	314454	1.506	1	105586	1	1.619	1	120272	2	2	1.628	1	121278	2
Ohio 21	4157545	19.905	19	189053	20	21.411	21	79723	21	21	21.522	21	100849	21
Oregon 2	413536	1.980	1	204668	2	2.130	2	25172	2	2	2.141	2	27184	2
Pennsylvania 30	6302115	30.173	30	36075	30	32.455	32	88291	32	32	32.624	32	120483	33
Rhode Island 2	428556	2.052	2	10820	2	2.207	2	40192	2	2	2.218	2	42204	2
South Carolina 7	1340316	6.417	6	87108	6	6.902	6	175224	7	7	6.938	6	181260	7
South Dakota 2	390638	1.870	1	181770	2	2.012	2	2274	2	2	2.022	2	4286	2
Tennessee 10	2020616	9.674	9	140804	10	10.406	10	78796	10	10	10.460	10	88856	10
Texas 13	3048710	14.596	14	124558	15	15.700	15	135980	16	16	15.782	15	151070	16
Utah 1	275277	1.318	1	66409	1	1.418	1	81095	1	1	1.425	1	82101	1
Vermont 2	343641	1.645	1	134773	2	1.770	1	149459	2	2	1.779	1	150465	2
Virginia 10	1854184	8.877	8	183240	9	9.549	9	106546	9	10	9.598	9	115600	10
Washington 2	515572	2.468	2	97836	2	2.655	2	127208	3	3	2.669	2	129220	3
West Virginia 4	958800	4.590	4	123328	5	4.938	4	182072	5	5	4.963	4	186096	5
Wisconsin 10	2067385	9.898	9	187573	10	10.647	10	125565	11	11	10.702	10	135625	11
Wyoming 1	92531	0.443	0	92531	1	0.477	0	92531	1	1	0.479	0	92531	1
United States	74565906	357.000	335	4595126	357	384.000	360	4660386	384	386	386.000	363	4443018	387

Hopkins was opposed to increasing the size of the House. When questioned by Stanyarne Wilson (D-SC) about 357, he replied that just because the current House size was 357, that was not the "controlling element," but 357 was the "best number." Hopkins then justified his comment with the remark, "The point is, as stated by one great French writer, that if you increase a legislative body beyond a certain point it becomes a mob."[14]

A short time later, Hopkins was probably sensing the weakness of his arguments in the House and the opposition was getting to him.[15]

> Now, who is it that is taking the lead in opposition to the bill of the committee? The gentleman from Maine. Why does he do it? He does it because under the bill reported by our committee the representation of Maine in this House is reduced by one member.
>
> The gentleman from Kansas is another gentleman earnestly in favor of the Burleigh bill and earnestly opposed to the committee bill. Why? Because under the committee bill Kansas will lose a Representative. My honored friend from Nebraska is another gentleman who is opposed to our bill. We find that under the bill as reported by the committee Nebraska will lose a member.

Regarding Kansas Hopkins explained, "Kansas has been cursed for ten long years with Populism." He continued, "How is it in the State of Nebraska? Nebraska, lying alongside of Kansas, is suffering not from this bill of the committee, but from Bryanism and Populism in that State."[16] Such comments do not serve as a model for how to win an argument.

James Richardson (D-TN) asked Hopkins why he did not take the House size of 357 and then add three more seats to accommodate the major fractions for Colorado, Florida, and North Dakota. Hopkins said there was no constitutional authority to do that.[17] Later, in commenting on the Burleigh bill, Hopkins made the careless statement that "with their 386 members, as they are figuring it, they have violated the Constitution of the United States and have a separate ratio for every State." Shortly afterwards he made another careless remark stating that he did not know what method Burleigh had in mind in creating that bill.[18]

Opponents to the Hopkins bill probably felt like sharks that just smelled blood in the water. John Shafroth, a Silver Republican from Colorado, ended the first day of debate by eloquently summarizing the objections.[19]

> Mr. Speaker, I am opposed to this bill. I think it is predicated on a wrong basis, on a wrong theory, and I believe that if such iniquities as I have pointed out in the

---

[14] Ibid, 4 January 1991: 564.
[15] Ibid: 565.
[16] Ibid.
[17] Ibid.
[18] Ibid: 566.
[19] Ibid: 570-1.

cases of Colorado, Maine, and West Virginia had appeared among the tables that were presented to Congress in 1850, when this system was first adopted, the Senate and House would have found that the old system of fixing a given number of inhabitants for each Representatives and for each major fraction would come nearer doing equity among the States.

The Census Bureau included two sets of tables in its report to Congress. The first tabulated apportionments for House sizes 350-400 based on Hamilton's method. The second tabulated apportionments based on Webster's method using divisors from 213000 down to 186500 in increments of 500. Shafroth examined the Webster method tables and noted that there was no Alabama paradox. Hence, the Webster method immediately had two appealing aspects: no Alabama paradoxes and every state with a majority fraction was awarded an additional seat.

The next day, Saturday, 5 December, began with an acerbic exchange between Hopkins and Charles Littlefield (R-ME). Littlefield came prepared and he was going to enjoy this. He started with the Alabama paradox applied to Colorado.[20]

> I do not say that the chairman of this committee adopted that basis of 357, the only basis that would leave out Colorado above 350, because Populists happen to come from Colorado, as he sneeringly suggested in his speech upon this floor. I do not make that insinuation. I call attention to the remarkable coincidence, however, because I conceive, and I suppose the chairman now, if his attention were called to it, would rise and say, that he thinks that Colorado, even though her people are Populists, has the same right to a proportional representation on the floor of this House as does even godlike Illinois or even Maine, that seems to be the bugbear in the mind of the chairman of this committee.

But Mr. Littlefield was saving his best for his home state of Maine.

> Let me strike another paradox in connection with belabored and assaulted Maine, nonprogressive Maine, that is behind the procession, whose men in Illinois lead the procession there. Now, Maine loses on 382. She does not lose when the House is increased to 383, 384, or 385. She loses again with 386, and does not lose with 387 or 388. Then she loses again on 389 and 390, and then ceases to lose.
>
> Not only is Maine subjected to the assaults of the chairman of this committee, but it does seem as though mathematics and science had combined to make a shuttlecock and battledore of the State of Maine in connection with the scientific basis upon which this bill is presented to this House.
>
> "Now you see it and now you don't." In Maine comes and out Maine goes. The House increases in size, and still she is out. It increases a little more in size, and then forsooth, in she comes. A little further increase, and out she goes, and then a little further increase, and in she comes. God help the State of Maine when

---

[20] Ibid: 592-3.

mathematics reach for her and undertake to strike her down in this manner in connection with her representation on this floor—more cruel even than the chairman of this great committee.

Subsequent to having fun with the Alabama paradox manifestations for Colorado and Maine, Mr. Littlefield then proceeded to shred the careless statements made by Mr. Hopkins the day before: that rounding by moiety was unconstitutional, that the size of the House should not be increased, and that Hopkins just couldn't image what method was used to construct the Burleigh bill. After his remarks, Littlefield was given a loud round of applause.[21]

The debate was continued on Monday; but most of the discussion focused on the Crumpacker adjustment and, as such, was irrelevant to the apportionment method. On Tuesday, 8 January 1901, Wesley Jones (R-WA) got the apportionment debate back on track. Jones opposed the Hopkins bill because it gave him the perception of freezing the size of the House. Jones felt that the size of the House should increase to reflect the increase in the population of the country. He was not concerned about the comments on the size of the House because he felt that most of the business of the House was conducted in small committees.[22]

Peter Otey (D-VA) followed with a collage of interesting ideas. From a theoretical point of view based on the pros and cons of the competing Hopkins and Burleigh bills, the House size should be 395 because at that size the Hamilton and Webster methods yield the same result. Further, 395 is the only House size between 350 and 400 for which the Hamilton and Webster methods agree. He appealed to his colleagues to vote "First, that no State shall lose a Representative; Second, that every State shall have the full benefit of the majority fraction."[23]

Otey closed by appending a "striking letter of Mr. Frank Abial Flower," written to the Honorable John J. Jenkins, a representative from Wisconsin. Mr. Flower wrote that the problem in constructing a fair apportionment bill is due to fractions. This fraction problem can be equitably solved by using a system of fractional voting. For example, suppose Alabama's quotient is 8.898. Then award Alabama 9 representatives of which 8 representatives are elected from districts whose representatives will have one vote each. The 9th representative will be elected at large and will have 0.898 vote in Congress. The "striking letter," however, although entered into the Congressional Record, did not receive a single comment. Congress was not interested in the idea of a representative having only a partial vote.

Hopkins was the final speaker to close the House debate. He began by noting that the six signers of the Burleigh minority report were all from states that would gain a seat under the Burleigh bill in comparison to the Hopkins bill. He accused them of political motivation in opposing his bill. Consequently, he initiated his remarks with a partisan tone which would only guarantee a partisan reception for his remarks. His main remark of substance was that the

---

[21] Ibid: 593-9.
[22] Ibid, 8 January 1901: 714-7.
[23] Ibid: 718-22.

Burleigh bill was created by starting with House size 384. But, then the Hamilton method left two states with major fractions without an additional seat. The Burleigh bill simply adjusted the situation awarding an additional seat to those two states, Nebraska, and Virginia; hence, making the House size 386. Hopkins noted from the tables provided by the Census Bureau that at House size 386, the correct apportionment would award the two additional seats to New York and Pennsylvania, not Nebraska and Virginia.

It was now time to decide. The Speaker directed the Clerk to read the first section of the Hopkins bill. After the reading, Burleigh offered a substitute replacing Section 1 of the Hopkins bill with Section 1 of the Burleigh bill. Then Burleigh Spalding (R-ND) offered an amendment to the Hopkins bill by adding an additional seat to Colorado, Florida, and North Dakota, bringing the House size to 360.[24] Dorsey Shackleford (D-MO) proposed to amend the Hopkins bill to House size 400.[25] William Alden Smith (R-MI) proposed to amend the Hopkins bill to House size 395.[26]

The Speaker then announced the parliamentary situation and the order of voting. First, the Spalding amendment to the Hopkins bill passed. Next, the William Alden Smith amendment to set the House size to 395 failed, 85-136. Then, the Burleigh substitute passed: yea 166, nay 102, present 10, not voting 77. The remainder of the bill was cleaned up to reflect the House size 386. The committee amendment to make congressional districts "contiguous and compact" also passed.[27] Then a vote was taken on the entire amended bill, which passed. Crumpacker moved to recommit the bill to the Select Committee on the Census for adjustments according to the Fourteenth Amendment; failed, 94-136. Subsequently the bill was sent to the Senate for concurrence.

The Senate rubber stamped the House bill. On 9 January the Senate received the bill, read it twice, and referred it to the Senate's Committee on the Census.[28] Two days later the committee reported favorably on the bill without amendment. Thomas Carter (R-MT), on behalf of the committee, asked for unanimous consent for the bill. An objection was made, so the President of the Senate specified that the bill would go to the calendar. Later that same day, Carter renewed his request for unanimous consent for a vote on the bill. This time the consent was granted and the bill passed with no debate.[29] President McKinley approved the bill on 16 January 1901.

---

[24] Ibid: 732.

[25] Ibid: 739.

[26] Ibid: 741.

[27] Ibid: 742-8.

[28] Ibid, 9 January 1901: 754.

[29] Ibid: 851-2, 883-4.

Section 4.1.3   Aftermath

What method was used to create the final version of H.R. 12740? Balinski and Young state,[30]

> The results produced by Hamilton's method proved to be more than Congress could accept. Hopkins's bill failed, and Hamilton's method was finally abandoned altogether—three decades after the phenomenon of the Alabama paradox had first come to the attention of Congress. Instead, Webster's method was applied to a House enlarged to 386 members. At 386 no state would lose a seat.

So, what method was used: Hamilton's or Webster's? For each, perhaps a better answer is "yes and no." Hamilton's method was followed to initiate the congressional bill, but not to complete it. Technically one might assert that Webster's method may apply from a mathematical point of view but not from a political point of view. The bill was created by first deciding on House size 384. Then Hamilton's method was applied. However, in examining the results, the proponents noticed that two states, Nebraska, and Virginia, had major fractions but not an additional seat from the lower quota. Hence, they supplemented the 384 Hamilton result by adding an additional seat each for Nebraska and Virginia. Accordingly, Littlefield claimed that the Hopkins and Burleigh bills were "built precisely on the same basis."[31]

Hence, the method may be called a supplemented Hamilton method. The final result was not consistent with Hamilton's method for 386. Thus, Hamilton's method was not really abandoned altogether, at least not from the political point of view.

Was Webster's method used? Balinski and Young define it as follows.[32]

> *The Method of Webster*. Choose the size of the house to be apportioned. Find a divisor x so that the whole numbers nearest to the quotients of the states sum to the required total. Give to each state its whole number.

This definition conforms to the Webster modified divisor method described previously in Chapter 2, Section 4.5. The initial key in the Webster modified divisor method is that one first chooses the size of the House to be apportioned. In creating the congressional bill, proponents started with House size 384; but, ended with House size 386. The method used may be called Webster's method if the proponents actually started with 386. The method is perhaps Webster's method from the mathematical point of view that if I start with House size 386, apply the divisor 193176, and finally round the resulting quotients by major fractions, then I do achieve House size 386. However, proponents did not begin the process by aiming to construct a House of size 386. The only thing "Webster" about the method is that it used Webster's method of rounding; i.e., rounding by moiety.

---

[30] Michel L. Balinski and H. Peyton Young, *Fair Representation: Meeting the Ideal of One Man, One Vote*, Second Edition, Brookings Institution Press, Washington, D. C.: 42.
[31] Congressional Record, 5 January 1901: 591.
[32] Ibid: 32.

Another approach about methodology is to look at it from the political point of view and consider that a Webster basic divisor method was applied. First, the proponents decided on a divisor as follows: divide House size 384 into the national population 74565906 and obtain 193176. Using this divisor and applying Webster's method of rounding, we obtain House size 386. Although this is what happened, this kind of thinking appears forced to assert that a basic divisor method was used. If one were truly using the Webster basic divisor method, then the initial approach would involve the question, how many people should a congressman represent? The response 193100 seems more natural than 193176 for producing a House with 386 members.

Hamilton's method was not yet abandoned altogether. Congress realized that sticking strictly to a mathematical algorithm caused problems. Sticking to a divisor method caused quota rule violations as Hopkins noted in criticizing the Burleigh bill. Sticking to the quota method caused paradoxes as Littlefield, Shaforth and Burleigh used in criticizing the Hopkins bill. This aspect of a political component of the debate was captured by Wesley Jones (R-WA).[33]

> An examination of the debates in connection with the apportionments in the past and an examination of the tables submitted in the report of the committee show that no system has ever yet been devised that has carried out the provision of the Constitution. It seems to me, from the very nature of things, that it is absolutely impossible to devise a mathematical system by which injustice will not be done. The population of the various states is not based upon any mathematical system.
> ... if we could so apportion the Representatives that each district would have exactly the number that could be represented by one member, this would be in exact accord with the requirements of the Constitution. As it is impossible to do this, then it seems to me that we should get as near to it as possible. If we have to do violence to any mathematical system in order to do it, it is but our plain duty to see that it is done, as justice should be placed above mathematics in such a matter.

Finally, it should be noted that "at 386 no state would lose a seat" is true for the Webster method of apportionment but false for the Hamilton method. At House size 386 under the Hamilton method, Nebraska would lose a seat. The minimum House size under the Hamilton method for no state to lose a seat was 387. The majority of Congress wanted that when apportionment was done, no state would lose a seat and that each state with a major fraction would be awarded an additional seat. The only Hamilton House size to meet this requirement was 395 in the 350-400 Census Bureau tables. However, these criteria were met under the Burleigh bill with House size 386. Hence, Congress opted for the Burleigh bill.

There was a final irony in the adoption of the apportionment bill based on the 1900 census. The final report published in December 1901 for the population of the 45 states showed four discrepancies from the populations issued in the apportionment tables to Congress a year

---

[33] Ibid, 8 January 1901: 715.

earlier: Connecticut, 908420; Maryland, 1188044; Nebraska, 1066300; and New York, 7264183.[34] The main irony is that at House size 384 Nebraska would not have had a major fraction (Table 4.2). Hence, the Burleigh bill corrected an "injustice" for Nebraska that did not exist. Using the final population figures, Nebraska's quota for House size 384 would have been 5.491. Accordingly, the corresponding Burleigh bill would not have achieved its goal of an apportionment where no state lost a seat. Apportionment under the Hopkins bill would be the same.

In order to achieve the goal of the Burleigh bill, Burleigh would have had to use the Hamilton table for House size 385; then, rounding by moiety would have resulted in a House of size 390. This would have resulted in an additional seat for Michigan, Nebraska, New York, Iowa, and Pennsylvania beyond the Hamilton formula. The smallest House size using the Hamilton method that would accomplish the goals that no state loses representation and each state with a quota/quotient greater than moiety would receive an additional seat was 399.

Congress did not change the apportionment bill based on the final population.

Table 4.2 (next page). The table gives a spreadsheet analysis for the competing Hopkins and Burleigh bills using the final census figures adjusting the populations for Connecticut, Maryland, Nebraska, and New York. The Quota 357/Lower/Seats columns show the calculations needed for the Hopkins Bill. The Quota 384/Lower/Seats columns show the Hamilton method for House size 384. Note the quotient for Nebraska is 5.491. The Burleigh Quota 385/Lower/Seats columns show the calculations needed for the Burleigh bill: first, take the Hamilton quotas for House size 385, round the quotas by moiety, and thus obtain the Burleigh House size of 390.

---

[34] The Twelfth Census of the United States taken in the Year 1900 may be obtained as a free ebook from https://books.google.com/books?id=EfdYAAAAYAAJ&pg=PR227&lpg=PR227&dq=congressional+apportionment+b ased+on+the+twelfth+census&source=bl&ots=QZTWJmKLAw&sig=XRieXkKOriuPQwoP- ZA9eZic8Ws&hl=en&sa=X&ei=kE4IVduEF4SEsAXApoKgBA&ved=0CEcQ6AEwBQ#v=onepage&q=congressional%20a pportionment%20based%20on%20the%20twelfth%20census&f=false

State	Population	Quota 357	Lower	Seats	Quota 384	Lower	Seats	Burleigh Quota 385	Lower	Seats
Alabama	1828697	8.756	8	9	9.418	9	9	9.442	9	9
Arkansas	1311564	6.280	6	6	6.755	6	7	6.772	6	7
California	1483504	7.103	7	7	7.640	7	8	7.660	7	8
Colorado	539103	2.581	2	2	2.776	2	3	2.784	2	3
Connecticut	908420	4.349	4	4	4.678	4	5	4.691	4	5
Delaware	184735	0.884	0	1	0.951	0	1	0.954	0	1
Florida	528542	2.531	2	2	2.722	2	3	2.729	2	3
Georgia	2216331	10.612	10	11	11.414	11	11	11.444	11	11
Idaho	159475	0.764	0	1	0.821	0	1	0.823	0	1
Illinois	4821550	23.085	23	23	24.831	24	25	24.896	24	25
Indiana	2516462	12.049	12	12	12.960	12	13	12.994	12	13
Iowa	2231853	10.686	10	11	11.494	11	11	11.524	11	12
Kansas	1470495	7.041	7	7	7.573	7	8	7.593	7	8
Kentucky	2147174	10.281	10	10	11.058	11	11	11.087	11	11
Louisiana	1381625	6.615	6	7	7.115	7	7	7.134	7	7
Maine	694466	3.325	3	3	3.577	3	4	3.586	3	4
Maryland	1188044	5.688	5	6	6.118	6	6	6.134	6	6
Massachusetts	2805346	13.432	13	13	14.448	14	14	14.485	14	14
Michigan	2420982	11.591	11	12	12.468	12	12	12.501	12	13
Minnesota	1749626	8.377	8	8	9.011	9	9	9.034	9	9
Mississippi	1551270	7.427	7	7	7.989	7	8	8.010	8	8
Missouri	3106665	14.874	14	15	15.999	15	16	16.041	16	16
Montana	232583	1.114	1	1	1.198	1	1	1.201	1	1
Nebraska	1066300	5.105	5	5	5.491	5	5	5.506	5	6
Nevada	40670	0.195	0	1	0.209	0	1	0.210	0	1
New Hampshire	411588	1.971	1	2	2.120	2	2	2.125	2	2
New Jersey	1883669	9.019	9	9	9.701	9	10	9.726	9	10
New York	7264183	34.780	34	35	37.411	37	37	37.508	37	38
North Carolina	1893810	9.067	9	9	9.753	9	10	9.779	9	10
North Dakota	314454	1.506	1	1	1.619	1	2	1.624	1	2
Ohio	4157545	19.906	19	20	21.411	21	21	21.467	21	21
Oregon	413536	1.980	1	2	2.130	2	2	2.135	2	2
Pennsylvania	6302115	30.174	30	30	32.456	32	32	32.541	32	33
Rhode Island	428556	2.052	2	2	2.207	2	2	2.213	2	2
South Carolina	1340316	6.417	6	6	6.903	6	7	6.921	6	7
South Dakota	390638	1.870	1	2	2.012	2	2	2.017	2	2
Tennessee	2020616	9.675	9	10	10.406	10	10	10.433	10	10
Texas	3048710	14.597	14	15	15.701	15	16	15.742	15	16
Utah	275277	1.318	1	1	1.418	1	1	1.421	1	1
Vermont	343641	1.645	1	2	1.770	1	2	1.774	1	2
Virginia	1854184	8.878	8	9	9.549	9	9	9.574	9	10
Washington	515572	2.469	2	2	2.655	2	3	2.662	2	3
West Virginia	958800	4.591	4	5	4.938	4	5	4.951	4	5
Wisconsin	2067385	9.898	9	10	10.647	10	11	10.675	10	11
Wyoming	92531	0.443	0	1	0.477	0	1	0.478	0	1
United States	74562608	357.000	335	357	384.000	360	384	385.000	362	390

Section 4.1.4   The New States Paradox

The decade of the 1900s saw only one new state admitted to the union, Oklahoma. On 16 November 1907 President Theodore Roosevelt issued Presidential Proclamation 780 admitting Oklahoma as the 46th state of the Union.[35] The state was awarded five representatives upon admission.[36] The representative allocation is consistent with an estimated population of 1000000 for Oklahoma using a divisor of 194182, the Burleigh divisor used in the 1901 apportionment act. Although the population of Oklahoma for statehood was not based on a census, it was based on a reasonable estimate. In advocating for statehood for Oklahoma, Senator Chester Long (R-KS) argued, "The Bureau of the Census, in its estimate of the population of all the States and Territories for the year 1905, placed the number of people in Oklahoma and Indian Territory at 1056261."[37]

Section 2 of the 1901 apportionment act read,[38]

> That whenever a new State is admitted to the Union the Representative or Representatives assigned to it shall be in addition to the number three hundred and eighty-six.

This is reasonable in that established apportionments need not be re-calculated because of the admission of a new state. What would be the result if a re-calculation had been done? Initially it seems that the admission of a new state should have nothing to do with the apportionment of the other states. However, the admission of a new state changes the national population, thereby changing the ratio of representation, thereby changing the decimal quotients. In the case of apportionment based on the 1900 census, based on Hamilton's method this would have resulted in New York losing a seat to Maine (Table 4.3, next page).

Thus, the New States Paradox was discovered.[39] Formally, we have the

> **New State Paradox** When a new state is added to the Union and given its share of seats, then upon recalculation for the new House size the allotted number of seats of other states may be affected.

This paradox adds more difficulty for the Hamilton method of apportionment.

---

[35] http://www.archives.gov/legislative/features/oklahoma/.
[36] Statutes at Large, 59th Congress, 1st Session, Chap. 3335, 16 June 1906: 267-85.
[37] Congressional Record—Senate, 59th Congress, 1st Session, 6 March 1906: 3385.
[38] Statutes at Large, 56th Congress, 2nd Session, Chap. 93, 16 January 1901: 733-4.
[39] https://www.youtube.com/watch?v=VSLsfvftr7A.

Table 4.3. Spreadsheet analysis displaying the 1907 New States Paradox.

State	Population	h=386	Lower	Seats	State	Population	h=391	Lower	Seats
Alabama	1828697	9.467	9	9	Alabama	1828697	9.463	9	9
Arkansas	1311564	6.790	6	7	Arkansas	1311564	6.787	6	7
California	1483504	7.680	7	8	California	1483504	7.676	7	8
Colorado	539103	2.791	2	3	Colorado	539103	2.790	2	3
Connecticut	908420	4.703	4	5	Connecticut	908420	4.701	4	5
Delaware	184735	0.956	0	1	Delaware	184735	0.956	0	1
Florida	528542	2.736	2	3	Florida	528542	2.735	2	3
Georgia	2216331	11.474	11	11	Georgia	2216331	11.468	11	11
Idaho	159475	0.826	0	1	Idaho	159475	0.825	0	1
Illinois	4821550	24.961	24	25	Illinois	4821550	24.949	24	25
Indiana	2516462	13.027	13	13	Indiana	2516462	13.021	13	13
Iowa	2231853	11.554	11	11	Iowa	2231853	11.549	11	11
Kansas	1470495	7.613	7	8	Kansas	1470495	7.609	7	8
Kentucky	2147174	11.116	11	11	Kentucky	2147174	11.111	11	11
Louisiana	1381625	7.152	7	7	Louisiana	1381625	7.149	7	7
Maine	694466	3.595	3	3	Maine	694466	3.594	3	4
Maryland	1188044	6.150	6	6	Maryland	1188044	6.148	6	6
Massachusetts	2805346	14.523	14	14	Massachusetts	2805346	14.516	14	14
Michigan	2420982	12.533	12	12	Michigan	2420982	12.527	12	12
Minnesota	1749626	9.058	9	9	Minnesota	1749626	9.053	9	9
Mississippi	1551270	8.031	8	8	Mississippi	1551270	8.027	8	8
Missouri	3106665	16.083	16	16	Missouri	3106665	16.075	16	16
Montana	232583	1.204	1	1	Montana	232583	1.204	1	1
Nebraska	1066300	5.520	5	5	Nebraska	1066300	5.518	5	5
Nevada	40670	0.211	0	1	Nevada	40670	0.210	0	1
New Hampshire	411588	2.131	2	2	New Hampshire	411588	2.130	2	2
New Jersey	1883669	9.752	9	10	New Jersey	1883669	9.747	9	10
New York	7264183	37.606	37	38	New York	7264183	37.589	37	37
North Carolina	1893810	9.804	9	10	North Carolina	1893810	9.800	9	10
North Dakota	314454	1.628	1	2	North Dakota	314454	1.627	1	2
Ohio	4157545	21.523	21	21	Ohio	4157545	21.513	21	21
Oregon	413536	2.141	2	2	Oklahoma	1000000	5.175	5	5
Pennsylvania	6302115	32.625	32	33	Oregon	413536	2.140	2	2
Rhode Island	428556	2.219	2	2	Pennsylvania	6302115	32.610	32	33
South Carolina	1340316	6.939	6	7	Rhode Island	428556	2.218	2	2
South Dakota	390638	2.022	2	2	South Carolina	1340316	6.935	6	7
Tennessee	2020616	10.460	10	10	South Dakota	390638	2.021	2	2
Texas	3048710	15.783	15	16	Tennessee	2020616	10.456	10	10
Utah	275277	1.425	1	1	Texas	3048710	15.776	15	16
Vermont	343641	1.779	1	2	Utah	275277	1.424	1	1
Virginia	1854184	9.599	9	10	Vermont	343641	1.778	1	2
Washington	515572	2.669	2	3	Virginia	1854184	9.594	9	10
West Virginia	958800	4.964	4	5	Washington	515572	2.668	2	3
Wisconsin	2067385	10.703	10	11	West Virginia	958800	4.961	4	5
Wyoming	92531	0.479	0	1	Wisconsin	2067385	10.698	10	11
United States	74562608	386.001	363	386	Wyoming	92531	0.479	0	1
					United States	75562608	390.999	368	391

Section 4.2: Reapportionment Based on the 1910 Census

Section 4.2.1 Background

The decade of the 1900s saw important changes in the Census Bureau. The *Permanent Census Act* approved by President Theodore Roosevelt on 6 March 1902 established a permanent Census Office. The Director of the Census was to be appointed by the President with the consent of the Senate. The Director was to appoint four chief statisticians to direct the work of analyzing the data collected. Further, employees of the Census Office were placed under the provisions of the Civil Service Act, approved 16 January 1883 by President Chester Arthur.[1]

Figure 4.1 Walter F. Willcox.

One of the chief statisticians who worked on the 1900 census was **Walter Francis Willcox** (Figure 4.1), an important statistician not only in the history of congressional apportionment but also in the development of the science of statistics in the United States.[2][3] Willcox was a professor at Cornell University from 1901 to 1931, serving as professor of economics and statistics. On 15 December 1910 Willcox met with Edgar Crumpacker (R-IN), chair of the House Committee on the Census. Crumpacker was eager to have an apportionment bill passed during the 3rd session of the 61st Congress (5 December 1910 - 3 March 1911). In response to the meeting, Willcox sent Crumpacker "tables showing the apportionment of each number of Representatives from 390 to 440, inclusive, according to the results of the census of 1910 by a method which, I believe, deserves the consideration of the Committee on the Census." Willcox called his method "the method of major fractions."[4] Crumpacker subsequently formulated an apportionment bill based on Willcox's analysis.

Arizona and New Mexico were still territories; however, it was anticipated that they would soon be admitted to statehood. Accordingly, Willcox included both Arizona and New Mexico in his tables as if they were states.

The Willcox tables (Table 4.4, next page) showed apportionment for House size 390-440 inclusive. For each House size the table displayed a "Ratio for division," the result of division to two decimal places, the final apportionment, and the gain or loss from the current apportionment.[5] One may also deduce from the tables that 435 (including one seat each for the anticipated statehoods of Arizona and New Mexico) is the smallest House size for which no state would lose a seat in the House.

---

[1] https://www.census.gov/history/www/reference/legislation/legislation_1902_-_1941.html.

[2] https://amstat.tandfonline.com/doi/abs/10.1080/00031305.1964.10482639.

[3] Eugene William Seneta. "Walter Francis Willcox" (version 2). *StatProb: The Encyclopedia Sponsored by Statistics and Probability Societies.* Freely available at https://encyclopediaofmath.org/wiki/Willcox,_Walter_Francis.

[4] 61st Congress, 3rd Session, House Report No. 1911, letter from W. F. Willcox to Hon. E. D. Crumpacker: 9-10.

[5] 61st Congress, 3rd Session, House Report No. 1911

Table 4.4. The Willcox table for House size 434 and 435.

TABLE 1.—Apportionment of each number of Representatives between 390 and 440, inclusive, by method of major fractions—Continued.

	Ratio for division, 211,944. Total number of Representatives, 434.				Ratio for division, 211,877. Total number of Representatives, 435.			
	Result of division.	Final apportionment.	Changes from present apportionment. Gain.	Loss.	Result of division.	Final apportionment.	Changes from present apportionment. Gain.	Loss.
United States..	....	434	43	....	....	435	44	....
Alabama..........	10.08	10	1	....	10.09	10	1	....
Arizona...........	.85	1	1	....	.85	1	1	....
Arkansas..........	7.42	7	....	....	7.43	7	....	....
California.........	11.21	11	3	....	11.21	11	3	....
Colorado..........	3.76	4	1	....	3.76	4	1	....
Connecticut.......	5.25	5	....	....	5.26	5	....	....
Delaware..........	.95	1	....	....	.95	1	....	....
Florida...........	3.55	4	1	....	3.55	4	1	....
Georgia...........	12.30	12	1	....	12.31	12	1	....
Idaho.............	1.52	2	1	....	1.52	2	1	....
Illinois...........	26.60	27	2	....	26.61	27	2	....
Indiana...........	12.74	13	....	....	12.74	13	....	....
Iowa..............	10.49	10	....	1	10.50	11	....	....
Kansas............	7.97	8	....	....	7.98	8	....	....
Kentucky..........	10.80	11	....	....	10.80	11	....	....
Louisiana.........	7.81	8	1	....	7.81	8	1	....
Maine............	3.50	4	....	....	3.50	4	....	....
Maryland..........	6.11	6	....	....	6.11	6	....	....
Massachusetts......	15.88	16	2	....	15.89	16	2	....
Michigan..........	13.26	13	1	....	13.26	13	1	....
Minnesota.........	9.78	10	1	....	9.79	10	1	....
Mississippi........	8.47	8	....	....	8.48	8	....	....
Missouri..........	15.54	16	....	....	15.54	16	....	....
Montana..........	1.72	2	1	....	1.72	2	1	....
Nebraska..........	5.65	6	....	....	5.62	6	....	....
Nevada...........	.38	1	....	....	.38	1	....	....
New Hampshire.....	2.03	2	....	....	2.03	2	....	....
New Jersey........	11.97	12	2	....	11.97	12	2	....
New Mexico........	1.49	1	1	....	1.49	1	1	....
New York..........	42.97	43	6	....	42.99	43	6	....
North Carolina.....	10.40	10	....	....	10.41	10	....	....
North Dakota......	2.71	3	1	....	2.71	3	1	....
Ohio.............	22.49	22	1	....	22.49	23	1	....
Oklahoma.........	7.81	8	3	....	7.82	8	3	....
Oregon...........	3.17	3	1	....	3.17	3	1	....
Pennsylvania.......	36.16	36	4	....	36.13	36	4	....
Rhode Island.......	2.55	3	1	....	2.56	3	1	....
South Carolina.....	7.14	7	....	....	7.15	7	....	....
South Dakota......	2.71	3	1	....	2.71	3	1	....
Tennessee.........	10.30	10	....	....	10.31	10	....	....
Texas.............	18.38	18	2	....	18.39	18	2	....
Utah.............	1.75	2	1	....	1.75	2	1	....
Vermont..........	1.67	2	....	....	1.68	2	....	....
Virginia...........	9.72	10	....	....	9.73	10	....	....
Washington........	5.37	5	2	....	5.38	5	2	....
West Virginia......	5.76	6	1	....	5.76	6	1	....
Wisconsin.........	11.00	11	....	....	11.01	11	....	....
Wyoming..........	.68	1	....	....	.68	1	....	....

Section 4.2.2   The Constitutional Minimum

In addition to the Willcox report, Crumpacker received a letter from William F. Willoughby, Acting Director of the Census Bureau, which transmitted apportionment tables constructed by the Bureau. The first table gave the state apportionment populations along with the territory populations for Arizona and New Mexico. The total U. S. population came to 91569325, excluding Indians not taxed since they were excluded constitutionally from the apportionment populations. The second table gave apportionments for House sizes 390 to 440 using the "method prescribed by the census act of 1850" (Hamilton's method). Using this method Willoughby noted that 440 was the minimum House size for which no state lost a seat.

The Census Bureau tables used a unique technique for applying Hamilton's method. By Hamilton's method, Arizona, Delaware, Nevada, and Wyoming would not receive a seat due to their small populations. So, the Bureau applied the constitutional minimum of one seat to each of these four states, then deducted them from the data set, and then distributed the remaining seats by reapplying Hamilton's method. Previously, the constitutional minimum requirement was applied at the end of Hamilton's method.

We now investigate three ways to apply the constitutional minimum requirement within Hamilton's method.

- Hamilton 1. After computing the apportionments using Hamilton's method, then apply the constitutional minimum, if needed.
- Hamilton 2. If a state has a quota with an integer part of 0, then assign the state one representative and then remove that state from further consideration. In particular, deduct that state's population from the total population.
- Hamilton 3. First allot one representative to each state. Then subtract the number of states from the House size to account for the constitutional minimum for each state. Apply Hamilton's method to this adjusted House size. No further adjustment in Hamilton's method is needed.

Table 4.5 (next page) displays the three variations of the Hamilton method for House size 390, the smallest House size in the Census Bureau's tables submitted by Willoughby. The first set contains the State/Population/Quota1/Lower/Seats columns and shows the result of using the Hamilton 1 method. Quota1 uses a national divisor of 234793. The constitutional minimum requirement needs to be applied only to one state, Nevada. To satisfy this requirement, a seat must be subtracted from Indiana and given to Nevada. Indiana is the only state without an additional seat for moiety. Although the integer part of the quota is zero for four states, three have a sufficiently large fraction that they would receive a seat by the regular Hamilton method. Only Nevada and Indiana are affected by the constitutional minimum rule.

The second set in Table 4.5 with Quota2, which uses a national divisor 235652, displays the results of using the Hamilton method 2. The final apportionment result is the same. However, assigning each state its lower quota distributes 365 seats; hence, an additional 21 seats need to be distributed. Assigning an additional seat to each state satisfying moiety brings the distribution to 385 seats, one short of the 386 needed. The next state in line by fractions is

Maryland with a quota of 5.4969. Hence, an additional seat is awarded for a minor fraction, a feature that Crumpacker wanted to avoid.

Table 4.5. Spreadsheet analysis for the constitutional minimum requirement using Hamilton's method.

State	Population	Quota1 D = 234793	Lower	Seats
AL 9	2138093	9.1063	9	9
AZ	180225	0.7676	0	1
AR 7	1574449	6.7057	6	7
CA 8	2376561	10.1219	10	10
CO 3	798572	3.4012	3	3
CT 5	1114756	4.7478	4	5
DE 1	202322	0.8617	0	1
FL 3	752619	3.2055	3	3
GA 11	2609121	11.1124	11	11
ID 1	323440	1.3776	1	1
IL 25	5638591	24.0152	24	24
IN 13	2700876	11.5032	11	11
IA 11	2224771	9.4755	9	9
KS 8	1690949	7.2019	7	7
KY 11	2289905	9.7529	9	10
LA 7	1656388	7.0547	7	7
ME 4	742371	3.1618	3	3
MD6	1295346	5.5170	5	6
MA 14	3366416	14.3378	14	14
MI 12	2810173	11.9687	11	12
MN 9	2074376	8.8349	8	9
MS 8	1797114	7.6540	7	8
MO 16	3293335	14.0265	14	14
MT 1	366338	1.5603	1	2
NE 6	1192214	5.0777	5	5
NV 1	80293	0.3420	0	1
NH 2	430572	1.8338	1	2
NJ 10	2537167	10.8060	10	11
NM	316983	1.3501	1	1
NY 37	9108934	38.7956	38	39
NC 10	2206287	9.3967	9	9
ND 2	574403	2.4464	2	2
OH 21	4767121	20.3035	20	20
OK 5	1657155	7.0579	7	7
OR 2	672765	2.8654	2	3
PA 32	7665111	32.6463	32	33
RI 2	542610	2.3110	2	2
SC 7	1515400	6.4542	6	6
SD 2	575676	2.4518	2	2
TN 10	2184789	9.3052	9	9
TX 16	3896542	16.5956	16	17
UT 1	371864	1.5838	1	2
VT 2	355956	1.5160	1	2
VA 10	2061612	8.7806	8	9
WA 3	1140134	4.8559	4	5
WV 5	1221119	5.2008	5	5
WI 11	2332853	9.9358	9	10
WY 1	144658	0.6161	0	1
USA	91569325	390.0002	367	390

State	Population	Quota2 D = 235652	Lower	Seats
AL 9	2138093	9.0731	9	9
AR 7	1574449	6.6812	6	7
CA 8	2376561	10.0850	10	10
CO 3	798572	3.3888	3	3
CT 5	1114756	4.7305	4	5
FL 3	752619	3.1938	3	3
GA 11	2609121	11.0719	11	11
ID 1	323440	1.3725	1	1
IL 25	5638591	23.9276	23	24
IN 13	2700876	11.4613	11	11
IA 11	2224771	9.4409	9	9
KS 8	1690949	7.1756	7	7
KY 11	2289905	9.7173	9	10
LA 7	1656388	7.0290	7	7
ME 4	742371	3.1503	3	3
MD6	1295346	5.4969	5	6
MA 14	3366416	14.2855	14	14
MI 12	2810173	11.9251	11	12
MN 9	2074376	8.8027	8	9
MS 8	1797114	7.6261	7	8
MO 16	3293335	13.9754	13	14
MT 1	366338	1.5546	1	2
NE 6	1192214	5.0592	5	5
NH 2	430572	1.8272	1	2
NJ 10	2537167	10.7666	10	11
NM	316983	1.3451	1	1
NY 37	9108934	38.6542	38	39
NC 10	2206287	9.3625	9	9
ND 2	574403	2.4375	2	2
OH 21	4767121	20.2295	20	20
OK 5	1657155	7.0322	7	7
OR 2	672765	2.8549	2	3
PA 32	7665111	32.5272	32	33
RI 2	542610	2.3026	2	2
SC 7	1515400	6.4307	6	6
SD 2	575676	2.4429	2	2
TN 10	2184789	9.2713	9	9
TX 16	3896542	16.5352	16	17
UT 1	371864	1.5780	1	2
VT 2	355956	1.5105	1	2
VA 10	2061612	8.7485	8	9
WA 3	1140134	4.8382	4	5
WV 5	1221119	5.1819	5	5
WI 11	2332853	9.8996	9	10
USA	90961827	386.0007	365	386

State	Population	Quota3 D = 267746	Lower	Seats	SEATS
AL 9	2138093	7.9855	7	8	9
AZ	180225	0.6731	0	1	2
AR 7	1574449	5.8804	5	6	7
CA 8	2376561	8.8762	8	9	10
CO 3	798572	2.9826	2	3	4
CT 5	1114756	4.1635	4	4	5
DE 1	202322	0.7556	0	1	2
FL 3	752619	2.8109	2	3	4
GA 11	2609121	9.7448	9	10	11
ID 1	323440	1.2080	1	1	2
IL 25	5638591	21.0595	21	21	22
IN 13	2700876	10.0875	10	10	11
IA 11	2224771	8.3093	8	8	9
KS 8	1690949	6.3155	6	6	7
KY 11	2289905	8.5525	8	9	10
LA 7	1656388	6.1864	6	6	7
ME 4	742371	2.7727	2	3	4
MD6	1295346	4.8380	4	5	6
MA 14	3366416	12.5732	12	13	14
MI 12	2810173	10.4957	10	10	11
MN 9	2074376	7.7476	7	8	9
MS 8	1797114	6.7120	6	7	8
MO 16	3293335	12.3002	12	12	13
MT 1	366338	1.3682	1	1	2
NE 6	1192214	4.4528	4	4	5
NV 1	80293	0.2999	0	0	1
NH 2	430572	1.6081	1	2	3
NJ 10	2537167	9.4760	9	9	10
NM	316983	1.1839	1	1	2
NY 37	9108934	34.0208	34	34	35
NC 10	2206287	8.2402	8	8	9
ND 2	574403	2.1453	2	2	3
OH 21	4767121	17.8046	17	18	19
OK 5	1657155	6.1893	6	6	7
OR 2	672765	2.5127	2	2	3
PA 32	7665111	28.6283	28	29	30
RI 2	542610	2.0266	2	2	3
SC 7	1515400	5.6598	5	6	7
SD 2	575676	2.1501	2	2	3
TN 10	2184789	8.1599	8	8	9
TX 16	3896542	14.5531	14	15	16
UT 1	371864	1.3889	1	1	2
VT 2	355956	1.3295	1	1	2
VA 10	2061612	7.6999	7	8	9
WA 3	1140134	4.2583	4	4	5
WV 5	1221119	4.5607	4	5	6
WI 11	2332853	8.7129	8	9	10
WY 1	144658	0.5403	0	1	2
USA	91569325	342.0007	319	342	390

The third set with Quota3, which uses a national divisor of 267746, displays Hamilton method 3. In this variation one seat is initially assigned to each state; hence, the constitutional minimum is satisfied for all states at the start. In 1910 there were 48 states; hence, the goal of distributing 390 seats is reduced by 48. The remaining 342 seats are then distributed by Hamilton's method. The result shows several differences from the previous methods, some of which are paradoxical. For example, Arizona has a population of only 180225. The divisor is 267746; yet, Arizona is awarded two seats. First, Arizona is awarded one seat for the constitutional minimum requirement. Arizona's quota is 0.6731. The fraction is large enough to be awarded a seat among the remaining 342 seats distributed by Hamilton's method. A similar thing happens to Delaware and Wyoming. The Census Bureau's decision to apply the Hamilton method 2 is needed to avoid this type of paradox exhibited in Hamilton method 3.

Willoughby's transmission letter alluded to apportionment tables prepared by "assigning an additional Representative whenever the remainder exceeded one-half." Willoughby noted that such tables were prepared for the 1900 apportionment; however, they were not used by Congress. He offered that the Bureau was ready to prepare such tables on request. However, Crumpacker had already received the needed tables from Willcox. These tables presented apportionment based on moiety in a novel way and in a manner that avoided the anomalies of applying the constitutional minimum requirement in the Hamilton method. Willcox displayed apportionments for House size 390 to 440 using a Webster modified divisor method. Willcox simply called his method the "method of major fractions."

Willcox's Table 2 (see Table 4.6, next page) was visionary. He began by assigning one seat to each state thereby satisfying the constitutional minimum requirement at the start. This process distributed 48 seats. He then asked which state would receive the next seat if the House size were increased to 49. He noted that if one divides the population of each state by 1.5, then the most populous state, New York, would obtain a quotient satisfying moiety with a divisor of 6072623; however, all of the other states would have minor fractions and thus not satisfy moiety (Table 4.6, 1.5 column). The next populous state, Pennsylvania, would achieve moiety using a divisor of 5110074; hence, creating a House with 50 members. Thus, a divisor between 6072623 and 5110075 inclusively would yield a House of 49 members by moiety. Willcox referred to these populations as "boundary ratios" for each House size. He used the midpoint of each boundary interval as the "ratio for division."

Willcox's Table 2 (see Table 4.6) shows the results for dividing relevant state populations by 1.5, 2.5, ..., 45.5. He summarized the results in Table 3 (see Table 4.7 following Table 4.6). Willcox's Table 3 is creative, displaying which state gets the next seat when the House size is increased by one.

Table 4.6. Willcox Table 2.

APPORTIONMENT OF REPRESENTATIVES. 37

TABLE 2.—Constitutional population, "excluding Indians not taxed."

	Total.	Divided by—				
		1.5	2.5	3.5	4.5	5.5
United States	91,569,325					
Alabama	2,128,093	1,418,395	855,237	610,883	475,131	388,744
Arizona	130,225					
Arkansas	1,574,449	1,049,632	629,770	449,842	349,877	286,263
California	2,376,561	1,584,374	950,624	679,017	528,124	432,102
Colorado	799,572	532,381	319,428	228,163		
Connecticut	1,114,756	743,170	445,902	318,501	247,723	202,682
Delaware	202,322					
Florida	752,619	501,746	301,047	215,034		
Georgia	2,609,121	1,739,414	1,043,648	745,463	579,805	474,385
Idaho	323,440	215,626				
Illinois	6,638,591	3,759,061	2,255,436	1,611,026	1,253,020	1,025,198
Indiana	2,700,876	1,800,584	1,080,350	771,679	600,194	491,068
Iowa	2,224,771	1,483,180	889,908	635,649	494,393	404,504
Kansas	1,690,949	1,127,299	676,379	483,128	375,766	307,445
Kentucky	2,289,905	1,526,603	915,962	654,258	508,867	416,346
Louisiana	1,656,388	1,104,259	662,555	473,253	258,086	301,181
Maine	742,371	494,914	296,948	212,106		
Maryland	1,295,346	863,564	518,138	370,099	287,855	235,517
Massachusetts	2,805,416	2,203,277	1,348,566	901,833	748,092	612,075
Michigan	2,810,173	1,873,448	1,124,069	802,906	624,482	510,940
Minnesota	2,074,376	1,382,917	829,750	592,679	460,972	377,159
Mississippi	1,797,114	1,198,076	718,845	513,461	399,358	326,748
Missouri	3,293,335	2,195,556	1,317,334	940,952	731,852	598,788
Montana	266,333	244,225				
Nebraska	1,192,214	794,809	476,886	340,632	264,936	216,766
Nevada	80,268					
New Hampshire	430,572	287,048				
New Jersey	2,537,167	1,691,445	1,014,867	724,905	563,815	461,303
New Mexico	316,933	211,322				
New York	9,108,934	6,072,623	3,643,574	2,602,553	2,024,208	1,656,169
North Carolina	2,206,287	1,470,858	882,515	630,368	490,286	401,143
North Dakota	574,703	382,935	229,761			
Ohio	4,767,121	3,178,081	1,906,848	1,362,035	1,059,360	866,749
Oklahoma	1,657,155	1,104,770	662,862	473,472	368,256	301,301
Oregon	672,765	448,510	269,106			
Pennsylvania	7,665,111	5,110,074	3,066,044	2,190,031	1,703,358	1,393,656
Rhode Island	542,610	361,740	217,044			
South Carolina	1,515,400	1,010,267	606,160	432,971	336,755	275,527
South Dakota	575,676	383,784	230,270			
Tennessee	2,184,789	1,456,526	873,915	624,225	485,508	397,234
Texas	3,896,542	2,597,695	1,558,617	1,113,298	865,898	708,462
Utah	371,864	247,909				
Vermont	355,956	237,304				
Virginia	2,061,612	1,374,408	824,644	589,032	458,126	374,838
Washington	1,140,134	760,089	456,053	325,752	253,363	207,297
West Virginia	1,221,119	814,079	488,447	348,891	271,359	222,021
Wisconsin	2,332,853	1,555,235	933,141	666,529	518,412	424,155
Wyoming	144,658					

Table 4.7. Willcox Table 3.

APPORTIONMENT OF REPRESENTATIVES. 89

TABLE 2.—*Constitutional population, "excluding Indians not taxed"*—Continued.

	Divided by—					
	34.5	35.5	36.5	37.5	38.5	39.5
New York	264,018	256,581	249,551	242,897	236,588	230,598
Pennsylvania	222,177	215,918	210,003	204,402		

	Divided by—					
	40.5	41.5	42.5	43.5	44.5	45.5
New York	224,912	219,485	214,321	209,393	204,688	200,189

**TABLE 3.—*Boundary ratios and ratios for division, down to 200,000, with total number of Representatives in House, State gaining one, and number falling to that State according to each ratio for division.*

Boundary ratios arranged in order of size.	Ratios for division midway between boundary ratios.	Total number of Representatives in House.	State gaining one over preceding apportionment.	Total number of Representatives for State gaining one.	Boundary ratios arranged in order of size.	Ratios for division midway between boundary ratios.	Total number of Representatives in House.	State gaining one over preceding apportionment.	Total number of Representatives for State gaining one.
6,072,623					1,555,235				
	5,591,348	49	N. Y.	2		1,540,919	72	Wis.	2
5,110,074					1,526,603				
	4,434,567	50	Pa.	2		1,504,891	73	Ky.	2
3,759,061					1,483,180				
	3,701,317	51	Ill.	2		1,477,019	74	Iowa	2
3,643,574					1,470,858				
	3,410,827	52	N. Y.	3		1,463,692	75	N. C.	2
3,178,081					1,456,526				
	3,122,062	53	Ohio	2		1,440,960	76	Tenn.	2
3,066,044					1,425,395				
	2,834,298	54	Pa.	3		1,413,384	77	Ala.	2
2,602,553					1,401,374				
	2,600,124	55	N. Y.	4		1,397,515	78	N. Y.	7
2,597,695					1,392,656				
	2,426,565	56	Tex.	2		1,388,286	79	Pa.	6
2,255,436					1,382,917				
	2,249,856	57	Ill.	3		1,378,662	80	Minn.	2
2,244,277					1,374,408				
	2,219,916	58	Mass.	2		1,368,221	81	Va.	2
2,195,556					1,362,035				
	2,192,798	59	Mo.	2		1,354,300	82	Ohio	4
2,190,031					1,346,566				
	2,107,119	60	Pa.	4		1,331,950	83	Mass.	3
2,024,208					1,317,334				
	1,965,528	61	N. Y.	5		1,285,177	84	Mo.	3
1,906,848					1,253,020				
	1,890,148	62	Ohio	3		1,233,772	85	Ill.	5
1,873,448					1,214,525				
	1,837,016	63	Mich.	2		1,206,309	86	N. Y.	8
1,800,584					1,198,076				
	1,769,999	64	Ind.	2		1,188,661	87	Miss.	2
1,739,414					1,179,247				
	1,721,386	65	Ga.	2		1,153,273	88	Pa.	7
1,703,358					1,127,299				
	1,697,401	66	Pa.	5		1,125,664	89	Kans.	2
1,691,445					1,124,069				
	1,673,807	67	N. J.	2		1,118,683	90	Mich.	3
1,656,109					1,113,298				
	1,633,596	68	N. Y.	6		1,108,534	91	Tex.	4
1,611,024					1,104,770				
	1,597,699	69	Ill.	4		1,104,514	92	Okla.	2
1,584,374					1,104,258				
	1,571,408	70	Cal.	2		1,092,304	93	La.	2
1,558,517					1,080,350				
	1,556,936	71	Tex.	3		1,075,904	94	Ind.	3

Section 4.2.3   The 61st Congress

With these reports in hand, Representative Crumpacker quickly went to work and on 6 January 1911 submitted an apportionment bill, H.R. 30566.[6] The bill was referred to the Committee on the Census for which Crumpacker was the chairman.

On 13 January Crumpacker, on behalf of the Committee on the Census, reported favorably on behalf of H.R. 30566. He also submitted House Report 1911 in support of the committee's recommendation. House Report 1911 contains the letters and tables from both Willcox and Willoughby.

On 16 January Crumpacker received unanimous consent for two amendments to his proposed bill. One amendment concerned the expected statehoods for Arizona and New Mexico. Based on the population returns from the 1910 census, Willcox apportioned one seat to each state. However, the enabling act for New Mexico statehood specified two representatives upon admission.[7] The amendment specified that Arizona and New Mexico would be allotted one state each upon admission. The other amendment added a new section that would establish a permanent apportionment procedure, similar in spirit to the Vinton act of 1850. The Crumpacker proposal specified that the Secretary of the Interior and Labor, upon receiving the census report, would calculate apportionments using a divisor of the national population divided by 430 with the resulting quotients rounded by moiety. The Secretary would issue certificates notifying Congress and the governor of each state of the results.[8]

Debate on the Crumpacker proposal was limited to one day in the House.[9] It began with the House acting as a Committee of the Whole on the state of the Union. Crumpacker first urged that Congress quickly pass an apportionment bill this session so states will not have to call special sessions of their legislatures to deal with redistricting. He explained that his bill was a natural because it satisfied the two criteria favored by most congressmen. First, no state would lose representation. Second, each state with a major fraction would be awarded an additional seat for that fraction. House size 433 (excluding Arizona and New Mexico) was the smallest House size meeting those two criteria. Accordingly, he summarized his bill as follows. First, start with the ratio 211877. Second, divide the ratio into each state's population. Third, round each state's quotient by moiety to obtain each state's apportionment.

Crumpacker also made some comments contrasting his bill against the main opposition, H.R. 30894, submitted by Philip Campbell (R-KS)[10]. The interesting drama here is that after the Committee on the Census recommended passage of the Crumpacker bill, the Republican caucus met and voted to support the competing H.R. 30894 submitted by Philip Campbell (R-KS). The

---

[6] Congressional Record, 61st Congress, 3rd Session, 13 January 1911: 614.
[7] Statutes at Large, 61st Congress, 2nd Session, Chap. 310, Sec. 5, 20 June 1910: 561.
[8] Ibid, 16 January 1911: 956.
[9] Congressional Record, 61st Congress, 3rd Session, 9 February 1911: 2205-31.
[10] Ibid: 708.

Campbell bill used the Willcox method (excluding Arizona and New Mexico) for House size 391, the current House size.

Crumpacker's main argument against the Campbell bill was that keeping the House size at 391 would result in a loss of seats for 13 states with Missouri losing two seats. Campbell's main argument was that the Crumpacker House size of 433 was too large. Much of the debate revolved around what House size is effective for representing the people and getting the business of the House accomplished.

Voting then began on the three sections of the Crumpacker bill, one section at a time.[11] Section 1 specified a House size of 433 apportioned as displayed in Table 4.4, House size 435 but without Arizona and New Mexico. William Stafford (R-WI) moved to amend by replacing 433 with 391. Charles Thomas (D-NC) moved to amend Stafford's amendment by using House size 437 and Hamilton's method; failed. Then a vote was taken on Stafford's amendment; failed, 125-168. Politte Elvins (R-MO) moved to amend by replacing 433 with 402. This way, Missouri would only lose one seat; failed, 73-201. This ended any further amendments and Section 1 was accepted.

Section 2 specified one seat each for Arizona and New Mexico upon admission. These seats would be in addition to the 433 seats specified in Section 1. The section passed with no comment. Finally, the new Section 3 establishing the permanent apportionment mechanism passed, 159-142.

William Bennet (R-NY) then proposed a 7-section substitute bill that mostly focused on mechanisms for adjusting the apportionment populations by enforcing the Fourteenth Amendment to the U. S. Constitution; failed, 90-154. Earlier the Republican Club of the City of New York adopted a resolution protesting any action on apportionment without attention to enforcing suffrage rights specified in the Fourteenth Amendment.[12]

Crumpacker then requested that the Committee of the Whole rise and report to the House; agreed. A vote was taken to recommit the Campbell bill to the Committee on the Census for recommendation; failed, 133-171. A vote was taken on the Crumpacker bill; passed (no vote count recorded).

The bill was then sent to the Senate for concurrence. The Senate referred the bill to its Committee on the Census. On 3 March, the last full day of the 3rd Session of the 61st Congress, Eugene Hale (R-ME) submitted Senate Report 1280 to accompany H.R. 30566. The report simply stated that the majority of the committee recommended passage without amendment and noted that Robert La Follette (R-WI) dissents.[13] La Follette was chair of the Senate

---

[11] Ibid: 2223-31.
[12] Ibid: 2229-30.
[13] 61st Congress, 3rd Session Senate Report 1280, 3 March 1911. Accessed from https://books.google.com/books?id=22I3AQAAIAAJ&pg=PR8-IA139&lpg=PR8-IA139&dq=61st+congress+3rd+session+Senate+Report+1280&source=bl&ots=ClqW5ODRD8&sig=Ujbl6iSrK5EduM

Committee on the Census, but he was ill, so he asked Hale to report the bill as a courtesy on behalf of the House. Hale asked for unanimous consent for the bill to be presented to the Senate. Porter McCumber (R-ND) objected. He said he was a member of the committee and that the committee had never considered the bill. Hale responded that La Follette had tried to call a meeting, but there was no quorum; hence, he asked the clerk of the committee to poll the members. Elihu Root (R-NY) supported McCumber's objection asserting the bill was too important to simply rubber stamp. Shortly afterwards the Senate dropped the issue, took up other matters, and adjourned the 3rd Session of the 61st Congress the next morning.[14]

Section 4.2.4   The 62nd Congress

Congress reconvened as the 62nd Congress. The first session met from 4 April 1911 to 22 August 1911. The Democrats were quite successful during the national elections and took control of the House. The party make-up of the House was 230 Democrats, 180 Republicans, 1 Socialist, and 1 Independent.[15]

The chairmanship of the Committee on the Census passed from Edgar Crumpacker (R-IN) to William Houston (D-TN). Being a new Congress, the legislative process began all over again. Houston wasted no time getting the ball rolling on apportionment. On 10 April he introduced H.R. 2983, a basic apportionment bill.[16] Crumpacker reintroduced his old bill as H.R. 27. On 25 April Houston reported from the Committee on the Census with a favorable recommendation for H.R. 2983. The bill was accompanied by House Report 12,[17] read twice, and referred to the Committee of the Whole on the state of the Union. This set up the machinery for debate and resolution in the House.

The machinery was well-oiled and set in motion two days later on 27 April. Houston began by explaining the basics of the bill. The bill specified a House size of 433 with one additional seat each for Arizona and New Mexico when they became states. In these respects, the Crumpacker and Houston bills were identical. Before providing further details, Houston explained the difficulty of the apportionment procedure.[18]

> In the apportionment of the Representatives among the different States the committee was confronted with the question as to the manner and method of arriving at a just and fair apportionment, and upon this point I must say that there is a very great diversity of opinion. It is rather remarkable that after more than 100 years in the history of our Government there has been no uniform method agreed upon, either by Congress or by the officials of the Census Bureau or by

---

KRjWsERpoOFHI&hl=en&sa=X&ei=piNqVZvLLJCmyASS9YLoDA&ved=0CDMQ6AEwAw#v=onepage&q=61st%20cong
ress%203rd%20session%20Senate%20Report%201280&f=false.

[14] Congressional Record, 61st Congress, 3rd Session, 3 March 1911: 4149-53.

[15] http://en.wikipedia.org/wiki/62nd_United_States_Congress.

[16] Congressional Record, 62nd Congress, 1st Session, 10 April 1911: 147.

[17] United States serial set, Issue 6078. Available from https://books.google.com/books?id=Q-
s3AQAAIAAJ&pg=PP1#v=onepage&q&f=false.

[18] Congressional Record, 62nd Congress, 1st Session, 10 April 1911: 669.

statisticians in general. However, the method adopted in the formation of this bill, to my mind, adopts the simplest and the plainest and as fair a method as is available under the present conditions. The method adopted was the method known as the method of majority fractions. By that method a ratio is ascertained, and that ratio is divided among the population of the different States, each State getting a Member in the House for each full ratio and one for each majority fraction thereof.

With respect to House size, method of apportionment, new states, and the nature of congressional districts, the Crumpacker and Houston bills were identical. The methodology of apportionment was a modified divisor method. House size 433 was chosen because it was the smallest House size for which no state lost a representative when rounding by major fractions. The ratio of representation, 211877, was divided into each state's population to obtain the state's quotient. The quotient was then rounded by moiety to obtain a state's apportionment and achieve the House size of 433. The proposal had several appealing advantages. The method and results were fairly easy to understand: rounding by moiety was included and no state lost a representative.

The details behind the method are a bit convoluted. The ratio of representation was proposed by Walter Willcox in his Table 1.[19] It is the midway divisor needed to construct a House of 435 members using the method of major fractions. The 435 House size anticipated the admission of Arizona and New Mexico. Dropping Arizona and New Mexico from the calculations, but retaining the divisor 211877, achieves the House size 433 and is consistent with an additional seat for Arizona and New Mexico upon obtaining statehood. Further, the "same result is reached by the ratio the committee has determined upon, 211877, and the number 433, as would be reached by this method suggested by the chief statistician, Dr. Hill." Hill's method, which he called the method of alternate ratios, was described in a letter from Hill to the Committee on the Census and included in House Report 12 (details in Section 4.2.5).

Although Crumpacker, a Republican, and Houston, a Democrat, agreed on the basics, there were dissenters. Most opposition to the recommended Houston bill came from congressmen who opposed increasing the size of the House. Most congressmen opposed to increasing the House favored keeping the current House size, 391. Some objections were raised by strict state's rights advocates that Congress should not be regulating congressional districts. And, others did not like the section in the Crumpacker bill that defaulted apportionment to the Secretary of the Interior and Labor who would apply the Webster basic divisor method in which the ratio of representation was the national population divided by 430.

Edward Saunders (D-VA) captured the essence of the disagreement. He said, "there are two propositions on which we are all agreed. We do not favor too large a House. All agree to that. We do not favor too large constituencies. On that too, we are agreed." The problem is that House size and constituency are inversely related to each other. Several congressmen simply

---

[19] House Report 12: 31 or House Report 1911: 33.

focused on the one that advanced their agenda. Saunders further offered the view that an increase in House size is simply "a necessary and inevitable incident of our growth."[20]

After the debate time was up, it was time to vote. John Nelson (R-WI) moved to amend the bill by replacing the House size of 433 with 391; failed, 91-134.[21] J. Swagar Sherley (D-KY) moved to amend the bill by including Crumpacker's Secretary of the Interior and Labor provision; failed, 80-111.[22] Caleb Powers (R-KY) moved to amend the bill by requiring that congressional districts be of equal size within 20000; failed, 66-107. A similar motion within 50000 also failed, 69-104.[23] Another similar motion within 75000 also failed. Crumpacker made a final effort to rescue his section regarding the Secretary of the Interior and Labor by moving to amend the bill to insert the corresponding section from his bill and then send the bill back to the Committee on the Census for further evaluation; failed, 99-177.[24] After these attempts at amending the bill all failed, a vote was taken on the bill; passed.[25]

The Senate received the bill H.R. 2983 on 28 April 1911 and sent it to the Committee on the Census.[26] On 6 July Benjamin Shively (D-IN) on behalf of the committee reported the bill to the Senate and submitted the accompanying Senate Report No. 94. Finally, on 2 August the Senate resumed consideration of H.R. 2983. James O'Gorman (D-NY) gave a summary of the bill and of its rationale. He then strongly urged support and passage of the bill. The subsequent debate focused mainly on the House size vs. constituency and on gerrymandering. The next day the Senate ended debate and proceeded with amendments.

The first amendment, offered by Theodore Burton (R-OH), involved Section 4:

> That in case of an increase in the number of Representatives in any State under this apportionment such additional Representative or Representatives shall be elected by the State at large and the other Representatives by the districts now prescribed by law until such State shall be redistricted by the legislature thereof in the manner herein prescribes; and if there be no change in the number of Representatives from a State, the Representatives thereof shall be elected from the districts now prescribed by law until such State shall be redistricted as herein prescribed.

The Burton amendment was to strike out the phrase "by the legislature thereof in the manner therein prescribed" and replace by "in a manner provided by the laws thereof and in accordance with the rules enumerated in Section 3 of the act."[27] The rationale for the

---

[20] Congressional Record, 62nd Congress, 1st Session, 27 April 1911: 687.

[21] Ibid: 290-692.

[22] Ibid: 692-5.

[23] Ibid: 695-700.

[24] Ibid: 704-5.

[25] Ibid: 705.

[26] Ibid: 722.

[27] Ibid: 3555.

amendment was a spillover from the House debate on the same issue: who has the authority to set congressional districts? Earlier only state legislatures had authority for redistricting. However, several states recently enabled the capacity for initiatives and referendums enacted by the people. Some states allowed for independent redistricting commissions. This issue was intimately tied to the gerrymandering issue since independent commissions were created to overcome gerrymandering. The Burton amendment passed 39-28 with 23 not voting.

Then Burton proposed another amendment to add a short Section 5.

> That candidates for Representative or Representatives to be elected at large in any State shall be nominated in the same manner as candidates for governor, unless otherwise provided by the laws of such State.

This amendment passed without debate. Subsequently Elihu Root (R-NY) moved to amend Section 1 to specify a House size of 391; failed 23-46 with 21 not voting.[28] Then Asle Gronna (R-ND), on behalf of his absent colleague, Porter McCumber (R-ND), offered an amendment to specify a House size of 405 members; failed, 22-47 with 21 not voting. Finally, the amendments were engrossed into the bill, read a third time, and routinely passed (no roll call vote was ordered).[29] The next day, on 4 August, the House agreed to the Senate amendments.[30] President William Howard Taft approved the bill on 8 August 1911.

Section 4.2.5   Joseph Adna Hill

The Census Bureau has been fortunate to have a line of skilled, honest, professional, and dedicated statisticians including Charles Seaton, Francis Walker, Walter Willcox, and now Joseph Adna Hill (Figure 4.2[31]). Hill graduated from Harvard in 1885 and subsequently earned his Ph.D. from the University of Halle (Germany) in 1892. In 1898 he began work for the Census Bureau, becoming chief statistician in 1909.[32]

Figure 4.2. Joseph Hill.

House Report 12 contained a letter from Hill to Representative Houston, chair of the House Committee on the Census.[33] The considerate letter is reprinted in Figure 4.3. Note that Hill submitted the letter not as an official of the Census Bureau but as a private citizen. Hill was perhaps aware that new ideas on apportionment never got adopted on presentation, but usually had to sink in for at least a decade before given serious consideration.

---

[28] Ibid: 3557.

[29] Ibid: 3558.

[30] Ibid: 3604.

[31] https://sites.google.com/site/huntingtonhillmethod/home.

[32] https://www.census.gov/history/www/census_then_now/notable_alumni/joseph_adna_hill.html.

[33] 62nd Congress, 1st Session, House Report 12, 25 April 1911: 48

DEPARTMENT OF COMMERCE AND LABOR,
BUREAU OF THE CENSUS,
Washington, April 25, 1911.

Hon. WILLIAM C. HOUSTON,
Chairman House Committee on Census,
Washington, D. C.

DEAR SIR: I have the honor to transmit herewith a statement explaining a method of apportionment which I have worked out as the result of a very careful consideration of the problem. Appended to the statement is a table showing the application of the method to the apportionment of each number of Representatives from 390 up to 440, inclusive.

While I am not submitting this document as the representative of the Census Bureau, but rather as a private citizen and on my individual responsibility, I am at liberty to say that the Director of the Census, Dr. E. Dana Durand, has carefully examined this method of apportionment and gives it his approval. I wish also to acknowledge my indebtedness to him for valuable criticisms and suggestions.

For convenience I have designated the method as the method of alternate ratios, although the appropriateness of the term will only be apparent to one who reads the explanatory statement herewith submitted.

It was not my expectation that this method would be applied in the pending apportionment. The method is new and not so readily explained or understood as the methods which have been used in the past. It is a matter of interest, however, that as applied to the apportionment of 433 Representatives among the existing States this method gives exactly the same result as is obtained by the method of major fractions adopted by your committee and applied in the bill they have introduced. Usually, however, the results of these two methods differ more or less.

It only remains for me to express my thanks for your courtesy in appending this statement to your report and thereby giving me an opportunity to bring this method to the attention of Congress and the American public so far as they may be interested in the subject.

Respectfully,

JOSEPH A. HILL,
Chief Statistician of the Division of Revision and Results,
Bureau of the Census.

Figure 4.3. Letter from Joseph Hill to Representative Houston reprinted in House Report 12.

Hill's letter was a cover for his report on apportionment. Hill knew that the Hamilton method suffered deal-breaking paradoxes. But the general basis for the quota method (if a state has 10% of the population, then it should have 10% of the seats in the House) seemed so natural and obvious that it should be the basis for apportionment. Hill concluded that the fault did not lie with the quota method, but in the mechanism for awarding additional seats. He concluded that paradoxes were produced by awarding additional seats to states with the largest decimal fractions. Hill agreed with Webster's interpretation of the Constitution that representatives should be apportioned according to the population *as near as may be*. But what does *as near as may be* mean?

Recall that Hamilton's method first decides on the House size, h. Then h is divided into the national population to obtain the standard divisor, D. Divide D into each state's population to obtain each state's quota. Allot to each state its lower quota. This distributes most, but not all, of h. Suppose the sum of the lower quotas is k. Accordingly, there are h-k seats yet to be distributed. Hamilton distributes the remaining h-k seats to those h-k states with the highest quota fractions. Hill concluded that merely ranking states by the quota decimal fraction was insufficient because it did not consider the size of the state. He believed that a priority list needed to be established for the decimal quotas that would rank fractions in reference to the size of the state.

Hill made his case by presenting a numerical example. Suppose that one more seat is to be awarded between two states, State A and State B. The population for A is given by $p_A = 160000$ and $p_B = 480000$. Further suppose that the ratio of representation is given by $D = 100000$. Then the quotas are $Q_A = 1.6$ and $Q_B = 4.8$. So, Hamilton awards the additional seat to B. This results in the apportionment $a_A = 1$ and $a_B = 5$, since, with only one additional seat to distribute, A's quota would be rounded down and B's quota rounded up.

As a result of the Hamilton apportionment, Hill noted that $p_B/p_A = 3$ but $a_B/a_A = 5$. If we reversed the award of the additional seat so that $a_A = 2$ and $a_B = 4$, then $p_B/p_A = 3$ and $a_B/a_A = 4/2 = 2$. This yields a result that is better from the viewpoint of *as near as may be*.

Hill then expands the example further to obtain a general rule for how to award additional seats after each state has been awarded its lower quota. For the two states A and B, we consider two apportionment alternates.

> Alternate 1: $a_A = 1$ and $a_B = 5$.
> Alternate 2: $a_A = 2$ and $a_B = 4$.

Let $c_A = p_A/a_A$ and $c_B = p_B/a_B$ denote the resulting constituencies of A and B, respectively. For alternate 1 we have $c_A = 160000/1 = 160000$ and $c_B = 480000/5 = 96000$. For alternate 2 we have $c_A = 160000/2 = 80000$ and $c_B = 480000/4 = 120000$. Hill then interprets *as near as may be* as the ratio of the two constituencies should be as close to 1 as possible.

To compare the two alternates fairly, one must compose the two ratios so that they are both larger than one or both smaller than one. For ease of comparison, we compare ratios that are larger than one. Accordingly, we obtain:

> Alternate 1: $c_A/c_B = 160000/96000 = 5/3 = 1.666...$.
> Alternate 2: $c_B/c_A = 120000/80000 = 3/2 = 1.5$.

Since alternate 2 provides a ratio of constituencies that is closer to 1, then alternate 2 apportions better *as near as may be*.

A general rule may be formulated as follows. Suppose one more additional seat is to be distributed between states A and B. Let n_A and n_B be the lower quotas of the two states. The two alternates are

Alternate 1: $a_A = n_A$ and $a_B = n_B + 1$.
Alternate 2: $a_A = n_A + 1$ and $a_B = n_B$.

Let $c_A^{(1)}$ and $c_B^{(1)}$ be the constituencies for A and B under alternate 1; similarly, for alternate 2. Then, State A has priority over State B for an additional seat if and only if

$$\frac{c_B^{(2)}}{c_A^{(2)}} < \frac{c_A^{(1)}}{c_B^{(1)}}$$

$$\Leftrightarrow \quad \frac{\left(\frac{p_B}{n_B}\right)}{\left(\frac{p_A}{n_A+1}\right)} < \frac{\left(\frac{p_A}{n_A}\right)}{\left(\frac{p_B}{n_B+1}\right)}$$

$$\Leftrightarrow \quad \frac{p_B^2}{n_B(n_B+1)} < \frac{p_A^2}{n_A(n_A+1)}$$

$$\Leftrightarrow \quad \frac{p_B}{\sqrt{n_B(n_B+1)}} < \frac{p_A}{\sqrt{n_A(n_A+1)}}$$

Hence, additional seats should not be distributed according to the priority of greatest quota decimal fractions as in Hamilton's method, but according to the priority list obtained by dividing a state's population by $\sqrt{n(n+1)}$ where n represents the state's lower quota.

Nerds everywhere will recognize $\sqrt{n(n+1)}$ as the geometric mean of the two options n and $n+1$. Hence, the Hill priority list is obtained by dividing each state's population by the geometric mean of its round down, round up options.

The Hill criterion represents an alternate quota method. Begin the same way as the Hamilton method up to and including awarding each state its lower quota. Then distribute the needed remaining seats according to the Hill priority numbers in descending order. As Representative Houston noted in his presentation in Congress, Hill's method agreed with his proposed apportionment bill, H.R. 2983, for House size 433. A spreadsheet analysis comparing the methods of Hamilton, Hill, and Webster is given in Table 4.8 and verifies Houston's claim.

A nuance to note is that the national divisor is the integer part of the national population divided by the House size. This introduces a bit of round-off error leading to the quota column adding up to 433.0004 instead of 433. Applying the rule of three would avoid this annoyance. Since Congress used the national divisor rather than the rule of three, so do we.

Table 4.8 (next page) displays the results of apportionment based on the 1910 census using the methods in play in Congress. The State/Seats/Population columns lists the 46 states with their current number (1910) of representatives and the population. Arizona and New Mexico are treated as territories, not yet as states, but their upcoming statehood is anticipated.

The Quota $D=210328$/Moiety/Hamilton columns show apportionment based on the quota which uses the national divisor. The Moiety column displays the result of apportionment using the hybrid method of apportionment based on the 1900 census. First, the national divisor is computed: D = (national population)/433 = 91072177/433 = 210328. The national divisor is divided into each state's population to obtain its quota. Each quota is rounded by moiety to produce a House of 436. A straightforward application of Hamilton's method to distribute 433 seats would deny seats to Idaho (quota 1.5265), Maine (3.5038), and Texas (18.5260).

The Quotient $d=211877$/Webster columns show the results of applying a divisor of 211877, a modified divisor that produces a House of 433 using Webster's method of rounding. Note that Hamilton's method uses the quotas obtained by applying the national divisor, 210328. Webster's method uses the modified divisor 211877 to achieve the 433 House size. This feature bothered Hill in that, for example, Texas and Ohio have a moiety using the national divisor but not using the modified divisor. Hence, the effect of the directive *round by moiety* depends on what apportionment method one uses, even for producing the same House size (here, 433). In comparing Hamilton vs. Webster for House size 433, under Webster Idaho and Maine each gain a seat at the expense of Mississippi and Ohio.

The case for Ohio was particularly troubling since Ohio's quota of 433 seats is 22.6652; but Ohio's quotient using the Webster modified divisor of 211877 is 22.4995. To create a House of 433 members using Webster's method, any divisor between 211873 and 211882, inclusive, works. The divisor 211877 is simply a midpoint of the allowable Webster modified divisors. If 211873 is chosen, then annoyingly Ohio's quotient is 22.4999.

The Quota/Lower/Hill Priority/Seats column set displays the calculations needed to apportion by Hill's method. Begin like in Hamilton's method by calculating each state's quota based on the national divisor. Allotting each state its lower quota distributes 412 seats; hence, there are 21 more seats to be distributed to bring the House size to 433. Hill then creates a priority list by dividing each state's population by the square root of the product of the lower quota and the upper quota. The 21 states with the highest priority numbers are then awarded an additional seat. Note that the methods of Hill and Webster agree while Hill differs from Hamilton for four states—Idaho and Maine gain a seat at the expense of Mississippi and Ohio.

Hill's method of alternate ratios was the last of four variations of the quota method presented to Congress in American history. They all began the same way: first, determine the size of the House. Second, calculate the national divisor, D, the integer part of the national population, divided by the House size. Third, determine each state's quota by dividing the state population by the national divisor. Fourth, allocate each state its lower quota. This distributes

Table 4.8. A spreadsheet analysis comparing the methods of Hamilton, Hill, and Webster.

State	Seats	Population	Quota $D=210328$	Moiety	Hamilton	Quotient $d=211877$	Webster	Quota	Lower	Hill Priority	Seats
Alabama	9	2138093	10.1655	10	10	10.0912	10	10.1655	10	203859	10
Arkansas	7	1574449	7.4857	7	7	7.4310	7	7.4857	7	210395	7
California	8	2376561	11.2993	11	11	11.2167	11	11.2993	11	206853	11
Colorado	3	798572	3.7968	4	4	3.7690	4	3.7968	3	230528	4
Connecticut	5	1114756	5.3001	5	5	5.2613	5	5.3001	5	203526	5
Delaware	1	202322	0.9619	1	1	0.9549	1	0.9619	0		1
Florida	3	752619	3.5783	4	4	3.5522	4	3.5783	3	217262	4
Georgia	11	2609121	12.4050	12	12	12.3143	12	12.4050	12	208897	12
Idaho	1	323440	1.5378	2	1	1.5265	2	1.5378	1	228707	2
Illinois	25	5638591	26.8086	27	27	26.6126	27	26.8086	26	212815	27
Indiana	13	2700876	12.8413	13	13	12.7474	13	12.8413	12	216243	13
Iowa	11	2224771	10.5776	11	11	10.5003	11	10.5776	10	212124	11
Kansas	8	1690949	8.0396	8	8	7.9808	8	8.0396	8	199280	8
Kentucky	11	2289905	10.8873	11	11	10.8077	11	10.8873	10	218334	11
Louisiana	7	1656388	7.8753	8	8	7.8177	8	7.8753	7	221344	8
Maine	4	742371	3.5296	4	3	3.5038	4	3.5296	3	214304	4
Maryland	6	1295346	6.1587	6	6	6.1137	6	6.1587	6	199876	6
Massachusetts	14	3366416	16.0056	16	16	15.8885	16	16.0056	16	204119	16
Michigan	12	2810173	13.3609	13	13	13.2632	13	13.3609	13	208304	13
Minnesota	9	2074376	9.8626	10	10	9.7905	10	9.8626	9	218658	10
Mississippi	8	1797114	8.5443	9	9	8.4819	8	8.5443	8	211792	8
Missouri	16	3293335	15.6581	16	16	15.5436	16	15.6581	15	212584	16
Montana	1	366338	1.7417	2	2	1.7290	2	1.7417	1	259040	2
Nebraska	6	1192214	5.6684	6	6	5.6269	6	5.6684	5	217668	6
Nevada	1	80293	0.3818	1	1	0.3790	1	0.3818	0		1
New Hampshire	2	430572	2.0471	2	2	2.0322	2	2.0471	2	175780	2
New Jersey	10	2537167	12.0629	12	12	11.9747	12	12.0629	12	203136	12
New York	37	9108934	43.3082	43	43	42.9916	43	43.3082	43	209415	43
North Carolina	10	2206287	10.4897	10	10	10.4131	10	10.4897	10	210361	10
North Dakota	2	574403	2.7310	3	3	2.7110	3	2.7310	2	234499	3
Ohio	21	4767121	22.6652	23	23	22.4995	22	22.6652	22	211924	22
Oklahoma	5	1657155	7.8789	8	8	7.8213	8	7.8789	7	221447	8
Oregon	2	672765	3.1986	3	3	3.1753	3	3.1986	3	194211	3
Pennsylvania	32	7665111	36.4436	36	36	36.1772	36	36.4436	36	210023	36
Rhode Island	2	542610	2.5798	3	3	2.5610	3	2.5798	2	221520	3
South Carolina	7	1515400	7.2049	7	7	7.1523	7	7.2049	7	202504	7
South Dakota	2	575676	2.7370	3	3	2.7170	3	2.7370	2	235019	3
Tennessee	10	2184789	10.3875	10	10	10.3116	10	10.3875	10	208311	10
Texas	16	3896542	18.5260	19	18	18.3906	18	18.5260	18	210701	18
Utah	1	371864	1.7680	2	2	1.7551	2	1.7680	1	262948	2
Vermont	2	355956	1.6924	2	2	1.6800	2	1.6924	1	251699	2
Virginia	10	2061612	9.8019	10	10	9.7302	10	9.8019	9	217313	10
Washington	3	1140134	5.4207	5	5	5.3811	5	5.4207	5	208159	5
West Virginia	5	1221119	5.8058	6	6	5.7633	6	5.8058	5	222945	6
Wisconsin	11	2332853	11.0915	11	11	11.0104	11	11.0915	11	203049	11
Wyoming	1	144658	0.6878	1	1	0.6827	1	0.6878	0		1
USA	391	91072117	433.0004	436	433	429.8348	433	433.0004	409		433

most, but not all, of the *h* seats in the House. Fifth, an additional seat must then be given to some states in order to bring the House size to *h*. The four variations of the quota methods are variants of the fifth step. The four variants of the quota method are:

- Hamilton: largest fractions;
- Lowndes: largest constituencies;
- Seaton: smallest deviation from D using the upper quota;
- Hill: largest alternate ratios.

A spreadsheet displaying the results of the four quota methods for House size 483 is provided in Table 4.9 (next page). The national divisor is int(91072117/483) = 210328. Seaton's priority numbers are calculated by D − (state population)/(upper quota). The blanks in the Hill priority numbers are a result of division by zero. One may consider the priority numbers in this case to be infinity. A slightly cleaner spreadsheet could be made by using the rule of three to compute the quota rather than using the national division since it needs to be rounded to an integer, thus creating the awkward quota sum of 433.0004 due to round-off error.

All four of these quota methods yield different results. In comparison with the Hamilton method, Lowndes affects 8 states—Arizona, Idaho, Maine, and Washington gain at the expense of Illinois, Iowa, Missouri, and Ohio. In comparison with the Hamilton method, Seaton affects 14 states—Georgia, Michigan, New York, North Carolina, Pennsylvania, Tennessee, and Texas gain at the expense of Florida, Montana, North Dakota, Rhode Island, South Dakota, Utah, and Vermont. In comparison with the Hamilton method, Hill affects 4 states—Idaho and Maine gain at the expense of Mississippi and Ohio.

Section 4.2.6   Premonitions

Two items were introduced in Congress with great intensity yet failed to be fully heeded. One item was a mechanism for automatic apportionment. The other was a headlong clash between rural vs. urban interests, needs, and values.

Concerns for an automatic apportionment mechanism were first introduced by Representative Samuel Vinton in the apportionment act based on the 1850 census. Vinton was the key driver behind the act, also known also as the Vinton act. He was particularly concerned about having a mechanism in place in case Congress failed to pass an apportionment act based on a new census. He felt in that event Congress lost its constitutional power to operate and feared the demise of the government. The Vinton plan would have apportionment carried out by the Secretary of the Interior using Hamilton's quota method with House size 233.

During the 61st and 62nd Congresses, Edgar Crumpacker (R-IN) introduced legislation that had a similar purpose in that it contained a provision for a permanent apportionment mechanism. Apportionment would be automatically calculated by the Secretary of the Interior and Labor. The Census Bureau was housed within the Department of the Interior and Labor. As soon as the census was completed, the Secretary would compute the apportionment using Webster's method with a divisor of the national population divided by 430.

Table 4.9. Comparison of the Quota methods of Hamilton, Lowndes, Seaton, and Hill for a House of 433.

State	Seats	Population	Quota D=210328	Seats Hamilton	Constituency	Seats Lowndes	Priority Seaton	Seats Seaton	Priority Hill	Seats Hill
Alabama	9	2138093	10.1655	10	213809	10	15956	10	203859	10
Arkansas	7	1574449	7.4857	7	224921	8	13522	7	210395	7
California	8	2376561	11.2993	11	216051	11	12281	11	206853	11
Colorado	3	798572	3.7968	4	266191	4	10685	4	230528	4
Connecticut	5	1114756	5.3001	5	222951	5	24535	5	203526	5
Delaware	1	202322	0.9619	1	202322	1	8006	1		1
Florida	3	752619	3.5783	4	250873	4	22173	3	217262	4
Georgia	11	2609121	12.4050	12	217427	12	9626	13	208897	12
Idaho	1	323440	1.5378	1	323440	2	48608	1	228707	2
Illinois	25	5638591	26.8086	27	216869	26	1491	27	212815	27
Indiana	13	2700876	12.8413	13	225073	13	2568	13	216243	13
Iowa	11	2224771	10.5776	11	222477	10	8076	11	212124	11
Kansas	8	1690949	8.0396	8	211369	8	22445	8	199280	8
Kentucky	11	2289905	10.8873	11	228991	11	2155	11	218334	11
Louisiana	7	1656388	7.8753	8	236627	8	3280	8	221344	8
Maine	4	742371	3.5296	3	247457	4	24735	3	214304	4
Maryland	6	1295346	6.1587	6	215891	6	25279	6	199876	6
Massachusetts	14	3366416	16.0056	16	210401	16	12304	16	204119	16
Michigan	12	2810173	13.3609	13	216167	13	9601	14	208304	13
Minnesota	9	2074376	9.8626	10	230486	10	2890	10	218658	10
Mississippi	8	1797114	8.5443	9	224639	9	10649	9	211792	8
Missouri	16	3293335	15.6581	16	219556	15	4495	16	212584	16
Montana	1	366338	1.7417	2	366338	2	27159	1	259040	2
Nebraska	6	1192214	5.6684	6	238443	6	11626	6	217668	6
Nevada	1	80293	0.3818	1	80293	1	130035	1		1
New Hampshire	2	430572	2.0471	2	215286	2	66804	2	175780	2
New Jersey	10	2537167	12.0629	12	211431	12	15161	12	203136	12
New York	37	9108934	43.3082	43	211836	43	3307	44	209415	43
North Carolina	10	2206287	10.4897	10	220629	10	9756	11	210361	10
North Dakota	2	574403	2.7310	3	287202	3	18860	2	234499	3
Ohio	21	4767121	22.6652	23	216687	22	3062	23	211924	22
Oklahoma	5	1657155	7.8789	8	236736	8	3184	8	221447	8
Oregon	2	672765	3.1986	3	224255	3	42137	3	194211	3
Pennsylvania	32	7665111	36.4436	36	212920	36	3163	37	210023	36
Rhode Island	2	542610	2.5798	3	271305	3	29458	2	221520	3
South Carolina	7	1515400	7.2049	7	216486	7	20903	7	202504	7
South Dakota	2	575676	2.7370	3	287838	3	18436	2	235019	3
Tennessee	10	2184789	10.3875	10	218479	10	11711	11	208311	10
Texas	16	3896542	18.5260	18	216475	18	5247	19	210701	18
Utah	1	371864	1.7680	2	371864	2	24396	1	262948	2
Vermont	2	355956	1.6924	2	355956	2	32350	1	251699	2
Virginia	10	2061612	9.8019	10	229068	10	4167	10	217313	10
Washington	3	1140134	5.4207	5	228027	6	20306	5	208159	5
West Virginia	5	1221119	5.8058	6	244224	6	6808	6	222945	6
Wisconsin	11	2332853	11.0915	11	212078	11	15924	11	203049	11
Wyoming	1	144658	0.6878	1	144658	1	65670	1		1
USA	391	91072117	433.0004	433		433		433		433

Crumpacker's motivation was different than Vinton's. Crumpacker did not worry about the government coming to a halt, but wanted to take the politics and tediousness of apportionment out of Congress. He felt that Congress had now settled the problem of apportionment mechanism and House size. The House had basically reached its limit for efficient and effective operation; hence, House size around 430 would serve the needs of the nation. Further, Congress wanted to retain the method of major fractions as a fundamental rule of fairness.

However, concerns about what would happen if Congress failed to pass an apportionment act based on a new census basically went unheeded and even vigorously opposed. First, most congressmen thought it was such a constitutional duty to apportion based on the census that they could not conceive of Congress failing to do its constitutional job; hence, the Crumpacker provision was unnecessary. Second, some Congressmen vigorously opposed the idea of apportionment on automatic calculation done by the Secretary of the Interior and Labor. Why, this would result in Congress handing over important constitutionally mandated authority to an outside entity; hence, the Crumpacker provision was unwarranted and even unconstitutional!

Concerns about conflicts between rural and urban values were passionately presented by Thetus Sims (D-TN).[34]

> Now, my friends, the population of the great cities is increasing out of all proportion to the increase of population in the country districts; and if you are going to limit the number of Representatives, the day will come when the great cities will have the balance of power in this body, as they have in other countries. Small legislative bodies are more easily controlled wrongfully, either by passion or pelf. It is easier to corruptly control a small body than a larger one.
>
> But you know and I know, my friends, that the foreign element of our population is increasing in greater ratio in the cities than in the country and that the negroes are flocking to the cities. If I had the power to redistrict the States, I would put all the big districts in the cities and the little ones in the country among the agricultural classes, the landowning classes, the classes that have made our institutions what they are that will have to maintain them if they are to be maintained. Where do revolutions arise? My friends, where does the only Socialist in this House hail from? Does he come from a country district? I mean no reflection on him. He is a man of brains, ability, and patriotism. I know of some people who tremble at the increase of socialism, which is confined largely to the cities.
>
> Let us not reduce the representation of the agricultural sections of this country. If we fix the number in the next House at 391, it will mean to take representation from those States that I think, judged by everything that goes to make good legislators, will average higher than those of the great cities.

---

[34] Congressional Record, 62nd Congress, 1st Session, 27 April 1911: 686.

Sims's views did not receive much in the way of further expansion during the debates based on the 1910 census. But the sentiment was clear. Gerrymandering was a hot-button issue during the debates. But most congressmen represented rural interests. Gerrymandering was simply a way to isolate urban masses into large districts. Rural interests could then be expanded into more numerous smaller districts. Still today the effects of gerrymandering trump the efforts made to balance the issues of fairness and power involved in the history of congressional apportionment.

John Langley (R-KY) added an important regional element into the urban vs. rural conflict.

> I am frank to say, gentlemen, that so far as I am personally concerned, one of the reasons why I am going to vote for the increase of membership in the House is that if the membership were left at 391, the State of Kentucky would lose one Representative in this body and one vote in the electoral college, and I do not wish to see that happen. And another reason is that the State of Virginia would lose one, and other Southern States would lose; and I am not in favor of any legislation, apportionment or otherwise, that will reduce the representation of the great South in the Congress of the United States or in the electoral college. [Prolonged applause.]
>
> I want to say further that, barring the question of politics and the very undesirable views that they have on certain questions, I believe that no harm, and perhaps considerable good, would come to the country if we had here a few more of the broad-minded, big-hearted men like those which the South sends to the Congress of the United States. [Applause.]

The two items, the mechanism of congressional apportionment and the clash of urban vs. rural values, gave a sneak preview of what would come to a colossal head within a decade.

Section 4.3:   Reapportionment Based on the 1920 Census

Section 4.3.1   Background

The story of reapportionment based on the 1920 census can be stated in one simple sentence: it did not happen. It is the only decade where reapportionment based on the census failed. It was not due to lack of effort—in the House there were 42 bills introduced during the decade to apportion based on the 1920 census, but none passed.[1] The immediate question is, why? The answer is not simple and involves a complex tapestry incorporating at least six fabrics that illustrate issues and forces of the time: new states, World War I, women's suffrage, prohibition, the census, and the head-on clash between rural vs. urban values.

New States

As anticipated, during the decade of 1910, Arizona and New Mexico were admitted as new states. On 6 January 1912 President William Howard Taft signed the proclamation admitting New Mexico as the 47th state in the Union.[2] On 14 February 1912 President Taft signed the proclamation admitting Arizona as the 48th state.[3]

With the admissions of New Mexico and Arizona, the continental (in the sense of contiguous) United States of America was completed with 48 states. The House size was brought to 435: 433 seats apportioned to the 46 states based on the 1910 census plus one representative each for New Mexico and Arizona based on their admission to statehood. The House has remained at 435 from each census-based reapportionment since then up to the present time. This includes reapportionment based on the census 1930-2010.

World War I

World War I broke out in Europe during the summer of 1914.[4] Initially most Americans wanted nothing to do with Europe's problems. President Wilson proclaimed American neutrality. Toward the end of 1915, under pressure from hawks such as Teddy Roosevelt, Wilson announced a preparedness program, a crash endeavor to increase American army and navy capabilities.

The election of 1916 was one of the closest in American history. Wilson supporters advanced the campaign slogan, "He kept us out of war." His promise not to send American troops to Europe assisted him in carrying 10 of the 12 states that had already adopted women's suffrage. Without the women's vote, Wilson would not have been reelected.[5] [6]

---

[1] Emanuel Celler, Congressional Apportionment: Past, Present, and Future, *Law and Contemporary Problems*, 14(2) Legislative Reapportionment (Spring, 1952):271. Accessed from http://www.jstor.org/stable/1190232.
[2] https://www.presidency.ucsb.edu/documents/proclamation-1175-admitting-new-mexico-the-union.
[3] http://clickamericana.com/eras/1910s/arizona-statehood-is-achieved-1912.
[4] http://www.worldwar1.com/tlplot.htm.
[5] Eric Foner, *Give Me Liberty! An American History*, W. W. Norton & Co., New York, second edition, 2009: 688.
[6] https://library.whitman.edu/blog/presidential-election-1916/.

World events changed, however, and on 2 April 1917 Wilson asked Congress for a declaration of war against Germany. The request passed Congress by a huge margin. Shortly after, a Lenin-led communist revolution overthrew the czar in Russia. American troops arrived in large numbers in the spring and summer of 1918 as the United States devoted substantial manpower and material resources to the war. American support turned the tide of the stalemate of the war. The war ended 11 November 1918. Although 116000 Americans died during the war, this was only 1.4% of the total military combat deaths suffered by all participants. In addition, 204000 Americans returned wounded from the war.[7]

Women's Suffrage

Several states enacted full women's suffrage well before the Nineteenth Amendment to the Constitution. Others enacted partial suffrage, allowing women to vote in school district elections. In 1913 Illinois allowed women to vote in municipal and presidential elections but not elections for state-wide offices. Finally, on 18 August 1920 the Nineteenth Amendment was ratified.[8]

> The right of citizens of the United States to vote shall not be denied or abridged by the United States or by any State on account of sex.
> Congress shall have power to enforce this article by appropriate legislation.

Prohibition

For an understanding of the role of this topic in American history, we ardently recommend *Prohibition*, a film by Ken Burns and Lynn Novick.[9] Prohibition played a gridlock role for reapportionment based on the 1920 census since the dries (those favoring retention of Prohibition) in Congress would not yield on any measure that would provide the wets (those favoring repealing Prohibition) with more power. The Eighteenth Amendment to the U. S. Constitution that established Prohibition as the law of the land was ratified on 16 January 1919 and remained in force throughout the 1920s. It was not repealed until 5 December 1933.

The Census

Of course, reapportionment is based on the decennial census. However, the census of 1920 showed a major shift in the nature of the U. S. population. For the first time in American history a majority of the population was associated with urban areas (Table 4.10, next page).[10] Up until this time America was perceived primarily as a rural country with rural values. Things were about to happen. On this point we recommend the charming 6-minute *Backstory: Urbanization and the 1920 Census.*[11] This population shift would lead to major conflicts in public policy featuring a headlong clash of rural vs. urban values.

---

[7] http://www.worldwar1.com/sfnum.htm.
[8] https://www.womenshistory.org/resources/timeline/womans-suffrage-timeline.
[9] http://www.pbs.org/kenburns/prohibition/watch-video/#id=2082675582.
[10] U. S. Census Bureau, Abstract of the Fourteenth Census of the United States 1920. Downloaded from https://www.census.gov/prod/www/decennial.html.
[11] http://backstoryradio.org/shows/the-meaning-of-numbers-a-history-of-the-u-s-census/.

Table 4.10. 1920 Census comparing urban vs. rural populations for 1910 and 1920.

54   POPULATION—URBAN AND RURAL.

No. 33.—DISTRIBUTION OF POPULATION AS URBAN AND RURAL, WITH PER CENT URBAN, 1900, 1910, AND 1920: By States and Geographic Divisions.[1]

[Source: Reports of the Bureau of the Census, Department of Commerce.]

State.	1900 Urban.	1900 Rural.	1910 Urban.	1910 Rural.	1920 Urban.	1920 Rural.	Per cent urban. 1900	1910	1920
Alabama	216,714	1,611,983	370,431	1,767,662	509,317	1,838,857	11.9	17.3	21.7
Arizona	19,495	103,436	63,260	141,094	117,527	216,635	15.9	31.0	35.2
Arkansas	111,733	1,199,831	202,681	1,371,768	290,497	1,461,707	8.5	12.9	16.6
California	777,699	707,354	1,469,739	907,810	2,331,729	1,095,132	52.4	61.8	68.0
Colorado	260,651	279,049	404,840	394,184	453,259	486,370	48.3	50.7	48.2
Connecticut	543,755	364,665	731,797	382,959	936,339	444,292	59.9	65.6	67.8
Delaware	85,717	99,018	97,085	105,237	120,767	102,236	46.4	48.0	54.2
District of Columbia	278,718	....	331,069	....	437,571	....	100.0	100.0	100.0
Florida	107,031	421,511	219,080	533,539	355,825	612,645	20.3	29.1	36.7
Georgia	346,382	1,869,949	538,650	2,070,471	727,859	2,167,973	15.6	20.6	25.1
Idaho	10,003	151,769	69,898	255,696	119,037	312,829	6.2	21.5	27.6
Illinois	2,616,368	2,205,182	3,476,929	2,161,662	4,403,153	2,082,127	54.3	61.7	67.9
Indiana	862,689	1,653,773	1,143,835	1,557,041	1,482,855	1,447,535	34.3	42.4	50.6
Iowa	572,386	1,659,467	680,054	1,544,717	875,495	1,528,526	25.6	30.6	36.4
Kansas	330,903	1,139,592	493,790	1,197,159	617,964	1,151,293	22.5	29.2	34.9
Kentucky	467,668	1,679,506	555,442	1,734,463	633,543	1,783,087	21.8	24.3	26.2
Louisiana	366,288	1,015,337	496,516	1,159,872	628,163	1,170,346	26.5	30.0	34.9
Maine	232,827	461,639	262,248	480,123	299,569	468,445	33.5	35.3	39.0
Maryland	591,206	596,838	658,192	637,154	869,422	580,239	49.8	50.8	60.0
Massachusetts	2,567,098	238,248	3,125,367	241,049	3,650,248	202,108	91.5	92.8	94.8
Michigan	952,323	1,468,659	1,327,044	1,483,129	2,241,560	1,426,852	39.3	47.2	61.1
Minnesota	598,100	1,153,294	850,294	1,225,414	1,051,593	1,335,532	34.1	41.0	44.1
Mississippi	120,035	1,431,235	207,311	1,589,803	240,121	1,550,497	7.7	11.5	13.4
Missouri	1,128,104	1,978,561	1,398,817	1,894,518	1,586,903	1,817,152	36.3	42.5	46.6
Montana	84,554	158,775	133,420	242,633	172,011	376,878	34.7	35.5	31.3
Nebraska	252,702	813,598	310,852	881,362	405,306	891,066	22.7	26.1	31.3
Nevada	7,195	35,140	13,367	68,508	15,254	62,153	17.0	16.3	19.7
New Hampshire	226,260	185,319	255,099	175,473	279,761	163,322	55.0	59.2	63.1
New Jersey	1,329,162	554,507	1,907,210	629,957	2,474,936	680,964	70.6	75.2	78.4
New Mexico	27,381	167,929	46,571	280,730	64,960	295,390	14.0	14.2	18.0
New York	5,298,111	1,970,783	7,185,494	1,928,120	8,589,844	1,795,383	72.9	78.8	82.7
North Carolina	186,790	1,707,020	318,474	1,887,813	490,370	2,068,753	9.9	14.4	19.2
North Dakota	23,413	295,733	63,236	513,820	88,239	558,633	7.3	11.0	13.6
Ohio	1,998,382	2,159,183	2,665,143	2,101,978	3,677,136	2,082,258	48.1	55.9	63.8
Oklahoma[2]	58,417	731,974	320,155	1,337,000	539,480	1,488,803	7.4	19.3	26.6
Oregon	133,180	280,356	307,060	365,705	391,019	392,370	32.2	45.6	49.9
Pennsylvania	3,448,610	2,853,505	4,630,669	3,034,442	5,607,815	3,112,202	54.7	60.4	64.3
Rhode Island	407,647	20,909	524,654	17,956	589,180	15,217	95.1	96.7	97.5
South Carolina	171,256	1,169,060	224,832	1,290,568	293,987	1,389,737	12.8	14.8	17.5
South Dakota	40,936	360,634	76,673	507,215	101,872	534,675	10.2	13.1	16.0
Tennessee	326,639	1,693,977	441,045	1,743,744	611,226	1,726,659	16.2	20.2	26.1
Texas	520,759	2,527,951	938,104	2,958,438	1,512,689	3,150,539	17.1	24.1	32.4
Utah	105,427	171,322	172,934	200,417	215,584	233,812	38.1	46.3	48.0
Vermont	75,831	267,810	98,917	257,039	109,976	242,452	22.1	27.8	31.2
Virginia	340,067	1,514,117	476,529	1,585,083	673,984	1,635,203	18.3	23.1	29.2
Washington	211,477	305,626	605,530	536,460	748,735	607,886	40.8	53.0	55.2
West Virginia	125,465	833,335	228,242	992,877	369,007	1,094,694	13.1	18.7	25.2
Wisconsin	790,213	1,278,829	1,004,320	1,329,540	1,244,558	1,387,499	38.2	43.0	47.3
Wyoming	26,657	65,874	43,221	102,744	57,348	137,054	28.8	29.6	29.5
Total	30,380,433	45,614,142	42,166,120	49,806,146	54,304,603	51,406,017	40.0	45.8	51.4
Geographic divisions.[3]									
New England	4,053,427	1,538,590	4,998,082	1,554,599	5,865,073	1,535,836	72.5	76.3	79.2
Middle Atlantic	10,075,883	5,378,795	13,723,373	5,592,519	16,672,595	5,588,549	65.2	71.0	74.9
East North Central	7,219,975	8,755,600	9,617,271	8,633,350	13,049,272	8,426,271	45.2	52.7	60.8
West North Central	2,946,544	7,400,879	3,873,716	7,764,205	4,727,372	7,816,877	28.5	33.3	37.7
South Atlantic	2,232,632	6,210,848	3,092,153	9,102,742	4,338,792	9,651,480	21.4	25.4	31.0
East South Central	1,131,056	6,416,701	1,574,229	6,835,672	1,994,207	6,899,100	15.0	18.7	22.4
West South Central	1,057,197	5,475,093	1,957,456	6,827,078	2,970,829	7,271,395	16.2	22.3	29.0
Mountain	541,363	1,133,294	947,511	1,686,006	1,214,980	2,121,121	32.3	36.0	36.4
Pacific	1,122,356	1,294,336	2,382,329	1,809,975	3,471,483	2,095,388	46.4	56.8	62.4

[1] Urban population comprises that residing in cities and other incorporated places of 2,500 inhabitants or more, and in towns of 2,500 or more in Massachusetts, New Hampshire, and Rhode Island.
[2] Includes population of Indian Territory for 1900.
[3] For States included in each division, see note 5, p. 37.

Rural vs. Urban Values

The decade of 1920 is known today as the "roaring 20s."[12] However, the decade is far more complex than flappers and speakeasies. The previously mentioned *Prohibition* film by Ken Burns and Lynn Novick presents an engaging documentary of fabrics woven into the tapestry of the decade. We also recommend the comprehensive study by Charles Eagles of the urban-rural conflict in apportionment during the decade.[13] The urban-rural conflict is not a simple, total explanation of the gridlock that prevented a reapportionment based on the census of 1920. The urban-rural conflict is a wide collage of items that change from location to location and year to year. Many different fabrics are woven into those various collages; however, two fabrics are consistent: white supremacy and Protestant fundamentalism.

The most prominent of the white supremacy groups in national politics was the Ku Klux Klan. The Klan is mostly remembered today as a domestic terrorist group that operated primarily in the South. However, the Klan was a force throughout much of the nation. From 1920 to 1925 some three to six million Americans were members.[14] The Klan had a notable presence in the rural Midwest. During the first half of 1920 Indiana had the strongest Klan presence of any state. In 1923 David Curtis Stephenson rose to prominence, not only as the Grand Dragon for Indiana, but the overseer for Klan activities in 23 northern states. Under his leadership, Klan membership exceeded 300000 in Indiana, about 30% of native-born whites. Stephenson is noted for bragging, "I am the law in Indiana." In 1923, his newspaper, *The Fiery Cross*, had a circulation of around half a million. In the 1924 elections in Indiana, Klan favorites won all but one of Indiana's 13 seats in the U. S. House of Representatives.[15] [16]

The Klan saw itself as the guardian of white Protestant values and a protector for white Christian women. The white robe was not only a color of white supremacy but the color of Protestant virtue. The Klan was virulently anti-Catholic, anti-Jewish, and anti-immigrant. Accordingly, the Klan freely aligned itself with Christian groups that championed Prohibition; for example, the Women's Christian Temperance Union.[17] The various marriages between white supremacy and Christian fundamentalist groups formed a powerful political alliance that not only spurred Prohibition but was a major roadblock responsible for the non-apportionment based on the 1920 census. An evolution of this alliance still exists today in the so-called "Tea Party," a name perhaps even more apt for the Prohibition era.

---

[12] http://www.1920-30.com/.

[13] Charles W. Eagles, *Democracy Delayed: Congressional Reapportionment and Urban-Rural Conflict in the 1920s*, The University of Georgia Press, Athens, Georgia, 1990.

[14] Rory McVeigh, Power Devaluation, the Ku Klux Klan, and the Democratic National Convention of 1924, *Sociological Forum*, 16(1) March 2001: 1-30.

[15] http://www.smithsonianmag.com/history/murder-wasnt-very-pretty-the-rise-and-fall-of-dc-stephenson-18935042/?no-ist; http://www.thepress.purdue.edu/titles/format/9781557530462; https://historymuseumsb.org/the-golden-era-of-indiana/.

[16] Richard K. Tucker, *The Dragon and the Cross: The Rise and Fall of the Ku Klux Klan in Middle America*, Archon Books, Hamden, CT, 1 July 1991.

[17]https://www.alcoholproblemsandsolutions.org/the-kkk-and-the-wctu-close-partners-in-prohibition/; https://leben.us/kkk-wctu-partners-prohibition/.

Section 4.3.2 The 66th U. S. Congress.

Congressional action on apportionment based on the 1920 census began in the 3rd session of the 66th Congress which met from 6 December 1920 to 3 March 1921. The Republicans gained control of Congress after the 1918 election. The House consisted of 192 Democrats, 1 Prohibition, 1 Farmer-Labor, and 240 Republicans.[18] On 26 September 1919 President Woodrow Wilson suffered an incapacitating stroke; hence, presidential leadership came to a halt for the remainder of his term. On 2 November Republican Warren Harding was elected President in a landslide. However, Harding was way over his head in this position and provided no guidance. Congress took over. On the first day of the 3rd session of the 66th Congress, several new bills were introduced in the House. Among them Isaac Siegel (R-NY) introduced H.R. 14498, a bill to re-apportion the House based on the 1920 census.[19] The bill was referred to the Committee on the Census of which Siegel was chair. Three other apportionment bills were quickly introduced and referred to the Committee on the Census.[20]

On 14 December Siegel, as chair of the Committee on the Census, asked unanimous consent that a House document be printed; granted. The document contained apportionment tables prepared by the Census Bureau for House size 435 to 483 using the method of major fractions.[21] The Siegel bill specified House size 483, the smallest House size for which no state lost a representative. The current House size was 435. The tables were to be used as reference for the upcoming apportionment debate.

On 31 December 1920 Oscar Bland (R-IN) made some insightful comments about the upcoming apportionment debate during the debate on an agriculture bill.[22] He noted that the Siegel bill would bring the size of the House to 483 members, an increase of almost 50 members from the current size of 435. The debate would mostly center about House size: 483 vs. 435. Bland noted that there were good arguments for both. The issue boiled down to efficiency vs. constituency. The larger the House, the more cumbersome, unwieldy, costly, and inefficient it becomes. However, a larger House size means reduced constituency resulting in a decreased workload for the individual congressman. A greater constituency naturally results in an increased workload. The workings of the House and the workload of a congressman are inversely related to each other. The debate must then be about seeking the right balance between House size and constituency.

A week later on 8 January 1921 Siegel, as chair of the Committee on the Census, referred the bill H.R. 14498 for the apportionment of Representatives in Congress amongst the several States under the Fourteenth Census, reported it without amendment, and accompanied by House Report No. 1173. The report and bill were then referred to the Committee of the Whole House on the state of the Union.[23]

---

[18] https://en.wikipedia.org/wiki/66th_United_States_Congress.
[19] Congressional Record, 66th Congress, 3rd Session, 6 December 1920: 10.
[20] Ibid: 305, 447, 544.
[21] Ibid: 332.
[22] Ibid: 859-61.
[23] Ibid: 1181.

On 18 January 1920 debate began in earnest for two days. Siegel began by summarizing H.R. 14498. It would set the House size at 483. The seats were distributed by using a divisor of 218986 and applying the method of major fractions. The key components in the thinking underlying the bill are that no state would lose representation and that each state with a major fraction would be awarded a seat for that fraction. He argued that objections to the House becoming unwieldy and inefficient can be overcome by some changes in the House rules.[24]

Louis Fairfield (R-IN), a signer of the minority report issued by the Committee on the Census, argued in favor of H R. 15021 submitted by Henry Barbour (R-CA), a bill similar to the Siegel bill but retaining the House size at 435 using the ratio of representation 242415. Fairfield argued that the relative influence of any state is the same regardless of House size.[25] Hence, the argument is about the effects of House size 483 vs. 435 and a corresponding constituency of 218986 vs. 242415.

James Aswell (D-LA) expressed sensitivity to the workload of an individual congressman: "Of course, each Member represents the Nation, but he serves best when he is in touch with his constituents individually. The larger the number of constituents, of course, the more difficult the task." Aswell noted that a compromise could be reached with one of the alternate proposals specifying a House of 460 members with a ratio of representation of 218986. At House size 460 only Maine and Missouri would lose a seat. Under the Barbour bill keeping the House size at 435, 11 states would lose a seat and Missouri would lose 2 seats.[26] Although Aswell noted the compromise, he ardently supported the Siegel bill.

> Mr. Chairman, an argument against this bill is an argument to reduce the representation of 11 agricultural States; it is an argument for the pernicious lobbyist here, against the will of the people; it is an argument for special privilege against the average citizen; it is an argument for the rich and mighty against the poor and the weak; it is an argument for the reactionary against the progressive; it is an argument for autocracy and centralization against democracy and popular government. Let each Member decide for himself and let the country now know on which side he stands. If we still believe in a republican form of government in popular government, this bill will be enacted into law. [Applause]

Samuel Brinson (D-NC) stated that the only significant role Congress plays in apportionment is to determine the House size. He subsequently argued vigorously against the Siegel bill because the House "is already too unwieldy." Because of the current House size, the important work of the House is done in committees. An increase in the size of the House would not only make things worse, but would be too costly. He stated, "the financial condition of the country is calling for curtailment and all practical economies." Further, he implored,[27]

---

[24] Ibid: 1627.
[25] Ibid: 1628.
[26] Ibid: 1628-30.
[27] Ibid 1630-1.

If there is need of enlarged membership, is that need so urgent that this burden should be put upon the country, now in the midst of financial depression, when the business of the country and citizens generally are feeling the effects of the tremendous loss sustained by the farmers of the country?

Carlos Bee (D-TX) countered by focusing on constituency rather than the effects of House size.[28] He argued that "especially since the war, the Government has become a living, breathing, moving force in the life of every man and woman in this country." He particularly noted, "The granting of suffrage to women has brought into governmental activity and governmental interest thousands and thousands of women who want to be informed, who want their Congressman's advice; they want their Congressman's information upon a great many subjects." He decried leaving this chore to an increased clerical staff. But his main concern was for the rural community.

I say to you in all solemnity that by defeating this bill you are taking a measurable control of the Government away from the rural districts and throwing it into the congested districts, and doing it unfairly.

Paul Johnson (D-MS) lamented the use of the timing of the census figures. The census was taken in January 1920 (ironically at the urging of the Department of Agriculture). Thousands had left rural areas for the cities for the war effort, but now, after the census, they are returning home. Accordingly, Johnson felt this would erroneously skew the population figures to favor the urban interests.[29]

For the last two years there have been special trains carrying thousands of Negroes and a great many white people to the northern cities, and since this financial condition has come about in the country hundreds and thousands of those same people are trying to return to the South.

Carlos Bee then used the remaining time allotted to him to decry that a lesser House size will deprive farmers of their power in government, "unless you increase this membership you are going to take away the strength and the power and the control of the Government from the rural districts of this country and center it in the congested districts."[30]

Clarence McLeod (R-MI) spoke about the increased workload for a congressman. The important concern was "that the ex-service man's needs are constantly growing and will continue to grow in years to come and, I believe, that added Representatives in Congress is the only way the above-stated needs of these men can be properly taken care of." He emphasized that the various soldier bureaus were not equipped to deal with the unexpected workload of

---

[28] Ibid 1633-4.
[29] Ibid: 1633.
[30] Ibid: 1634.

caring for returning wounded veterans: "increased Representatives is the one present remedy to care for these men, until Congress can put through appropriate hospitals."[31]

Oscar Bland (R-IN) picked up the theme of the census figures introduced earlier by Paul Johnson of Mississippi. He claimed that "errors in the census ... would probably change the representation in as many as six states." He argued that the war drained men from the rural areas to the cities "like a magnet." But these men are in the process of returning to their farms. Hence, "the great industrial centers will, in my judgment, receive undue representation in Congress after the tide sets back to the farm."[32] Accordingly, Bland was opposed to increasing the size of the House because, he felt, the additional representatives would go to urban areas. The next day Bland moved to strike out the enacting clause of the bill.

An interesting point is that both Bland and Bee held the same reference point of view but came to the opposite conclusion on apportionment. Bland wanted to keep the House size at 435 because the new seats would go to urban areas. Bee wanted to increase the House size to 483 so that the rural states would not lose representatives.

Then, just before voting was to begin, Siegel introduced an unexpected fly in the ointment. He insisted on presenting a letter that he had just that morning received from Professor Edward Huntington asserting that the apportionment computations may be erroneous.[33]

> Harvard University,
> The Harvard Engineering School,
> *Cambridge, Mass., January 17, 1921.*

Hon. ISAAC SIEGEL,
>   *Chairman   Committee on the Census,*
>   *House of Representatives, Washington, D. C.*

DEAR SIR: I thank you for your letter of January 14 in reply to mine of January 8, and am glad that you took the matter up with Dr. Hill. It was indeed through his request that the need of a strictly mathematical solution of this problem was first called to my attention a few weeks ago.

At the time I wrote to you I had not yet had opportunity to lay my theory before Dr. Hill, so that I am not surprised that he advised you that Prof. Willcox's method (the method of major fractions) was deemed the fairest up to the present time.

Within the last few days, however, I have finished the formal exposition of my method and its application to the 1920 census, and only yesterday sent a copy to Dr. Hill.

Prof. Persons, Prof. Holcombe, and other statistical experts in the university who have examined my plan have pronounced it the only scientific method, and have

---

[31] Ibid: 1634.
[32] Ibid: 1678.
[33] Ibid: 1678-9.

given me permission to state so. I have, therefore, every reason to hope that Dr. Hill also will indorse my plan as soon as he has had time to examine it.

I shall be in Washington on Friday of this week, attending a statistical conference of the National Research Council, and if your committee or any members of it would be willing at this late date to let me lay my plan before you, I should gladly meet any appointment you wish to make for Friday afternoon, January 21, or for Saturday, January 22.

I am preparing some simple charts and tables by which, without going into any mathematical technicalities, I believe I can make the reasonableness of my plan entirely evident.

The importance of the problem is increased by the possible adoption of 435 as the total, for the Willcox tables for 435 are incorrect (according to my view) in the case of no less than three pairs of States.

1920	New Mexico	New York	Rhode Island	North Carolina	Vermont	Virginia
Willcox method	1	43	2	11	1	10
Improved method	2	42	3	10	2	9

I can be reached by telegram at 27 Everett Street, Cambridge, Mass., up to Thursday noon, or by letter at the Cosmos Club, Washington, on Friday.

Thanking you again for your courteous attention to this matter, I am

Sincerely, yours,   EDWARD V. HUNTINGTON.

Presenting the letter to Congress merely produced confusion. Some thought that perhaps the census figures were being questioned. Others thought that the subject should be sent back to committee for more study. Siegel and Barbour assured the House that the census figures were the correct population figures. Accordingly, the members of the House demanded votes rather than opening another squabble about apportionment methodology.

Voting started with the Bland amendment to delete the enactment portion of the bill; failed, 92-197. This vote made it clear that the House wanted to act on apportionment. Henry Barbour (R-CA) moved to amend by replacing the House size 483 with 435. Burton Sweet (R-IA) moved to use 460. John Jones (D-TX) moved to use 307. The Jones motion failed decisively, 27-203. The Sweet motion failed, 55-180. The Barbour amendment passed, 198-77.[34] Attempts to alter language in some other sections of the bill quickly failed.[35] The House was on a roll and wanted to complete their part in enacting this legislation. Siegel moved to report the amended bill to the whole House; agreed.

The House, now acting as the full House and not just a committee, passed the Barbour amendment: yeas 269, nays 76, present 3, not voting 82. It was decisive! A vote (untallied) was taken on the bill; passed.[36] For reference, a spreadsheet analysis is presented in Table 4.11 (page 218) for House sizes 435 and 483 using the method of major fractions. The

[34] Ibid: 1679-80.
[35] Ibid: 1688-1693.
[36] Ibid: 1694.

apportionment populations are taken from House Report No. 1173.[37] In Table 4.11 the State/Seats/Population column set lists the 48 states with their current number of seats in the House and their 1920 census-based apportionment populations (resident population minus Indians not taxed).

The *h*=435/Seats column set in Table 411 presents the results for House size 435 using the Willcox method of major fractions. They show a dramatic shift in representation affecting 19. Eight states gain in representation: California (3), Connecticut, Michigan (2), New Jersey, North Carolina, Ohio (2), Texas, and Washington. Eleven states lose in representation: Indiana, Iowa, Kansas, Kentucky, Louisiana, Maine, Mississippi, Missouri (2), Nebraska, Rhode Island, and Vermont. For comparison, the *h*=483/Seats column set presents the results for House size 483 using the same method of major fractions.

By applying the rural vs. urban data from the Census Bureau (see Table 4.10), one begins to see the shift in representation from rural to urban states. Although rudimentary, a simple application of a 50% cutoff line shows that among the states that lose representation, 10 seats come from rural states and two from urban states (Indiana and Rhode Island). Among the eight states which gain seats, 6 are urban states and 2 are rural (North Carolina and Texas). The urban states gain 10 out of the 12 seats.

The bill was sent to the Senate for concurrence. The Senate referred the bill to its Committee on the Census.[38] And there it died. There would be no apportionment bill based on the 1920 census passed by the 66th Congress. The process would need to begin anew in the next Congress.

Two other items affecting apportionment were placed on the table in the House. On 9 December 1920 Porter Dale (R-VT) introduced House Joint Resolution 399 advocating a constitutional amendment that would set the minimum number of representatives for any state as two rather than one.[39] On 22 January 1921 William Hill (R-NY) introduced House Joint Resolution 455 advocating a constitutional amendment that would exclude aliens from the apportionment populations.[40] Both resolutions were referred to the Committee on the Judiciary. Neither resolution made it out of committee.

---

[37] 66th Congress, 3rd Session, House Report No. 1173, 8 January 1921: 6; accessed from https://play.google.com/books/reader?id=CctGAQAAIAAJ&printsec=frontcover&output=reader&hl=en&pg=GBS.PA69.

[38] Ibid: 1697.

[39] Ibid: 146.

[40] Ibid: 1913.

Table 4.11. Spreadsheet analysis for House size 435 and 483 using the method of major fractions based on the 1920 census. The divisor for House size 435 is 242415; for House size 483, 218986.

State	Seats	Population	h=435	Seats	h=483	Seats
Alabama	10	2348174	9.6866	10	10.7229	11
Arizona	1	309495	1.2767	1	1.4133	1
Arkansas	7	1752204	7.2281	7	8.0014	8
California	11	3426031	14.1329	14	15.6450	16
Colorado	4	939161	3.8742	4	4.2887	4
Connecticut	5	1380631	5.6953	6	6.3047	6
Delaware	1	223003	0.9199	1	1.0183	1
Florida	4	968470	3.9951	4	4.4225	4
Georgia	12	2895832	11.9458	12	13.2238	13
Idaho	2	430442	1.7756	2	1.9656	2
Illinois	27	6485280	26.7528	27	29.6150	30
Indiana	13	2930390	12.0883	12	13.3816	13
Iowa	11	2404021	9.9170	10	10.9780	11
Kansas	8	1769257	7.2985	7	8.0793	8
Kentucky	11	2416630	9.9690	10	11.0355	11
Louisiana	8	1798509	7.4191	7	8.2129	8
Maine	4	768014	3.1682	3	3.5071	4
Maryland	6	1449661	5.9801	6	6.6199	7
Massachusetts	16	3852356	15.8916	16	17.5918	18
Michigan	13	3668412	15.1328	15	16.7518	17
Minnesota	10	2385656	9.8412	10	10.8941	11
Mississippi	8	1790618	7.3866	7	8.1769	8
Missouri	16	3404055	14.0423	14	15.5446	16
Montana	2	541511	2.2338	2	2.4728	2
Nebraska	6	1296372	5.3477	5	5.9199	6
Nevada	1	75820	0.3128	1	0.3462	1
New Hampshire	2	443083	1.8278	2	2.0233	2
New Jersey	12	3155900	13.0186	13	14.4114	14
New Mexico	1	353428	1.4579	1	1.6139	2
New York	43	10380589	42.8216	43	47.4030	47
North Carolina	10	2559123	10.5568	11	11.6862	12
North Dakota	3	643953	2.6564	3	2.9406	3
Ohio	22	5759394	23.7584	24	26.3003	26
Oklahoma	8	2028283	8.3670	8	9.2622	9
Oregon	3	783389	3.2316	3	3.5773	4
Pennsylvania	36	8720017	35.9714	36	39.8200	40
Rhode Island	3	604397	2.4932	2	2.7600	3
South Carolina	7	1683724	6.9456	7	7.6887	8
South Dakota	3	631239	2.6040	3	2.8826	3
Tennessee	10	2337885	9.6441	10	10.6760	11
Texas	18	4663228	19.2365	19	21.2946	21
Utah	2	448388	1.8497	2	2.0476	2
Vermont	2	352428	1.4538	1	1.6094	2
Virginia	10	2309187	9.5258	10	10.5449	11
Washington	5	1354596	5.5879	6	6.1858	6
West Virginia	6	1463701	6.0380	6	6.6840	7
Wisconsin	11	2631305	10.8545	11	12.0159	12
Wyoming	1	193487	0.7982	1	0.8836	1
USA	435	105210729	434.0108	435	480.4450	483

Section 4.3.3   The 67th U. S. Congress.

The first session of the 67th Congress met from 11 April to 23 November 1921. Six apportionment bills were introduced in the House and referred to the Committee on the Census.[41] Isaac Siegel (R-NY) was successful in his re-election bid and retained chairmanship of the committee. On 29 July Siegel, on behalf of the committee, reported H.R. 7882 without amendment.[42] Siegel authored the bill and introduced it a week earlier.[43] The bill was accompanied by House Report No. 312.[44] The bill with report was referred to the Committee of the whole House on the state of the Union.

Earlier, on 21 June 1921 Wallace White (R-ME) testified in hearings before a subcommittee of the Committee on the Census. He summarized that the debate is a contest on finding a balance between House size vs. constituency.[45]

> It seems to me there are two principal considerations which may properly influence this committee and the House in this matter. If the efficiency of the House as a parliamentary body is of first importance, then we must concede that the House may be of such size that it will become less orderly and that its effectiveness as a deliberative, legislative body will be impaired. One who believes that a Member's first duty is the consideration of measures upon the floor of the House is justified in refusing to cast his vote at this time to add further to its Members. Indeed, he might well justify a vote to reduce even the present membership. But if we give heed to the changes which have taken place about us, if we consider the demands now made upon the time, the energy, and the thought of a Representative outside of and beyond the consideration of legislative proposals, we must conclude that every Member is now working to the limit of his capacity and that to take a single Representative from any State is a wrong to that State and to its citizens.

Debate began on 14 October and fully lived up to White's analysis.[46] Siegel began by explaining the details of apportionment bill H.R. 7882. It set the House size at 460 and distributed the seats by adopting the "ratio of 228882 for each Representative." As the report claimed, it was not necessary to discuss the method because the method of major fractions and the "Huntington, or Harvard method, agree with each other when the number of the House is fixed at 460."[47]

---

[41] Congressional Record, 67th Congress, 1st Session: 90-2, 2357, 2468, 4199.

[42] Ibid: 4470.

[43] Ibid: 4199.

[44] House Report No. 312 is available by download from https://babel.hathitrust.org/cgi/pt?id=uc1.b3994244&view=1up&seq=185. Accessed 13 August 2019.

[45] Apportionment of Representatives, Hearings before a Subcommittee of the Committee on the Census, House of Representatives, 67th Congress, 1st Session, 27-29 June 1921: 5; downloaded from https://play.google.com/books/reader?id=7Ioqu4bYu8YC&printsec=frontcover&output=reader&hl=en&pg=GBS.PA1.

[46] Congressional Record, 67th Congress, 1st Session: 6307-48.

[47] House Report No. 312: 2.

At House size 460 each state with a major fraction is given an additional seat for that fraction. In addition, no state loses a seat except Maine and Missouri. The choice of House size 460 was a compromise for Siegel. His bill from the previous Congress using 483 was defeated by amending the House size to 435. House size 460 was a half-way point where competing methods of apportionment agreed. Siegel noted that the committee was split evenly between 460 and 435 (no increase). Two members who favored 435 signed the majority report so that the bill would be referred to the whole House where debate and resolution could take place. The debate exposed a variety of viewpoints:

- The House is too unwieldy and should be decreased in size;
- The House has reached its efficiency limit and should remain at its current size, 435;
- The House should increase to reflect the increase in population;
- No apportionment based on the 1920 census should take place.

Many arguments about 460 vs. 435 were virtual repeats between 483 vs. 435 in the previous Congress. Some of those arguments became refined. Siegel referred to an increased workload caused by the war.[48]

> We find in the recent war 4,764,670 men were called into the service of the country, and each congressional district on the average gave 11,000 men.
> Now, the minority report calls attention to the fact that we can obtain additional secretaries in order to attend in the wants of these men. … I say to you frankly that the soldier boys, the marines, and those who served in the Navy in this late war are entitled to have their individual cases handled by the Members of the House individually and not by additional secretaries. When they were called out into the service, they were called out by a selective draft law passed by us. Now, when they come back to us, as they are coming back to us and will continue to come back to us for at least another several years, they are entitled to receive the personal attention of the individual Members of the house and not the attention of secretaries.

Louis Fairfield (R-IN) and Eugene Black (D-TX) argued strongly to keep the House the same at 435 citing increased expenses and inefficiencies that go along with an increased size. William Bourke Cockran (D-NY) made the astute observation that no matter what was done, "It is impossible to keep this House as it is … . Either the membership of the House must be increased or each constituency must be enlarged. And to enlarge each constituency is to change very materially the character of the House." Accordingly, many viewpoints focused on the advantages or disadvantages of a larger or smaller House size or constituency.

For example, Theodore Burton (R-OH) spoke for retaining the current House.[49] He argued that an increased House came with increased rules and more limited debate time, leading to

---

[48] Congressional Record, 67th Congress, 1st Session: 6308-9.
[49] Ibid: 6326-7.

diminished opportunity and prestige of an individual member. He also argued that a greater House size leads to a decrease in national vision.

> One point which should not be overlooked is that the larger the House the more a Member becomes a mere agent of a locality; his vision is not so broad; his spirit of loyalty to the whole country is diminished; his efforts for a pork barrel are materially increased rather than his interest in legislation which would be of general benefit.

Further, he countered Siegel's argument for the need for lessening the burden of increased constituency caused by returning servicemen.

> We owe to them undying gratitude, but will the difference between 11,000 and 10,300 in each district materially increase the efforts of Congressmen in aiding this class of their constituents. What is needed more than this personal touch is the passage of helpful legislation for their good, which shall be general in its nature, which will provide proper organization of the activities for the ex-soldier.

John Cable (R-OH) supported no increase in House size, "This administration was elected on a platform of economy." In this regard he asked whether it was

> consistent for this House to vote itself an increase of 25 new Members and during the same session of Congress by refusing appropriations cause to be stricken from the rolls of the executive Civil Service Commission in the District of Columbia over 1,000 employees and from this same roll for the balance of the United States over 35,000 employees? Is it consistent to cut down appropriations of the Navy and cause a reduction in the enlisted men of more than 26,000 and by that same method cause a reduction of almost 100,000 of enlisted men in the Army, many of whom may now be numbered among those 5,000,000 of unemployed throughout the United States?

Cable further argued that Congress needs to practice what it preached. In addition, he argued, the country does not need an increase in legislative proposals that an increase of 25 congressmen would generate.

> The records show that an average of at least 20,000 bills have been introduced into the House each year for the last 14 sessions; that an average of almost 2,000 have been reported out, with many more bills considered and killed in the committees; that an average of more than 700 of these bills introduced have become laws.

Cable closed his address with the plea, "When will this decennial increase in the number of Representatives cease? No more auspicious time exists than the present."[50]

---

[50] Ibid: 6332.

Rufus Hardy (D-TX) supported increasing the House size and refuted arguments about the increase in cost that an increased House size would bring. First, he argued that the House represented the people. Since the population increased, so should the House. He further argued that saving money by not increasing the House was petty. If Congress was serious about saving money, "shut off the big things." For example, one less battleship would save $40000000, let alone the $2000000 annual operating costs. He summarized his position with an engaging adage, "We save at the spigot and lose at the bunghole."[51]

Thomas Blanton (D-TX) argued for a smaller House size.[52] He already had introduced a bill that would reduce the size to 304. He then challenged the supporters of the Siegel bill increasing the House size to 460 because agricultural districts need more representation. Referring to the additional 25 seats provided by the Siegel bill, Blanton argued:

> The agricultural districts do not get them under this bill. Boston gets its extra Representative, New York City gets its two, Pittsburgh and Philadelphia get their two, Cincinnati and Cleveland get their three, Detroit gets its three, Chicago gets its one, San Francisco gets its four, and yet gentlemen talk about agricultural districts. The big cities gobble up the new Members, and it will be the big cities in Texas that will gobble up all new Members.

John Rankin (D-MS) passionately introduced the idea that no apportionment should take place based on the 1920 census.

> Mr. Chairman, I presume it is violating no rules of the Census Committee, of which I am a member, to tell you that I was opposed to reporting any bill at all providing for the reapportionment of the membership of this House under the census of 1920. I was opposed to it because of the fact that the census was taken at a time when we were just emerging from the World War and when so many thousands of people had left the farms and the small towns temporarily and gone to the large cities of the North and East, that a reapportionment under that census would necessarily take from Mississippi and other agricultural states their just representation and place it to the credit of the congested centers.
>
> If the census could be taken today, since our boys have returned from the service and those who were engaged in the various manufacturing industries and war activities have gone back to their homes, I dare say that an apportionment under such a census would justify little or no shifting of representation with the House remaining at its present membership.

Cyrenus Cole (R-IA) was a staunch conservative Republican who believed in rural values. He was a first term representative and gave his first floor speech on apportionment. His short, eloquent address received two rounds of applause. His first main point was that the census was inaccurate. He concurred with Rankin's assessment that the wave of farmers who left for

---

[51] Ibid: 6334.
[52] Ibid: 6330

the military or for wartime industry in the cities did not return en masse until the after the 1920 census was taken. Hence, he argued in favor of increasing the House size to 460 so that the agricultural states would not lose seats.[53]

> I need not say to you that the representation of the so-called agricultural States is vital to the Nation. A home on the farm stands for something more than a tenement in a city. From the time when the poet's embattled farmers fired the shot heard around the world the toilers on the land have been a large part of the safety and security of American institutions.
>
> To transfer more of the power in this House from the farms to the cities is so serious a thing, so fraught with meaning, if not mischief, that it should not be undertaken on the basis of a census taken under the conditions that existed in January, 1920. For one, I think it would be better if no reapportionment were made on that showing, but this bill, while it adds some Members to the cities, at least does not deprive the great agricultural States of any part of their representation.

After the allotted four hours of debate was completed, action on the bill was to take place section by section. After section 1 was read, Henry Barbour (R-CA) moved to amend by changing 460 to 435.

Debate on amendments was limited. However, William Vaille (R-CO) emphasized the factor of immigration to argue against the Barbour amendment.[54] He offered that the proportional make-up in a House of 435 would be very different from the current make-up because of "districts of largely foreign make-up and the decreased proportion which will accrue to districts of more distinctly American population." He further admonished, "the conclusion will be unavoidable that those of you who vote for a membership of 435 in the next House, by voting for the pending amendment, will be voting for an increase in the proportional weight of these alien elements." Vaille noted that in a House of 435 members eight states would lose in representatives which would not lose in a House of 460. In their behalf he argued,

> in the first place, these eight States have attracted a larger percentage of agricultural immigrants, who have anchored themselves to the soil, reared their families, and become identified with the communities in which they live, while in the large cities of the East the immigrants have been largely laborers, without the same personal interest in the country and in the soil of the country which would make them desire naturalization. In the second place, the very presence of larger numbers of their own kind tends to separate the immigrant to a greater degree from the people who are already here, to make him less dependent upon them, and to increase his association with and dependence upon the people of his own foreign speech and habit.

---

[53] Ibid: 6317.
[54] Ibid: 6339-40.

Vaille closed by urging a constitutional amendment that would exclude noncitizens from the apportionment populations.

The Barbour amendment failed, 123-140. This was a dramatic reversal of the position taken by the previous session of the House. Then, George Tinkham (R-MA) moved to amend by changing 460 to 425; failed.[55] Accordingly, Section 1 setting the House size at 460 remained unchanged. Shortly afterwards, Louis Fairfield (R-IN) moved to recommit the bill to the Committee on the Census; passed: yeas 146, nays 142, present 3, not voting 140.[56]

Curiously, there was no debate about the method of apportionment. Perhaps the debate was pre-empted by a comment in Report No. 312.[57]

> It is not necessary to discuss the method adopted, as both plans commonly known as the Wilcox (sic), or Cornell method, and the Huntington, or Harvard method, agree with each other when the number of the House is fixed at 460.

In reporting the apportionment bill H.R. 7882 out of the Committee on the Census, Siegel presented this same idea. However, he never described what the Huntington method actually was and it was not described in Report 312. The tables included in Report 312 were prepared by Joseph Hill, a statistician in the Census Bureau, and were computed using the Willcox method, the method of major fractions. It is interesting that the Hamilton quota method and the method of major fractions agreed for both House size 435 and 460. Hence, neither Siegel, in advocating H.R. 7882 with House size 460, nor Barbour, in advocating his amendment to use House size 435, had any need to contest about methodology in this regard.

What is odd is that Siegel said, "The proposition has been advanced to use as a basis the Harvard system of calculation which is known as a proportional system, and others have urged the old system known as the majority fraction system."[58] A proportional system was first presented earlier by Hill in connection with reapportionment based on the census of 1910. The Huntington method is an adaptation of Willcox's priority calculation technique that utilizes Hill's method of calculating priorities.

Table 4.12 (next page) supplies a spreadsheet to follow the calculations comparing the Huntington (Harvard) method with the method of major fractions (also known as the Webster or Willcox method) for House size 435 and 460. For convenience, the quota for each House size is given. The State/Seats/Population column set gives the number of seats each state currently has along with its apportionment population. The $h = 435$/Willcox/Harvard column set gives the apportionment using those methods for House size 435 which uses a national divisor of 242000. House size 460 uses a national divisor of 228882.

---

[55] Ibid: 6340.
[56] Ibid: 3648.
[57] House Report 312: 2.
[58] Congressional Record, 14 October 1921: 6308.

Table 4.12. A comparison of the Webster and Huntington (Harvard) methods for House size 460 and 483.

State	Seats	Population	h = 435	Willcox	Harvard	h = 460	Willcox	Harvard
Alabama	10	2348174	9.7087	10	10	10.2666	10	10
Arizona	1	309495	1.2796	1	1	1.3532	1	1
Arkansas	7	1752204	7.2446	7	7	7.6609	8	8
California	11	3426031	14.1651	14	14	14.9792	15	15
Colorado	4	939161	3.8830	4	4	4.1062	4	4
Connecticut	5	1380631	5.7083	6	6	6.0364	6	6
Delaware	1	223003	0.9220	1	1	0.9750	1	1
Florida	4	968470	4.0042	4	4	4.2343	4	4
Georgia	12	2895832	11.9730	12	12	12.6611	13	13
Idaho	2	430442	1.7797	2	2	1.8820	2	2
Illinois	27	6485280	26.8138	27	27	28.3548	28	28
Indiana	13	2930390	12.1159	12	12	12.8122	13	13
Iowa	11	2404021	9.9396	10	10	10.5108	11	11
Kansas	8	1769257	7.3151	7	7	7.7355	8	8
Kentucky	11	2416630	9.9917	10	10	10.5659	11	11
Louisiana	8	1798509	7.4360	7	7	7.8634	8	8
Maine	4	768014	3.1754	3	3	3.3579	3	3
Maryland	6	1449661	5.9937	6	6	6.3382	6	6
Massachusetts	16	3852356	15.9278	16	16	16.8432	17	17
Michigan	13	3668412	15.1673	15	15	16.0389	16	16
Minnesota	10	2385656	9.8636	10	10	10.4305	10	10
Mississippi	8	1790618	7.4034	7	7	7.8289	8	8
Missouri	16	3404055	14.0743	14	14	14.8831	15	15
Montana	2	541511	2.2389	2	2	2.3676	2	2
Nebraska	6	1296372	5.3599	5	5	5.6680	6	6
Nevada	1	75820	0.3135	1	1	0.3315	1	1
New Hampshire	2	443083	1.8320	2	2	1.9372	2	2
New Jersey	12	3155900	13.0483	13	13	13.7982	14	14
New Mexico	1	353428	1.4613	1	2	1.5453	2	2
New York	43	10380589	42.9192	43	42	45.3858	45	45
North Carolina	10	2559123	10.5808	11	10	11.1889	11	11
North Dakota	3	643953	2.6625	3	3	2.8155	3	3
Ohio	22	5759394	23.8126	24	24	25.1811	25	25
Oklahoma	8	2028283	8.3861	8	8	8.8680	9	9
Oregon	3	783389	3.2390	3	3	3.4251	3	3
Pennsylvania	36	8720017	36.0534	36	36	38.1255	38	38
Rhode Island	3	604397	2.4989	2	3	2.6425	3	3
South Carolina	7	1683724	6.9615	7	7	7.3615	7	7
South Dakota	3	631239	2.6099	3	3	2.7599	3	3
Tennessee	10	2337885	9.6661	10	10	10.2216	10	10
Texas	18	4663228	19.2804	19	19	20.3885	20	20
Utah	2	448388	1.8539	2	2	1.9604	2	2
Vermont	2	352428	1.4571	1	2	1.5409	2	2
Virginia	10	2309187	9.5475	10	9	10.0962	10	10
Washington	5	1354596	5.6007	6	6	5.9225	6	6
West Virginia	6	1463701	6.0518	6	6	6.3996	6	6
Wisconsin	11	2631305	10.8793	11	11	11.5045	11	11
Wyoming	1	193487	0.8000	1	1	0.8460	1	1
USA	435	105210729	435.0000	435	435	460.0000	460	460

Although the Huntington and Willcox methods agreed for House size 460, as Siegel claimed, they needed to apply different divisors (ratios of representation) to achieve 460, a fact which Siegel did not mention. He merely said, "Under this bill the House would be increased to 460 based on an average of 228882 persons for each congressional district."[59] Applying the Huntington method with a divisor of 228882 yields a House of 461. The Huntington method gives an additional seat to Wisconsin whose quotient was 11.4963. Huntington's equivalent rounding criterion is based on the geometric mean of 11 (the round-down option) and 12 (the round-up option). Since Wisconsin's quotient of 11.4963 is greater than the geometric mean of 11 and 12, which is 1.4891, then Huntington awarded Wisconsin 12 seats. The smallest divisor that Huntington's method could use to distribute 460 seats was 229026. For House size 435 there are discrepancies for six states between the Huntington method and the method of major fractions. Using the Huntington method, New Mexico, Rhode Island, and Vermont each gain a seat at the expense of New York, North Carolina, and Virginia.

It appears that the members of the Committee on the Census were simply happy to use Hill's tables. Their concern was on the big question of what size the House should be, not on the fine mathematical points of apportionment methodology.

The Committee on the Census was as split as Congress where some wanted to increase the House size, others wanted to keep the current size, a few wanted to decrease the House size, and some wanted no reapportionment based on the census of 1920. The Committee on the Census had 16 members including Isaac Siegel (R-NY), Louis Fairfield (R-IN), Henry Barbour (R-CA), Carroll Beedy (R-ME), and John Rankin (D-MO). Siegel, the chair, strongly supported an increase in House size. Fairfield, Barbour and Beedy were articulate and outspoken in opposing any increase in the House. And Rankin was outspoken in opposing any apportionment based on the 1920 census. Since the committee could not come to terms about what to do, nothing further was reported out of committee during the remainder of the sixty-seventh Congress.

After all this action with no resolution, there was only one other proposal regarding apportionment that was of note. On 17 December 1921 William Larsen (D-GA) introduced H. J. 235, a proposed amendment to the Constitution that would exclude aliens (foreign born noncitizens) from the apportionment population. The resolution was sent to the Committee on the Judiciary where it died. Although the proposal died, the anti-immigrant sentiments were alive and contributed to positions which solidified positions regarding transferring representation to urban districts where most of those aliens resided. Larsen presented historical data along with a set of tables that would show the distribution in the House for size 400, 410, 435, 460 and 483 members in which the alien population was excluded from the apportionment populations.[60]

---

[59] Ibid.
[60] Congressional Record, 67th Congress, 2nd Session, 17 December 1921: 475-7.

Section 4.3.4   Edward V. Huntington[61]

Two important contributions were made to apportionment methodology during the discussions based on the census of 1910. One was made by Walter Willcox and the other by Joseph Hill.

Willcox introduced the computational technique of priority tables. Willcox first apportioned 1 seat to each state, thus satisfying the constitutional minimum criterion. In 1910 this apportioned 46 seats. Willcox then asked, what state has the greatest priority for the 47th seat, 48th seat, etc. To obtain priority numbers Willcox divided each state's population by 1.5, 2.5, 3.5, etc. The state with the highest priority number was given the 47th seat; next highest the 48th seat, etc. In this way Willcox listed the additional state with greatest priority for House size from 47 to 440. Willcox's computational technique produces the same apportionments as Webster's method, also known as the method of major fractions.

Joseph Hill, at the time a statistician in the Census Bureau, was troubled by the paradoxes produced by Hamilton's method. His intuition led him to believe that the paradoxes were caused by the way Hamilton's method awarded a state an additional seat. He was concerned with the problem of which of two competing states should get an additional seat (see Section 3.5: 29-35). Suppose states A and B had populations p_A and p_B and apportionments a and b. Suppose an additional seat became available. Which of the two states has priority for the additional seat? Hill's conclusion was that state A had priority over state B for the additional seat if and only if

$$\frac{p_B}{\sqrt{b(b+1)}} < \frac{p_A}{\sqrt{a(a+1)}}$$

The quantity $\sqrt{a(a+1)}$ is the geometric mean of a and $a+1$. Hence Hill suggested adjusting Hamilton's priority list of greatest fractions by substituting a priority list calculated from a state's population divided by the geometric mean of its round-down, round-up options based on the state's quota.

On 8 January 1921, Isaac Siegel, acting as chair of the House Committee on the Census, reported the apportionment bill H.R. 14498 out of committee. The bill was accompanied by House Report No. 1173. The report contained tables prepared by Joseph Hill, now assistant director of the Census Bureau, for House sizes 435-483 using the method of major fractions (also known as Webster's or Willcox's method).

Debate on the bill began on 18 January 1921. During the debate on 19 January Siegel introduced a letter written two days before by Edward V. Huntington (see pp. 214-5). Although Huntington was presenting Siegel with a new apportionment method, no action was taken using Huntington's ideas. The bill passed the House and was sent to the Senate.

---

[61] For a biographical sketch, visit the website of the Mathematical Association of America:
http://www.maa.org/about-maa/governance/maa-presidents/edward-vermilye-huntington-1918-maa-president.

On 18 February 1921 Senator Howard Sutherland (R-WVA) sent a letter (probably to Joseph Hill or to the Director of the Census Bureau) asking for a clarification and analysis of Huntington's proposal.[62] In particular, Huntington noted a discrepancy in the apportionments made by his method in contrast to the method of major fractions for House size 435, the size contained in the House bill. A response was not obtained before the end of the 66th Congress on 4 March 1921. Hence, the bill died.

On 15 April 1921 Huntington published a paper detailing his method.[63] Huntington essentially combined Willcox's computational technique of constructing a priority list with Hill's method for calculating the priorities. Huntington's method consists of first, like Willcox, assigning one seat to each state. Then a priority list is constructed by dividing each state's population by $\sqrt{1 \times 2} = \sqrt{2}$, $\sqrt{2 \times 3} = \sqrt{6}$, $\sqrt{3 \times 4} = \sqrt{12}$, $\sqrt{4 \times 5} = \sqrt{20}$, etc. Thus, Huntington's method is based on the following inquiry: if a state has n representatives, then what is its priority for having $n+1$ representatives. Huntington called his method *The Method of Equal Proportions*. In today's literature it is also known as the Huntington-Hill method.

Huntington argued that the method of equal proportions was mathematically superior to the method of major fractions. Huntington was a gifted expositor. He spent a great deal of his academic time advancing the teaching of mathematics to engineers. He was a major supporter of *The American Mathematical Monthly* advocating the advancement and teaching of mathematics. This talent shows in his short, readable article explaining the method.

He began by acknowledging that apportionment cannot be made exactly based on populations because of the involvement of fractions. The problem is then to replace a decimal by a natural number in such a way that "the resulting injustice shall be as small as possible."[64] This echoes Daniel Webster's sentiments during the debates based on the 1830 census.

So, what does it mean for a discrepancy between two positive numbers, a and b, to be *as small as possible*? In that case we would like a to be approximately equal to b (denote $a \approx b$). There are two ways to measure that $a \approx b$: (1) $a - b \approx 0$, or (2) $a/b \approx 1$.

Suppose A and B are two states with apportionments a and b, respectively. In an equitable apportionment, $p_A/a \approx p_B/b$; i.e., the constituencies of A and B are as near as possible. Further, we should expect $p_A/p_B \approx a/b$, $p_B/p_A \approx b/a$, and $a/p_A \approx b/p_B$. Huntington noticed that if we adopt the difference criterion (1), that the difference between two quantifies should be close to zero, then different fractions lead to different apportionments. In particular, choosing $p_A/a \approx$

---

[62] C. W. Doten, E. F. Gay, W. C. Mitchell, E. R. A. Seligman, A. A. Young and W. S. Rossiter, Report Upon the Apportionment of Representatives, *Quarterly Publications of the American Statistical Association*, 17(136), December 1921: 1004-13. Accessed from http://www.jstor.org/stable/2965270.

[63] Edward V. Huntington, The Mathematical Theory of the Apportionment of Representatives, *Proceedings of the National Academy of Sciences of the United States of America*, 7(4), 15 April 1921: 123-7. Accessed from https://www.ncbi.nlm.nih.gov/pmc/articles/PMC1084767/.

[64] Ibid: 123.

p_B/b leads to Dean's method; but, choosing $a/p_A \approx b/p_B$ leads to Webster's method.[65] He concluded that the difference approach leads to conflicting results. Hence, Huntington argued that, given positive numbers a and b where $a > b$, $a \approx b$ should be measured by $a/b \approx 1$.

To understanding this process, recall the target range for Dean's method (Figure 4.4). Let d be the ratio of representation and $q_A = p_A/d$ be the resulting state quotient. Let $a = \text{int}(q_A)$.

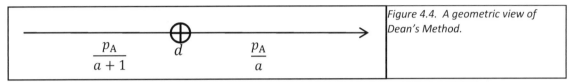

Figure 4.4. A geometric view of Dean's Method.

Dean's criterion is that the state's apportionment should be $a + 1$ (i.e., given an additional seat) if and only if $p_A/(a+1)$ is closer to d than p_A/a. This leads to

$$\text{use } a+1 \iff d - \frac{p_A}{a+1} < \frac{p_A}{a} - d \iff \frac{2}{\frac{1}{a}+\frac{1}{a+1}} < \frac{p_A}{d} \iff HM(a, a + 1) < q_A.$$

Using the reciprocal of the graphic in Figure 4.4, we arrive at Webster's method of apportionment based on the arithmetic mean. To arrive at Huntington's method, start with the Dean graphic and divide through by d obtaining a dimensionless target range (Figure 4.5).

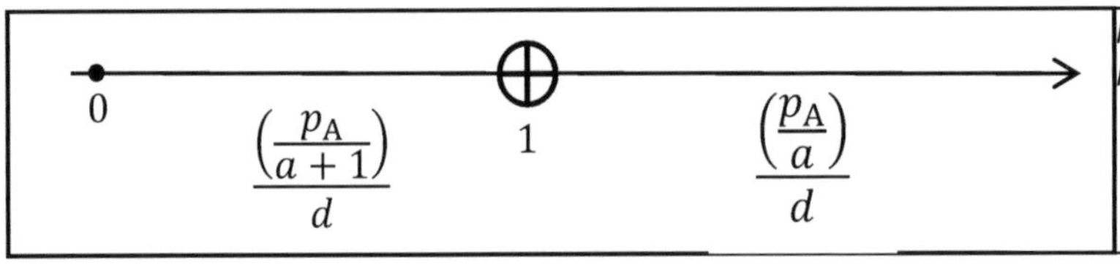

Figure 4.5. A geometric view of Huntington's method.

Recall: if $0 < x < 1$, then $1 < 1/x$. Huntington's criterion is to round the quotient up if and only if the reciprocal of the left fraction is less than the right fraction; i.e.,

$$\text{use } a + 1 \text{ if and only if } \frac{d}{\left(\frac{p_A}{a+1}\right)} < \frac{\left(\frac{p_A}{a}\right)}{d}.$$

Applying some basic algebra yields

$$\text{use } a + 1 \iff \frac{d}{\left(\frac{p_A}{a+1}\right)} < \frac{\left(\frac{p_A}{a}\right)}{d}$$

$$\iff d^2 < \frac{p_A^2}{a(a+1)}$$

$$\iff a(a + 1) < \left(\frac{p_A}{d}\right)^2$$

$$\iff \sqrt{a(a + 1)} < q_A$$

$$\iff GM(a, a + 1) < q_A \qquad GM = \text{geometric mean}$$

---

[65] Charles Biles, Congressional Apportionment Based on the Census 1800-1840, Section 5.6: 50-3.

We would achieve the same result if we stated the criterion as the reciprocal of the right-hand fraction is greater than the left-hand fraction. The enlightening point here is that the Huntington-Hill arithmetical rounding procedure is mathematically equivalent to: round the quotient according to which shot is "closer" on a dimensionless shooting range.

During 27-29 July 1921 a subcommittee of the Committee on the Census held hearings to accept testimony on apportionment.[66] Almost all of the testimony concerned the size of the House, congressional districts, or whether no apportionment based on the 1920 census should occur because of the vast migration from urban areas back to the farm since the census was taken. There was only one item that briefly concerned apportionment methodology.[67]

> Hon. Louis W. Fairfield presiding.
>   Mr. Fairfield. The committee will come to order. I have a telegram that was referred to me this morning, reading as follows:
>
> Providence, R. I., *June 27, 1921.*
> Hon. LeBabon B. Colt,
>   *United States Senate, Washington, D. C.*
> In the matter of reapportionment of Representatives, I heartily indorse Prof. Huntington's "method of equal proportions in." I believe this method is scientific and equitable and hope you will use your influence to secure its adoption by Congress, as it will insure three Representatives for Rhode Island.
>   EMERY J. SANSOUCI,
>   *Governor of Rhode Island.*

The telegram, however, generated no discussion of methodology. The subcommittee report further contained a statement from a 14 July committee meeting in which the corrected figures from the 1920 census were used for tables constructed by Joseph Hill that presented apportionments for House sizes 435-483 using the method of major fractions.

In December 1921 a report on apportionment was published by the Joint Committee of the American Statistical Association and the American Economic Association to Advise the Director of the Census in the form of a letter to Senator Howard Sutherland, chair of the Senate Committee on the Census.[68] The final conclusion of the joint ASA and ESA committee was, "the 'method of equal proportions,' consistent as it is with the literal meaning of the words of the Constitution, is logically superior to the 'method of major fractions.'" Accordingly, Senator Sutherland probably felt pleased that he did not take action on the House bill at the close of the 66th Congress.

---

[66] Subcommittee Hearings accessed from
https://play.google.com/books/reader?id=7loqu4bYu8YC&printsec=frontcover&output=reader&hl=en&pg=GBS.PA17.
[67] Ibid: 13.
[68] Doten et al (see Reference 62 in this section).

For comparison we provide an illustration contrasting the priority technique for the method of major fractions (Webster or Willcox methods) against the priority technique for method of equal proportions (Huntington-Hill). Table 4.13 (next page) provides computational details. The State/Population column set displays the 48 states with their respective populations. The 1.5/2.5/3.5 column set shows Willcox priorities, the state populations divided by 1.5, 2.5, and 3.5, respectively. This provides the first three tiers of the Willcox priority numbers. When the third tier is reached for any state, then the fourth tier must be computed for that state before the procedure can be continued. Similarly, the sqrt(2)/sqrt(6)/sqrt(12) column set provides the first three tiers for the Huntington-Hill priority numbers obtained by dividing the state populations by $\sqrt{2}$, $\sqrt{6}$, and $\sqrt{12}$, respectively. Notice that by either priority method, for any given state the priority numbers decrease as the divisor increases.

We now illustrate the use of the Willcox priority tables. First assign one seat to each of the 48 states, creating a House with 48 members. If the House is now increased by one, then New York is assigned the 49th seat since it has the highest priority number, 6920392. Then Pennsylvania is assigned the 50th seat (priority number 5813344). Illinois is assigned the 51st seat (priority number 4323520). New York is assigned the 52nd seat because its priority number for a third seat, 4152235, is greater than any unused state priority number for a second seat. Ohio is assigned the 53rd seat (priority number 3839596). Pennsylvania is assigned the 54th seat since its priority number for a third seat, 3488006, is greater than any unused state priority number for a second seat. Texas is assigned the 55th seat (priority number 3108818). Massachusetts is the next state in line to receive a second seat with priority number 2568237; however, New York's priority number for a fourth seat (2965882) and Illinois's priority number for a third seat (2594112) are higher. Hence, the 56th seat is assigned to New York, the 57th seat to Illinois, and the 58th seat to Massachusetts.

The Huntington-Hill priority tables are used in the same manner as the Willcox tables to assign seats in the House. The Huntington-Hill priorities assign seats in the same manner as the Willcox priorities for House size 40-56. However, the Willcox priority assigns the 57th seat to Illinois and the 58th seat to Massachusetts, but the Huntington-Hill priority assigns them in reverse order with Massachusetts receiving the 57th seat (H-H priority number 2724027) and Illinois receiving the 58th seat (H-H priority number 2647604). Similarly, Willcox awards the 59th seat to Pennsylvania (Willcox priority 2491433) and the 60th seat to Michigan (Willcox priority 2445608); Huntington-Hill reverses the assignment giving the 59th seat to Michigan (H-H priority 2593959) and the 60th seat to Pennsylvania (H-H priority 2517252).

Which method to use then becomes crucial when deciding to increase the House size by even one seat.

Table 4.13. Spreadsheet showing the first three levels for Willcox's (1.5/2.5/3.5) and Hill's (sqrt(2)/sqrt(6)/sqrt(12)) priority numbers. The notation sqrt(2) means the square root of 2, etc.

State	Population	1.5	2.5	3.5	sqrt(2)	sqrt(6)	sqrt(12)
Alabama	2348174	1565449	939269	670906	1660409	958638	677859
Arizona	309495	206330	123798	88427	218846	126350	89343
Arkansas	1752204	1168136	700881	500629	1238995	715334	505817
California	3426031	2284020	1370412	978866	2422569	1398671	989009
Colorado	939161	626107	375664	268331	664087	383410	271112
Connecticut	1380631	920420	552252	394466	976253	563640	398553
Delaware	223003	148668	89201	63715	157686	91040	64375
Florida	968470	645646	387388	276705	684811	395376	279573
Georgia	2895832	1930554	1158332	827380	2047662	1182218	835954
Idaho	430442	286961	172176	122983	304368	175727	124257
Illinois	6485280	4323520	2594112	1852937	4585785	2647604	1872139
Indiana	2930390	1953593	1172156	837254	2072098	1196326	845930
Iowa	2404021	1602680	961608	686863	1699899	981437	693981
Kansas	1769257	1179504	707702	505502	1251053	722296	510740
Kentucky	2416630	1611086	966652	690465	1708815	986585	697620
Louisiana	1798509	1199006	719403	513859	1271737	734238	519184
Maine	768014	512009	307205	219432	543067	313540	221706
Maryland	1449661	966440	579864	414188	1025065	591821	418481
Massachusetts	3852356	2568237	1540942	1100673	2724027	1572717	1112079
Michigan	3668412	2445608	1467364	1048117	2593959	1497622	1058979
Minnesota	2385656	1590437	954262	681616	1686913	973939	688679
Mississippi	1790618	1193745	716247	511605	1266158	731016	516906
Missouri	3404055	2269370	1361622	972587	2407030	1389699	982666
Montana	541511	361007	216604	154717	382906	221070	156320
Nebraska	1296372	864248	518548	370392	916673	529241	374230
Nevada	75820	50546	30328	21662	53612	30953	21887
New Hampshire	443083	295388	177233	126595	313306	180887	127907
New Jersey	3155900	2103933	1262360	901685	2231558	1288390	911029
New Mexico	353428	235618	141371	100979	249911	144286	102025
New York	10380589	6920392	4152235	2965882	7340184	4237857	2996617
North Carolina	2559123	1706082	1023649	731178	1809573	1044757	738755
North Dakota	643953	429302	257581	183986	455343	262892	185893
Ohio	5759394	3839596	2303757	1645541	4072506	2351262	1662593
Oklahoma	2028283	1352188	811313	579509	1434212	828043	585514
Oregon	783389	522259	313355	223825	553939	319817	226144
Pennsylvania	8720017	5813344	3488006	2491433	6165983	3559932	2517252
Rhode Island	604397	402931	241758	172684	427373	246744	174474
South Carolina	1683724	1122482	673489	481064	1190572	687377	486049
South Dakota	631239	420826	252495	180354	446353	257702	182223
Tennessee	2337885	1558590	935154	667967	1653134	954437	674889
Texas	4663228	3108818	1865291	1332350	3297400	1903754	1346157
Utah	448388	298925	179355	128110	317058	183053	129438
Vermont	352428	234952	140971	100693	249204	143878	101737
Virginia	2309187	1539458	923674	659767	1632841	942721	666604
Washington	1354596	903064	541838	387027	957844	553011	391038
West Virginia	1463701	975800	585480	418200	1034992	597553	422534
Wisconsin	2631305	1754203	1052522	751801	1860613	1074225	759592
Wyoming	193487	128991	77394	55282	136815	78990	55854

Section 4.3.5   The 68th U. S. Congress.

The term of the 68th Congress was 4 March 1923 to 4 March 1925. The 1st Session met from 3 December 1923 to 7 June 1924. The 2nd Session met from 1 December 1924 to 3 March 1925.

During the first session, eight bills concerning apportionment were introduced in the House and subsequently referred to the Committee on the Census. However, on 14 March 1924, Henry Barbour (R-CA) stated, "I am advised that on March 8 the Committee on the Census met and determined it would not report out an apportionment bill this session. Failure to act is inexcusable."[69]

In reply, Ira Hersey (R-ME) said, "I do not think an apportionment should be made under a census taken four or five years ago, because the population has radically changed." He further argued that there should be another census before a new apportionment is made because the 1920 census was unreliable.[70]

On 4 June 1924, just before the close of the 1st session, Clarence McLeod (R-MI), commented, "It appears, however, from the research of scholars and specialists, that there is no law to compel Congress to make a reapportionment of our representatives." Nevertheless, he implored his colleagues to do their constitutional duty. Clearly the Committee on the Census could not get it together to refer a bill out of committee. In accordance with a new rule, the committee was already taking signatures to petition to be released of duty.[71]

The second session of the 68th Congress saw even less action on apportionment. Only one new apportionment bill was introduced. It was referred to the Committee on the Census where it died.

The only discussion on apportionment occurred during debate on an appropriation bill. Thomas Blanton (D-TX) moved an amendment to the appropriation bill that would set the House size at 304. Blanton's justification was the constitutional guideline that representatives and direct taxes shall be apportioned among the several states according to their respective numbers. He was ruled out of order.

Thus, the 68th Congress ended with no action taken on apportionment. The sentiment for no reapportionment based on the 1920 census appeared to be solidifying.

Section 4.3.6   The 69th U. S. Congress.

The term of the 69th Congress was from 4 March 1925 to 4 March 1927. The 1st Session of Congress met from 7 December 1925 to 3 July 1926. During the first day four apportionment bills were introduced in the House and referred to the Committee on the Census.[72] The House

---

[69] Congressional Record, 68th Congress, 1st Session, 14 March 1924: 4181.

[70] Ibid: 4183.

[71] Ibid: 10552.

[72] Congressional Record 69th Congress, 1st Session, 7 December 1925: 398, 404, 448.

Committee on the Census for the 69[73] Congress was formed on 16 December.[73] The committee had 17 members, 10 Republicans and 7 Democrats. On 5 January 1926 Albert Carter (R-CA) resigned from the committee.[74] He was replaced by Florence Kahn (R-CA), the first woman to serve on the Committee on the Census.

The Committee on the Census held hearings on the four submitted apportionment bills on 25 February, 3 March, and 22 March 1926.[75] On 7 April Ernest Gibson (R-VT) rose to insert some remarks on apportionment. He noted that all of the pending bills before the Committee on the Census used the method of major fractions although the Doten Report (see Reference 62 of this section) concluded that "the method of equal proportions" is preferred to "major fractions." Accordingly, he asked and received consent to insert the Doten Report into the Congressional Record.[76] No discussion about apportionment followed Gibson's remarks.

Henry Barbour (R-CA), a member of the House Committee on the Census and author of H.R. 111, realized that nothing was going to be referred out of committee regarding apportionment during this session of the 69th Congress. On 8 April 1926 he rose to "present a privileged question under the Constitution."[77]

> Mr. BARBOUR moves to discharge the Committee on the Census from consideration of house bill 111, a bill for the apportionment of Representatives in Congress amongst the several States under the Fourteenth Census, and that the House proceed to the immediate consideration thereof.

A week earlier Barbour alerted the Speaker of the House about this move and to be prepared to make a ruling. The opposition also came prepared. Immediately Bertrand Snell (R-NY) rose to make a point of order against Barbour's motion "because the consideration of the bill does not present a question of constitutional privilege." Snell was from upstate New York. He was also chair of the powerful House Rules Committee.[78]

William Bankhead (D-AL) joined Snell's objection and added that there is no procedure under the rules for Barbour's motion. A debate then ensued that occupied the next ten pages of the Congressional Record. The main thrust of the argument against Barbour's motion was initiated by Snell, "there is no mandatory provision in the Constitution itself which provides for immediate apportionment." The opposition argued that the census and apportionment were two different items. Although the Constitution specified that the census be taken every ten years, it did not specify that an apportionment had to follow, or when afterwards. Snell and company argued that *if* an apportionment was to take place, *then* it must be based on the census. Snell said, "It seems to me it follows that when you do make that apportionment it

---

[73] Ibid, 16 December 1925: 932.
[74] Ibid, 5 January 1926: 1504.
[75] Ibid 24 February 1926: 4527; 3 March 1926: 4955; 22 March 1926: 6049.
[76] Ibid: 7077-80.
[77] Ibid, 8 April 1926: 7138-7149.
[78] https://en.wikipedia.org/wiki/Bertrand_Snell.

must be in accordance with the last census, but I cannot read anywhere in the provisions of the Constitution where it provides that the apportionment itself is a mandatory proposition."

Despite Barbour's pleas that Congress had a constitutional duty to apportion each decade based on the census, the opposition was gathering force from several points. Was decennial reapportionment constitutionally mandated? Should not the usual rules and procedures of the House be followed? Then there were those who wanted reapportionment, but with an increased House size. And there were those that openly opposed any reapportionment based on the 1920 census.

Finally, the Speaker said that if he had to rule without the basis of precedent, he would rule against Barbour's motion; i.e., that it was out of order. However, the Speaker left it to a vote of the House. In that vote on 8 April 1926 the Barbour motion was soundly defeated: yeas 87, nays 265, not voting 79. It was clear then that no apportionment bill would be forthcoming from the Committee on the Census and that reapportionment based on the 1920 census was dead for the 1st session of the 69th Congress.

The last voice on the floor of the House regarding apportionment came from Florence Kahn (R-CA). She summarized the history of congressional apportionment and then chastised, "Why then should not a reapportionment bill have been passed? It is a constitutional mandate—and it our duty, as I see it, to obey this mandate. [Applause.]"[79] The only other activity regarding reapportionment for the remainder of the first session was that five additional apportionment bills were submitted and referred to the Committee on the Census.[80]

It became clear that the House and the Committee on the Census were split into three deadlocked factions, neither of which could muster a majority:

- There should be no reapportionment based on the census of 1920;
- Reapportionment based on the 1920 census should take place with an increase in the size of the House;
- Reapportionment based on the 1920 census should take place with no increase in the size of the House.

The second session of the 69th Congress met from 6 December 1926 to 3 March 1927. The House Committee on the Census was chaired by Edward Fenn (R-CT). On 6 December Fenn submitted his own apportionment bill which was referred to the Committee on the Census.

Fenn called for a series of seven committee hearings that extended from 8 January to 26 February.[81] The committee received considerable testimony about the method of equal proportions, including testimony from Hill, Willcox, and Professors Huntington and Young from Harvard. However, the committee could not agree on a bill to report to the House.

---

[79] Ibid, 29 April 1926: 8457-9.
[80] Ibid, 27 April 1926: 8338; 11 May 1926: 9248; 11 May 1926: 9400; 11 May 1926: 11423; 11 May 1926: 11723.
[81] Congressional Record, 69th Congress, 2nd Session: 1256, 1317, 1754, 1908, 2406, 3315, 3928.

Fenn became annoyed with the inability to refer an apportionment bill out of committee for consideration by the House. Just before the close of the 69th Congress, Fenn decided to take action. On 1 March he introduced H.R. 17378 which was referred to the Committee on the Census.[82] The committee refused to refer the bill to the House. So, the next day Fenn rose in the House to move to suspend the rules and bring H.R. 17378 to the floor. In a prearranged deal the Speaker had the Clerk report the bill. The bill contained eight sections. The enactment (first) section specified a House of 435 after 3 March 1933. The second section specified that as soon as the 1930 census was completed the Secretary of Commerce would calculate the apportionments based on the method of equal proportions. Sections 3-4 specified the Secretary to submit the results to the Clerk of the House and directed the Clerk to send a certificate of notification to each state. Section 5 specified that congressional districts were to be compact, contiguous, and of as equal size as possible with one representative per district. Sections 6-8 specified when congressmen could be elected at large rather than from districts.

Debate was limited to 20 minutes for each side with the pro side managed by Fenn and the con side managed by John Rankin (D-MS). The pro side basically argued that the country needed protection to guard against another apportionment failure by Congress for the upcoming 1930 census. Some proponents spoke about the necessity of not increasing the House size.[83] But Fenn's chosen lead proponent was Clarence McLeod (R-MI) who urged Congress to recognize the constitutional duty towards census-based reapportionment. He spent time advocating for the method of equal proportions. But he described the method as "based on the principle that the ratio of population to Representatives or the number of people per Representative shall be as nearly as possible the same in all States."[84] He further said, "That being the case, it becomes a question of making the congressional districts as nearly uniform as it is possible to make them" and that "it can be mathematically demonstrated that the method of equal proportions accomplishes that result." However, McLeod's explanation describes Dean's method, not the Huntington method of equal proportions.

Rankin brilliantly managed the opposition. Rankin was an experienced member of the Committee on the Census and throughout the decade starting with the 66th Congress he was an outspoken opponent of any reapportionment based on the 1920 census. Rankin chose to recognize speakers who were committed to a reapportionment based on the 1920 census. They were appalled at the idea of this Congress failing to act on the basis of the 1920 census and simply punting their constitutional duty to the 1930 census. Other speakers were outraged that Congress would abrogate its constitutional duty to the Secretary of Commerce. Rankin also engaged speakers that were opposed to tying the size of the House down to 435. Although Rankin's personal agenda was to block any apportionment legislation based on the 1920 census, he skillfully used other viewpoints opposed to specific components of Fenn's bill.

---

[82] Ibid: 5288.
[83] Ibid, 2 March 1927: 5414-5428.
[84] Ibid: 5416.

Finally, a vote was taken on the Fenn bill. It narrowly failed: yeas 183, nays 197, not voting 52. The bill had no realistic chance of passing into law anyway. Even if the bill had passed the House, the Senate would have had only a day to approve the bill since the 69th Congress ended at noon on 4 March 1927. The most likely scenario if the bill passed is that the Senate simply would have referred it to committee and let it die there. Hence, the 69th Congress ended with no reapportionment bill based on the census of 1920.

Section 4.3.7   The 70th U. S. Congress.

The first session of the 70th Congress met from 5 December 1927 to 29 May 1928. On opening day six different apportionment bills were submitted and referred to the Committee on the Census. Fenn won re-election to his seat and retained chairmanship of the committee.

Soon chairman Fenn called a series of Hearings that dealt considerably with methods of apportionment. The committee received testimony from a variety of mathematicians and statisticians including Joseph Hill, Walter Willcox, Leonard Ayers (President of the American Statistical Association) and E. R. Hedrick (editor, Bulletin of the American Mathematical Society). Most of the testimony favored the method of equal proportions.[85]

John Rankin, still a member of the Committee on the Census, wanted to get to the main point. He said, "You three statisticians agree with me that if you are going to reapportion the House, you must fix one of two things, either fix the size of the House in advance or fix the basis of reapportionment."[86] Rankin recognized that there were only two approaches to apportionment—a constituency approach or a House size approach. All the methods under discussion had to do with what to do with the resulting decimal fraction.

Willcox presented a set of tables that compared the methods of rejected fractions (Jefferson's method), major fractions (Webster's method), Vinton (Hamilton's quota method), equal proportions (Huntington-Hill method), and minimum range (Table 4.14).[87] Willcox did quite well at explaining that the choice of method depended on the goal of apportionment. Did Congress want to create congressional districts equal in size as near as possible? Or did Congress want to create the same number of representatives per million people as near as possible? Or some other goal? The method of choice depended on the goal of choice.

Figure 4.14 (next page). Apportionment for House size 435 based on the 1920 census using five historical divisor methods and the Hamilton quota method. The divisors needed to obtain House size 435 for Jefferson (230000), Dean (244600), Huntington-Hill (H-H (244523)), Webster (242000), Adams (256700), and Hamilton (241864) were those supplied by Willcox.

---

[85] Apportionment of Representatives, Hearings before the Committee of the Census, Seventieth Congress, First Session, on H.R. 130; accessed from
http://babel.hathitrust.org/cgi/pt?id=umn.31951d035927993;view=1up;seq=1.
[86] Ibid: 51.
[87] Ibid: 52-55.

State	Seats	Population	Jefferson	Dean	H-H	Webster	Adams	Hamilton
Alabama	10	2348174	10	10	10	10	10	10
Arizona	1	309495	1	1	1	1	2	1
Arkansas	7	1752204	7	7	7	7	7	7
California	11	3426031	14	14	14	14	14	14
Colorado	4	939161	4	4	4	4	4	4
Connecticut	5	1380631	6	6	6	6	6	6
Delaware	1	223003	1	1	1	1	1	1
Florida	4	968470	4	4	4	4	4	4
Georgia	12	2895832	12	12	12	12	12	12
Idaho	2	430442	1	2	2	2	2	2
Illinois	27	6485280	28	27	27	27	26	27
Indiana	13	2930390	12	12	12	12	12	12
Iowa	11	2404021	10	10	10	10	10	10
Kansas	8	1769257	7	7	7	7	7	7
Kentucky	11	2416630	10	10	10	10	10	10
Louisiana	8	1798509	7	7	7	7	8	7
Maine	4	768014	3	3	3	3	3	3
Maryland	6	1449661	6	6	6	6	6	6
Massachusetts	16	3852356	16	16	16	16	16	16
Michigan	13	3668412	15	15	15	15	15	15
Minnesota	10	2385656	10	10	10	10	10	10
Mississippi	8	1790618	7	7	7	7	7	7
Missouri	16	3404055	14	14	14	14	14	14
Montana	2	541511	2	2	2	2	3	2
Nebraska	6	1296372	5	5	5	5	6	5
Nevada	1	75820	1	1	1	1	1	1
New Hampshire	2	443083	1	2	2	2	2	2
New Jersey	12	3155900	13	13	13	13	13	13
New Mexico	1	353428	1	2	2	1	2	1
New York	43	10380589	45	42	42	43	41	43
North Carolina	10	2559123	11	10	10	11	10	11
North Dakota	3	643953	2	3	3	3	3	3
Ohio	22	5759394	25	24	24	24	23	24
Oklahoma	8	2028283	8	8	8	8	8	8
Oregon	3	783389	3	3	3	3	4	3
Pennsylvania	36	8720017	37	36	36	36	34	36
Rhode Island	3	604397	2	3	3	2	3	2
South Carolina	7	1683724	7	7	7	7	7	7
South Dakota	3	631239	2	3	3	3	3	3
Tennessee	10	2337885	10	10	10	10	10	10
Texas	18	4663228	20	19	19	19	19	19
Utah	2	448388	1	2	2	2	2	2
Vermont	2	352428	1	2	2	1	2	1
Virginia	10	2309187	10	9	9	10	9	10
Washington	5	1354596	5	6	6	6	6	6
West Virginia	6	1463701	6	6	6	6	6	6
Wisconsin	11	2631305	11	11	11	11	11	11
Wyoming	1	193487	1	1	1	1	1	1
USA	435	105210729	435	435	435	435	435	435

However, Willcox at times gave confusing descriptions of what the various methods did, especially with his description of minimum range. He described the method as a priority technique which first assigned one seat to each state. Then, the next state in line to get the next seat was that state with the largest population per representative. Willcox then said that this makes congressional districts nearly as possible the same size. However, the technique described by Willcox yields Adams's method. The resulting achieved goal described by Willcox describes Dean's method. The table provided by Willcox for minimum range is consistent only with Adams's method of apportionment.

Later Hill gave the same confused explanation as Willcox. Hill said, "I will define the method of minimum range as the method by which absolute difference between the several states as measured by the number of inhabitants per Representative are made as small as possible."[88] However, this describes Dean's method. If only Willcox had included a column showing apportionment based on the harmonic mean, he could have seen the situation (Table 4.14).

After the hearings Fenn proposed H.R. 11725 which was referred to his committee.[89] Finally on 4 April the bill along with House Report 1137 was reported out of committee.[90] The bill was anticipatory in that it did not apportion based on the 1920 census but was written in anticipation of the census of 1930. It specified that if the Congress failed to pass a reapportionment bill by the end of the term in which it received the census report, then reapportionment will be done automatically by the President using House size 435 and the method of major fractions.

The House debated the bill using familiar old issues and some new ones. Some congressmen lamented that Congress was ignoring its duty to make the decennial apportionment based on the 1920 census. Some argued that aliens (noncitizen immigrants) should not be counted in the apportionment populations. Others went further and argued that only native-born Americans should be represented. Some said it was unconstitutional for the current Congress to dictate to a future Congress. Others lamented ceding congressional power to the executive. In the end, the House voted to send the bill back to committee, 186-164.[91] This ended consideration of apportionment in the House for the first term of the 70th Congress.

Figure 4.6. Senator Arthur Vandenberg.

Meanwhile Senator Woodridge Ferris (D-MI) died on 23 March 1928. To take his place, Michigan Governor Fred Green appointed Arthur Vandenberg (R-MI) who then joined the Senate on 31 March 1928. Vandenberg (Figure 4.6[92]) was appalled that Congress did not reapportion based on the 1920 census. Although just a freshman Senator appointed until the

---

[88] Ibid: 93.
[89] Congressional Record, 70th Congress, 1st Session, 3 March 1928: 4054.
[90] Ibid, 4 April 1928: 5916.
[91] Ibid: 9004-9032, 9085-9107.
[92] Public Domain from Wikiwand: https://www.wikiwand.com/en/Arthur_Vandenberg.

upcoming election, on 24 May he submitted S. 4554,[93] an apportionment bill identical to the 1921 bill passed by the House that died in the Senate. In the election held in November 1928 Vandenberg ran to maintain his seat in the Senate. He campaigned on a pledge that reapportionment was of highest priority; in particular, to fight for automatic reapportionment. He won handily.[94] Subsequently, he "would play a significant role in the final passage of apportionment legislation."[95]

The second session of the 70th Congress met from 3 December 1928 to 4 March 1930. This time both chambers of Congress initiated action. On 20 December[96] Senator Vandenberg spoke to condemn the non-apportionment based on the 1920 census. He requested that the Senate delay action on a pending census bill that would define the administration and scope of the 1930 census. Vandenberg asked for the delay to add a section that would authorize automatic reapportionment. On 3 January 1929 he presented his amendment.[97]

The Republican House leadership, motivated by Vandenberg's actions in the Senate, spearheaded action on apportionment. Speaker of the House Nicholas Longworth (R-OH), Majority Leader John Tilson (R-CT), and chair of the Rules Committee Bertrand Snell (R-NY) all promised support and action on the Fenn bill. The Fenn bill called for automatic reapportionment done by the Secretary of Commerce using House size 435 and the method of major fractions, but only if the Congress receiving the census failed to re-apportion before adjournment. In that event it also called for compact, contiguous, and equal sized (as near as practical) districts and contained provisions for when a congressman could be elected at large. On 5 January 1929 the bill made it out of committee on a close 7-6 vote. All 7 yes votes were from Republicans; the no votes were from 6 Democrats and 1 Republican. The bill was accompanied by House Report No. 2010. A minority report authored by Rankin was submitted on 8 January.

When formal debate launched on 10 January, arguments against the Fenn bill were familiar but more intense. A special nastiness was introduced by Homer Hoch (R-KS) who was on a crusade to exclude aliens from apportionment populations. Fiorello LaGuardia (R-NY) charged that Hoch was only advancing the Evans Plan, the agenda of Hiram Evans, Imperial Wizard of the Ku Klux Klan.[98] John Schafer (R-WI) portrayed Hoch as a front man for the KKK and the Anti-Saloon League.

House rules limited debate to three hours. Further, a vote had to be taken before adjournment on 11 January. At the end of the debate in a surprising maneuver Fenn moved to strike the last three sections of his bill, the sections regulating districts and controlling at large representatives. The motion passed on a voice vote without debate. This was probably a

---

[93] Ibid: 9677.
[94] https://en.wikipedia.org/wiki/Arthur_H._Vandenberg.
[95] Charles Eagles, Democracy Delayed: 69.
[96] Congressional Record, 70th Congress, 2nd Session, 20 December 1928: 933.
[97] Ibid, 3 January 1929: 1033.
[98] https://en.wikipedia.org/wiki/Hiram_Wesley_Evans.

political move to enhance passage of what Fenn perhaps perceived as a too-close-to-call vote. Debate then ended. A motion was made to send the bill back to committee; failed, 134-226. The Fenn bill then passed by voice vote. For the second time in the decade of 1920 the House passed an apportionment bill. The bill was then sent to the Senate for concurrence. However, the Senate had less than two months before the 70th session of Congress ended.

The Senate referred the bill to the Committee on Commerce. The committee held no hearings and reported it to the Senate. Unfortunately, the chair of the Republican Steering Committee was Frederic Sackett (R-KY). He opposed the bill because Kentucky would lose a seat; hence, he assigned the bill a low priority on the Senate calendar.

Despite Sackett's intransigence, on 24 January Vandenberg moved to interrupt considerations of a bill to construct navy cruisers in order to consider the Fenn Bill; passed, 53-23. Vandenberg denounced the failure of Congress to carry out its constitutional duty and apportion based on the census. The plea was joined by Senator David Walsh (D-MA). Despite the pleas, the Senate cut short the debate and returned to its consideration of navy cruisers.

On 14 February Vandenberg tried again but failed to renew the debate in the Senate. The Senate did not take up the Fenn bill until the last week of the session. At this late time the opposition pounced with vigor, led by Senators Hugo Black (D-AL) and Byron Harrison (D-MS). Black ranted against handing congressional power to the Secretary of Commerce and the method of major fractions since it favored large states over small states. Harrison railed that the Senate was too busy with a complex appropriation bill to pause and consider the apportionment bill. Vandenberg saw he had no chance. Accordingly, he proposed to send the bill back to committee. Hence, just like with the 68th Congress, the House-passed apportionment bill died in the Senate.

Although defeated at the time, Vandenberg persisted. He immediately began planning for the upcoming 71st Congress. He met with the key members of the Republican leadership in Congress: Charles Curtis (R-KS), the outgoing majority leader and new Vice-President; Nicholas Longworth (R-OH), Speaker of the House; John Tilson (R-CT), House majority leader; and Charles Watson (R-IN), the new Senate majority leader. They all gave assurances to Vandenberg that the Senate would take up apportionment in an upcoming special session of Congress.

On 4 February 1929 the National Academy of Sciences issued a report on apportionment.[99] The report was prepared at the request of Speaker of the House Nicholas Longworth (R-OH). The panel of prestigious mathematicians issuing the report consisted of Raymond Pearl (chair), Gilbert Bliss, Ernst Brown, and Luther Eisenhart. The report stated that the panel had studied five methods of congressional apportionment: smallest divisors (also known as rejected fractions, Jefferson), harmonic mean (Dean), equal proportions (geometric mean, Huntington-Hill), major fractions (arithmetic mean, Webster), and greatest divisors (accepted fractions,

---

[99] Report of the National Academy of Sciences, Fiscal Year 1928-9: 21-23.

Adams). The panel unanimously recommended the method of equal proportions. The report was printed in the Congressional Record on 2 March.[100]

About the same time that the Academy issued its reports, *Science* published a letter submitted by Walter Willcox written to explain the apportionment situation in Congress.[101] Willcox noted that the bill before Congress was not "a real apportionment bill," but "a bill authorizing a future apportionment by the secretary of commerce after the results of the census of 1930 or of any subsequent census have been announced and Congress has failed to pass an apportionment bill in the following session."

Willcox also wrote, "Upon the moot question of method," the census committee has been concerned with two main problems. First, "What method is likely to give the bill the best chance of passing Congress?" Second, "What method is most likely to satisfy Congress when its results are brought home to the members by a specific apportionment?" Hence, Willcox is giving the impression that politics, not fairness, is the main driver for passage of an apportionment bill. Willcox further stated, "The choice of a method seems to me of little importance compared with the need of securing congressional compliance with the constitution." It seemed that apportionment methodology was adding confusion rather than enlightenment towards resolution.

Willcox noted that "As many persons interested in the practical problem seem to be baffled by the mathematics of apportionment." An exchange in the House debate on 10 January clearly illustrated the point in Congress.[102] Randolph Perkins (R-NJ) interrupted a presentation by Arthur Greenwood (D-IN) that there is "uncertainty among some of us as to what the method of major fractions is; will the gentleman kindly explain that?" Greenwood answered, "I do not pretend to know." He offered that maybe Jacobstein (R-NY) could possibly explain. Greenwood added, "I do not think there is another member of the committee who could explain it or who understands it. We should wait and see the results and not tie our hands."

Later, Perkins made a similar interruption during a presentation by Lester Dickinson (R-IA) in which Perkins asked, "some of us are waiting to hear the theory of major fractions explained. Will the gentleman kindly do that?" Dickinson simply responded, "No." He added, "I will refer you to the gentleman from New York, but I will say to you that I am going to offer an amendment by which I change from major fractions to equal proportions. [Applause.]" Fenn, chairman of the Committee on the Census, then asked Dickinson, "May I ask the gentleman whether he can explain the theory of equal proportions?" Dickinson responded, "No, I can not, and I do not think that the chairman of the committee, who has been studying this thing for six or seven years can explain them either."[103]

---

[100] Congressional Record, 70th Congress, 2nd Session, 2 March 1929: 4966-7.

[101] Walter Willcox, The Apportionment Situation in Congress, *Science*, New Series 69(1780), 8 February 1929: 163-65.

[102] Congressional Record, 10 January 1929: 1495.

[103] Ibid: 1498.

Why would some congressmen favor the method of equal proportions over the method of major fractions if they were clueless about how the method worked? The answer is that they knew the result: when variances between the two methods occurred, equal proportions always favored a smaller state over a larger state. This result set well with rural advocates.

But Willcox himself was partly to blame for the confusion. In his *Science* article, Willcox announced, "let me state again, as simply as possible and without argument, the essential differences between the different methods." He said, "At one extreme is the method of rejected fractions used in all apportionments before 1840." He continued, "At the other extreme is the method of the harmonic mean, or as I have preferred to call it in arguing before the census committee, the method of minimum range. By it every decimal fraction, no matter how small, entitles the state to a representative." However, the method of the harmonic mean describes Dean's method, but the method of minimum range (accepted fractions) yields Adams's method. Willcox then gave his personal ranking of the methods: major fractions, minimum range, rejected fractions, and finally equal proportions.

Willcox concluded his analysis with his judgment that the most desirable goal for apportionment should be done with either one of two viewpoints:

(1) To give the residents of the United States as nearly as may be equal representation in the House of Representatives, irrespective of the state of residence; or

(2) To give the members of the House of Representatives as nearly as may be equal number of constituents.

Willcox's goal (1) is actualized by the method of major fractions; goal (2), by Dean's method of harmonic means.

Section 4.3.8   The 71st U. S. Congress.

In the 1928 election Republicans retained their power, capturing both chambers of Congress. Republican Herbert Hoover was elected in a landslide over his Democratic opponent Al Smith. Arguably, after George Washington, Hoover was perhaps the most qualified candidate ever to run for President of the United States. After his inauguration on 4 March 1929, Hoover called a special session of Congress specifically to deal with the pressing issues of relief for agriculture and revision of the tariff. He sent a message to Congress about the agenda.[104]

> It is my understanding that it is the purpose of the leaders of Congress to confine the deliberations of the session mainly to the questions of farm relief and tariff. In this policy I concur. There are, however, certain matters of emergency legislation that were partially completed in the last session, such as the decennial census, the reapportionment of congressional representation, and the suspension of the

---

[104] Herbert Hoover, Message to the Special Session of the Congress on Farm Relief, Tariff, antedating Emergency Legislation, 16 April 1929; accessed from https://www.presidency.ucsb.edu/documents/message-the-special-session-the-congress-farm-relief-tariff-antedating-emergency.

national origins clause of the immigration act of 1924, [p.81] together with some minor administrative authorizations. I understand that these measures can be reundertaken without unduly extending the session. I recommend their consummation as being in the public interest.

The special session lasted only two days, 4-5 March 1929. Although Fenn introduced two bills, they were referred to the Committee on the Census. No action was taken during the special session since the committee was not yet formed.

The first session of the 71st Congress met from 15 April to 22 November 1929. Finally, success was achieved when on 18 June 1929 President Hoover signed *An Act To provide for the fifteenth and subsequent decennial censuses and to provide for apportionment of Representatives in Congress*.[105] The details of the story are fascinating but require a separate essay of their own. We refer the interested reader to the Congressional Record, Democracy Delayed[106], and a paper by Sweeting[107]. Eagles especially follows the leadership of Senator Vandenberg in spearheading the passage of a joint census and apportionment bill in the Senate. Sweeting describes the brilliant political craftsmanship of House majority leader Tilson (R-CT) in saving the bill and steering it to passage in the House. Differences in the House and Senate versions were ironed out in a joint committee. The House approved the final measure in a voice vote on 11 June 1929. The Senate passed the final bill on 13 June by a vote of 48-37. The Census and Apportionment Act of 1929 contained 22 sections. The first 21 sections described the management and content for the census of 1930. Only section 22 was devoted to apportionment.

SEC. 22. (a) On the first day, or within one week thereafter, of the second regular session of the Seventy-first Congress and of each fifth Congress thereafter, the President shall transmit to the Congress a statement showing the whole number of persons in each State, excluding Indians not taxed, as ascertained under the fifteenth and each subsequent decennial census of the population, and the number of Representatives to which each State would be entitled under an apportionment of the then existing number of Representatives made in each of the following manners:

(1) By apportioning the then existing number of Representatives among the several States according to the respective numbers of the several States as ascertained under such census, by the method used in the last preceding apportionment, no State to receive less than one Member;

(2) By apportioning the then existing number of Representatives among the several States according to the respective numbers of the several States as

---

[105] Statutes at Large, 71st Congress, 1st Session, CHAP. 28, 18 June 1929: 21-27; accessed from https://www.loc.gov/law/help/statutes-at-large/71st-congress/session-1/c71s1ch28.pdf.

[106] Charles Eagles, Democracy Delayed, 1928-1929: 62-84.

[107] Orville Sweeting, John. Q. Tilson and the Reapportionment Act of 1929, *The Western Political Quarterly* 9(2) June 1956: 435-453.

ascertained under such census, by the method known as the method of major fractions, no State to receive less than one Member; and

(3) By apportioning the then existing number of Representatives among the several States according to the respective numbers of the several States as ascertained under such census, by the method known as the method of equal proportions, no State to receive less than one Member.

(b) If the Congress to which the statement required by subdivision (a) of this section is transmitted, fails to enact a law apportioning Representatives among the several States, then each State shall be entitled, in the second succeeding Congress and in each Congress thereafter until the taking effect of a reapportionment under this Act or subsequent statute, to the number of Representatives shown in the statement based upon the method used in the last preceding Certificate thereof to apportionment. It shall be the duty of the Clerk of the last House of Representatives forthwith to send to the executive of each State a certificate of the number of Representatives to which such State is entitled under this section. In case of a vacancy in the office of Clerk, or of his absence or inability to discharge this duty, then such duty shall devolve upon the officer who, under section 32 or 33 of the Revised Statutes, is charged with the preparation of the roll U.S.C., p.4. of Representatives-elect.

(c) This section shall have no force and effect in respect of the apportionment to be made under any decennial census unless the statement required by subdivision (a) of this section in respect of such census is transmitted to the Congress within the time prescribed in subdivision (a).

Approved, June 18, 1929.

This action finalized that there would be no reapportionment based on the census of 1920. However, when the 71st Congress receives the apportionment report based on the census of 1930 from the President, they would need to act by the end of that Congress or an automatic reapportionment would go into effect. In effect this would mean a House with 435 seats apportioned by the method of major fractions.

The passage of this bill came just in time. Black Thursday, 24 October 1929, initiated the worst stock market crash in U. S. history. The Great Depression was underway and would occupy the major attention of the country for the next decade.[108] The country became too busy to be concerned with apportionment. This law, with a few adjustments, is still the cornerstone of congressional apportionment methodology.

---

[108] http://useconomy.about.com/od/glossary/g/Black-Thursday-1929.htm.

Section 4.4: Reapportionment Based on the 1930 Census

Section 4.4.1   Background

On 5 December 1930 the Speaker laid several items from the President before the House. Among them was the following message.[1]

> *To the Congress of the United States:*
>
> In compliance with the provisions of section 22 (a) of the act approved June 18, 1929, I transmit herewith a statement prepared by the Bureau of the Census, Department of Commerce, giving the whole number of persons in each State, exclusive of Indians not taxed, as ascertained under the Fifteenth Decennial Census of Population, and the number of Representatives to which each State would be entitled under an apportionment of the existing number of Representatives by the method known as the method of major fractions, which was the method used in the last preceding apportionment, and also by the method known as the method of equal proportions.
>
> HERBERT HOOVER,
>
> THE WHITE HOUSE, *December 4, 1930.*

The automatic provisions specified in the act of 1929 were underway and working. The statement by President Hoover consisted of a table showing the list of the 48 states, their respective apportionment populations, and the apportionments for a House with 435 Representatives based on the method of major fractions and the method of equal proportions. Fortunately, the two methods agreed and yielded the same apportionments.

Table 4.15 (next page) displays a spreadsheet analysis of the information in President Hoover's message to Congress. The State/Seat/Population column set lists the 48 states, their current number of Representatives, and their apportionment populations based on the 1930 census. The Webster/Seats column set shows the results for the method of major fractions which uses a divisor of 279500 to obtain a House of 435. Notice that Nevada needs its constitutional minimum of 1 seat due to its quotient being under 0.5. The Huntington-Hill (H-H)/Seats column set displays the numbers obtained by the method of equal proportions. Interestingly, the integer part of the national divisor works for the method of equal proportions. This indicates that the Huntington-Hill method will produce the same result as Hamilton's method. Hence, the 1930 census results were fortunate in that the methods of Webster, Huntington-Hill, and Hamilton all agreed. Accordingly, methodology would not be an issue for apportionment based on the census of 1930. However, the underlying political elements and current events provided sufficient tensions for any issue in Congress.

Table 4.15 (next page). Report based on the 1930 census. The Webster method of distributing 435 seats uses a divisor of 279500; Huntington-Hill and Hamilton, 280675.

---

[1] Congressional Record, 71st Congress, 3rd Session, 5 December 1930: 246.

State	Seats	Population	Webster	Seats	H - H	Seats	Quota	Seats
Alabama	10	2646242	9.4678	9	9.4281	9	9.4281	9
Arizona	1	389375	1.3931	1	1.3873	1	1.3873	1
Arkansas	7	1854444	6.6349	7	6.6071	7	6.6071	7
California	11	5668241	20.2799	20	20.1950	20	20.1951	20
Colorado	4	1034849	3.7025	4	3.6870	4	3.6870	4
Connecticut	5	1606897	5.7492	6	5.7251	6	5.7251	6
Delaware	1	238380	0.8529	1	0.8493	1	0.8493	1
Florida	4	1468191	5.2529	5	5.2309	5	5.2309	5
Georgia	12	2908446	10.4059	10	10.3623	10	10.3623	10
Idaho	2	441536	1.5797	2	1.5731	2	1.5731	2
Illinois	27	7630388	27.3001	27	27.1858	27	27.1859	27
Indiana	13	3238480	11.5867	12	11.5382	12	11.5382	12
Iowa	11	2470420	8.8387	9	8.8017	9	8.8017	9
Kansas	8	1879498	6.7245	7	6.6963	7	6.6964	7
Kentucky	11	2614575	9.3545	9	9.3153	9	9.3153	9
Louisiana	8	2101593	7.5191	8	7.4876	8	7.4876	8
Maine	4	797418	2.8530	3	2.8411	3	2.8411	3
Maryland	6	1631522	5.8373	6	5.8129	6	5.8129	6
Massachusetts	16	4249598	15.2043	15	15.1406	15	15.1407	15
Michigan	13	4842052	17.3240	17	17.2515	17	17.2515	17
Minnesota	10	2551583	9.1291	9	9.0909	9	9.0909	9
Mississippi	8	2008154	7.1848	7	7.1547	7	7.1547	7
Missouri	16	3629110	12.9843	13	12.9299	13	12.9300	13
Montana	2	524729	1.8774	2	1.8695	2	1.8695	2
Nebraska	6	1375123	4.9199	5	4.8993	5	4.8993	5
Nevada	1	86390	0.3091	1	0.3078	1	0.3078	1
New Hampshire	2	465292	1.6647	2	1.6578	2	1.6578	2
New Jersey	12	4041319	14.4591	14	14.3986	14	14.3986	14
New Mexico	1	395982	1.4168	1	1.4108	1	1.4108	1
New York	43	12587967	45.0374	45	44.8489	45	44.8490	45
North Carolina	10	3167274	11.3319	11	11.2845	11	11.2845	11
North Dakota	3	673340	2.4091	2	2.3990	2	2.3990	2
Ohio	22	6646633	23.7804	24	23.6809	24	23.6809	24
Oklahoma	8	2382222	8.5232	9	8.4875	9	8.4875	9
Oregon	3	950379	3.4003	3	3.3860	3	3.3861	3
Pennsylvania	36	9631299	34.4590	34	34.3148	34	34.3148	34
Rhode Island	3	687497	2.4597	2	2.4494	2	2.4494	2
South Carolina	7	1738760	6.2210	6	6.1949	6	6.1949	6
South Dakota	3	673005	2.4079	2	2.3978	2	2.3978	2
Tennessee	10	2616497	9.3613	9	9.3222	9	9.3222	9
Texas	18	5824601	20.8394	21	20.7521	21	20.7521	21
Utah	2	505741	1.8094	2	1.8019	2	1.8019	2
Vermont	2	359611	1.2866	1	1.2812	1	1.2812	1
Virginia	10	2421829	8.6649	9	8.6286	9	8.6286	9
Washington	5	1552423	5.5543	6	5.5310	6	5.5310	6
West Virginia	6	1729199	6.1868	6	6.1609	6	6.1609	6
Wisconsin	11	2931721	10.4892	10	10.4453	10	10.4453	10
Wyoming	1	223630	0.8001	1	0.7968	1	0.7968	1
U. S.	435	1.22E+08	436.8281	435	434.9994	435	435.0000	435

Section 4.4.2   Automatic Pilot

The rural vs. urban values struggle was intense. On 16 December 1930 Bishop James Cannon sent the following letter to all members of Congress.[2]

BOARD OF TEMPERANCE AND SOCIAL SERVICE,
METHODIST EPISCOPAL CHURCH SOUTH,
Washington, D. C., December 16, 1930.

DEAR SIR: At a meeting of the executive committee of the Board of Temperance and Social Service of the Methodist Episcopal Church South, held in Washington on December 10, 1930, it was ordered that a resolution adopted by the full board at its annual meeting at Lake Junaluska, N. C., July 2-4, 1930, with reference to alien representation be sent to the Members of Congress. We are hereby sending to you the resolution appended below.

Yours very truly,

JAMES CANNON, Jr.,
E. L. CRAWFORD,
A. C. MILLAR,
LEVIN SMITH,
S. C. HATCHER,
Executive Committee.

Resolved, In view of the fact that under the new apportionment several States will suffer the loss of numbers of Members of Congress, which losses are principally in dry States, and since the States with the large wet-dominated cities now have approximately 30 Congressmen—30 electoral votes and 60 delegates to the national nominating conventions—who represent not American citizens but seven and one-half million of unnaturalized aliens, we heartily approve the Stalker resolution providing for an amendment to the Constitution of the United States which will eliminate entirely all the unnaturalized aliens in the enumeration of the population to determine congressional or electoral representation, thus placing control of the Government of the country in its own citizens. We believe that such action will be most helpful in eliminating a factor which is unfriendly to prohibition and law enforcement.

Bishop Cannon's letter with the Resolution was introduced into the Congressional Record by Robert Clancy (R-MI) while giving a scathing rebuttal.[3] Clancy equated the religious support of prohibition to the support that Southern churches gave to slavery before the Civil War. Clancy asserted that the South had disenfranchised over 10000000 blacks from voting in violation of the fourteenth amendment. If the Fourteenth Amendment were enforced the South would lose 35 Congressmen, 35 electoral votes, and 70 delegates to the national conventions. Clancy argued, "Since these unearned and illegal votes are dry votes, Bishop Cannon fights fiercely to

---

[2] Ibid, 17 December 1930: 997-8.
[3] Ibid.

retain them as against Representative Tinkham's efforts to right the wrong." When Congressman Tinkham (R-MA) submitted legislation to enforce the Fourteenth Amendment, Bishop Cannon denounced Tinkham as "an enemy of the Southland."

John Cochran (D-MO) was getting concerned that Congress was not going to take any action on apportionment. In that event the apportionment announced in President Hoover's message would take effect automatically. Cochran's concern was that by the 1929 statute the Clerk of the House would notify the state executives at the end of the current session of Congress, which occurred on 4 March 1931.[4] Cochran noted that many state legislatures which were now in session would be adjourned by then. Cochran stressed that redistricting was necessary because there were outrageous inequalities in congressional districts throughout the country. He stressed that the 1930 census showed that 56.2% of the population resides in urban areas. However, the current House has "268 Representatives classed as representing rural populations, while ... 160 as being Representatives of urban districts." He also noted as an example that one district in Missouri had a constituency of 715772, while a neighboring district had but 116495.

Accordingly, Cochran urged that the Clerk be authorized to officially notify the states now so that state legislatures will have time to redistrict before they adjourn. In response Bertrand Snell (R-NY), chair of the Rules Committee, simply dismissed Cochran's concern claiming that States can act on their own initiative. Subsequently, Cochran introduced H.R. 15983 to actualize his proposal. However, the bill was sent to the Committee on the Census where it died, as did all other apportionment legislation proposed during this session of Congress.

The key struggle regarding apportionment was over the issue of counting aliens. The rural-dry coalition valiantly tried to stem the tide of decreasing rural representation with increased urban representation. The efforts were neutralized by forces threatening to push Tinkham's efforts to enforce the Fourteenth Amendment. A final cap was placed in the Senate by a revealing table submitted by Senator Vandenberg.[5] He noted, "The study is interesting in view of the movement to emphasize citizenship by the exclusion of aliens from the apportionment count." Vandenberg hypothetically proposed basing the apportionment population on the voter count; hence, exclude all but voters. His tables showed an enormous loss of 64 seats in the southern states. The table was a blow to nativist arguments.

On 2 March 1931 a jubilant Robert Clancy proclaimed, "Mr. Speaker, a tremendous victory for orderly government in the Republic was won when this Congress recently frustrated all efforts to delay or block congressional reapportionment." The full Committee on the Census met on 27 February and voted 13 to 8 not to report any bills out of committee. Hence, all efforts to block or delay apportionment based on the census of 1930 were dead. Automatic reapportionment would take effect on 4 March 1931.

---

[4] Ibid, 9 January 1931: 1887-95.
[5] Ibid, 20 January 1931: 2633.

Chapter 5

Congressional Apportionment

Based on the Census

1940-2000

The Huntington-Hill Era

Chapter 5
Congressional Apportionment Based on the Census 1940-2010
The Huntington-Hill Era

Table of Contents

Reference:

The cover map is courtesy of http://www.1940census.net/1940_us_map.php.

However, the history of apportionment in the House of Representatives up to the present day clearly indicates that the solution of our founding fathers was just a compromise and not a real solution.[1]

Representative Emanuel Celler, New York

Introduction

This chapter describes the history of apportionment of the national House of Representatives based on the census 1940-2010. The Constitution directs that representation in the House shall be based on an enumeration of the people as determined by a decennial census. The censuses 1940-2010 feature the Huntington-Hill modified divisor method for House apportionment.

During the first six census decades, 1790-1840, Congress applied a basic divisor method, a census-based method initiated by a constituency approach to congressional apportionment: how many people should a congressman represent? The answer is called the ratio, divisor, or constituency. The ratio is divided into a state's population to calculate the state's quotient. During the first five censuses, 1790-1830, the fractional remainder was dropped to obtain a state's apportionment. In 1840 the first mutation in apportionment methodology occurred when Webster's rounding criterion was applied to the quotients. The quotient was rounded normally to obtain a state's apportionment. Experience taught that there are political effects to the choice of divisor and the rounding technique.

In 1850 forces emerged to change the approach to apportionment from a constituency approach to a House size approach. The constituency initiating question, how many people should a congressman represent, was replaced by, what should be the size of the House? The resulting seats in the House were then distributed by Hamilton's method, also referred to as the Vinton plan. Legislators hoped the new approach would take the politics out of reapportionment of the House. This time, however, it was not unacceptable political consequences that doomed the method but unexpected mathematical consequences. Over the next fifty years unintuitive paradoxes began to emerge. The situation known as the Alabama Paradox led to the ultimate demise of Hamilton's method.

Quota rule violations doomed the basic divisor method. Paradoxes doomed the Hamilton-Vinton method. Congress scrambled to invent an alternative. The eventual result was a modified divisor method where the House size was first established and then set aside as a goal for a divisor method. A new method of rounding the quotient decimal, the Huntington-Hill method, was established as the method of choice in 1940.

---

[1] Emanuel Celler, Congressional Apportionment: Past, Present, and Future, *Law and Contemporary Problems*, 17(2) Legislative Reapportionment (Spring, 1952): 268-75.

Section 5.1: Reapportionment Based on the 1940 Census

Section 5.1.1 The Twentieth Amendment

The act of 1929 put congressional apportionment on automatic pilot if Congress failed to act in a timely manner. The procedure worked well for reapportionment based on the 1930 census. But a constitutional amendment intervened on the way to the 1940 census. The Twentieth Amendment, ratified on 23 January 1933, contains six sections and deals in part with the timing for the terms of principal federal office holders. The first two sections read as follows.[1]

> **Section 1.** The terms of the President and Vice President shall end at noon on the 20th day of January, and the terms of Senators and Representatives at noon on the 3d day of January, of the years in which such terms would have ended if this article had not been ratified; and the terms of their successors shall then begin.
> **Section 2.** The Congress shall assemble at least once in every year, and such meeting shall begin at noon on the 3d day of January, unless they shall by law appoint a different day.

The Twentieth Amendment was nicknamed "the lame duck amendment." One purpose of the amendment was to eliminate the lame duck component in the terms of President and members of Congress. It seemed to present a desirable streamlining of the calendar of government presented in the Constitution. The Heritage Guide to the Constitution notes "that the amendment was ratified by the states more quickly than any other constitutional amendment before or since supports this impression of an uncontroversial technical revision."[2]

The problem with The Twentieth Amendment is that the change in commencement for the term of the President and the start of Congress made it impossible for compliance with the calendar mandated by the apportionment law of 1929. To comply with the timetable of the 1929 law, the President would have to present the apportionment results to Congress based on the 1940 census before the 1940 census was taken. Oops.

Section 5.1.2 54 STAT 162 (1940)

The first session of the 76th Congress met from 3 January to 5 August 1939. On 26 May 1939 Senator Arthur Vandenberg (R-MI) introduced Senate bill S2505 to amend the census act of 1929 so that the specified calendar would be compatible with the Twentieth Amendment. Upon presenting S2505 to the Senate he asked, "consent to introduce a bill to amend the act of 1929 merely to revise the calendar so that the report of the President may follow the taking of the census." Without objection the bill was received and sent to the Senate Committee on Commerce (the Census Bureau is housed in the Department of Commerce).[3]

---

[1] https://www.law.cornell.edu/constitution/amendmentxx
[2] http://www.heritage.org/constitution#!/amendments/20/essays/182/presidential-terms
[3] Congressional Record, 26 May 1939: 6201-2.

Senator Vandenberg was determined to have the Senate focus on the task of making this technical calendar change in the apportionment act of 1929. He did not want to allow other issues to delay apportionment as it did in the 1920s. Riptides for other issues had already begun, especially the issue of counting aliens in the apportionment population. On 1 February 1939 Senator Arthur Capper (R-KS) introduced Senate Joint Resolution 54 to amend the Constitution to exclude aliens who have not completed their naturalization from the apportionment population.[4]

Mr. Capper argued that there were 14 million foreign born persons in the U. S. Of these, 8 million were naturalized citizens, leaving 6 million alien noncitizens. He presented a typical rural values point of view by noting that 1.5 million of these noncitizen aliens lived in New York State thereby yielding four representatives for New York. He contended that representation must be based on citizenship, not residence. His justification was that "We are spending billions on defense." Further, many aliens are "active in un-American activities working and boring on from within." He concluded, "I favor the bill now before Congress that would cancel citizenship for those advocating communism, fascism, and nazism."[5]

On 7 June 1939 Mr. Vandenberg from the Committee on Commerce referred S2505 without amendment to the full Senate. The bill was augmented with Senate Report No. 556 which explained the technical details of the calendar conflicts between the act of 1929 and the Twentieth Amendment.[6] The report explains:[7]

> The act of 1929 calls for a census in 1940 and fixes April 1, 1940, as the day to commence the enumeration of population. It requires that the tabulation of total population shall be completed within eight months (which would be November 1, 1940) and reported within this time limit to the President of the United States.
>
> The President thereupon is required to report this enumeration and a calculation of Congressional reapportionment (by three different methods based thereon) to the Congress "on the first day or within one week thereafter of the second regular session of the Seventy-sixth Congress."
>
> Prior to the adoption of the twentieth amendment, the second regular session of the Seventy-sixth Congress would have convened December 1, 1940, 1 month after the president gets his completed census enumeration. But as a result of the twentieth amendment, the second regular session of the Seventy-sixth Congress convenes on January 3, 1940, which is 11 months before the President gets his enumeration, and it is 4 months before the census even starts. Therefore this "time table" is manifestly inoperative.

Hence, it was totally clear that the act of 1929 had to be amended if Congress wanted to maintain automatic apportionment. On 13 June 1939 the Senate proceeded to consider and

---

[4] Ibid, 1 February 1939: 999.
[5] Ibid: 1003-4.
[6] Ibid, 7 June 1939: 6741.
[7] 76th Congress, 1st Session, Senate, Report 556, 7 June 1939: 2.

pass S2505.[8] The bill was then sent to the House for concurrence. The House received the bill on 15 June and referred it to the House Committee on Commerce.[9]

On 24 July Clarence McLeod (R-MI) introduced H.R. 7348 which was referred to the House Committee on Commerce.[10] H.R. 7348 differed from S2505 only by the dates used to correct the act of 1929 which demanded a quicker decision by Congress. On 3 August the Speaker recognized Mr. McLeod for 1 minute who then appealed that Congress must amend the act of 1929 if decennial reapportionment is to be assured.[11] Nothing further on apportionment happened during the 1st Session. On 5 August the 1st Session of the 76th Congress ended.

The 2nd Session of the 76th Congress was brief, lasting only from 21 September to 3 November 1939. Apportionment was not a topic of consideration. The 3rd Session lasted a year from 3 January 1940 to 3 January 1941. Finally, the House had time to act on apportionment.

To spur the House to act, on 4 January 1940 President Franklin Roosevelt sent a letter to Matthew Dunn (D-PA), chair of the House Committee on the Census, urging action on S2505. The President stressed the necessity of congressional action so that he could comply with the mandates of the 1929 act for apportionment. For reference the letter was inserted into the Appendix of the Congressional Record by Representative Dunn.[12]

On 14 March 1940 the Vandenberg bill S2505 was reported out of the House Committee on Commerce to the Whole House on the State of the Union. The Committee reported favorably on S2505 with amendment. The bill was supplemented with House Report No. 1787 to explain the committee's recommendation.[13] The amendment had two features. The first feature amended the calendar to have Congress make a quicker decision on apportionment after receiving the report from the President transmitting the information from the Census Bureau. The purpose was to enable state legislatures to conduct timely redistricting decisions without calling special sessions of the state legislatures. Earlier Lindsay Warren (D-NC) introduced H.R. 8653 which was the same as Vandenberg's Senate bill but with earlier reporting dates. Mr. Warren reported to the House that Vandenberg approved the earlier timetable.[14]

The second feature contained the following loaded sentence:[15]

> In submitting the statement to Congress he shall exclude aliens from the population total in the several States and apportion the number of Representatives accordingly.

---

[8] Congressional Record, 13 June 1939: 7089.
[9] Ibid, 15 June 1939: 7277.
[10] Ibid, 24 July 1939: 9897.
[11] Ibid, 3 August 1939: 10949.
[12] Ibid, Appendix, 12 January 1940: 166.
[13] Ibid, 14 March 1940: 2916.
[14] Ibid, 11 April 1940: 4367.
[15] 76th Congress, 3d Session, House of Representatives, Report No. 1787: 1.

The component that excludes aliens reignited the debate between rural and urban values that impeded reapportionment based on the 1920 census. Accordingly, action on apportionment stalled. Some creative maneuver was needed to get things moving again. Consequently, instead of the usual House procedure, William Nelson (D-MO) brought forward House Resolution 456 from the Rules Committee. The resolution asked for the House to consider S2505 immediately. Hence, the first part of the debate was whether to adopt the resolution. After a half hour the resolution was adopted and formal debate on S2505 proceeded although most of the debate on the resolution concerned S2505.[16]

Mr. Warren added that although the committee "saw fit to provide an amendment providing for the exclusion of aliens from the population totals in making the apportionment," in his opinion this "is clearly unconstitutional." He further reported that after the alien provision of the amendment was added, the committee met again and authorized striking it. Mr. Dunn followed by verifying Mr. Warren's claim.[17]

In addition to Mr. Warren, William Nelson (D-MO), Hamilton Fish (R-NY), and Leland Ford (R-CA) spoke to urge the House to stay on task and pass legislation needed for the calendar adjustment enabling the act of 1929 to conform to the Twentieth Amendment. After a short inquiry about "Indians not taxed," John Rankin (D-MS), one of the principal players in the nonreapportionment based on the 1920 census and still in Congress,[18] spoke to interject a rambled variety of unrelated apportionment concerns.

Mr. Rankin first complained about the inequality of congressional district sizes, using New York and Illinois as examples. Then he advocated that state legislatures, not Congress, are responsible to correct this "rotten boroughs" situation.

Mr. Rankin opened his main remarks claiming that if this bill passes then it "freezes the House at 435 Members now and in perpetuity." Also, it transferred the "right to apportion" from Congress to the President. He then argued that the nonreapportionment based on the census of 1920 was justified. He repeated his old argument that the Constitution does not require that Congress reapportion after the census, but only that if Congress reapportions, then it must be based on the census. In addition he cautioned that if this bill passes, then "the probabilities are that Congress will never again reapportion the House of Representatives."[19]

Mr. McLeod got things back on track by stressing the urgency of quick passage so that state legislatures can enact appropriate redistricting legislation. Emanuel Celler (R-NY) rose not only to stress the urgency of S2505, but to squelch objections to including aliens in apportionment populations. First, Mr. Celler supported the proposal to strike the Census Committee's insertion to exclude aliens. Mr. Celler emphasized the Fourteenth Amendment, Section 2:

---

[16] 76th Congress, 3d Session, House of Representatives: 4366-4373.
[17] Ibid: 4367.
[18] Zechariah Chafee, Jr., Reapportioning the House of Representatives under the 1940 Census, *Proceedings of the Massachusetts Historical Society*, Third Series, Vol. 66 (Oct., 1936-May,1941):372.
[19] Ibid: 4368-4369.

Representatives shall be apportioned among the several States according to their respective numbers, counting the whole number of persons in each State, excluding Indians not taxed.

Mr. Celler emphasized that the constitutional term is "persons," not "citizens." Accordingly, aliens "are protected alike with citizens as to due process and equal protection of the law." He cited three Supreme Court cases which "unequivocally hold" that "persons" includes "aliens." Mr. Celler concluded, "If you want aliens out, you must amend the Constitution." He also deftly included that among the counted were "Negroes—originally three-fifths of the Negroes." One could not escape that as part of the Great Compromise to accommodate the slave states, the Constitution originally specified the counting of all free persons, excluding Indians not taxed, and three-fifths of all others. However, in slave states the slaves were not citizens. Hence, it was clear from the onset that *person* was not equivalent to *citizen*.

Mr. Celler then met head on Mr. Rankin's charge that the counting of aliens gave an unjust advantage to the larger states. Mr. Celler noted that over half the population was contained in just nine states; so, less than half the population resided in the other thirty-nine states. Considering the Senate and the Electoral College, the smaller states have a huge advantage in power over the more populous states. Mr. Celler concluded this argument with the observation that not counting aliens would only increase this discrepancy in power. The founding fathers recognized this point and accordingly in the Constitution based taxation and representation on an enumeration of the total population, not just citizens.

At the time of this debate in Congress, the most important topic of the day was the rise of Nazism and the war in Europe. Mr. Celler deftly exploited this situation. He started by reporting on hearings from the Committee on the Judiciary that addressed the issue of whether aliens were counted in assessing the population base for legislatures in other countries. The entire population was the enumeration basis, among others, in Argentina, Brazil, Chile, England, Canada, Australia, Union of South Africa, and France. He concluded, "The only nation that I have discovered that departed from the practice was Germany, and there, for purposes of reapportionment, only nationals are considered. I presume only Nazis would be considered of the amount for representation in their more popular legislative branch."[20]

The debate was over and it was time to make decisions. The Speaker announced, "The question is on agreeing to the resolution." The resolution was immediately agreed to. Accordingly, Mr. Dunn moved "that the House resolve itself into the Committee of the Whole House of the State of the Union for the consideration of the bill (S. 2505)." The motion passed.

Discussion began with a request by Francis Case (R-SD) for clarification on "Indians not taxed." Is this equivalent to "not subject to taxation?" The consensus was in the affirmative and there was agreement that all Indians would be included in the apportionment population.[21]

---

[20] Ibid: 4371-4373
[21] Ibid: 4373-4374.

Frederick Smith (R-OH) spoke against S2505 because he was opposed to automatic reapportionment. He asserted that the House would lose its power over apportionment because the Senate could kill any measure simply by not acting and thereby activating the automatic process. He emphasized that the basis for his concern was that the most important rationale for representation is the preservation of individual property rights.[22]

The remainder of the debate time was devoted mainly to Indians and aliens.[23] After the debate time expired the Clerk read the first portion of the bill and then amendments were in order. James Mott (R-OR) offered the amendment to change the House size to 300. His rationale was that the House was too large making it unwieldy. Mr. Warren objected with a point of order that the amendment was not germane. After some discussion the chairman (Marvin Jones, D-TX) ruled with Mr. Warren; hence, the Mott amendment was not admitted.[24]

Frederick Smith (R-OH) offered an amendment that would require the computation by the Census Bureau be done only by "the method used in the last apportionment." The effect of this proposal would be to adopt Webster's modified divisor method. After short discussion the amendment was rejected.[25]

The Clerk then read the bill as it stands. Afterwards Mr. Dunn offered the committee amendment to strike the part excluding aliens from the apportionment population. John Schafer (R-WI) offered an amendment that would enforce the Fourteenth Amendment to the Constitution and reduce apportionment for those states that denied citizens the right to vote. Again Mr. Warren objected with a point of order that the Schafer amendment was not germane. The chairman again ruled in Warren's favor. However, Schafer was allowed to make a statement in which he condemned the suppression of the black vote in the South.[26]

Clarence McLeod (R-MI) offered the amendment that the time allotted by Congress to take action once the Census Office report was transmitted to House by the President be restricted to 60 days rather than the entire session of Congress. His rationale was to give state legislatures time to redistrict while in session rather than imposing the need to call special sessions of state legislatures. A vote was taken and the McLeod amendment failed, 81-89. Immediately Michael Bradley (D-PA) demanded a recount by tellers. This time the McLeod amendment passed, 119-91. Subsequently the Dunn amendment was agreed to without further debate.[27]

The chairman of the House Committee on the Whole House on the State of the Union then rose to report the amended S2505 to the House for action. The Speaker of the House now took over as presider of the session. Malcolm Tarver (D-GA) demanded a vote of the House on the committee amendment on striking the exclusion of aliens from the enumeration of the

---

[22] Ibid: 4374-4377.
[23] Ibid: 4377-
[24] Ibid: 4382-4383.
[25] Ibid: 4384.
[26] Ibid 4384-4385.
[27] Ibid: 4385-4386.

population. So, a vote was taken sustaining the committee's recommendation to strike the phrase excluding aliens from the enumeration of the population, passed 209-23.[28] This was a resounding affirmation by the House that all people, not just citizens, were to be included in the apportionment populations of the various states.

The Speaker then called for a vote on the bill, passed. No vote count was recorded.[29] The amended bill was sent to the Senate. On 12 April 1940 Mr. Vandenberg made the motion to agree, which was immediately approved.[30] The bill was subsequently processed and then approved by President Franklin Roosevelt on 25 April 1940 (Figure 5.1.)[31]

Figure 5.1. 54 Stat. 162 (1940).

The final apportionment item for the 76th Congress was supplied by Mr. Rankin. On 5 December 1940 he introduced the apportionment bill H.R. 10718. Mr. Rankin was in his finest form in presenting this bill. His presentation obviously acknowledged that Congress wanted the safeguards of automatic apportionment. His bill had three features. First, the House size would be reset to 450. Second, the method of equal proportions would be used in the apportionment calculations. Third, the bill supplied provisions governing election of representatives in states whose number of representatives changed in the event that the state legislature did not redistrict in time for the next national election.[32]

---

[28] Ibid: 4386.

[29] Ibid: 4386.

[30] Ibid: 4402.

[31] United States Statutes at Large, Volume 54, Chap. 152: 162. Available as Pub. Law 76-162 or 54 Stat. 162 from https://www.loc.gov/law/help/statutes-at-large/76th-congress/session-3/c76s3ch152.pdf.

[32] Congressional Record, 76th Congress, 3rd Session, 5 December 1940: 13845-13848, 13857.

Mr. Rankin argued that at House size 450 no state would lose representation except for Kansas and Oklahoma who would lose one representative each. Sadly, both states lost population over the 1930 decade due to the Dust Bowl. Further, as Albert Rutherford (R-PA) pointed out, only Kansas would need to redistrict since one of Oklahoma's representatives, Will Rogers (D-OK), was elected at-large.[33] Hence, House size 450 would provide maximum convenience with a minimal increase in House size.

The main debate centered on House size. Earl Michener (R-MI) argued that the House was already too large and that he would vote to reduce the House size to 300. The discussion pointed out two sides to the issue. On one side Mr. Michener argued that the greater the House size, the more unwieldy the House becomes. Mr. Rankin countered that the smaller the House size, the greater the workload for the individual congressman.[34]

One of Mr. Rankin's key points was to advocate for the method of equal proportions. He emphasized that in keeping the House size at 435, the method of major fractions in contrast to the method of equal proportions would affect only two states. Using the method of major fractions, the default method under the act of 1929, Arkansas would lose a seat and Michigan would gain a seat. Apportionment for all other states would be the same under either method. Mr. Rankin supported equal proportions since both Arkansas and Michigan would retain their current number of seats. Further, he referred to earlier studies that concluded the method of equal proportions is "logically superior to the method of major fractions."[35]

Mr. Rankin's bill was sent to the Committee on the Census. Since there was little time left in the 76th Congress, the committee took no action. Besides, the committee had yet to perform the daunting task of digesting the extensive information contained in a report by Edward Huntington, printed as a Senate document at the request of Senator David Walsh (D-MA).[36] However, Mr. Rankin's proposal set the stage for the major fractions vs. equal proportions fight in the House, 77th Congress. The contest was set up to feature Michigan vs. Arkansas. This should be quite a game!

Section 5.1.3   55 STAT 761 (1941)

The first session of the 77th Congress opened on 3 January 1941. On 8 January President Roosevelt transmitted to Congress the apportionment information based on the 1940 census prepared by the Census Bureau as required by law. President Roosevelt noted that the Director of the Census included all Indians in the apportionment populations.[37] The next day Senator Vandenberg asked that the apportionment tables for House size 435 (Table 5.1, next page) be included in the Congressional Record. There was no objection.

---

[33] Ibid: 13847.

[34] Ibid.

[35] Ibid: 13845.

[36] Edward V. Huntington, Methods of Apportionment in Congress, 76th Congress, 3[d] Session, Senate Document No. 304: 1940. Accessed on 28 August 2019 from https://babel.hathitrust.org/cgi/pt?id=uc1.b3996194&view=1up&seq=1221.

[37] Congressional Record, 77th Congress, 1st Session, 8 January 1941: 51, 70-71.

Congress was now on high alert that it had only sixty days to act before the automatic apportionment provisions kicked in. On 24 January Ezekiel Gathings (D-AR) introduced H.R. 2665, a bill to provide for apportioning Representatives in Congress by the equal proportions method. The bill was then sent to the House Committee on the Census.[38]

On 5 February Guy Moser (D-PA), as chair of the Committee on the Census, reported favorably without amendment on both H.R. 2665 and H.R. 1619. H.R. 1619, known also as the Rankin bill, not only specified the method of equal proportions, but also increased the House size to 450. As explanation of the committee's position, H.R. 2665 was accompanied by House Report No. 30 and H.R. 1619 by House Report No. 31. Both reports cited the report of the National Academy of Sciences issued in 1929 to justify its endorsement of equal proportions.[39]

Debate about apportionment began on 17 February.[40] Mr. Moser began by summarizing the position of the Committee on the Census. First, equal proportions and major fractions apportioned the 435 seats in the House in the same way except for Arkansas and Michigan. At House size 434 Arkansas had 6 seats and Michigan 17. The 435th seat would be given to one of these two states. Equal proportions awarded the seat to Arkansas while major fractions awarded the seat to Michigan. The act of 1929 directed the Census Bureau to compute the apportionment of 435 seats by both the equal proportions and the major fractions methods (Table 5.1, next page). By the amendment enacted in 1940, if Congress did not act within 60 days, then the method last used, the method of major fractions, would act as default. Hence, the committee felt that Congress should decide who gets the 435th seat, Arkansas or Michigan.

Mr. Moser advanced that the committee made its decision by asking, Which method is fairest? All the testimony from experts, including mathematicians, statisticians, the Census Bureau, except Professor Willcox, advocated equal proportions over major fractions. The scientific case for major fractions was further weakened by Willcox's change of heart, now preferring the method of smallest divisors (Adams's method) over major fractions.[41]

---

[38] Ibid, 24 January 1941: 303.
[39] Ibid, 5 February 1941: 679.
[40] Ibid, 17 January 1941: 1080-1089.
[41] Ibid, 1080.

Table 5.1. Apportionment table presented to Congress from the Census Bureau.

TABLE 1.—*Populations of the States, 1940; and apportionment of Representatives in Congress, 1940 and 1930*

State	Population Apr. 1, 1940	Present number of Representatives	Apportionment of 435 Representatives, 1940					
			Method of major fractions			Method of equal proportions		
			Number of Representatives	Change from 1930		Number of Representatives	Change from 1930	
				Gain	Loss		Gain	Loss
	(1)	(2)	(3)	(4)	(5)	(6)	(7)	(8)
United States	131,669,275	435	435	16	16	435	9	9
Alabama	2,832,961	9	9			9		
Arizona	499,261	1	2	1		2	1	
Arkansas	1,949,387	7	6		1	7		
California	6,907,387	20	23	3		23	3	
Colorado	1,123,296	4	4			4		
Connecticut	1,709,242	6	6			6		
Delaware	266,505	1	1			1		
District of Columbia	663,091							
Florida	1,897,414	5	6	1		6	1	
Georgia	3,123,723	10	10			10		
Idaho	524,873	2	2			2		
Illinois	7,897,241	27	26		1	26		1
Indiana	3,427,796	12	11		1	11		1
Iowa	2,538,268	9	8		1	8		1
Kansas	1,801,028	7	6		1	6		1
Kentucky	2,845,627	9	9			9		
Louisiana	2,363,880	8	8			8		
Maine	847,226	3	3			3		
Maryland	1,821,244	6	6			6		
Massachusetts	4,316,721	15	14		1	14		1
Michigan	5,256,106	17	18	1		17		
Minnesota	2,792,300	9	9			9		
Mississippi	2,183,796	7	7			7		
Missouri	3,784,664	13	13			13		
Montana	559,456	2	2			2		
Nebraska	1,315,834	5	4		1	4		1
Nevada	110,247	1	1			1		
New Hampshire	491,524	2	2			2		
New Jersey	4,160,165	14	14			14		
New Mexico	531,818	1	2	1		2	1	
New York	13,479,142	45	45			45		
North Carolina	3,571,623	11	12	1		12	1	
North Dakota	641,935	2	2			2		
Ohio	6,907,612	24	23		1	23		1
Oklahoma	2,336,434	9	8		1	8		1
Oregon	1,089,684	3	4	1		4	1	
Pennsylvania	9,900,180	34	33		1	33		1
Rhode Island	713,346	2	2			2		
South Carolina	1,899,804	6	6			6		
South Dakota	642,961	2	2			2		
Tennessee	2,915,841	9	10	1		10	1	
Texas	6,414,824	21	21			21		
Utah	550,310	2	2			2		
Vermont	359,231	1	1			1		
Virginia	2,677,773	9	9			9		
Washington	1,736,191	6	6			6		
West Virginia	1,901,974	6	6			6		
Wisconsin	3,137,587	10	10			10		
Wyoming	250,742	1	1			1		

Advocates for equal proportions pushed their advantage by examining district size under both proposals. Mr. Gathings presented the following specifics. Michigan's population was 5256106 while Arkansas's was 1949387. If Michigan is awarded the seat, then Michigan's average district size is 5256106/18 = 292006. If Arkansas is awarded the seat, then Arkansas's average district size is 1949387/6 = 324898. The resulting disparity is that Arkansas has a district size 32892 larger than Michigan. Reversing the apportionment gives Michigan 17 seats with resulting district size 309182 and Arkansas 7 seats with district size 278484. The corresponding disparity is that Michigan has an average district size 30699 larger than Arkansas. Thus, the raw numbers show that equal proportions results in a smaller disparity between the two states when average district size is taken as the measure of fairness.[42]

Fred Gilchrist (R-IA) argued that aliens should not be counted in the apportionment figures. He provided preliminary figures from the Department of Justice, Immigration and Naturalization Service, that showed that Arkansas only had 3210 aliens while Michigan had 290730. The implication seemed to be that Michigan was underserving of the additional seat because of Michigan's alien population.[43]

Carl Curtis (R-NE) countered Mr. Gathings argument in the following way. The U. S. population divided by 435 seats yields a national average district size of 301163. Providing Michigan with the additional seat yields an average district size of 292006 for the 18 congressmen. Providing Arkansas with the additional seat yields an average district size of 278484 for the 7 congressmen. Hence, it is fairer to award the seat to Michigan because it brings Michigan's average district size closer to the national average.[44]

Debate resumed the next day.[45] John Murdock (D-AZ), a member of the House Committee on the Census, countered Mr. Curtis's argument. Start with the national average district size of 301163. Before the 435th seat is assigned, Michigan has 17 representatives and Arkansas has 6. Thus, Michigan represents in general 17x301163 = 5119771 people, leaving a residue of 136335 people. And Arkansas represents in general 6x301163 = 1806978 people, leaving a residue of 142415 people. Hence, he concluded that "Arkansas has more than 6000 persons over Michigan for that four hundred and thirty-fifth congressman."[46]

Further statements were mostly a rehash of arguments already presented with occasional nastiness included. J. Roland Kinzer (R-PA) moved to recommit H.R. 2665 back to the Committee on the Census; failed, 146-206. A vote was then taken on the bill; passed, 210-146.[47] Balinski and Young specifically note the partisan nature of the vote.[48]

---

[42] Ibid: 1086-1087.

[43] Ibid: 1085-1086.

[44] Ibid: 1088.

[45] Ibid, 18 February 1941: 1123-1130.

[46] Ibid: 1123.

[47] Ibid: 1129-30.

[48] Michel L. Balinski and H. Peyton Young, *Fair Representation: Meeting the Ideal of One Man, One Vote*, second edition, Brookings Institution Press, Washington, D. C., 2001: 58.

The political motives were only too apparent. Arkansas was a safe Democratic state, Michigan's normal leanings were Republican. Every Democrat, except those from Michigan, voted for Gathings's bill, and every Republican voted against.

The next day the bill was sent to the Senate. The Senate referred it to the Senate Committee on Commerce.[49] The committee soon held hearings on the bill.[50] The committee heard testimony on the background and main thinking from the House Committee on the Census for passing H.R. 2665 which specified the method of equal proportions for calculating congressional apportionment. Testimony was given by Meyer Jacobstein, a key player in the House as a representative from New York facilitating the passage of the act of 1929. Mr. Jacobstein, now with the Brookings Institution, argued strongly and cogently in favor of the equal proportions method.[51] He advanced that Congress made great progress and has done "two things which are splendid: You have got 435 as the number of Members of the House." Further, "You have preserved the automatic feature of the law." The final third step was to "write into law the method known as equal proportions." His final appeal was:

> If that is written into the law I think you will have for all time—at least until some mathematician like Einstein comes along with a better method—something that will fill the bill. Thus far we know of no better method than this which is embodied in the bill before you.

It was clear that the competing apportionment methods were equal proportions and major fractions. The only expert testifying in favor of major fractions over equal proportions was Walter Willcox.[52] He noted that the National Academy of Sciences had previously "reported in 1929 on five methods which were mathematically satisfactory." Willcox also stated that the NAS was asked to report on just the mathematical aspects, not the political aspects of apportionment. Willcox opined, "It is my conviction that the mathematical aspects of apportionment have been greatly exaggerated." Willcox stated that apportionment is "primarily a political question."

Willcox then proceeded to embrace the method of smallest divisors as his most preferred method. Although not mentioned by name, the method of smallest divisors is the Adams method of apportionment where all decimal quotients are rounded up. Willcox's confusing testimony basically destroyed any scientific basis for supporting major fractions. From expert opinion, the method of equal proportions was the final method left standing.

Finally, on 22 July the Senate Committee on Commerce reported favorably on H.R. 2665 with amendment and recommended that the amended bill pass. The amended bill was

---

[49] Congressional Record, 71st Congress, 1st Session, 19 February 1941: 1150.
[50] Apportionment of Representatives in Congress, Hearings before a Subcommittee of the Committee on Commerce on H.R. 2665, February 27, 28, and March 1, 1941, United States Government Printing Office, Washington, 1941; https://babel.hathitrust.org/cgi/pt?id=umn.31951d02156449y&view=1up&seq=5.
[51] Ibid: 7-9.
[52] Ibid: 14-17.

accompanied by Senate Report 573. The committee noted in their report that the 60-day window for congressional action had expired and that automatic apportionment using the method of major fractions was thereby in progress. The report stated that the Senate was too busy with the land lease bill among other things to deal with apportionment. Noting that the 60-day window had expired, the Senate committee amended H.R. 2665 to retract the automatic apportionment in progress under major fractions and reissue any certificates of notification if needed. The Committee on Commerce approved this action by a vote of 11 to 6.

The Senate debated H.R. 2556 with amendment on 20-21 October.[53] Included in the Record was a carefully written statement by Calvert Dedrick, chief statistician for the Census Bureau.[54] The statement explained the fairness rationale for the methods of equal proportions and major fractions as they affected Michigan and Arkansas. Equal proportions had the effect of minimizing the disparity in average district size between the two states. Major fractions had the effect of minimizing the disparity in number of representatives per one million people, a criterion which is the reciprocal of district size.

Mr. Dedrick faced the question from Arkansas that "By the method of major fractions you propose to take a member away from Arkansas and give it to Michigan. Why?" Mr. Dedrick replied that "The answer is simple." At 7 Arkansas has 3.5909 representatives per million people. Michigan at 17 has 3.2343 representatives per million. Thus, Michigan is underrepresented by 0.3566 votes in the House per million people in comparison with Arkansas. If Arkansas has 6 and Michigan 18 congressmen, then the respective ratios are 3.0779 and 3.4246 leaving Arkansas underrepresented by 0.3467 votes in the House per million people. Hence, the transfer of the representative from Arkansas to Michigan is justified.

Mr. Dedrick concluded his presentation with the observation that "major fractions does not equalize as nearly as possible the average congressional districts among the States. It only equalizes the votes in the House of Representatives per million people in the States." He then noted that there is a method that minimizes the disparity in district size between the states as measured by the absolute difference. He explained, "The reason this method is not mentioned in the apportionment law is its awesome title; it is the method of the harmonic mean."

When measured in terms of absolute difference, making the fairness criterion for apportionment the average district size leads to the method of the harmonic mean (Dean's method). Making the fairness criterion the number of representatives per person, or more conveniently per million people, leads to the method of major fractions (Webster's method). However, if we use ratios (equal proportions) rather than absolute difference, then it does not matter whether the focus is on district size or representatives per million.

---

[53] Ibid: 8050-8059, 8076-8088.
[54] Ibid: 8058-8059.

Mr. Dedrick concluded by quoting the conclusion in the extensive and daunting report submitted by Professor Edward Huntington.[55]

> The method of equal proportions may be defined as the only method which will apportion a given number of Representatives among the several States, so that the ratios of population to Representatives, and also the ratios of Representatives to population, shall be equal as may be among the several States.

The definitive presentation bended the debate over what is the fairest method of apportionment as far as the Senate was concerned. However, Prentiss Brown (D-MI) was upset over the retroactive feature of the Senate amendment. He moved to amend the amendment striking features that would make equal proportions retroactive and apply to the 1940 census.[56] The motion failed 19-44.[57] Then, in quick succession without a recorded vote, the amendment recommended by the Committee on Commerce passed. Then, the amended H.R. 2556 passed. On 6 November the House agreed to the Senate amendment.[58] President Roosevelt approved the bill on 15 November 1941.[59] The relevant section of the act is given below in Figure 5.2.

Number of Representatives in 78th Congress.	SEC. 2. (a) Each State shall be entitled, in the Seventy-eighth and in each Congress thereafter until the taking effect of a reapportionment under a subsequent statute or such section 22, as amended by this Act, to the number of Representatives shown in the statement transmitted to the Congress on January 8, 1941, based upon the method known as the method of equal proportions, no State to receive less than one Member.

Figure 5.2. Section 2 of 55 Stat 571.

The report from the Census Bureau contained priority list tables using major fractions and equal proportions. First, as the Constitution requires, one seat is given to each state. This distributed 48 seats. Using either method, seat 49 went to New York and seat 50 to Pennsylvania. But then differences in results between the two methods began to show. By major fractions, seat 51 went to New York and seat 52 went to Illinois. Under equal proportions this result was reversed as seat 51 went to Illinois and seat 52 went to New York.[60]

The Arkansas vs. Michigan conflict could have been resolved by increasing the House size to 436. Under major fractions, seat 435 went to Michigan and seat 436 went to Arkansas. Equal proportions reversed this assignment. However, Congress did not want to make House size a political football again. The main purpose of the automatic apportionment feature of the act of 1929 is to write the rules of the game before the game begins. Congress did not like the idea of adjusting the rules of the game while the game was in progress.

---

[55] Edward V. Huntington, Methods of Apportionment in Congress, 76th Congress, 3d Session, Senate Document No. 304: 6.

[56] Congressional Record, 77th Congress, 1st Session, 21 October 1941: 8083.

[57] Ibid: 8088.

[58] Ibid: 8579-8582.

[59] United States Statutes at Large, Volume 55, 77th Congress, 1st Session, Chap. 470: 761-2; available at https://www.loc.gov/law/help/statutes-at-large/77th-congress/c77s1.pdf.

[60] Congressional Record, 77th Congress, 1st Session, 6 November 1941: 8085-8087.

The method of equal proportions was now written into law as the method of congressional apportionment. Automatic apportionment is now in place unless Congress acts within 60 days of the Census Report as transmitted by the President: the House will have 435 seats apportioned by the method of equal proportions.

Section 5.1.4   The Aftermath

From experience the political and mathematical aspects of congressional apportionment became sharpened and precipitated into a comprehensive theory. It also became clear that understanding two basic arithmetical principles help considerably in understanding the history, politics, and mathematics of congressional apportionment: (1) how to average two positive numbers, and (2) how to round a decimal. These two principles may at first sound simple, perhaps even trivial, but they turn out to be profound.[61]

Two Arithmetical Principles

First consider the averaging process. Suppose that a and b are two positive numbers where a < b. There are five ways to average them. The choice depends on context and rationale. Denote the average of a and b by ave(a,b). Then the five choices are given by ave(a,b) =

1.   max(a,b) = b; i.e., the maximum of a and b.
2.   min(a,b) = a; i.e., the minimum of a and b.
3.   AM(a,b) = ($a + b$)/2; i.e., the arithmetic mean (the "usual" way to average).
4.   GM(a,b) = $\sqrt{ab}$; i.e., the geometric mean.
5.   HM(a,b) = 2/(1/a + 1/b) = 2ab/($a + b$); i.e., the harmonic mean.

Second, these five averaging methods can be applied to the problem of how to round a decimal. Suppose that q is a positive number with a nonzero decimal fraction component; i.e., not a whole number. Sometimes it is convenient to round the decimal number. Suppose that n is the integer component of the decimal number. Then a round for q, denoted by round(q), is either n (q rounded down) or n+1 (q rounded up). The general rounding criterion is to round up if and only if $q \geq$ ave(n,n+1). Hence, there are five mechanisms for the rounding process. By default round down, but round up if and only if

1. $q \geq$ max(n,n+1). Since this never happens, always round down.
2. $q \leq$ max(n,n+1). Since this always happens, always round up.
3. $q \geq$ AM(n,n+1). This is called arithmetic mean rounding (the "usual" way).
4. $q \geq$ GM(n,n+1). This is called geometric mean rounding.
5. $q \geq$ HM(n,n+1). This is called harmonic mean rounding.

Note how the decimal rounding procedure is intimately paired with an averaging procedure. The history of congressional apportionment is intricately tied to the rounding procedure. Rounding procedure 1 defines Jefferson's method; rounding procedure 2, Adams's method;

---

[61] Charles Biles, *An Average Lesson*, 2015. Available at http://nia977.wixsite.com/drbcap/resources.

rounding procedure 3, Webster's method; rounding procedure 4, the Huntington-Hill method; and rounding procedure 5, Dean's method. Further, Jefferson's method became known as the method of largest divisors (LD), Adams's method as the method of smallest divisors (SD), Webster's method as the method of major fractions (MF), Dean's method as the method of the harmonic mean (HM), and the Huntington-Hill method as the method of equal proportions (EP). The key point here is that an understanding of these five apportionment methods necessitates the understanding of the five methods for how to round a decimal and how to average.

Political and Mathematical Aspects

Congress resolved the political process of congressional apportionment with the act of 1929 and the two amendments in 1940 and 1941. The resolution had three components.

1. An automatic feature to guarantee an apportionment based on the census.
2. The House size is fixed at 435.
3. The method of equal proportions is the method for computing apportionment which results in the distribution of the 435 seats among the states.

History clarified several aspects, showing once again that experience is a wonderful teacher. First, there are only two approaches to the congressional apportionment problem: the constituency approach and the House size approach. The constituency approach starts with the question, how many people should a congressperson represent? The House size approach starts with the question, how many seats should there be in the House? Each approach leads to different methods. Further, natural notions of fairness conflict between the two approaches.

Second, history shows that a constituency approach can result in excessive political gamesmanship. The House size approach leads to either a quota method or a modified divisor method. A quota method leads to deal breaking paradoxes. Hence, in 1910 Congress settled on a modified divisor method. The controversy then narrowed to which of the five decimal rounding methods to use within the modified divisor algorithm. This led to the natural question, which method is fairest?

Third, history showed that the mechanism of computation can facilitate the apportionment process. There are two mechanisms for a modified divisor method: ad hoc and priority. An ad-hoc technique specifies the House size and then determines the apportionment for that House size. The algorithm needs to be rerun to consider a different House size. A priority technique first assigns one seat to each state. In today's world, this assigns the first 50 congressional seats. The priority list then identifies which state has priority for the 51st seat, 52nd seat, and currently up to the 440th seat. The priority list then takes us directly back to the question of how to average the round-up, round-down options, since the priority for a state with n seats to receive an additional seat is computed by dividing the state's population by ave($n,n+1$). For the average, LD uses min, SD uses max, EP uses GM, MF uses AM, and Dean uses HM.[62]

---

[62] Charles Biles, *Congressional Apportionment: A Liberal Arts Perspective*, 2016: 32-36. Available from http://nia977.wixsite.com/drbcap/resources.

Fourth, algorithms for basic divisor, quota, and modified divisor methods became well defined. The algorithms rely on the methods for how to round a decimal. Each rounding method comes with its own political justification.[63] Table 5.2 displays the apportionment for a House with 435 representatives based on the 1940 census using the five historical methods.

The methods of Greatest Divisors (Jefferson) and Smallest Divisors (Adams) display quota violations. Jefferson displays upper quota violations for California, Ohio, Pennsylvania, and New York which has a two-seat upper quota violation. Adams displays lower quota violations for Illinois and New York. Adams also displays several glaring examples of bias favoring small states over large states. For example, South Dakota has a quota of 2.1349 and is awarded three seats while Ohio has a quota of 22.9364 and is awarded 22 seats. The other three methods, Harmonic Mean (Dean), Equal Proportions (Huntington-Hill), and Major Fractions (Webster) display no quota rule violations. Those three methods yield the same apportionments except that Webster awards a seat to Arkansas at the expense of Michigan.

The quota was featured in previous decades but did not appear in the Arkansas vs. Michigan debate. Arkansas could have appealed to quota fractions. Michigan's quota of 435 seats was 17.457 and Arkansas's was 6.473 giving Arkansas a close call edge over Michigan. Further, the method of equal proportions agreed with the Hamilton quota method, whereas major fractions differed for both Arkansas and Michigan. Although the quota method suffers from paradoxes, these anomalies only occur when comparing various House sizes or varying populations. At a fixed House size, the Alabama paradox is not an issue. The quota method has a natural appeal as a "fair share" method.

The concept of district size appeared jumbled and confused in the debate. References were made to the national average district size, 301163, obtained by dividing the total U. S. population by 435. However, this national divisor would not work for apportioning 435 seats using either equal proportions or major fractions. The national divisor was too large to apportion 435 seats by equal proportions and too small by major fractions. Using equal proportions, one must use a divisor between 299906 and 300384. Using major fractions, one must use a divisor between 300472 and 300795. Hence, a convenient and workable average district size for equal proportions is 300000 and 300500 for major fractions. In comparing equal proportions with major fractions, arguing from the viewpoint of district size can be an apples vs. oranges comparison since the methods involve different average district sizes. Congressmen arguing their point of view by using district sizes produced by the final results were really and unknowingly appealing, as Calvert Dedrick emphasized, to the method of harmonic means. For comparison, Harmonic Means works with the national divisor, Smallest Divisor 316700, and Greatest Divisor 285000 to achieve House size 435.

Table 5.2 (next page). Apportionment based on the 1940 census comparing the five historical divisor methods is displayed, along with the quota based on a House size of 435. EP is Equal Proportions (Huntington-Hill), MF is Major Fraction (Webster), HM is Harmonic Mean (Dean), SD is Smallest Divisor (Adams), GD is greatest divisor (Jefferson).

---

[63] Ibid

State	Seats	Population	EP	MF	HM	SD	GD	Quota	Hamilton
Alabama	9	2832961	9	9	9	9	9	9.4067	9
Arizona	1	499261	2	2	2	2	1	1.6578	2
Arkansas	7	1949387	7	6	7	7	6	6.4728	7
California	20	6907387	23	23	23	22	24	22.9357	23
Colorado	4	1123296	4	4	4	4	3	3.7299	4
Connecticut	6	1709242	6	6	6	6	5	5.6755	6
Delaware	1	266505	1	1	1	1	1	0.8849	1
Florida	5	1897414	6	6	6	6	6	6.3003	6
Georgia	10	3123723	10	10	10	10	10	10.3722	10
Idaho	2	524873	2	2	2	2	1	1.7428	2
Illinois	27	7897241	26	26	26	25	27	26.2224	26
Indiana	12	3427796	11	11	11	11	12	11.3818	11
Iowa	9	2538268	8	8	8	9	8	8.4282	8
Kansas	7	1801028	6	6	6	6	6	5.9802	6
Kentucky	9	2845627	9	9	9	9	9	9.4488	9
Louisiana	8	2363880	8	8	8	8	8	7.8492	8
Maine	3	847226	3	3	3	3	2	2.8132	3
Maryland	6	1821244	6	6	6	6	6	6.0474	6
Massachusetts	15	4316721	14	14	14	14	15	14.3335	14
Michigan	17	5256106	17	18	17	17	18	17.4527	17
Minnesota	9	2792300	9	9	9	9	9	9.2717	9
Mississippi	7	2183796	7	7	7	7	7	7.2512	7
Missouri	13	3784664	13	13	13	12	13	12.5668	13
Montana	2	559456	2	2	2	2	1	1.8576	2
Nebraska	5	1315834	4	4	4	5	4	4.3692	4
Nevada	1	110247	1	1	1	1	1	0.3661	1
New Hampshire	2	491524	2	2	2	2	1	1.6321	2
New Jersey	14	4160165	14	14	14	14	14	13.8136	14
New Mexico	1	531818	2	2	2	2	1	1.7659	2
New York	45	13479142	45	45	45	43	47	44.7569	45
North Carolina	11	3571623	12	12	12	12	12	11.8594	12
North Dakota	2	641935	2	2	2	3	2	2.1315	2
Ohio	24	6907612	23	23	23	22	24	22.9364	23
Oklahoma	9	2336434	8	8	8	8	8	7.7580	8
Oregon	3	1089684	4	4	4	4	3	3.6182	4
Pennsylvania	34	9900180	33	33	33	32	34	32.8731	33
Rhode Island	2	713346	2	2	2	3	2	2.3686	2
South Carolina	6	1899804	6	6	6	6	6	6.3082	6
South Dakota	2	642961	2	2	2	3	2	2.1349	2
Tennessee	9	2915841	10	10	10	10	10	9.6819	10
Texas	21	6414824	21	21	21	21	22	21.3001	21
Utah	2	550310	2	2	2	2	1	1.8273	2
Vermont	1	359231	1	1	1	2	1	1.1928	1
Virginia	9	2677773	9	9	9	9	9	8.8914	9
Washington	6	1736191	6	6	6	6	6	5.7649	6
West Virginia	6	1901974	6	6	6	7	6	6.3154	6
Wisconsin	10	3137587	10	10	10	10	11	10.4182	10
Wyoming	1	250742	1	1	1	1	1	0.8326	1
US	435	131006184	435	435	435	435	435	435.0000	435

Despite the invariable post-mortem arguments that will probably occur in the future, the apportionment debate based on the 1940 census set in place a matured procedure having an automatic procedure with a fixed House size and fixed apportionment method. Results were communicated from the Census Bureau to the President and Congress in the form of a priority list up to 440 seats. A well-defined precedent is now in place. Any future proposal for change carries the burden of proof about being an improvement.

Section 5.2:   Reapportionment Based on the 1950 Census

Section 5.2.1   Automatic Apportionment

The 1950 census saw many innovations at the Census Bureau. For the first time the enumeration included citizens and their dependents living abroad, "including the armed forces of the United States, employees of the U. S. Government, and crews of vessels in the American Merchant Marine at sea or in foreign ports."[1] The Bureau experienced technological advancement and innovations in the use of the first nonmilitary computer, UNIVAC I.[2]

On 9 January 1951 President Truman transmitted the report from the Director of the Census which gave the population of each state along with its corresponding apportionment.[3] Also provided, as prescribed by law, was the apportionment based on the 1950 census using House size 435 and the method of equal proportions (Table 5.3).[4]

Table 5.3. Apportionment table based on the census of 1950.

DEPARTMENT OF COMMERCE, BUREAU OF THE CENSUS, Washington 25, D. C.

Population of the United States, by States, 1950, and apportionment of Representatives in Congress, 1950 and 1940

State	Population, 1950	Present number of Representatives	Apportionment of 435 Representatives according to 1950 population			State	Population, 1950	Present number of Representatives	Apportionment of 435 Representatives according to 1950 population		
			Number	Change from present number of Representatives					Number	Change from present number of Representatives	
				Increase	Decrease					Increase	Decrease
(1)	(2)	(3)	(4)	(5)	(6)	(1)	(2)	(3)	(4)	(5)	(6)
United States	150,697,361	435	435	14	14	Montana	591,024	2	2		
						Nebraska	1,325,510	4	4		
Alabama	3,061,743	9	9			Nevada	160,083	1	1		
Arizona	749,587	2	2			New Hampshire	533,242	2	2		
Arkansas	1,909,511	7	6		1	New Jersey	4,835,329	14	14		
California	10,586,223	23	30	7		New Mexico	681,187	2	2		
Colorado	1,325,089	4	4			New York	14,830,192	45	43		2
Connecticut	2,007,280	6	6			North Carolina	4,061,929	12	12		
Delaware	318,085	1	1			North Dakota	619,636	2	2		
District of Columbia	802,178					Ohio	7,946,627	23	23		
Florida	2,771,305	6	8	2		Oklahoma	2,233,351	8	6		2
Georgia	3,444,578	10	10			Oregon	1,521,341	4	4		
Idaho	588,657	2	2			Pennsylvania	10,498,012	33	30		3
Illinois	8,712,176	26	25		1	Rhode Island	791,896	2	2		
Indiana	3,934,224	11	11			South Carolina	2,117,027	6	6		
Iowa	2,621,073	8	8			South Dakota	652,740	2	2		
Kansas	1,905,299	6	6			Tennessee	3,291,718	10	9		1
Kentucky	2,944,806	9	8		1	Texas	7,711,194	21	22	1	
Louisiana	2,683,516	8	8			Utah	688,862	2	2		
Maine	913,774	3	3			Vermont	377,747	1	1		
Maryland	2,343,001	6	7	1		Virginia	3,318,680	9	10	1	
Massachusetts	4,690,514	14	14			Washington	2,378,963	6	7	1	
Michigan	6,371,766	17	18	1		West Virginia	2,005,552	6	6		
Minnesota	2,982,483	9	9			Wisconsin	3,434,575	10	10		
Mississippi	2,178,914	7	6		1	Wyoming	290,529	1	1		
Missouri	3,954,653	13	11		2						

---

[1] U. S. Census Bureau, https://www.census.gov/programs-surveys/decennial-census/library/publications/decennial.1950.html.

[2] Ibid, https://www.census.gov/history/www/through_the_decades/overview/1950.html.

[3] Special Message to the Congress on the Need for More Equal Apportionment of Congressional Districts, accessed from http://trumanlibrary.org/publicpapers/index.php?pid=203&st=&st1=. Also, House of Representatives Document No. 36, 82nd Congress, 1st Session, 1951.

[4] Congressional Record, 82nd Congress, 1st Session, 9 January 1951: 114-115.

Census 1950

A debate on apportionment was not going to happen.[5]

> Is there any chance of a revival of Willcox's method? It would affect just one seat.
> Kansas would lose one congressman and California would get him. No sane man
> is going to get up in the capitol and urge giving eight new seats to California, which
> will gain seven anyway. At a recent conference, Willcox joined in a unanimous
> resolution, that there is "no practical reason" for departing from the present
> method. Therefore, the best mathematical method—Huntington's, called the
> method equal proportions—is here for good.

The only possible challenge from the automatic apportionment results would come from
interests preferring the method of major fractions over the method of equal proportions.
However, the two methods gave the same results except for two states. Equal proportions
assigned 30 seats to California (a gain of 7 seats) and 6 seats to Kansas (no change). Major
proportions assigned 31 seats to California and 5 to Kansas. Not even California spoke up to
replace equal proportions with major fractions.

Sixteen states experienced a change in apportionment based on the 1950 census. Seven
states gained: California 7, Florida 2, Maryland, Michigan, Texas, Virginia, and Washington.
Nine states lost: Arkansas, Illinois, Kentucky, Mississippi, Missouri 2, New York 2, Oklahoma 2,
Pennsylvania 3, and Tennessee.

In his transmission letter to Congress President Truman noted the automatic features of the
apportionment process. However, President Truman wrote, "certain problems have arisen with
respect to the creation of appropriate districts within the States, which merit the consideration
of Congress." The problems all concerned redistricting within the states. In particular,
President Truman noted the "widespread discrepancies" in district size. He noted that one
state had a congressional district of 175000 and another of 900000. Further, some fifty districts
were under 250000 and another fifty districts over 450000. President Truman concluded that
although redistricting is the task of state legislatures, the problem is of national concern, "and
the Congress has a Constitutional obligation in this field which cannot be overlooked."

President Truman urged Congress to pass legislation mandating that all congresspersons
come from single member districts which are compact, contiguous, and "as nearly as
practicable an equal number of inhabitants." Although these were statutory requirements in
1911, the apportionment act of 1929 failed to incorporate those guidelines into law. President
Truman closed his letter by urging that "proper redistricting be done promptly."

In response on 14 February 1951 Emanuel Celler (R-NY) introduced H.R. 2648 specifying
that congressional districts must be continuous and compact. The bill was referred to the
House Committee on the Judiciary.[6] On 20 February Erwin Hall (R-NY) introduced a supporting

---

[5] Zechariah Chafee, Congressional Reapportionment under the Census of 1950, *Proceedings of the Massachusetts Historical Society*, Third Series, Vol. 70 (Oct., 1950 – May, 1953): 237-239.
[6] Congressional Record, 82 Congress, 1st Session, 14 February 1951: 1276.

273

bill, H.R. 2799, a bill to strengthen national security defenses by outlawing the gerrymander and saving representative government. Hall's bill was also sent to the Committee on the Judiciary.[7] National security was useful to promote legislation since the Korean War (25 June 1950 - 27 July 1953) was well underway.[8] Further, just a year before the anticommunist witch-hunts of Senator Joseph McCarthy (R-WI) started with a vengeance.[9]

In addition to these bills concerning redistricting, the usual anomalies were reintroduced. On 30 January Joseph Bryson (D-SD) introduced House Joint Resolution 140 proposing a constitutional amendment excluding aliens in counting the population for apportionment.[10]

On October 1951, well after the deadline for Congress to defer automatic reapportionment, John Rankin (D-MS) introduced H.R. 5771, a bill to postpone reapportionment until after the next census, a special census to be taken in 1955. The bill was referred to the Committee on the Judiciary.[11]

In March the American Political Science Association released their report strongly urging Congress to pass legislation requiring single member congressional districts that are compact, contiguous, and approximately of equal size with a deviation not to exceed 15% of the average congressional district size for the state. The unanimous report was widely distributed to the White House, Congress, and other government agencies.[12] [13]

No apportionment bill made it out of committee. The automatic feature mandated by the act of 1929 was the only action on apportionment. Congress took no action on redistricting.

Section 5.2.2   Methods Compared

Reapportionment based on the 1950 census was the first in which the apportionment procedure was set in advance and there were no mid-course changes, adjustments, or supplements. Consequently, we will review each of the apportionment methods thus far proposed. There are three categories of methods: basic divisor, quota, and modified divisor.

The key feature of a basic divisor method is that it starts with the constituency question, how many people should a congressperson represent? The answer is often called the divisor because it is divided into each state's population to determine each state's quotient. Variations in the divisor method occur from rounding the quotient decimal. We consider five rounding methods for rounding the quotient.

---

[7] Ibid, 20 February 1951: 1413.

[8] Korean War, 2009, accessed from http://www.history.com/topics/korean-war.

[9] McCarthyism, US History Online Textbook, 2016, accessed from http://www.ushistory.org/us/53a.asp.

[10] Congressional Record, 82 Congress, 1st Session, 30 January: 753-754.

[11] Ibid, 17 October 1951: 13406.

[12] The Reapportionment of Congress, *The American Political Science Review*, Vol. 45, No. 1 (Mar., 1951): 153-157.

[13] Congressional Record, 82 Congress, 1st Session, Appendix: 82.

- Jefferson: round down.
- Dean: harmonic mean rounding.
- Hill: geometric mean rounding.
- Webster: arithmetic mean rounding (the usual method of rounding a decimal).
- Adams: round up.

To start the method, we need a divisor. Since we are analyzing apportionment based on the 1950 census, we use the resulting national divisor: (national population)/435 = 149895183/435 which, taking the integer part of the answer, is 344586. The national divisor represents the average congressional district size for 435 seats based on the nation as a whole. The results are shown in Table 5.4.

Each of the five methods results in a different House size: Jefferson 410, Webster 438, Hill 439, Dean 440, and Adams 455. In comparison with Webster, Hill gives an additional seat to Oklahoma whose quotient is 6.4813. Since the decimal part is less than .5, Webster rounds the quotient down. However, the geometric mean of the round down, round up options is given by GM(6,7) = 6.4807. Thus, Hill rounds Oklahoma up to 7 seats since Oklahoma's quotient exceeds the geometric mean rounding criterion. Dean, in comparison to Hill, gives an additional seat to Michigan. Michigan's quotient, 18.4911, is larger than HM(18,19) = 18.4865 but smaller than GM(18,19) = 18.4932; hence, Dean awards Michigan 19 seats while Hill awards Michigan 18 seats. Thus, the method of rounding the quotient decimal is decisively important.

Congress used a basic divisor method for apportionment based on the census 1790-1840. In 1850 Congress switched to a quota method. To analyze results based on the 1950 census, each state's quota is obtained by multiplying each state's proportion of the national population by 435; i.e., (state quota) = 435 x (state population)/(national population). Subsequently each state is given its lower quota; i.e., the quota rounded down. This distributes 410 of the 435 seats. The remaining 25 seats are distributed according to a priority list.

Table 5.4 (next page). The State/Seats/Population column set lists the 48 states, the number of seats (based on the 1940 census), and the population from the 1950 census. The quotient column shows each state's quotient based on the national divisor 344586. In Jefferson's method the constitutional minimum of one seat comes into play for Delaware, Nevada, and Wyoming. Dean rounds the quotient up if the quotient exceeds the harmonic mean of the round down, round up options. Similarly, Huntington-Hill (H-H) and Webster round the quotient up if the quotient exceeds the geometric mean or arithmetic mean, respectively. The constitutional minimum requirement comes into play for the Webster basic divisor method only for Nevada. Adams rounds all decimals up.

State	Seats	Population	quotient	Jefferson	Dean	H-H	Webster	Adams
Alabama	9	3061743	8.8853	8	9	9	9	9
Arizona	2	749587	2.1753	2	2	2	2	3
Arkansas	7	1909511	5.5415	5	6	6	6	6
California	23	10586223	30.7216	30	31	31	31	31
Colorado	4	1325089	3.8455	3	4	4	4	4
Connecticut	6	2007280	5.8252	5	6	6	6	6
Delaware	1	318085	0.9231	1	1	1	1	1
Florida	6	2771305	8.0424	8	8	8	8	9
Georgia	10	3444578	9.9963	9	10	10	10	10
Idaho	2	588637	1.7082	1	2	2	2	2
Illinois	26	8712176	25.2830	25	25	25	25	26
Indiana	11	3934224	11.4172	11	11	11	11	12
Iowa	8	2621073	7.6064	7	8	8	8	8
Kansas	6	1905299	5.5292	5	6	6	6	6
Kentucky	9	2944806	8.5459	8	9	9	9	9
Louisiana	8	2683516	7.7877	7	8	8	8	8
Maine	3	913774	2.6518	2	3	3	3	3
Maryland	6	2343001	6.7995	6	7	7	7	7
Massachusetts	14	4690514	13.6120	13	14	14	14	14
Michigan	17	6371766	18.4911	18	19	18	18	19
Minnesota	9	2982483	8.6553	8	9	9	9	9
Mississippi	7	2178914	6.3233	6	6	6	6	7
Missouri	13	3954653	11.4765	11	11	11	11	12
Montana	2	591024	1.7152	1	2	2	2	2
Nebraska	4	1325510	3.8467	3	4	4	4	4
Nevada	1	160083	0.4646	1	1	1	1	1
New Hampshire	2	533242	1.5475	1	2	2	2	2
New Jersey	14	4835329	14.0323	14	14	14	14	15
New Mexico	2	681187	1.9768	1	2	2	2	2
New York	45	14830192	43.0377	43	43	43	43	44
North Carolina	12	4061929	11.7879	11	12	12	12	12
North Dakota	2	619636	1.7982	1	2	2	2	2
Ohio	23	7946627	23.0614	23	23	23	23	24
Oklahoma	8	2233351	6.4813	6	7	7	6	7
Oregon	4	1521341	4.4150	4	4	4	4	5
Pennsylvania	33	10498012	30.4656	30	30	30	30	31
Rhode Island	2	791896	2.2981	2	2	2	2	3
South Carolina	6	2117027	6.1437	6	6	6	6	7
South Dakota	2	652740	1.8943	1	2	2	2	2
Tennessee	10	3291718	9.5527	9	10	10	10	10
Texas	21	7711194	22.3781	22	22	22	22	23
Utah	2	688862	1.9991	1	2	2	2	2
Vermont	1	377747	1.0962	1	1	1	1	2
Virginia	9	3318680	9.6309	9	10	10	10	10
Washington	6	2378963	6.9038	6	7	7	7	7
West Virginia	6	2005552	5.8202	5	6	6	6	6
Wisconsin	10	3434575	9.9673	9	10	10	10	10
Wyoming	1	290529	0.8431	1	1	1	1	1
US	435	149895183	435.0008	410	440	439	438	455

Table 5.5 (next page) shows quota method results using three different priority lists: Hamilton, Lowndes, and Hill. In Hamilton's method the lower quotas distribute 407 of the 435 seats. Hence, 28 more seats need to be distributed to reach House size 435. First, Hamilton assigns a seat to any state with a lower quota of 0 to satisfy the constitutional requirement that each state must receive at least one seat. This distributes a seat each to Delaware, Nevada, and Wyoming. These states then are removed from further consideration. The remaining 25 seats are distributed using Hamilton's priority list which consists of the decimal fraction component of a state's quota. Hamilton's method suffered from the politically inconvenient result that three states (Arkansas, Kansas, Kentucky) had decimal fractions greater than .5 but did not make the priority for an additional seat since the last used Hamilton priority number for seat 435 was 0.6064 (Nebraska).

Lowndes's priority list consists of each state's constituency (average district size) using the adjusted lower quota where any state with a lower quota of 0 is adjusted to 1. Hill's priority list consists of dividing each state's population by the geometric mean of the lower and upper quotas. However, if the lower quota is 0, then this leads to a division by zero. In that case, the state has top priority and is automatically given a seta. In practice, Hamilton's priority was the only one ever used. Lowndes's priority was a flash in the pan proposal, but the thinking behind the proposal was frequently used in debate as evidence that one method was better than another. Hill's priority was never used in the context of a quota method. But Huntington picked up on Hill's proposal and adapted it to a modified divisor method. This yielded the Huntington-Hill method used for apportionment based on every census since 1940.

Table 5.6 (page 280) shows the results of applying a modified divisor method. To achieve a House size of 435, Jefferson's method must use a divisor between 329555 and 329559, inclusively; Dean, between 347651 and 347922; Huntington-Hill between 347136 and 347684; Webster between 346497 and 347089; and Adams between 365043 and 365746. Note that in a basic divisor method the divisor is constant but the resulting House size can vary depending on the quotient rounding mechanism. In a modified divisor method the House size is fixed but the resulting divisor needed to achieve that result varies. In this case all five basic divisor methods yield different results. Further, none of the five modified divisor methods agree with Hamilton's method. Also, Jefferson's and Adams's modified methods contain blatant quota rule violations displaying their intrinsic bias towards large and small states, respectively.

Among the thirteen methods displayed (five basic divisor, three quota, and five modified divisor methods), only two of them agree: the Huntington-Hill modified divisor method and the Hill quota method. As a result, theoretical questions came to the forefront after the method and technique of apportionment were settled. What is the fairest method and how can fairness be measured? What is bias and how can bias be measured? What specific political goal should apportionment strive to reach? Such questions will soon serve as a launch pad for future research into the congressional apportionment problem.

Table 5.5. *The spreadsheet displays the results of apportioning the 435 seats in congress using the three quota methods presented in U. S. history: Hamilton, Lowndes, and Hill.*

State	Seats	Population	Quota	Lower	Hamilton	Lowndes	Seats	Hill	Seats
Alabama	9	3061743	8.8853	8	9	382717	9	360830	9
Arizona	2	749587	2.1753	2	2	374793	3	306018	2
Arkansas	7	1909511	5.5415	5	5	381902	6	348627	6
California	23	10586223	30.7215	30	31	352874	30	347136	30
Colorado	4	1325089	3.8454	3	4	441696	4	382520	4
Connecticut	6	2007280	5.8252	5	6	401456	6	366478	6
Delaware	1	318085	0.9231	0	1	318085	1		1
Florida	6	2771305	8.0424	8	8	346413	8	326601	8
Georgia	10	3444578	9.9963	9	10	382730	10	363090	10
Idaho	2	588637	1.7082	1	2	588637	2	416229	2
Illinois	26	8712176	25.2830	25	25	348487	25	341720	25
Indiana	11	3934224	11.4172	11	11	357656	11	342430	11
Iowa	8	2621073	7.6064	7	8	374439	8	350256	8
Kansas	6	1905299	5.5292	5	5	381059	6	347858	6
Kentucky	9	2944806	8.5459	8	8	368100	8	347049	8
Louisiana	8	2683516	7.7876	7	8	383359	8	358600	8
Maine	3	913774	2.6518	2	3	456887	3	373047	3
Maryland	6	2343001	6.7995	6	7	390500	7	361533	7
Massachusetts	14	4690514	13.6120	13	14	360808	13	347684	14
Michigan	17	6371766	18.4910	18	18	353987	18	344546	18
Minnesota	9	2982483	8.6552	8	9	372810	8	351489	9
Mississippi	7	2178914	6.3233	6	6	363152	6	336214	6
Missouri	13	3954653	11.4765	11	11	359513	11	344208	11
Montana	2	591024	1.7152	1	2	591024	2	417917	2
Nebraska	4	1325510	3.8467	3	4	441836	4	382642	4
Nevada	1	160083	0.4646	0	1	160083	1		1
New Hampshire	2	533242	1.5475	1	2	533242	2	377059	2
New Jersey	14	4835329	14.0323	14	14	345380	14	333669	14
New Mexico	2	681187	1.9768	1	2	681187	2	481672	2
New York	45	14830192	43.0376	43	43	344888	43	340946	43
North Carolina	12	4061929	11.7878	11	12	369266	11	353546	12
North Dakota	2	619636	1.7982	1	2	619636	2	438149	2
Ohio	23	7946627	23.0613	23	23	345505	23	338231	23
Oklahoma	8	2233351	6.4812	6	6	372225	6	344614	6
Oregon	4	1521341	4.4150	4	4	380335	5	340182	4
Pennsylvania	33	10498012	30.4655	30	30	349933	30	344243	30
Rhode Island	2	791896	2.2981	2	2	395948	3	323290	2
South Carolina	6	2117027	6.1437	6	6	352837	6	326664	6
South Dakota	2	652740	1.8943	1	2	652740	2	461557	2
Tennessee	10	3291718	9.5527	9	10	365746	9	346978	9
Texas	21	7711194	22.3781	22	22	350508	22	342804	22
Utah	2	688862	1.9991	1	2	688862	2	487099	2
Vermont	1	377747	1.0962	1	1	377747	2	267107	1
Virginia	9	3318680	9.6309	9	10	368742	9	349820	10
Washington	6	2378963	6.9038	6	7	396493	7	367082	7
West Virginia	6	2005552	5.8202	5	6	401110	6	366162	6
Wisconsin	10	3434575	9.9672	9	10	381619	10	362036	10
Wyoming	1	290529	0.8431	0	1	290529	1		1
US	435	149895183	435.0000	407	435		435		435

Table 5.6. The five historic modified divisor methods applied for
apportionment based on the census of 1950.

State	Seats	Population	LD	HM	GM	AM	SD
Alabama	9	3061743	9	9	9	9	9
Arizona	2	749587	2	2	2	2	3
Arkansas	7	1909511	5	6	6	6	6
California	23	10586223	32	30	30	31	29
Colorado	4	1325089	4	4	4	4	4
Connecticut	6	2007280	6	6	6	6	6
Delaware	1	318085	1	1	1	1	1
Florida	6	2771305	8	8	8	8	8
Georgia	10	3444578	10	10	10	10	10
Idaho	2	588637	1	2	2	2	2
Illinois	26	8712176	26	25	25	25	24
Indiana	11	3934224	11	11	11	11	11
Iowa	8	2621073	7	8	8	8	8
Kansas	6	1905299	5	6	6	5	6
Kentucky	9	2944806	8	8	8	8	9
Louisiana	8	2683516	8	8	8	8	8
Maine	3	913774	2	3	3	3	3
Maryland	6	2343001	7	7	7	7	7
Massachusetts	14	4690514	14	14	14	14	13
Michigan	17	6371766	19	18	18	18	18
Minnesota	9	2982483	9	9	9	9	9
Mississippi	7	2178914	6	6	6	6	6
Missouri	13	3954653	11	11	11	11	11
Montana	2	591024	1	2	2	2	2
Nebraska	4	1325510	4	4	4	4	4
Nevada	1	160083	1	1	1	1	1
New Hampshire	2	533242	1	2	2	2	2
New Jersey	14	4835329	14	14	14	14	14
New Mexico	2	681187	2	2	2	2	2
New York	45	14830192	45	43	43	43	41
North Carolina	12	4061929	12	12	12	12	12
North Dakota	2	619636	1	2	2	2	2
Ohio	23	7946627	24	23	23	23	22
Oklahoma	8	2233351	6	6	6	6	7
Oregon	4	1521341	4	4	4	4	5
Pennsylvania	33	10498012	31	30	30	30	29
Rhode Island	2	791896	2	2	2	2	3
South Carolina	6	2117027	6	6	6	6	6
South Dakota	2	652740	1	2	2	2	2
Tennessee	10	3291718	9	9	9	9	10
Texas	21	7711194	23	22	22	22	22
Utah	2	688862	2	2	2	2	2
Vermont	1	377747	1	1	1	1	2
Virginia	9	3318680	10	10	10	10	10
Washington	6	2378963	7	7	7	7	7
West Virginia	6	2005552	6	6	6	6	6
Wisconsin	10	3434575	10	10	10	10	10
Wyoming	1	290529	1	1	1	1	1
US	435	149895183	435	435	435	435	435

Section 5.3:   Reapportionment Based on the 1960 Census

Section 5.3.1   Background

The completion of the 50 states in the union was accomplished just before the 1960 census. Alaska was admitted as the 49th state on 3 January 1959.[1] Hawaii was admitted as the 50th state on 21 August 1959.[2] Alaska and Hawaii's statehoods are the only times a video was made of a Presidential proclamation for a state.[3] President Eisenhower signed both statehood proclamations. Each state was granted one representative upon admission temporarily bringing the House size to 437 until reapportionment based on the 1960 census reverted the House back to 435 seats.

The 1960 census also saw further evolution in census methodology. It was the first census for which the mail was used as the primary means of data collection. Census forms were mailed to each household. A member of the household completed the form and saved it for collection by a census enumerator. The collected data were computer analyzed by a method called FOSDIC, film optical screening device for input to computers.[4]

Statisticians began using sampling techniques in 1937. The 1940 census was the first in which sampling techniques were used to obtain data beyond the basic questions.[5] In the 1960 census sampling was used for data collection except for apportionment purposes. At this time 80% of the population was classified as urban. The census bureau estimated that sampling resulted in a 75% reduction in the cost of processing the census.[6]

Congress had its plate full with several complex issues such as the war in Vietnam and the birth of the civil rights movement with the Supreme Court's Brown vs. Board of Topeka ruling in 1954. Thus, Congress seemed content to allow automatic reapportionment.

Section 5.3.2   Automatic Reapportionment

Census day was 1 April 1960. Following the directions in the act of 1929 as amended in 1940 and 1941, on 15 November 1960 Robert Burgess, Director of the Census Bureau, sent a memorandum to Frederick Mueller, Secretary of Commerce, transmitting "a statement showing the population of each State and the District of Columbia on April 1, 1960 as ascertained by the Eighteenth Decennial Census of the United States, and the number of Representatives to which

---

[1] https://www.eisenhowerlibrary.gov/research/online-documents/alaska-statehood.

[2] https://www.eisenhowerlibrary.gov/research/online-documents/hawaii-statehood.

[3] http://www.history.com/topics/us-states/hawaii/videos/eisenhower-proclaims-hawaii-the-50th-state; http://www.history.com/topics/us-states/alaska/videos/eisenhower-proclaims-alaska-the-49th-state.

[4] https://www.census.gov/history/www/through_the_decades/overview/1960.html.

[5] https://www.census.gov/history/www/innovations/data_collection/developing_sampling_techniques.html.

[6] https://www.census.gov/history/pdf/1960overview.pdf.

each State is entitled." The report contained the apportionments based on the 1960 census computed using the method of equal proportions (Table 5.7). The information was subsequently sent to Congress by President Eisenhower on 10 January 1960.[7]

Table 5.7. Automatic apportionment results based on the 1960 census.

2   RELATING TO THE EIGHTEENTH DECENNIAL CENSUS

TABLE 1.—*Population of the United States by States, 1960, and apportionment of Representatives in Congress, 1960 and 1950*

State	Popula-tion, 1960	Present number of Represent-atives	Apportionment of 435 Representatives according to 1960 population		
			Number	Change from present number of Representatives	
				Increase	Decrease
United States	179,323,175	437	435	19	21
Alabama	3,266,740	9	8		1
Alaska	226,167	1	1		
Arizona	1,302,161	2	3	1	
Arkansas	1,786,272	6	4		2
California	15,717,204	30	38	8	
Colorado	1,753,947	4	4		
Connecticut	2,535,234	6	6		
Delaware	446,292	1	1		
District of Columbia	763,956				
Florida	4,951,560	8	12	4	
Georgia	3,943,116	10	10		
Hawaii	632,772	1	2	1	
Idaho	667,191	2	2		
Illinois	10,081,158	25	24		1
Indiana	4,662,498	11	11		
Iowa	2,757,537	8	7		1
Kansas	2,178,611	6	5		1
Kentucky	3,038,156	8	7		1
Louisiana	3,257,022	8	8		
Maine	969,265	3	2		1
Maryland	3,100,689	7	8	1	
Massachusetts	5,148,578	14	12		2
Michigan	7,823,194	18	19	1	
Minnesota	3,413,864	9	8		1
Mississippi	2,178,141	6	5		1
Missouri	4,319,813	11	10		1
Montana	674,767	2	2		
Nebraska	1,411,330	4	3		1
Nevada	285,278	1	1		
New Hampshire	606,921	2	2		
New Jersey	6,066,782	14	15	1	
New Mexico	951,023	2	2		
New York	16,782,304	43	41		2
North Carolina	4,556,155	12	11		1
North Dakota	632,446	2	2		
Ohio	9,706,397	23	24	1	
Oklahoma	2,328,284	6	6		
Oregon	1,768,687	4	4		
Pennsylvania	11,319,366	30	27		3
Rhode Island	859,488	2	2		
South Carolina	2,382,594	6	6		
South Dakota	680,514	2	2		
Tennessee	3,567,089	9	9		
Texas	9,579,677	22	23	1	
Utah	890,627	2	2		
Vermont	389,881	1	1		
Virginia	3,966,949	10	10		
Washington	2,853,214	7	7		
West Virginia	1,860,421	6	5		1
Wisconsin	3,951,777	10	10		
Wyoming	330,066	1	1		

[7] 87th Congress, 1st Session, House Document No. 46.

The big winners were California with a gain of 8 seats and Florida with a gain of 4 seats. Seven states gained 1 seat each: Arizona, Hawaii, Maryland, Michigan, New Jersey, Ohio, and Texas. Pennsylvania lost 3, Arkansas, Massachusetts, and New York each lost 2, and Alabama, Illinois, Iowa, Kansas, Kentucky, Maine, Minnesota, Mississippi, Missouri, North Carolina, and West Virginia each lost 1 seat.

Section 5.3.3   The Aftermath

Table 5.8 (next page) displays apportionment by each of the five modified divisor methods: LD (largest divisor, Jefferson), HM (harmonic mean, Dean), GM (geometric mean, Huntington-Hill), AM (arithmetic mean, Webster), and SD (smallest divisor, Adams). For reference the quota for each state determined by the rule of three is also displayed. The workable interval of divisors for each of the five modified divisor methods is provided below along with the easiest rounded divisor to use. The divisor represents the national average district size.

- LD   [390323, 391159]   391000
- HM   [412547, 413225]   413000
- GM   [412217, 413131]   413000
- AM   [411614, 411886]   411700
- SD   [435723, 436589]   436000

The apportionment determined by Dean, Huntington-Hill, and Webster all agree with the single exception that Webster awards an additional seat to Massachusetts at the expense of New Hampshire. Further, Dean, Huntington-Hill, and Webster have no quota rule violations. Jefferson displays two quota violations awarding California and New York one seat above the upper quota. Adams has five quota rule violations with California, Michigan, New York, Pennsylvania, and Texas each with one seat below the lower quota. These quota rule violations once again display the large state bias inherent in Jefferson's method and the small state bias inherent in Adams's method.

Differences in the five modified divisor methods can also be seen in a priority list for which state would get the next seat in the House. Jefferson and Webster award the 436th seat to Pennsylvania, Dean and Huntington-Hill to Massachusetts, and Adams to Kansas.

Despite the impression that apportionment under the amended act of 1929 was a done deal, stirrings continued in the academic community. In particular, Harris and Burt published two papers advocating the minimum range method advanced by Willcox. Harris and Burt argued that equal proportions applies a criterion of fairness between any two states, but not to the system as a whole. They described the method of minimum range as one having the criterion of minimizing the "differences in representation between the state that is most poorly represented and the state that is most favorably represented."[8]

---

[8] Curtis Harris and Oscar Burt, The Minimum Range method of Apportionment, *The Southwestern Social Science Quarterly*, Vol. 45, No. 2 (September 1965): 142-148.

Table 5.8 (next page). Apportionment results based on the 1960 census.

State	Seats	Population	LD	HM	GM	AM	SD	Quota
Alabama	9	3266740	8	8	8	8	8	7.9583
Alaska	1	226167	1	1	1	1	1	0.5510
Arizona	2	1302161	3	3	3	3	3	3.1723
Arkansas	6	1786272	4	4	4	4	5	4.3517
California	30	15717204	40	38	38	38	37	38.2897
Colorado	4	1753947	4	4	4	4	5	4.2729
Connecticut	6	2535234	6	6	6	6	6	6.1763
Delaware	1	446292	1	1	1	1	2	1.0872
Florida	8	4951560	12	12	12	12	12	12.0628
Georgia	10	3943116	10	10	10	10	10	9.6061
Hawaii	1	632772	1	2	2	2	2	1.5415
Idaho	2	667191	1	2	2	2	2	1.6254
Illinois	25	10081158	25	24	24	24	24	24.5594
Indiana	11	4662498	11	11	11	11	11	11.3586
Iowa	8	2757537	7	7	7	7	7	6.7178
Kansas	6	2178611	5	5	5	5	5	5.3075
Kentucky	8	3038156	7	7	7	7	7	7.4015
Louisiana	8	3257022	8	8	8	8	8	7.9346
Maine	3	969265	2	2	2	2	3	2.3613
Maryland	7	3100689	7	8	8	8	8	7.5538
Massachusetts	14	5148578	13	12	12	13	12	12.5428
Michigan	18	7823194	20	19	19	19	18	19.0586
Minnesota	9	3413864	8	8	8	8	8	8.3167
Mississippi	6	2178141	5	5	5	5	5	5.3063
Missouri	11	4319813	11	10	10	10	10	10.5238
Montana	2	674767	1	2	2	2	2	1.6438
Nebraska	4	1411330	3	3	3	3	4	3.4382
Nevada	1	285278	1	1	1	1	1	0.6950
New Hampshire	2	606921	1	2	2	1	2	1.4786
New Jersey	14	6066782	15	15	15	15	14	14.7797
New Mexico	2	951023	2	2	2	2	3	2.3169
New York	43	16782304	42	41	41	41	39	40.8845
North Carolina	12	4556155	11	11	11	11	11	11.0996
North Dakota	2	632446	1	2	2	2	2	1.5407
Ohio	23	9706397	24	24	24	24	23	23.6464
Oklahoma	6	2328284	5	6	6	6	6	5.6721
Oregon	4	1768687	4	4	4	4	5	4.3088
Pennsylvania	30	11319366	28	27	27	27	26	27.5759
Rhode Island	2	859488	2	2	2	2	2	2.0939
South Carolina	6	2382594	6	6	6	6	6	5.8044
South Dakota	2	680514	1	2	2	2	2	1.6578
Tennessee	9	3567089	9	9	9	9	9	8.6900
Texas	22	9579677	24	23	23	23	22	23.3377
Utah	2	890627	2	2	2	2	3	2.1697
Vermont	1	389881	1	1	1	1	1	0.9498
Virginia	10	3966949	10	10	10	10	10	9.6641
Washington	7	2853214	7	7	7	7	7	6.9509
West Virginia	6	1860421	4	5	5	5	5	4.5323
Wisconsin	10	3951777	10	10	10	10	10	9.6272
Wyoming	1	330066	1	1	1	1	1	0.8041
US	437	178559219	435	435	435	435	435	435.0000

Harris and Burt wrote that their motivation was a result of apportionment based on the 1960 census. Under equal proportions the state with the largest resulting district size is Maine with 484632 people per representative. The state with the smallest resulting district size is Alaska with 226167 people per representative. Hence, the difference between the largest and smallest district sizes is 258465. However, under the minimum range method, this difference is computed by Kansas minus Delaware = 435722 – 223146 = 212576. Thus, argue Harris and Burt, the minimum range method treats the whole picture better than equal proportions. However, the algorithm for computation for minimum range appeared dauntingly complex.[9] [10]

It was clear that the researchers were unaware that this method of minimum range was merely Adams's method, a method that can easily be discarded because of its frequent quota rule violations and intrinsic small state bias. However, Harris and Burt raised interesting questions about what is bias and how can bias be measured.

---

[9] Oscar Burt and Curtis Harris, Apportionment of the U.S. House of Representatives: A Minimum Range, Integer Solution, Allocation Problem, *Operations Research*, Vol. 11, No. 4 (July-August 1963.

[10] E. J. Gilbert, J. A. Schatz, (1964) Letter to the Editor—An Ill-Conceived Proposal for Apportionment of the U.S. House of Representatives. Operations Research 12(5):768-773. http://dx.doi.org/10.1287/opre.12.5.768.

Section 5.4: Reapportionment Based on the 1970 Census

Section 5.4.1   Background

The 1970 census experienced a much greater demand for accuracy because "the increased need for data resulted from the federal government's reliance on population and other information collected by the census when distributing funds to state and local governments." By 1970 apportionment was the only practical constitutional justification for the census since direct taxes were no longer an issue. However, Congress tied the funding of several programs to population. Hence, congressmen demanded accurate census counts. We refer the reader to the Census Bureau's 1970 Overview web page for related interesting items about the census.[1]

Congress was tied up in several difficult issues, especially the war in Vietnam. Thus, like with the 1960 census, Congress accepted the automatic reapportionment results.

Section 5.4.2   Automatic Reapportionment

Once again Congress did nothing to deviate from the apportionment provided by the amended Act of 1929. Hence, apportionment based on the 1970 census was based on a House size of 435 determined by the Huntington-Hill modified divisor method. Table 5.9 (next page) displays apportionment based on the 1970 census by each of the five modified divisor methods: LD (largest divisor, Jefferson), HM (harmonic mean, Dean), GM (geometric mean, Huntington-Hill), AM (arithmetic mean, Webster), and SD (smallest divisor, Adams). For reference the quota for each state determined by the rule of three is also displayed. The workable interval of divisors for each of the five modified divisor methods is provided below along with the easiest rounded figure to use. The divisor represents the national average district size for each method.

- LD   [446642, 446769]   446700
- HM   [472980, 473369]   473000
- GM   [471992, 472043]   472000
- AM   [468107, 469068]   469000
- SD   [495624, 496510]   496000

Apportionment determined by Dean, Huntington-Hill, and Webster all disagreed with each other. Webster, in comparison with Huntington-Hill, gave California a seat at the expense of Montana. In comparison with Dean, Webster gave a seat each to California and Connecticut at the expense of Montana and South Dakota while Huntington-Hill gave a seat to California at the expense of Oregon. Thus, only two states are involved comparing Huntington-Hill against either Webster or Dean. Four states are involved comparing Webster against Dean. However, there are no quota rule violations in either of the three methods.

---

[1] https://www.census.gov/history/www/through_the_decades/overview/1970.html.

State	Seats	Population	LD	HM	GM	AM	SD	Quota
Alabama	8	3475885	7	7	7	7	8	7.4099
Alaska	1	304067	1	1	1	1	1	0.6482
Arizona	3	1787620	4	4	4	4	4	3.8108
Arkansas	4	1942303	4	4	4	4	4	4.1406
California	38	20098863	44	42	43	43	41	42.8467
Colorado	4	2226771	4	5	5	5	5	4.7470
Connecticut	6	3050693	6	6	6	7	7	6.5035
Delaware	1	551928	1	1	1	1	2	1.1766
Florida	12	6855702	15	15	15	15	14	14.6150
Georgia	10	4627306	10	10	10	10	10	9.8645
Hawaii	2	784901	1	2	2	2	2	1.6732
Idaho	2	719921	1	2	2	2	2	1.5347
Illinois	24	11184320	25	24	24	24	23	23.8427
Indiana	11	5228156	11	11	11	11	11	11.1454
Iowa	7	2846920	6	6	6	6	6	6.0691
Kansas	5	2265846	5	5	5	5	5	4.8303
Kentucky	7	3246481	7	7	7	7	7	6.9208
Louisiana	8	3672008	8	8	8	8	8	7.8280
Maine	2	1006320	2	2	2	2	3	2.1453
Maryland	8	3953698	8	8	8	8	8	8.4285
Massachusetts	12	5726676	12	12	12	12	12	12.2081
Michigan	19	8937196	20	19	19	19	19	19.0523
Minnesota	8	3833173	8	8	8	8	8	8.1715
Mississippi	5	2233848	5	5	5	5	5	4.7621
Missouri	10	4718034	10	10	10	10	10	10.0579
Montana	2	701573	1	2	2	1	2	1.4956
Nebraska	3	1496820	3	3	3	3	4	3.1909
Nevada	1	492396	1	1	1	1	1	1.0497
New Hampshire	2	746284	1	2	2	2	2	1.5909
New Jersey	15	7208035	16	15	15	15	15	15.3661
New Mexico	2	1026664	2	2	2	2	3	2.1886
New York	41	18338055	41	39	39	39	37	39.0930
North Carolina	11	5125230	11	11	11	11	11	10.9259
North Dakota	2	624181	1	1	1	1	2	1.3306
Ohio	24	10730200	24	23	23	23	22	22.8746
Oklahoma	6	2585486	5	6	6	6	6	5.5117
Oregon	4	2110810	4	5	4	5	5	4.4998
Pennsylvania	27	11884314	26	25	25	25	24	25.3349
Rhode Island	2	957798	2	2	2	2	2	2.0418
South Carolina	6	2617320	5	6	6	6	6	5.5796
South Dakota	2	673247	1	2	2	1	2	1.4352
Tennessee	9	3961060	8	8	8	8	8	8.4442
Texas	23	11298787	25	24	24	24	23	24.0867
Utah	2	1067810	2	2	2	2	3	2.2764
Vermont	1	448327	1	1	1	1	1	0.9557
Virginia	10	4690742	10	10	10	10	10	9.9997
Washington	7	3443487	7	7	7	7	7	7.3408
West Virginia	5	1763331	3	4	4	4	4	3.7591
Wisconsin	10	4447013	9	9	9	9	9	9.4801
Wyoming	1	335719	1	1	1	1	1	0.7157
US	435	204053325	435	435	435	435	435	435.0000

Table 5.9. Apportionment based on the 1970 census.

Quota rule violations are manifested in Jefferson's and Adams's methods. Jefferson displays upper quota rule violations favoring California, Illinois, New York, and Ohio. Adams displays lower quota rule violations at the expense of California, New York, Pennsylvania, and Texas. Jefferson displays its large state bias by awarding upper quotas to Michigan, New York, and Texas even though their quotas are only 19.0523, 39.0930, and 24.0867. Adams displays its small state bias by awarding an upper quota to Nebraska even though its quota is only 3.1909.

Differences between the five modified divisor methods can also be seen from which state had preference for the next seat in Congress. Jefferson and Dean both would award the 436th seat to California, but Huntington-Hill would award the seat to Oregon, Webster to Wisconsin, and Adams to New York.

Section 5.5:   Reapportionment Based on the 1980 Census

Section 5.5.1   The McDade Amendment

As James Leach (R-IA) noted, "The 1980 census is the first billion-dollar census."[1] Even more than the cost, Congress became intensely concerned with the results and use of the census. James Jefford (R-VT) noted that "census figures are used by the Federal Government for the distribution of $50 billion in Federal moneys each year, and affect planning at all levels of government."[2] The census was not only for apportionment of representatives in the House, it was also the basis for the distribution of a large amount of money from the federal government to the states. The underlying importance of the big picture was stated by Representative Leach, "At stake in the reapportionment of the House seats in the 1980's is a rural versus urban battle with enormous partisan as well as philosophical ramifications."

The lightening rod issue was the counting of aliens in the apportionment population. The myriad of previous efforts to base the apportionment population on citizenship rather than residency made little progress. Accordingly, Joseph McDade (R-PA) introduced an amendment to an appropriations bill that would bypass the counting of aliens.[3]

> None of the funds appropriated or otherwise made available in this Act shall be obligated or expended to calculate or transmit, pursuant to section 2a of Title 2 of the United States code, the number of representatives in congress to which each state shall be entitled under the twentieth decennial census.

The Act of 1929 required the Census Bureau to submit a report to the President which contained the apportionment population for each state and provide the resulting number of congressional seats to each state based on the method of equal proportions. The President was then required to transmit the report to Congress. If the Congress did not act, then the results because automatic and effective in the next congressional election. The McDade amendment would thereby prevent the President from transmitting the results to Congress, thereby essentially nullifying the automatic apportionment feature of the Act of 1929.

The resulting debate highlighted every congressional concern over the census, including:

- the counting of aliens (noncitizens) in the apportionment populations,
- correcting for undercounts of the population,
- constitutionality concerns.

However, the purpose of the McDade amendment was to curtail the inclusion of aliens in the apportionment populations.[4]

---

[1] Congressional Record, 96th Congress, 2nd Session, 18 August 1980: 21863.
[2] Ibid, 20 August 1980: 22141.
[3] Ibid: 22140.
[4] Ibid: 22140-22149.

Most of the debate participants expressed opposition to the counting of aliens for apportionment arguing that representation should be based on citizenship, not residency. Lawrence Coughlin (R-PA) even went further, "it is just outrageous to count illegal aliens for the purpose of apportionment, or for other purposes, for that matter." Henry Hyde (R-IL) reported on the results of his annual district questionnaire in which he asked if one supported the including of illegal aliens in the reapportionment populations. Among the respondents, the result was 15% yes, 79% no, and 6% undecided. Mr. Hyde argued that when the framers determined that all persons should be counted, illegal aliens was not an issue. Now it is.

Robert Garcia (D-NY) argued strongly that the McDade amendment was unconstitutional. The Fourteenth Amendment states that "Representatives shall be apportioned among the several states according to their respective numbers, counting the whole numbers of persons." He quoted a statement from the Supreme Court, *Wesberry v. Sanders*, 376 U.S. 1, 13 (1964), in which the court declared that people meant inhabitants, not just citizens.

James Courter (R-NJ) supported the intent of the McDade amendment but argued that the only way to make the change and remove illegal aliens from the apportionment population is by an amendment to the Constitution. Mr. Courter further argued that to pass this 11th hour amendment would waste the billion dollars already spent on the census.

Mr. Garcia and Edward Derwinski (R-IL) argued that the situation of illegal aliens was not the fault of the Census Bureau. Mr. Garcia, who supported the counting of aliens, contended that if the illegal aliens were given the opportunity to become citizens, "they would all jump at the opportunity." Mr. Derwinski, who opposed the counting of aliens, proposed that the fault probably lies with the Judiciary Committee, and he chastised, "If they concentrated on writing a workable immigration law, that might help."

Mr. Leach favored apportionment based on citizenship rather than residency but noted that "the only way to deal with his concerns is through a constitutional amendment." He noted that Congress has had ample time to be proactive. Congress should accept the results and procedures based on the 1980 census "without political tinkering." He concluded, "Abide by the Constitution, and reject the McDade amendment today, then change the Constitution and apply the McDade logic to the next decennial census in 1990."

Tom Steed (D-OK) rose to make two points. First, the census should be taken by the Postal Service since they could have done the job at a fraction of the cost. Second, the mechanism of trying to solve a problem by an amendment to an appropriations bill is not good procedure. Solve a problem directly in the appropriate committee and do not go through the back door of an appropriations bill.

Finally, it was time to vote. The McDade amendment passed, 224 to 187, 21 not voting. However, this was only an amendment to an appropriation bill. The amendment was later stripped as several members of Congress, both House and Senate, became convinced that to remove aliens from the apportionment population would require a constitutional amendment.

This debate highlighted the main concerns of Congress. How should Congress deal with census undercounts? Should aliens be counted in the apportionment population? There was only one bill submitted regarding apportionment methodology. On 23 February 1981 Floyd Fithian (D-IN) introduced H.R. 1990, the Census Data Reform Act of 1990.[5] Included in the bill was to replace the Huntington-Hill equal proportions method with the Hamilton-Vinton quota method. He presented five reasons for the change: it is based on simple mathematical concepts, it "honors the concept of quota more often than any others," it is neutral between small and large states, it adheres more closely to the spirit of one man one vote than any other method, and it has been used for reapportionment more than any other method in U. S. history.[6] The proposal died in committee.

Section 5.5.2   Automatic Reapportionment

The automatic reapportionment based on the 1980 census was based on a House size of 435 determined by the Huntington-Hill modified divisor method. Table 5.10 displays apportionment based on the 1980 census by each of the five modified divisor methods: LD (largest divisor, Jefferson), HM (harmonic mean, Dean), GM (geometric mean, Huntington-Hill), AM (arithmetic mean, Webster), and SD (smallest divisor, Adams). For reference the quota for each state determined by the rule of three is also displayed.

The workable interval of divisors for each of the five modified divisor methods is provided below along with the easiest rounded figure to use. The divisor represents the national average district size for each method.

- LD   [490634, 490791]   490700
- HM   [524063, 524214]   524100
- GM   [523469, 524196]   524000
- AM   [520407, 522874]   521000
- SD   [546427, 547245]   547000

The apportionment determined by Dean and Huntington-Hill agreed with each other. Webster differed in awarding a seat to Indiana at the expense of New Mexico. Thus, only two states are involved comparing Webster against either Huntington-Hill or Dean. There are no quota rule violations in either of the three methods. The quota rule violations for Jefferson's method are glaring. California is given two seats over the upper quota while Illinois, New York, Ohio, and Pennsylvania are each given one seat above the upper quota. Adams's method only has one quota rule violation in that it gives California one seat less than its lower quota.

---

[5] https://www.congress.gov/bill/97th-congress/house-bill/1990?q=%7B%22search%22%3A%5B%22census%22%2C%22census%22%5D%7D.
[6] Congressional Record, 97th Congress, 1st Session, 23 February 1981: 2709.

State	Seats	Population	LD	HM	GM	AM	SD	Quota
Alabama	8	3475885	7	7	7	7	8	7.4099
Alaska	1	304067	1	1	1	1	1	0.6482
Arizona	3	1787620	4	4	4	4	4	3.8108
Arkansas	4	1942303	4	4	4	4	4	4.1406
California	38	20098863	44	42	43	43	41	42.8467
Colorado	4	2226771	4	5	5	5	5	4.7470
Connecticut	6	3050693	6	6	6	7	7	6.5035
Delaware	1	551928	1	1	1	1	2	1.1766
Florida	12	6855702	15	15	15	15	14	14.6150
Georgia	10	4627306	10	10	10	10	10	9.8645
Hawaii	2	784901	1	2	2	2	2	1.6732
Idaho	2	719921	1	2	2	2	2	1.5347
Illinois	24	11184320	25	24	24	24	23	23.8427
Indiana	11	5228156	11	11	11	11	11	11.1454
Iowa	7	2846920	6	6	6	6	6	6.0691
Kansas	5	2265846	5	5	5	5	5	4.8303
Kentucky	7	3246481	7	7	7	7	7	6.9208
Louisiana	8	3672008	8	8	8	8	8	7.8280
Maine	2	1006320	2	2	2	2	3	2.1453
Maryland	8	3953698	8	8	8	8	8	8.4285
Massachusetts	12	5726676	12	12	12	12	12	12.2081
Michigan	19	8937196	20	19	19	19	19	19.0523
Minnesota	8	3833173	8	8	8	8	8	8.1715
Mississippi	5	2233848	5	5	5	5	5	4.7621
Missouri	10	4718034	10	10	10	10	10	10.0579
Montana	2	701573	1	2	2	1	2	1.4956
Nebraska	3	1496820	3	3	3	3	4	3.1909
Nevada	1	492396	1	1	1	1	1	1.0497
New Hampshire	2	746284	1	2	2	2	2	1.5909
New Jersey	15	7208035	16	15	15	15	15	15.3661
New Mexico	2	1026664	2	2	2	2	3	2.1886
New York	41	18338055	41	39	39	39	37	39.0930
North Carolina	11	5125230	11	11	11	11	11	10.9259
North Dakota	2	624181	1	1	1	1	2	1.3306
Ohio	24	10730200	24	23	23	23	22	22.8746
Oklahoma	6	2585486	5	6	6	6	6	5.5117
Oregon	4	2110810	4	5	4	5	5	4.4998
Pennsylvania	27	11884314	26	25	25	25	24	25.3349
Rhode Island	2	957798	2	2	2	2	2	2.0418
South Carolina	6	2617320	5	6	6	6	6	5.5796
South Dakota	2	673247	1	2	2	1	2	1.4352
Tennessee	9	3961060	8	8	8	8	8	8.4442
Texas	23	11298787	25	24	24	24	23	24.0867
Utah	2	1067810	2	2	2	2	3	2.2764
Vermont	1	448327	1	1	1	1	1	0.9557
Virginia	10	4690742	10	10	10	10	10	9.9997
Washington	7	3443487	7	7	7	7	7	7.3408
West Virginia	5	1763331	3	4	4	4	4	3.7591
Wisconsin	10	4447013	9	9	9	9	9	9.4801
Wyoming	1	335719	1	1	1	1	1	0.7157
US	435	204053325	435	435	435	435	435	435.0000

Table 5.10. Apportionment based on the census of 1980.

The difference between methods is again illustrated by which state would be awarded the 436th seat: Jefferson to Texas, Dean and Huntington-Hill to Indiana, Webster to Georgia, and Adams to Hawaii.

Section 5.5.3   Balinski and Young

In 1980 Michel Balinski and H. Peyton Young published results[7] which contain the ingredients of what is known today as the Balinski and Young Impossibility Theorem.[8] The published paper on Webster's method of apportionment was written for a sophisticated mathematical audience. A treatment more accessible to a general audience appeared in Balinski and Young's seminal work, *Fair Representation*, in 1982.[9] A second edition of *Fair Representation* was published in 2001.[10] This classic is the starting point for anyone interested in an in-depth study of congressional apportionment today.

The Balinski and Young Impossibility Theorem essentially states that there are no perfect apportionment methods. There are only two approaches to apportionment. One can begin an apportionment process either by fixing the House size or fixing the constituency. Doing so leads to applying either a quota method or a divisor method to make the calculations. The work of Balinski and Young shows that any quota method is subject to the Alabama Paradox and that any divisor method is subject to quota rule violations.

Balinski and Young also built on previous work resolving issues concerning optimization and bias. *Fair Representation* is the starting point for anyone interested in apportionment from a modern perspective. The book has two parts. The first part is a readable narration of the history leading up to today's formulation of the congressional apportionment problem. The second part incorporates the necessary mathematical perspectives. The general reader will find the second part quite technical. Accordingly, we refer the reader to Balinski and Young Part 1 for an excellent historical summary leading to the modern congressional apportionment problem or to launch investigations into technical questions. In the remainder of this work, we focus on the continuing political concerns surrounding congressional apportionment.

---

[7] M. L. Balinski and H. P. Young, The Webster method of apportionment, *Proc. Natl. Acad. Sci. USA*, 77(1) January 1980: 1-4. Download available at https://www.ncbi.nlm.nih.gov/pmc/articles/PMC348194/.
[8] https://en.wikipedia.org/wiki/Apportionment_paradox.
[9] Michel Balinski and H. Peyton Young, *Fair Representation: Meeting the Ideal of One Man, One Vote*, Yale University Press, 1982.
[10] Michel Balinski and H. Peyton Young, *Fair Representation: Meeting the Ideal of One Man, One Vote*, Brookings Institution Press, 2001.

Section 5.6: Reapportionment Based on the 1990 Census

Congress did not concern itself with reapportionment results based on the 1990 census. Interest was limited to questions in the census, census undercounts, and counting American citizens overseas.

Section 5.6.1 Automatic Reapportionment

Automatic reapportionment based on the 1990 census was based on a House size of 435 using the Huntington-Hill modified divisor method. Table 5.11 (next page) displays the results by each of the five modified divisor methods: LD (largest divisor, Jefferson), HM (harmonic mean, Dean), GM (geometric mean, Huntington-Hill), AM (arithmetic mean, Webster), and SD (smallest divisor, Adams). The quota for each state determined by the rule of three is also displayed.

The workable interval of divisors for each of the five modified divisor methods is provided below along with the easiest rounded figure to use. The divisor represents the national average district size for each method.

- LD   [545194, 546032]   546000
- HM   [577049, 578075]   578000
- GM   [574848, 576049]   575000
- AM   [574110, 574195]   574150
- SD   [605240, 605459]   605300

Apportionments determined by Webster and Huntington-Hill agreed with each other. Dean differed in awarding a seat to Montana at the expense of Washington. The methods of Dean, Huntington-Hill, and Webster do not have any quota violations. Adams displays lower quota violations for four states: California (two seats below lower quota), Illinois, New York, and Ohio. Jefferson displays upper quota violations for three states: California, New York, and Texas.

Difference in methodology between the five methods is vividly displayed in the awarding of the 436th seat: Jefferson, Wisconsin; Dean, Washington; Huntington-Hill, Massachusetts; Webster, Oklahoma; and Adams, North Carolina.

The Census Bureau presents their apportionment findings also in the form of a priority list. First each state is awarded one seat in compliance with the constitutional mandate that each state receive at least one seat. This distributes the first 50 seats in the House. Then, the list identifies which state has priority for the 51st seat, 52nd seat, up to the 440th seat. This priority list is available at the Bureau's website.[1]

---

[1] https://www2.census.gov/programs-surveys/decennial/1990/data/apportionment/90pvalues.txt.

States	Seats	Population	LD	HM	GM	AM	SD	Quota
Alabama	7	4062608	7	7	7	7	7	7.0967
Alaska	1	551947	1	1	1	1	1	0.9642
Arizona	5	3677985	6	6	6	6	7	6.4248
Arkansas	4	2362239	4	4	4	4	4	4.1264
California	45	29839250	54	52	52	52	50	52.1240
Colorado	6	3307912	6	6	6	6	6	5.7784
Connecticut	6	3295669	6	6	6	6	6	5.7570
Delaware	1	668696	1	1	1	1	2	1.1681
Florida	19	13003362	23	23	23	23	22	22.7146
Georgia	10	6508419	11	11	11	11	11	11.3691
Hawaii	2	1115274	2	2	2	2	2	1.9482
Idaho	2	1011986	1	2	2	2	2	1.7678
Illinois	22	11466682	21	20	20	20	19	20.0303
Indiana	10	5564228	10	10	10	10	10	9.7197
Iowa	6	2787424	5	5	5	5	5	4.8692
Kansas	5	2485600	4	4	4	4	5	4.3419
Kentucky	7	3698969	6	6	6	6	7	6.4615
Louisiana	8	4238216	7	7	7	7	8	7.4034
Maine	2	1233223	2	2	2	2	3	2.1542
Maryland	8	4798622	8	8	8	8	8	8.3824
Massachusetts	11	6029051	11	10	10	11	10	10.5317
Michigan	18	9328784	17	16	16	16	16	16.2958
Minnesota	8	4387029	8	8	8	8	8	7.6634
Mississippi	5	2586443	4	5	5	5	5	4.5181
Missouri	9	5137804	9	9	9	9	9	8.9749
Montana	2	803655	1	2	1	1	2	1.4038
Nebraska	3	1584617	2	3	3	3	3	2.7681
Nevada	2	1206152	2	2	2	2	2	2.1069
New Hampshire	2	1113915	2	2	2	2	2	1.9458
New Jersey	14	7748634	14	13	13	13	13	13.5355
New Mexico	3	1521779	2	3	3	3	3	2.6583
New York	34	18044505	33	31	31	31	30	31.5206
North Carolina	11	6657630	12	12	12	12	11	11.6297
North Dakota	1	641364	1	1	1	1	2	1.1204
Ohio	21	10887325	19	19	19	19	18	19.0183
Oklahoma	6	3157604	5	6	6	5	6	5.5158
Oregon	5	2853733	5	5	5	5	5	4.9850
Pennsylvania	23	11924710	21	21	21	21	20	20.8304
Rhode Island	2	1005984	1	2	2	2	2	1.7573
South Carolina	6	3505707	6	6	6	6	6	6.1239
South Dakota	1	699999	1	1	1	1	2	1.2228
Tennessee	9	4896641	8	9	9	9	9	8.5536
Texas	27	17059805	31	30	30	30	29	29.8005
Utah	3	1727784	3	3	3	3	3	3.0181
Vermont	1	564964	1	1	1	1	1	0.9869
Virginia	10	6216568	11	11	11	11	11	10.8593
Washington	8	4887941	8	8	9	9	9	8.5384
West Virginia	4	1801625	3	3	3	3	3	3.1471
Wisconsin	9	4906745	8	9	9	9	9	8.5712
Wyoming	1	455975	1	1	1	1	1	0.7965
US	435	249022783	435	435	435	435	435	435.0000

Table 5.11. Apportionment based on the 1990 census.

Section 5.6.2   Montana

The automatic procedure assigned one representative to Montana based on the 1990 census. However, Montana had two representatives in the House since reapportionment based on the 1910 census. The loss of a representative meant that Montana's lone representative would be representing 803655 people, the largest congressional district in the nation, considerably more than the average district size of 572000.[2]

Accordingly, Montana filed suit in federal district court. Montana's motivation for doing so was to recover its lost seat.[3] Montana's legal justification was that the apportionment method used was unconstitutional. The three-judge panel voted 2-1 in favor of Montana and issued the following opinion:[4]

> ... holding the statute unconstitutional because the variance between the single district's population and that of the ideal district could not be justified under the "one person, one vote" standard developed in *Wesberry v. Sanders*, 376 U.S. 1, and other intrastate districting cases.

Montana's case centered on which state had priority for the 435th seat in the House, Montana or Washington. Huntington-Hill awarded the seat to Washington, thereby awarding nine seats to Washington and one seat to Montana. Montana contested that it was more deserving of the seat than Washington.

An appropriate divisor under the Huntington-Hill method is 575448. Awarding one seat to Montana leaves Montana with a district size of 803655. Awarding nine seats to Washington leaves Washington with an average district size of 543105. Using 575448 as the average district size leaves a disparity of 228207 over average for Montana and under 32343 for Washington, a spread of 260550 between the two states. Using Dean's method instead of the Huntington-Hill method reverses the apportionment leaving Montana with an average district size of 401828 and Washington 543105, a difference of only 141277. Since transferring a Huntington-Hill seat from Washington to Montana decreases the disparity in district size from 260550 to 141277, then the transfer should be made.

The Department of Commerce, home to the Census Bureau, immediately appealed the decision of the Montana District Court to the Supreme Court. The Supreme Court reversed the decision of the Montana District Court by a unanimous decision.[5] The Supreme Court held that

---

[2] Linda Greenhouse, *Supreme Court Upholds Method Used in Apportionment of House*, New York Times, 1 April 1992; available at http://www.nytimes.com/1992/04/01/us/supreme-court-upholds-method-used-in-apportionment-of-house.html.

[3] Christopher Yates, A House of Our Own or a House We've Outgrown? An argument for Increasing the size of the House of Representatives, *Journal of Law and Social Problems*, 25(2) 1992: 157-196; available as download from http://www.thirty-thousand.org/documents/Yates_1992.pdf.

[4] United States Department of Commerce v. Montana (91-860), 503 U.S. 442 (1992); https://www.law.cornell.edu/supct/html/91-860.ZS.html.

[5] Department of Commerce v. Montana, 503 U. S. 442 (1992); https://www.law.cornell.edu/supct/html/91-860.ZS.html.

the Huntington-Hill method does not violate the Constitution. The only constitutional requirement is that representatives shall be apportioned among the states "according to their respective numbers" as determined by a decennial census subject to two constraints, "The number of Representatives shall not exceed one for every thirty Thousand, but each State shall have at Least one Representative."[6] Clearly none of the constraints are violated in the automatic apportionment based on the 1990 census. Further, the Huntington-Hill method is certainly based on the population as determined by the census.

Section 5.6.3   Massachusetts

Massachusetts lost a seat as a result of reapportionment based on the 1990 census in which its congressional delegation fell from 11 to 10 representatives. Massachusetts filed suit in Federal district court to retain its 11 seats. The suit was based on two issues. First, the Huntington-Hill method is unconstitutional and Webster's method of apportionment should be used. Second, the inclusion of Federal employees serving abroad was improper since the methods used to count them was a violation of the Administrative Procedures Act.[7]

Massachusetts would have retained its 11 seats had Webster's method been applied for apportionment based on the 1990 census. Massachusetts argued that the Webster fairness criterion based on representatives per person was the criterion most consistent with the one-person one-vote mandate proclaimed by the Supreme Court. The district court ruled against this argument. The court's decision stated, "That 2 U.S.C. § 2a(a), insofar as it requires apportionment of seats in the House of Representatives among the states by the method known as equal proportions, is not in violation of the United States Constitution."[8]

Second, Massachusetts claimed that the method of enumeration of Federal employees was improper. The Massachusetts claim noted that 90% of these employees were members of the armed forces stationed overseas.[9] The problem of counting military personnel serving outside their place of residence has a long and convoluted history all its own.

For the 1970 census during the height of the Vietnam War the Census Bureau included overseas military personnel. Soldiers were assigned to their "home state" as provided in military records. A significant population, nearly 336000, were serving in Vietnam alone.[10] A direct enumeration in the battlefield is obviously impractical if not impossible. But in 1975 the Bureau declared that the "home state" designation was of "unknown reliability" and dropped including Federal employees serving overseas in the enumeration of the population for the 1980 census.

---

[6] U. S. Constitution, Article I, Section 2, Paragraph 3.

[7] Com. of Mass. v. Mosbacher, Civ. A. No. 91-11234-WD;
http://www.leagle.com/decision/19921015785FSupp230_1947.xml/COM.%20OF%20MASS.%20v.%20MOSBACHER.

[8] 785 F. Supp. 268.

[9] New York Times, Massachusetts Wins Census Fight And Will Retain 11 House Seats, 21 February 1992; accessed from http://www.nytimes.com/1992/02/21/us/massachusetts-wins-census-fight-and-will-retain-11-house-seats.html.

[10] https://en.wikipedia.org/wiki/1970_in_the_Vietnam_War.

In a reversal of procedure Secretary of Commerce Robert Mosbacher on 31 July 1989 announced that the Bureau would include Federal employees and their dependents serving abroad. The count would be based on government records of these people.

In the matter of including Federal employees serving abroad, the district court ruled in favor of Massachusetts. The court's opinion noted a litany of difficulties and problems with the counting of Federal employees serving overseas. The court's final decision included the following two key items.[106]

> That the administrative practice of the Executive Branch Defendants in counting overseas federal employees in the 1990 census for the purpose of apportioning seats in the United States House of Representatives among the states was arbitrary and capricious and an abuse of discretion in violation of the Administrative Procedure Act, 5 U.S.C. § 706(2)(A), and that consequently the use of the overseas census counts by the defendants in the certification of state entitlements to seats in the House of Representatives was improper.

> That the Executive Branch Defendants shall submit to defendant Anderson on or before March 31, 1992, a statement showing the number of Representatives to which each state would be entitled as a result of the 1990 decennial census under 2 U.S.C. § 2a(a), without inclusion of the overseas census counts in the apportionment count.

Massachusetts's victory was short lived. On 26 June 1992 in a unanimous 9-0 decision the Supreme Court reversed the district's court's conclusion in *Franklin v. Massachusetts*.[11] The key point in the ruling was that the Administrative Procedures Act did not apply in this case. Although this resolved the immediate case on a technical legal ground, it did not resolve the political dimensions of the issue of which and how to count Americans residing abroad.

Section 5.6.4   Congressional Apportionment and the Electoral College

George Bush and Albert Gore were the principal candidates in the 2000 presidential election. Al Gore won a close plurality of the popular vote, 48.87% to 48.38%.[12] However, George Bush was elected President by a close vote in the Electoral College, 271-266. The U. S. Constitution features a uniquely American method for selecting the national executive by applying a system of electors as specified in Article II, Section 1. This system is known today as the Electoral College. The 2000 election ignited another debate on whether the Constitution should be amended so that the President of the United States is chosen by direct popular vote.

An early flaw in the electoral system was uncovered in the presidential election of 1800 in which Thomas Jefferson defeated John Adams, or more precisely, eventually defeated Aaron

---

[11] 505 U. S. 788 (1992); https://supreme.justia.com/cases/federal/us/505/788/; https://www.oyez.org/cases/1991/91-1502.
[12] http://uselectionatlas.org/RESULTS/national.php?year=2000.

Burr who was Jefferson's running mate.[13] The flaw stemmed from the specification that each elector cast two votes. The top majority recipient among the electoral voters became the President and the next majority recipient was Vice-President. Thomas Jefferson and his running mate, Aaron Burr, tied with a majority of electors. Accordingly, the decision was sent to the House of Representatives where each state casts one vote. A majority of the 16 states was needed to declare a winner. Finally, on the 36th ballot Jefferson received the votes of 10 states, Burr 4 states, and 2 states abstained. Thomas Jefferson thus became the third president of the United States. The difficulty uncovered with the constitutional directions for electors was corrected with the ratification of the Twelfth Amendment to the Constitution on 15 June 1804.

Comparing the two methods, Electoral College vs. popular vote, by looking at the history of presidential elections, is not straight-forward. Early in American history electors in some states were chosen directly by state legislatures and there was no national popular vote for president.

The 2000 election was the 53rd presidential election. Arguably the 2000 election was the fourth presidential election where the electoral system chose a winner different than the plurality popular vote winner. Those previous three elections featured John Quincy Adams vs. Andrew Jackson in 1824, Rutherford Hayes vs. Samuel Tilden in 1876, and Benjamin Harrison vs. Grover Cleveland in 1888. With caveats an examination of these four elections is informative.

The 1824 Election

The election of 1824 featured four candidates: Andrew Jackson, John Quincy Adams, William Crawford, and Henry Clay. All four candidates were from the same political party, the Democratic-Republican Party. Hence, the campaign presented a strong regional feature. Andrew Jackson was the plurality winner of both the popular vote and the electoral vote. However, Jackson received only 99 of the 261 electoral votes, well short of the 136 needed to win in the Electoral College. Accordingly, following the stipulations of the Twelfth Amendment, the decision was sent to the House of Representatives to decide among the top three candidates from the Electoral College vote: Jackson, Adams, and Crawford. In the House each state gets one vote.

The 1824 election featured a fundamental problem with the Electoral College; i.e., what to do if no candidate receives a majority. The election is then sent to the House of Representatives to decide among the top three. That resulting decision is then subject to the politics of the House as the 1800 election previously showed. In the 1824 election Speaker of the House Henry Clay convinced Kentucky's representatives to vote for Adams contrary to instructions from the Kentucky state legislature. Ironically, although Clay came in last in both the popular and the electoral vote, Clay's political leadership was decisive in the House's selection of John Quincy Adams over Andrew Jackson.[14]

---

[13] Edward Larson, *A Magnificent Catastrophe*, Free Press, New York, 2007.
[14] Carter Smith, *Presidents: All You Need To Know*, Hylas Publishing, 2004: 48-51.

The key observation here is that a popular vote criterion would probably have selected Andrew Jackson over John Quincy Adams. All the Electoral College did in this case was to send the election to the House where that decision was subject to partisan power politics. The selection of John Quincy Adams had two consequences: four years of subsequent gridlock politics at the national level with a four-year delay in the presidency of Andrew Jackson.

In evaluating this election, however, the term "popular vote" carries serious caveats since there was no national popular vote. The state legislature in six of the twenty-four states in the union chose the electors and there was no popular vote in those states. Those six states were Delaware, Georgia, Louisiana, New York, South Carolina, and Vermont. Hence, the assertion that Jackson won the "popular vote" is really a stretch in this case.[15]

By 1836 state electors were chosen by statewide popular vote in every state except South Carolina. Hence, 1836 is the first presidential election where one might use the term "popular vote" in a national sense. South Carolina continued the practice of appointing electors by the state legislature until the 1860 presidential election.[16]

The popular vote in most states was very restricted by modern standards. The right to vote was usually reserved within a class of white males over 21 years of age. Further, the Electoral College vote was skewed since the infamous three-fifths rule was still in effect. The three-fifths rule counted a slave as 3/5ths of a person for congressional apportionment. This inflated the Electoral College voting power of slave states. As the historian Daniel Walker Howe noted, without the 3/5ths rule Jackson "would have received 77 electoral votes and Adams 83."[17]

Despite these caveats, the elections of 1800 and 1824 exposed the electoral system weakness that if the decision for who wins the presidency is sent to the House of Representatives, then that decision will be based on partisan politics rather than fairness.

The 1876 Election

The election of 1876 was the only presidential election where the majority winner of the popular vote did not win the Electoral College vote. Samuel Tilden lost to Rutherford Hayes in the Electoral College by one vote, 185-184. There are several issues that one can explore about this election, but one key fact the election exposed is that the winner of the Electoral College vote simply can be an artifact of the method used to apportion the House of Representatives.

After apportionment of the House based on the 1870 census, Congress passed a supplement adding some seats to the House. The supplement was based on a different method than the original 1870 apportionment. The revised method resulted in awarding a seat

---

[15] Richard Berg-Anderson, *by whom U. S. PRESIDENTIAL ELECTORS were "appointed": 1789 through 1832.* http://www.thegreenpapers.com/Hx/ByWhomElectorsWereAppointed.phtml .

[16] William Kimberling, *The Manner of Choosing Electors.* http://uselectionatlas.org/INFORMATION/INFOR1870 MATION/electcollege_choosing.php.

[17] Daniel Walker Howe, *What Hath God Wrought: The Transformation of America, 1815-1848*, Oxford University Press, 2007: 208.

to Florida, which went to Hayes, at the expense of New York, which went to Tilden. If the original methodology were followed in the supplement, then Tilden would have won the Electoral College vote, 185-184.[18] Accordingly, in a close election, the winner may be a result of the method used to apportion the House of Representatives.

The 1888 Election

The principal candidates in the election of 1888 featured incumbent Democrat Grover Cleveland against Republican Benjamin Harrison. Cleveland won the plurality popular vote by a narrow margin: 5538163 (48.63%) and Harrison 5443633 (47.80%).[19] However, Harrison won the Electoral College vote by a convincing margin, 233-168. The election result did not shed informative light on comparing the fairness of the electoral system vs. the popular vote for deciding who wins a presidential election. However, the result did highlight that the popular vote can be quite close while the Electoral College vote is decisive.

Among the presidential elections where the electoral system winner did not win a plurality of the popular vote, this election is considered to be the least contentious.[20] Nevertheless, the results did portray a strategy for winning a presidential election. The Republicans successfully conducted a vigorous campaign to victory by targeting a few swing states to gain an Electoral College victory. As a result, Republicans flipped New York and Indiana.[21] Although these were the only two states whose election results differed from the 1884 presidential election, it was enough for victory. Harrison won New York by 30231 out of a total of 1319748 and won Indiana by 9881 out of 536949 votes cast.[22]

The electoral system contributed little to the presidency by selecting Harrison over Cleveland. Basically, it served only as an interruption for Cleveland's second term. In the subsequent 1892 election Cleveland won a majority popular vote and the Electoral College vote, 277-145. Harrison "did little in office to distinguish himself."[23] He spent minimal time in the office and most days he was gone by lunchtime. Harrison's main contribution is that he produced many interesting items for history buffs.[24] In particular, by 2021 there have been 59 presidential elections. Joe Biden is the 46th President. However, only 45 men have served as President. This anomaly exists because Cleveland is the only President to serve non successive terms; accordingly, Cleveland is the 22nd President and the 24th President, the only President to be counted twice.

---

[18] See Chapter 3, Section 3.4: 136-138.

[19] http://uselectionatlas.org/RESULTS/national.php?year=1888. The popular vote figures differ slightly among the various sources; for example, https://en.wikipedia.org/wiki/1888_United_States_presidential_election. Also compare with Carter Smith, *Presidents: All You Need to Know*, Hylas Publishing, New York, 2004: 146.

[20] Election of 1888, http://constitution.laws.com/election-of-1888.

[21] Benjamin Harrison: Campaigns and Elections, https://millercenter.org/president/bharrison/campaigns-and-elections.

[22] http://uselectionatlas.org/RESULTS/data.php?year=1960&datatype=national&def=1&f=0&off=0&elect=0.

[23] Carter Smith, *Presidents*, Benjamin Harrison: 144.

[24] Noah McCullough, *The Essential Book of Presidential Trivia*, Random House, New York, 2006: 121-130.

The 2000 Election

The 2000 presidential election featured a close race between George W. Bush and Albert Gore. The Federal Election Commission reports the final popular vote as Bush 50456002 (47.87%) and Gore 50999897 (48.38%) out of a total of 105405100 votes cast.[25][26] The Electoral College vote came down to one state, Florida, which Bush won by 537 votes. This closeness is preserved in the media's memory with hanging chads or the presidential election decided by the Supreme Court.[27]

The 2000 election, however, displayed a major flaw in the electoral system that the selection of who wins a presidential election may be simply an artifact of the size of the House of Representatives. The website maintained by thirty-thousand.org posts a fascinating article by Neubauer and Zeitlin on *Outcomes of Presidential Elections and House Size*.[28] The article demonstrates how the result of the Gore vs. Bush presidential election was a consequence of the House size. The authors were professors of mathematics at California State University, Northridge. An earlier version featuring a mathematical exposition of the issue was published in the *College Mathematics Journal*.[29]

Really—should the size of the House matter more than the popular vote? Recall that the number of electoral votes that each state gets is equal to its number of national legislators: two senators plus the number of representatives in the House. The number of representatives for each state is determined every ten years based on the decennial census. The current size of the House is 435. That number was fixed by an act approved in 1929. The only constitutional restrictions on the size of the House are specified in Article I, Section 1: each state will receive at least one representative and the size of the House shall not exceed one for every thirty thousand. Hence, as a result of the 1990 census, the House must have at least 50 seats but no more than 8300. The Electoral College of 2000 was configured using congressional apportionment of the House based on the 1990 census. Congressional apportionment based on the 2000 census did not take effect until 2002.

Neubauer and Zeitlin calculated the Electoral College vote based on House size from 50 to 1000 inclusive using the current method of congressional apportionment. They concluded,

> As the House size ranges from 50 to 1000, the 2000 election would have produced ties for the following 25 House sizes: 491, 493, 505, 507, 533, 535, 537, 539, 541, 543, 545, 547, 551, 555, 557, 559, 561, 571, 573, 585, 587, 591, 593, 597, and 655.

[25] 2000 Presidential Election, https://www.fec.gov/introduction-campaign-finance/election-and-voting-information/federal-elections-2000/president2000/ [click Summary Tables (Excel)].

[26] https://www.infoplease.com/us/government/elections/presidential-election-of-2000-electoral-and-popular-vote-summary.

[27] Samantha Levine, *Hanging Chads: As the Florida Recount Implodes, the Supreme Court Decides Bush v. Gore*, 17 January 2008; http://www.usnews.com/news/articles/2008/01/17/the-legacy-of-hanging-chads.

[28] Michael Neubauer and Joel Zeitlin, *Outcomes of Presidential Elections and House Size*, PS: Political Science and Politics, October 2003; available at http://www.thirty-thousand.org/pages/Neubauer-Zeitlin.htm.

[29] Michael Neubauer and Joel Zeitlin, *Apportionment and the 2000 Election*, The College Mathematics Journal 34(1), January 2003: 2-10.

For all House sizes larger than 597, save for 655, which results in a tie, Gore would have won the election. For all House sizes smaller than 491 Bush would have won the election.

Further, in the intermediate House sizes, 492-597, the presidential winner oscillates between Bush and Gore in a way that makes no political sense. For this range of 106 House sizes Bush and Gore tie 24 times, Bush wins 53 times, and Gore wins 29 times.

Given the size of the U.S. population, the House size of 435 is rather low. On average a congressman in 2010 represents 711000 people. Accordingly, power is not only disproportionately skewed in favor of the small states in the Senate, but also in the House. The case that the winner of a presidential election merely may be the result of the size of the House is vividly displayed in the analysis for House sizes between 491 and 596, inclusive.

The 2000 presidential election also displays another potential problem with the electoral system. The number of electoral votes each state gets, for the most part, is based on the decennial census. Although the election was in 2000, the electoral votes were based on the 1990 census since apportionment of the House at that time was based on the 1990 census. An election held in a census year is based on an apportionment population that is ten years old. What would have been the result of Bush vs. Gore if the Electoral College vote were based on the 2000 census for congressional apportionment?

In comparison with the 1990 census, the 2000 census affected congressional apportionment for eighteen states: Arizona, gain 2; California, gain 1; Colorado, gain 1; Connecticut, lose 1; Florida, gain 2; Georgia, gain 2; Illinois, lose 1; Indiana, lose 1; Michigan, lose 1; Mississippi, lose 1; Nevada, gain 1; New York, lose 2; North Carolina, gain 1; Ohio, lose 1; Oklahoma, lose 1; Pennsylvania, lose 2; Texas, gain 2; Wisconsin, lose 1. Accordingly, the electoral vote would have changed from Bush 271 and Gore 266 to Bush 278 and Gore 259.

The key point here is that the Electoral College result may be at variance with the popular vote based on ten-year-old population data. Further, the population base is different. The apportionment calculation is based on the *resident* population for each state, whereas the popular vote can come only from people who are citizens in good standing of a given state. Although this scenario has not been an actual determinant in a presidential election, it could be a deciding factor in the Electoral College.[30]

A Popular Vote Alternative

Much of the discussion about abandoning the electoral system in favor of a national popular vote as the mechanism for deciding the winner of a presidential election assumes that the popular vote is a well-defined process. It is not.

---

[30] Paul Goldman and Mark Rozell, *Illegal Immigrants Could Elect Hillary*, 3 October 2015, http://www.politico.com/magazine/story/2015/10/illegal-immigrants-could-elect-hillary-clinton-213216.

Some analysts refer to the arguably four previous presidential elections where the electoral system did not select the plurality popular vote winner.[31, 32] However, the popular vote in an historical context, even for modern times, is ill-defined. Professor Brian Gaines, for example, argues that the John Kennedy vs. Richard Nixon election of 1960 should also be considered in the category where the electoral system chose a winner other than the plurality "popular vote" winner. The problem stems from how to determine the popular vote in Alabama, Georgia, and Mississippi. The ballot in Alabama did not list the presidential candidates, but "featured names of individual electors rather than slates." Gaines then analyzed the votes for electors and concluded that the popular vote corrected for the Democratic Split and Georgia's Long-Ballot shows that Nixon won the popular vote by 60132 votes.[33]

There are several specific issues about a national popular vote that must be addressed before a constitutional amendment can replace the electoral vote system with a popular vote system. Currently, each state regulates its own presidential ballot. A candidate in one state may not be a candidate in another. For example, in the 2016 presidential election the ballot in Utah featured 10 candidates. The ballot in California listed 6 candidates. In particular, Evan McCullin ran as an Independent in Utah. Utah was the only state in which McCullin was listed as a presidential candidate. McCullin won 21.5% of the vote in Utah. Such situations advance relevant "national popular vote" questions.

Question 1: should there be a uniform national presidential ballot? If yes, then what agency is responsible for the construction of the national ballot? Should there be a federal ballot access law for prospective presidential candidates; that is, what are the requirements to get on the ballot? You do not want just anybody who craves a vanity moment to be able to be on the ballot. Just recalling the 2016 media debacle about the Republican presidential debates should be warning enough about the problem of who to allow on stage.

Should there be a write-in option? Currently a candidate gets on the presidential ballot by means of a state's ballot access law. The laws in each of the states and D. C. are different. Nine states do not have a write-in option; the others have varying forms of a write-in option. To prevent frivolous voting, some states require a write-in candidate to be certified[34] or to file some appropriate paperwork; otherwise, the write-in vote is invalid.[35]

---

[31] E. J. Dionne, *If majority rules, democracy wins*, San Francisco Chronicle, 25 December 2016; accessed from http://www.sfchronicle.com/opinion/article/When-majority-rules-democracy-wins-10818017.php.

[32] George Will, *The electoral college is an excellent system*, Washington Post, 16 December 2016; accessed from https://www.washingtonpost.com/opinions/the-electoral-college-is-an-excellent-system/2016/12/16/30480790-c2ef-11e6-9a51-cd56ea1c2bb7_story.html?tid=a_inl&utm_term=.9b401f32a85d.

[33] Brian J. Gaines, Popular Myths about Popular Vote-Electoral College Splits, *PS: Political Science and Politics*, 34(1), March 2001: 70-75.

[34] Mike Donila and Jim Matheny, *Presidential write-ins skyrocket in 2016; names serious and silly*; https://www.wbir.com/article/news/local/presidential-write-ins-skyrocket-in-2016-names-serious-and-silly/51-350803984.

[35] https://ballotpedia.org/Ballot_access_for_presidential_candidates.

Question 2: should there be a uniform, national, federal requirement for voter registration for a national popular vote? Every state has different voter registration laws. Some states have recent restrictive "voter identification" laws that critics chastise as voter suppression laws.[36] So, how should the requirements for who can vote be set? For example, should all American citizens "in good-standing" be allowed to vote in a national election for President? In some states voting privileges are denied to felons; in others, there are no restrictions regarding felons.[37] So, who will be allowed to vote for president?

In considering all Americans in good standing, however that may be defined, what about American citizens who live in a U.S. territory but are not citizens of a state or residents of D. C.? For example, Americans living in Puerto Rico, the U. S. Virgin Islands, and Guam are U.S. citizens. They are subject to military duty (males between 18 and 25 must register with the Selective Service System[38]) and are subject to many federal taxes.[39] These territories have representation with voting privileges at the Republican and Democratic national nominating conventions. Further, the people in territories vote in presidential primary elections for selecting party nominees.[40] Why can American citizens in territories of the U.S. vote on all levels but not in the final election for president? Further, what about citizens living abroad or people with dual citizenship living in another country? So, in general, who should be allowed to vote in a national popular election for president?

Question 3: what should be the structure of the ballot in a national presidential election? Should the ballot merely list the candidates with the simple instruction "Vote for one"? How about other more comprehensive alternatives allowing for greater voter input, like the following two options, for example?

Option A: Vote for all candidates you approve. Thus, a voter gets a "say so" on each candidate: yes I approve, no I do not approve. The candidate with the most approvals then wins the election. This voting method is called *Approval Voting*.[41]

Option B: Rank the candidates from 1 on down. This method is referred to as a *Ranked Choice Voting* or *Instant Runoff Voting*.[42] Several localities use some form of a ranked choice system.[43] One form is a partial ranked order where a voter ranks their top three choices. In a full ranked-order system a voter may rank all the candidates. For example, if there are six candidates, then rank those candidates from 1 to 6. In the 2016 election Maine passed a full ranked order ballot method for all statewide offices.[44, 45]

---

[36] Simply Google *pros and cons of voter identification laws* to get a variety of viewpoints.
[37] http://ww2.kqed.org/lowdown/2014/02/26/felon-voting/
[38] https://www.sss.gov/Registration-Info/Who-Registration.
[39] http://www.pr51st.com/taxation-without-representation-in-puerto-rico/.
[40] http://www.fairvote.org/puerto-rico-and-other-territories-vote-in-primaries-but-not-in-general-election.
[41] https://electology.org/approval-voting.
[42] http://instantrunoff.com/instant-runoff-home/the-basics/.
[43] http://www.instantrunoff.com/instant-runoff-home/in-action/where-irv-is-used/in-the-united-states-2/.
[44] http://mainepublic.org/post/maine-passes-ranked-choice-voting#stream/0.
[45] https://ballotpedia.org/Maine_Ranked_Choice_Voting_Initiative,_Question_5_(2016).

The main point here is that the electoral system is subject to unavoidable flaws resulting from congressional reapportionment. Replacing the electoral system with a uniform national popular vote would require an amendment to the Constitution. However, advancing a constitutional amendment to eliminate the electoral system is not a simple matter. The amendment must be clearly but broadly crafted. Further, the shear politics that a constitutional amendment needs to be approved by a 2/3rds vote of both the House and the Senate and then by 3/4ths of the individual states is daunting by itself.[46]

As a more expedient mechanism to obtain change, the National Popular Vote movement has crafted a proposal that would not involve a constitutional amendment by working within the electoral system. Voting is kept as a "state's rights" matter. Ballot access, suffrage, ballot structure, and voting management are left up to each state. Then count the current popular vote separately in each state determined by state regulation as is currently done.[47]

This ingenious solution keeps the electoral system intact. The Constitution specifies,[48]

> Each State shall appoint, in such Manner as the Legislature thereof may direct, a Number of Electors, equal to the whole Number of Senators and Representatives to which the state may be entitled in Congress: but no senator or Representative, or Person holding an Office of Trust or Profit under the United States, shall be appointed an Elector.

Currently every electoral state legislature has directed that the electoral slate will be awarded to that slate of electors selected by plurality of the vote in that state. The National Popular Vote bill would have a state legislature simply direct that the electoral slate will be awarded to that slate of electors selected by the national plurality vote. The bill would take effect in those individual states that enact the bill when a consortium of states having a total of 270 or more electoral votes enact the National Popular Vote bill. The movement has made significant progress which can be tracked on their website. Interestingly, the National Popular Vote bill would be able to have the President and Vice-President selected by the national vote, yet it retains the electoral system. Currently the Electoral College consists of 538 electors. A majority of 270 electors is needed to elect a President. If a consortium of states with 270 electoral votes agrees to select a slate of electors pledged to the national popular winner, then that guarantees the election of the national popular vote winner.

---

[46] U. S. Constitution, Article V.
[47] http://www.nationalpopularvote.com/.
[48] U. S. Constitution, Article II, Section 1, Paragraph 2.

Section 5.7:   Reapportionment Based on the 2000 Census

Section 5.7.1   Background

As in the previous decade, Congress did not concern itself with the results of apportionment based on the 2000 census. However, there were some census issues that some members of Congress addressed, including privacy, accuracy, and inclusion of U. S. citizens living abroad.

Some members of Congress expressed apprehensions about what they perceived as the intrusive nature of the various questions asked in the census survey. For example, Helen Chenowith-Hage (R-ID) introduced H.R. 4198 to "declare the policy of the United States with regard to the constitutional requirement of a decennial census for purposes of the apportionment of Representatives in Congress among the several States." The bill declared that the sole purpose of the decennial census is the reapportionment of Representatives in Congress. The act further declared that "the only information needed in order to carry out that purpose are the names, ages, and the number of individuals residing in a household, and the address or location of such household." Finally, any penalties invoked for noncompliance with the Census Bureau's questionnaire would be restricted to that information. The bill was referred to the Committee on Government Reform and to the Committee on the Judiciary. The Committee on Government Reform sent the bill to its Subcommittee on the Census. The Committee on the Judiciary sent the bill to its Subcommittee on the Constitution. No further action was taken on the bill.[1]

Congress had major concerns over obtaining accurate census counts when the distribution of federal funds for programs was based on population. The Census Bureau relied heavily on sampling techniques to obtain population counts used for purposes other than congressional reapportionment.

Section 5.7.2   Automatic Reapportionment

Automatic reapportionment based on the 2000 census distributed 435 seats using the Huntington-Hill modified divisor method. Table 5.12 (next page) displays the results by each of the five modified divisor methods: LD (largest divisor, Jefferson), HM (harmonic mean, Dean), GM (geometric mean, Huntington-Hill), AM (arithmetic mean, Webster), and SD (smallest divisor, Adams). The quota for each state determined by the rule of three is also displayed.

The workable interval of divisors for each of the five modified divisor methods is provided below along with an easy rounded figure to use. The divisor represents the national average district size for each method.

- LD [615709, 615983] 615800
- HM [646449, 650503] 650000
- GM [645684, 645930] 645700

---

[1] https://www.congress.gov/bill/106th-congress/house-bill/4198/text.

State	Seats	Population	LD	HM	GM	AM	SD	Quota
Alabama	7	4461130	7	7	7	7	7	6.8956
Alaska	1	628933	1	1	1	1	1	0.9721
Arizona	6	5140683	8	8	8	8	8	7.9460
Arkansas	4	2679733	4	4	4	4	4	4.1421
California	52	33930798	55	52	53	53	50	52.4472
Colorado	6	4311882	7	7	7	7	7	6.6649
Connecticut	6	3409535	5	5	5	5	6	5.2702
Delaware	1	785068	1	1	1	1	2	1.2135
Florida	23	16028890	26	25	25	25	24	24.7760
Georgia	11	8206975	13	13	13	13	13	12.6856
Hawaii	2	1216642	1	2	2	2	2	1.8806
Idaho	2	1297274	2	2	2	2	2	2.0052
Illinois	20	12439042	20	19	19	19	19	19.2271
Indiana	10	6090782	9	9	9	9	9	9.4146
Iowa	5	2931923	4	5	5	5	5	4.5319
Kansas	4	2693824	4	4	4	4	4	4.1639
Kentucky	6	4049431	6	6	6	6	6	6.2592
Louisiana	7	4480271	7	7	7	7	7	6.9252
Maine	2	1277731	2	2	2	2	2	1.9750
Maryland	8	5307886	8	8	8	8	8	8.2044
Massachusetts	10	6355568	10	10	10	10	10	9.8239
Michigan	16	9955829	16	15	15	15	15	15.3888
Minnesota	8	4925670	7	8	8	8	8	7.6137
Mississippi	5	2852927	4	4	4	4	5	4.4098
Missouri	9	5606260	9	9	9	9	9	8.6656
Montana	1	905316	1	2	1	1	2	1.3994
Nebraska	3	1715369	2	3	3	3	3	2.6515
Nevada	2	2002032	3	3	3	3	3	3.0946
New Hampshire	2	1238415	2	2	2	2	2	1.9142
New Jersey	13	8424354	13	13	13	13	13	13.0216
New Mexico	3	1823821	2	3	3	3	3	2.8191
New York	31	19004973	30	29	29	29	28	29.3762
North Carolina	12	8067673	13	12	13	13	12	12.4703
North Dakota	1	643756	1	1	1	1	1	0.9951
Ohio	19	11374540	18	18	18	18	17	17.5817
Oklahoma	6	3458819	5	5	5	5	6	5.3463
Oregon	5	3428543	5	5	5	5	6	5.2995
Pennsylvania	21	12300670	19	19	19	19	19	19.0133
Rhode Island	2	1049662	1	2	2	2	2	1.6225
South Carolina	6	4025061	6	6	6	6	6	6.2216
South Dakota	1	756874	1	1	1	1	2	1.1699
Tennessee	9	5700037	9	9	9	9	9	8.8106
Texas	30	20903994	33	32	32	32	31	32.3115
Utah	3	2236714	3	4	3	3	4	3.4573
Vermont	1	609890	1	1	1	1	1	0.9427
Virginia	11	7100702	11	11	11	11	11	10.9756
Washington	9	5908684	9	9	9	9	9	9.1331
West Virginia	3	1813077	2	3	3	3	3	2.8025
Wisconsin	9	5371210	8	8	8	8	8	8.3023
Wyoming	1	495304	1	1	1	1	1	0.7656
US	435	281424177	435	435	435	435	435	435.0000

Table 5.12. Apportionment based on the 2000 census.

- AM [644237, 645413]   645000
- SD [678750, 681907]   680000

Apportionments determined by Webster and Huntington-Hill agreed with each other. Dean differed in awarding a seat to Montana and Utah at the expense of California and North Carolina. The methods of Dean, Huntington-Hill, and Webster do not have any quota violations. Adams displays lower quota violations for four states: California (two seats below lower quota), Florida, New York, and Texas. Jefferson displays upper quota violations for three states: California (two seats above upper quota) and Florida.

The Census Bureau presents their apportionment findings also in the form of a priority list. First each state is awarded one seat in compliance with the constitutional mandate that each state receive at least one seat. This distributes the first 50 seats in the House. Then, the list states which state has priority for the 51st seat, 52nd seat, up to the 440th seat. This priority list is available at the Bureau's website.[2] Difference in methodology between the five methods is again displayed in the awarding of the 436th seat: Jefferson, Minnesota; Dean, North Carolina; Huntington-Hill, Utah; Webster and Adams, New York.

Section 5.7.3   Utah

The Census Bureau's priority list for the awarding of seats 435 to 440 is displayed in Table 5.13.

Table 5.13. Priority List 435-440.

House Seat	State	State Seat	Priority Value
435	North Carolina	13	645931
436	Utah	4	645684
437	New York	30	644329
438	Texas	33	63276
439	Michigan	16	642646
440	Indiana	10	642025

Utah especially was unhappy with being "awarded" the 436th seat and thereby being deprived of an additional congressman. Accordingly, on 17 April 2001 Utah filed suit in U. S. District Court for the District of Utah to claim the 435th seat over North Carolina.[3] In determining the apportionment population for each state, the Census Bureau included all federal employees and their dependents living abroad. This practice heavily favored North Carolina over Utah since the federal overseas population added 18360 to the enumeration for North Carolina but only 3545 to Utah.[4]

However, all other Americans living abroad were excluded from the apportionment enumeration including 11159 Mormon missionaries from Utah living abroad under temporary assignment. If the missionaries had been included, then Utah would have been awarded the 435th House seat instead of North Carolina. Utah petitioned the District Court that either no Americans living abroad should be included in the apportionment enumeration or that the missionary count should be included for Utah. In short Utah asserted that "the Census Bureau's

[2] http://www2.census.gov/programs-surveys/decennial/2000/data/apportionment/00pvalues.txt.
[3] 143 F. Supp. 2d 1290 (D. Utah 2001); http://law.justia.com/cases/federal/district-courts/FSupp2/143/1290/2428922/.
[4] D'Vera Cohn, Census 2010: The Last Seat in Congress, Pew Research Center, 11 January 2011; accessed from http://www.pewresearch.org/2011/01/11/census-2010-the-last-seat-in-congress/.

failure to enumerate LDS missionaries living abroad, while including within its enumeration federal employees living abroad, violated various constitutional and statutory provisions."[5]

Utah included both procedures of redress, either include the missionaries or exclude all people living abroad, because Utah would have been awarded the 435th House seat under either proviso. Table 5.14 (next page) displays the spreadsheet for apportionment using only the resident population. In particular, observe that Utah and North Carolina are the only two states affected by applying only the resident population that excludes federal employees serving abroad along with their dependents living with them.[6]

The District Court ruled against Utah. The judicial panel concluded, using Census Bureau estimates, that there were about five million Americans living abroad on Census day that were not family members of federal employees. The inclusion of a mere 11159 Mormon missionaries would create an unfair advantage for Utah over all the other states. The panel advanced that deciding in favor of Utah would require that the 2000 census be retaken so that all Americans who are not federal employees living abroad would be included.

After losing in District Court, Utah appealed to the Supreme Court in *Utah v. Evans*.[7] It became clear to the Utah legal team that merely appealing the decision of the District Court would not yield a path to victory. The legacy of *Franklin v. Massachusetts* signaled that Utah was not going to convince the court to exclude the enumeration of federal employees living abroad by virtue of their being stationed in government service. Further, the narrow view that the case was merely about the priority of assigning a House seat between Utah and North Carolina would not work based on the single issue of whether to include the LDS Utah missionaries in Utah's enumeration. A different strategy based on a broad issue was needed.

Utah submitted its case based on two questions.[8]

> Does the Census Bureau's use of "hot-deck imputation," in the 2000 census, violate the statutory provision forbidding use of the statistical method known as sampling? Is this methodology inconsistent with the Constitution's statement that an "actual Enumeration be made?"

In particular, "Hot deck imputation is a method for handling missing data in which each missing value is replaced with an observed response from a "similar" unit."[9] [10] Utah charged

---

[5] 143 F. Supp. 2d 1290 (D. Utah 2001): 1293.

[6] Overseas populations obtained from U.S. Census Bureau, tab03.xls; accessed from http://www2.census.gov/programs-surveys/decennial/2000/data/apportionment/.

[7] 536 U. S. 452 (2002); https://supreme.justia.com/cases/federal/us/536/452/.

[8] Chicago-Kent College of Law at Illinois Tech. "Utah v. Evans." Oyez. https://www.oyez.org/cases/2001/01-714 (accessed March 31, 2017).

[9] U.S. Census Bureau, Center for Statistical Research and Methodology, Appendix F: Methods for Treating Missing Data, https://www.nap.edu/read/10907/chapter/18.

[10] Rebecca Andridge and Roderick Little, *A Review of Hot Deck Imputation for Survey Non-response*, Int Stat Rev. 2010 April; 789(1): 40-64. Accessed from https://www.ncbi.nlm.nih.gov/pmc/articles/PMC3130338/.

State	Population	Abroad	Resident	Seats	House
Alabama	4461130	14,030	4447100	7	7
Alaska	628933	2,001	626932	1	1
Arizona	5140683	10,051	5130632	8	8
Arkansas	2679733	6,333	2673400	4	4
California	33930798	59,150	33871648	53	53
Colorado	4311882	10,621	4301261	7	7
Connecticut	3409535	3,970	3405565	5	5
Delaware	785068	1,468	783600	1	1
Florida	16028890	46,512	15982378	25	25
Georgia	8206975	20,522	8186453	13	13
Hawaii	1216642	5,105	1211537	2	2
Idaho	1297274	3,321	1293953	2	2
Illinois	12439042	19,749	12419293	19	19
Indiana	6090782	10,297	6080485	9	9
Iowa	2931923	5,599	2926324	5	5
Kansas	2693824	5,406	2688418	4	4
Kentucky	4049431	7,662	4041769	6	6
Louisiana	4480271	11,295	4468976	7	7
Maine	1277731	2,808	1274923	2	2
Maryland	5307886	11,400	5296486	8	8
Massachusetts	6355568	6,471	6349097	10	10
Michigan	9955829	17,385	9938444	15	15
Minnesota	4925670	6,191	4919479	8	8
Mississippi	2852927	8,269	2844658	4	4
Missouri	5606260	11,049	5595211	9	9
Montana	905316	3,121	902195	1	1
Nebraska	1715369	4,106	1711263	3	3
Nevada	2002032	3,775	1998257	3	3
New Hampshire	1238415	2,629	1235786	2	2
New Jersey	8424354	10,004	8414350	13	13
New Mexico	1823821	4,775	1819046	3	3
New York	19004973	28,516	18976457	29	29
North Carolina	8067673	18,360	8049313	12	13
North Dakota	643756	1,556	642200	1	1
Ohio	11374540	21,400	11353140	18	18
Oklahoma	3458819	8,165	3450654	5	5
Oregon	3428543	7,144	3421399	5	5
Pennsylvania	12300670	19,616	12281054	19	19
Rhode Island	1049662	1,343	1048319	2	2
South Carolina	4025061	13,049	4012012	6	6
South Dakota	756874	2,030	754844	1	1
Tennessee	5700037	10,754	5689283	9	9
Texas	20903994	52,174	20851820	32	32
Utah	2236714	3,545	2233169	4	3
Vermont	609890	1,063	608827	1	1
Virginia	7100702	22,187	7078515	11	11
Washington	5908684	14,563	5894121	9	9
West Virginia	1813077	4,733	1808344	3	3
Wisconsin	5371210	7,535	5363675	8	8
Wyoming	495304	1,522	493782	1	1
US	281424177	574,330	280849847	435	435

Table 5.14. Spreadsheet for House apportionment based on the 2000 census excluding federal employees and their dependents living with them stationed overseas. The Resident column shows the apportionment population with the overseas (Abroad) population removed. The Seats column shows apportionment that excludes the Abroad population. The House column shows the corresponding apportionment that includes the Abroad population.

that hot-deck imputation violated the prohibition of sampling techniques in enumerating the population for apportionment. Hot deck imputation resulted in a 0.4% increase in the apportionment population for North Carolina, but only a 0.2% increase in the enumeration for Utah. Accordingly, Utah sought a court directive ordering a change in the official census report. The end result would have been that the priority for the 435th and 436th House seats would be awarded to Utah and North Carolina, respectively.[11]

The case was vigorously argued in the Supreme Court. The Court concluded with an answer of no to both questions brought by Utah. The first question resulted in an 8-1 decision. The second question was answered with a 5-4 decision.

Although Utah lost its case in court, *Evans v. Utah* underscored the problem of counting Americans serving abroad. Representative Carolyn Maloney (D-NY) spearheaded a drive that got the Census Bureau in 2004 to conduct a test to study the feasibility of enumerating Americans living abroad. The test resulted in failure. It cost $1450 to enumerate an American living abroad in the pilot study, compared with a cost of $56 to enumerate a resident. The Government Accountability Office recommended abandoning the project.[12] [13]

On 24 June 2009 Representatives Rob Bishop and Jason Chaffets (R-UT) introduced H.R. 3013, a bill to provide for the more accurate and complete enumeration of certain overseas Americans in the decennial census. The bill was referred to the Committee on Oversight and Government Reform.[14] The bill was reintroduced in the 112th Congress as H.R. 868. Senator Orin Hatch (R-UT) introduced a similar bill as S. 677. The bills never made it out of committee.

[11] Oyez, Utah. v. Evans.
[12] Matt Canham, *Census count to exclude overseas missionaries – again*, The Salt Lake Tribune, 16 August 2009; accessed from http://archive.sltrib.com/story.php?ref=/news/ci_13122213.
[13] The Hill, *Census Bureau finds it can't count Americans abroad*, 30 March 2006; accessed from http://thehill.com/homenews/administration/4231-census-bureau-finds-it-cant-count-americans-abroad.
[14] Congressional Record, 111th Congress, 1st Session, 24 June 2009: H7249.

Section 5.8: Reapportionment Based on the 2010 Census

Section 5.8.1 Automatic Reapportionment

The Census Bureau announced the apportionment results based on the 2010 census at a news conference on 21 December 2010.[1] Automatic reapportionment for House size 435 using the Huntington-Hill modified divisor method went smoothly.[2] As directed by law, on 5 January 2011 President Obama transmitted the results to Congress.[3] Table 5.15 (next page) displays the results by each of the five modified divisor methods: LD (largest divisor, Jefferson), HM (harmonic mean, Dean), GM (geometric mean, Huntington-Hill), AM (arithmetic mean, Webster), and SD (smallest divisor, Adams). The quota for each state from the rule of three is also displayed.

The workable interval of divisors for each of the five modified divisor methods is provided below along with an easy rounded figure to use. The divisor represents the national average district size for each method. By comparison, the total U. S. apportionment population divided by 435 yields an average House size of 710766.

- LD [675337, 677072] 676000
- HM [711341, 711814] 711500
- GM [709063, 741116] 710000
- AM [707233, 708576] 708000
- SD [749113, 750374] 750000

The Huntington-Hill and Webster methods differ in that Webster awards a seat to North Carolina at the expense of Rhode Island. Also, the two methods are at variance with the Dean method by awarding 53 seats to California and 1 seat to Montana. In contrast, Dean awards 2 seats to Montana and 52 seats to California. Jefferson's method has upper quota violations for California and Texas, awarding two seats over quota to California. Adams has lower quota violations for California, New York, and Texas, awarding two seats under quota to California.

Differences in the five methods can again be seen in which state has priority for the 436th seat: Jefferson, Washington; Dean, California; Huntington-Hill, North Carolina; Webster, Missouri; and Adams, Pennsylvania. The priority list for seats 50 through 440 for the Huntington-Hill method can be found on the Census Bureau's website.[4]

[1] https://www.census.gov/newsroom/releases/archives/2010_census/press-kits/apport.html.
[2] https://www.census.gov/data/tables/2010/dec/2010-apportionment-data.html (Table 1, Excel).
[3] Congressional Record—House, 112th Congress, 1st Session, 5 January 2011: H31; House Document 112-5; accessed from https://www.congress.gov/congressional-record/2011/1/5/house-section/article/H31-2.
[4] http://www.census.gov/data/tables/2010/dec/2010-apportionment-data.html (Table 1, PDF).

State	Seats	Population	LD	HM	GM	AM	SD	Quota
Alabama	7	4,802,982	7	7	7	7	7	6.7575
Alaska	1	721,523	1	1	1	1	1	1.0151
Arizona	8	6,412,700	9	9	9	9	9	9.0222
Arkansas	4	2,926,229	4	4	4	4	4	4.1170
California	53	37,341,989	55	52	53	53	50	52.5376
Colorado	7	5,044,930	7	7	7	7	7	7.0979
Connecticut	5	3,581,628	5	5	5	5	5	5.0391
Delaware	1	900,877	1	1	1	1	2	1.2675
Florida	25	18,900,773	27	27	27	27	26	26.5921
Georgia	13	9,727,566	14	14	14	14	13	13.6860
Hawaii	2	1,366,862	2	2	2	2	2	1.9231
Idaho	2	1,573,499	2	2	2	2	3	2.2138
Illinois	19	12,864,380	19	18	18	18	18	18.0993
Indiana	9	6,501,582	9	9	9	9	9	9.1473
Iowa	5	3,053,787	4	4	4	4	5	4.2965
Kansas	4	2,863,813	4	4	4	4	4	4.0292
Kentucky	6	4,350,606	6	6	6	6	6	6.1210
Louisiana	7	4,553,962	6	6	6	6	7	6.4071
Maine	2	1,333,074	1	2	2	2	2	1.8755
Maryland	8	5,789,929	8	8	8	8	8	8.1460
Massachusetts	10	6,559,644	9	9	9	9	9	9.2290
Michigan	15	9,911,626	14	14	14	14	14	13.9450
Minnesota	8	5,314,879	7	8	8	8	8	7.4777
Mississippi	4	2,978,240	4	4	4	4	4	4.1902
Missouri	9	6,011,478	8	8	8	8	9	8.4577
Montana	1	994,416	1	2	1	1	2	1.3991
Nebraska	3	1,831,825	2	3	3	3	3	2.5773
Nevada	3	2,709,432	4	4	4	4	4	3.8120
New Hampshire	2	1,321,445	1	2	2	2	2	1.8592
New Jersey	13	8,807,501	13	12	12	12	12	12.3916
New Mexico	3	2,067,273	3	3	3	3	3	2.9085
New York	29	19,421,055	28	27	27	27	26	27.3241
North Carolina	13	9,565,781	14	13	13	14	13	13.4584
North Dakota	1	675,905	1	1	1	1	1	0.9510
Ohio	18	11,568,495	17	16	16	16	16	16.2761
Oklahoma	5	3,764,882	5	5	5	5	6	5.2969
Oregon	5	3,848,606	5	5	5	5	6	5.4147
Pennsylvania	19	12,734,905	18	18	18	18	17	17.9171
Rhode Island	2	1,055,247	1	2	2	1	2	1.4847
South Carolina	6	4,645,975	6	7	7	7	7	6.5366
South Dakota	1	819,761	1	1	1	1	2	1.1533
Tennessee	9	6,375,431	9	9	9	9	9	8.9698
Texas	32	25,268,418	37	36	36	36	34	35.5509
Utah	3	2,770,765	4	4	4	4	4	3.8983
Vermont	1	630,337	1	1	1	1	1	0.8868
Virginia	11	8,037,736	11	11	11	11	11	11.3085
Washington	9	6,753,369	9	10	10	10	10	9.5015
West Virginia	3	1,859,815	2	3	3	3	3	2.6166
Wisconsin	8	5,698,230	8	8	8	8	8	8.0170
Wyoming	1	568,300	1	1	1	1	1	0.7996
US	435	309,183,463	435	435	435	435	435	435.0000

Table 5.15. Apportionment based on the 2010 census.

Section 5.8.2   Washington, District of Columbia

Exactly who the Census Bureau should count in enumerating the apportionment population has been an ongoing issue for 150 years. The contentious debate over whether to base the apportionment population on residents or citizens occupied more than a century. Since 1970 attention has been focused on Americans living abroad. The Census Bureau describes who is included in the apportionment population as follows.[5]

> The apportionment population count for each of the 50 states includes the state's total resident population (citizens and non-citizens) plus a count of the overseas federal employees (and dependents) who have that state listed as their home state in their employers' administrative records.

> For details on who is counted (and where they are counted) in the 2020 Census, see the 2020 Census Residence Criteria and Residence Situations.

Notice that nonmilitary citizens residing abroad are not counted. This is somewhat at odds with the Uniformed and Overseas Citizens Absentee Voting Act (UOCAVA) approved into law by President Ronald Reagan on 28 August 1986.[6] It seems inconsistent that military and embassy personnel and their families are counted in the apportionment population while most other citizens living abroad are not. Yet, both groups can vote in federal elections.

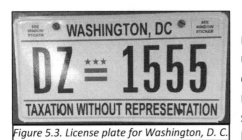

Figure 5.3. License plate for Washington, D. C.

The ongoing issue of enumeration of Americans residing overseas became entangled with another unrelated apportionment issue. A glaring inconsistency in equal representation is the status of citizens residing in the nation's capital, Washington, D. C.[7] The District is not a state, hence gets no full voting member in Congress. However, since 1970 the District has a delegate to the House of Representatives.[8] The delegate is a nonvoting member of the House. The delegate may serve on committees and vote in committee, may propose legislation, and may vote on procedural matters but not legislative matters. In 2000 the District actively began to voice its displeasure over lack of representation on its license plates (Figure 5.3).[9]

An intense effort to remedy the situation was spearheaded by Delegate Eleanor Holmes Norton (D-DC) (Figure 5.4[10], next page). The effort began with the introduction of H.R. 1285, No Taxation Without Representation Act of 2003, in the 108th Congress, 1st Session, on 13

---

[5] https://www.census.gov/topics/public-sector/congressional-apportionment/about/faqs.html#Q2.

[6] https://en.wikipedia.org/wiki/Uniformed_and_Overseas_Citizens_Absentee_Voting_Act.

[7] https://en.wikipedia.org/wiki/District_of_Columbia_voting_rights.

[8] Randy James, *A Brief History of Washington, D.C.*, Time Magazine, 16 February 2009; accessed from http://content.time.com/time/politics/article/0,8599,1881791,00.html.

[9] https://commons.wikimedia.org/wiki/File:Washington,_D.C._license_plate.JPG.

[10] By Federal Office of Eleanor Holmes Norton - http://www.norton.house.gov/images/stories/norton%20color%20official%20picture%202006.jpg. Public Domain, https://commons.wikimedia.org/w/index.php?curid=10505727

March 2003.[11] The bill had 139 cosponsors, all Democrats except
Bernie Sanders (I-VT). The bill mirrors the Twenty-Third Amendment
which treats the District as a state for the Electoral College. H.R. 1285
would extend the same treatment to the District for purposes of
representation in Congress. The District would be awarded two
senators and one representative. Further, the House size would be
reset to 436 so that apportionment would not otherwise be affected.
The bill did not make it out of the House Judiciary Committee. A
corresponding bill, S. 617, was introduced in the Senate by Joseph
Lieberman (I-CT) with similar results.[12]

*Figure 5.4. D.C. delegate
Eleanor Holmes Norton.*

In the 109th Congress on 16 May 2006 Tom Davis (R-VA) introduced H.R. 5388, District of
Columbia Fair and Equal House Voting Rights Act of 2006. The bill had two key features. First,
the District of Columbia would become a single congressional district with one representative.
Second, the size of the House would be reset to 437. The bill had 43 sponsors: 29 Democrats,
13 Republicans, and 1 Independent. The bill would provide no senators for the District.[13]

The bill was sent to the Committee on Government Reform. The bill was reported out of
committee on 24 July with an extensive 64-page report documenting the case for
representation in the House for the District.[14] The committee reported "favorably thereon
without amendment and recommend that the bill do pass." The favorable committee vote was
decisive, 29-4. Hearings were held in September but no further action on the bill was taken.

The important progress for the District was obtaining bipartisan support for representation.
The bill had two features which attracted Republican support. First, only the House would be
affected. Second, the House size would be increased from 435 to 437. This would allow Utah
to be awarded an additional seat in the House. Hence, the anticipated Democrat seat for the
District would be offset by an anticipated Republican seat for Utah. This mechanism would
solve Utah's problem as presented in Evans vs. Utah.

Sensing this opening, on 9 January 2007 Delegate Norton introduced H.R. 328, The District
of Columbia Fair and Equal House Voting Rights Act of 2007, into the 110th Congress. The bill
focused on the two features of one representative for the District and resetting the House size
to 437. If passed, then the bill would apply to reapportionment based on the 2010 census. The
bill garnered 24 cosponsors, 21 Democrats and 3 Republicans (none from Utah). The bill was
referred to the House Committee on the Judiciary where it died.[15]

---

[11] https://www.congress.gov/bill/108th-congress/house-bill/1285.
[12] https://www.congress.gov/bill/108th-congress/senate-bill/617/cosponsors.
[13] https://www.congress.gov/bill/109th-congress/house-bill/5388/.
[14] 109th Congress, 2d Session, Rept. 109-593, Part I; accessed from
https://www.congress.gov/109/crpt/hrpt593/CRPT-109hrpt593-pt1.pdf.
[15] https://www.congress.gov/bill/110th-congress/house-bill/328/all-actions.

Although H.R. 328 went nowhere, Eleanor Holmes Norton also introduced H.R. 1433 on 9 March 2007. The bill had 18 cosponsors, 6 Republicans and 18 Democrats. Among the original cosponsors introducing the bill were Republicans Tom Davis (VA), Todd Platts (PA), Christopher Shays (CT), and Darrell Issa (CA). The bill was referred to the Committee on Oversight and Government Reform and to the Committee on the Judiciary. Both committees reported favorably on the bill. The Committee on Oversight and Government reported favorably by a vote of 24-5 and issued H. Rept. 110-52, Part I, advancing their support. The Committee on the Judiciary reported favorably by a vote of 21-13 and issued Part II. Unfortunately, this vote was mostly on party lines. Democrats voted 19 aye, 0 nay, and 4 not voting. Republicans voted 2 aye, 13 nay, and 2 not voting. The two Republican aye votes were from Chris Cannon (R-UT) and Mike Pence (R-IN). Progress was being made in that a proposed District representation bill was vetted in committee and on 27 March the House proceeded to debate H.R. 1433.[16]

After the debate on 27 March, three weeks later Eleanor Holmes Norton introduced H.R. 1905, District of Columbia Voting Rights Act of 2007. Delegate Norton polished all the ideas from the previous committee reports and debates in formulating H.R. 1905. Accordingly, on 19 April the House tabled H.R. 1433 and proceeded to consider H.R. 1905. Subsequently, the House passed H.R. 1905, 241-177. The bill was then sent to the Senate who referred it to the Committee on Finance.[17]

To get things moving in the Senate, on 1 May Joe Lieberman (I-CT) introduced S. 1257, District of Columbia House Voting Rights Act of 2007, basically a clone of H.R. 1433. The Lieberman bill had 20 cosponsors. The two notable original cosponsors were Robert Bennett and Orrin Hatch, both Republican senators from Utah. Later, notable Democrats joined as cosponsors, including Hillary Clinton (NY), Barack Obama (IL), Edward Kennedy (MA), John Kerry (MA), and Christopher Dodd (CT). Also, Bernie Sanders (I-VT) joined as a cosponsor. The bill was referred to the Committee on Homeland Security and Governmental Affairs.

Action quickly progressed in the Senate. Hearings were held by the Committee on the Judiciary on 23 May. On 13 June the Committee on Homeland Security and Governmental Affairs reported favorably accompanied with Sen. Report No. 110-123. On 12 September a motion was made to proceed to consideration of the measure. However, on 18 September a cloture vote to proceed narrowly failed the 60-vote threshold, 57-42. Hence, the Senate failed to pass the bill by a mere 3 votes short of the supermajority needed to avoid filibuster.[18] Again, an unfortunate aspect was the pure power partisan nature of the vote. The 42 nay votes came from 41 Republicans and 1 Democrat. The 57 yea votes came from 8 Republicans, 47 Democrats, and 2 Independents.

---

[16] https://www.congress.gov/bill/110th-congress/house-bill/1433.

[17] https://www.congress.gov/bill/110th-congress/house-bill/1905

[18] S. 1257—110th Congress: District of Columbia House Voting Rights Act of 2007; https://www.govtrack.us/congress/bills/110/s1257.

Nevertheless, proponents of D. C. representation felt reinvigorated following the 2008 presidential election. Barack Obama was a cosponsor of S. 1257 during the previous Congress. Now he was President. During the campaign Obama said he would approve a bill awarding House representation for D.C. Accordingly, on 6 January 2009 Delegate Norton in the House introduced H.R. 157 – District of Columbia House Voting Rights Act of 2009.[19] Simultaneously, in the Senate Joe Lieberman and Orrin Hatch introduced the same bill as S. 160.[20]

The proposal had the most success in the Senate where an amended version passed on 26 February, 61 aye, 37 nay, and 1 not voting. Again, the vote was mostly on partisan lines. Five Republicans, including Senator Hatch (UT), joined 54 Democrats and 2 Independents in passing the bill. The 37 nay votes came from 35 Republicans and 2 Democrats. Surprisingly, Senator Bennett (R-UT) voted against the bill. On 27 February the bill was sent to the House where the bill was received and held at the desk. The bill advanced nowhere in the House.[21]

The main difficulty with the Senate bill is that it came laden with two irrelevant amendments. The most notorious was the Ensign amendment, S.Amdt.575 to S.160, proposed by John Ensign (R-NV). The amendment's purpose was to repeal all gun control regulations enacted by the District. The amendment passed in the Senate, 62-36. However, the Democrat controlled House was not about to support S. 160 with this amendment rider. Further, supporters of representation in Washington, D. C., would not support S. 106 with the amendment repealing the District's gun-control laws.[22]

H.R. 157 made even less progress. After introduction the bill was referred to the House Committee on the Judiciary. The bill with amendment was reported favorably out of committee on a party-line vote, 20-12, and accompanied by House Report 111-22. On March 2 the bill was place on the calendar, but no further action was taken.

Delegate Norton reintroduced the bill into the 112th Congress as H.R.267 – District of Columbia House Voting Rights Act of 2011. The bill was referred to committees but never resurfaced during the 112th Congress. A significant number of legislators began to question the constitutionality of awarding representation to the District of Columbia by legislative action. Many thought that it would need a constitutional amendment, much like the Twenty-Third Amendment which gave the District votes in the Electoral College. However, previously on 22 August 1978, Congress proposed the District of Columbia Voting Rights Amendment to the Constitution. This is the most recent constitutional amendment sent to the states for ratification. At the 7-year deadline the amendment was ratified by only 16 of the 51 states, well short of the 38 states needed for ratification.[23]

---

[19] https://www.congress.gov/bill/111th-congress/house-bill/157.

[20] https://www.congress.gov/bill/111th-congress/senate-bill/160.

[21] https://www.congress.gov/bill/111th-congress/senate-bill/160/all-actions.

[22] Tim Craig and Ann Marimow, *Gun law proposal snarls local support for D. C. voting rights*, The Washington Post, 20 April 2010; accessed from http://www.washingtonpost.com/wp-dyn/content/article/2010/04/19/AR2010041904954.html?hpid=newswell.

[23] https://en.wikipedia.org/wiki/District_of_Columbia_Voting_Rights_Amendment.

The latest effort to obtain representation for the District of Columbia is through statehood.[24] On 2 March 2017 Delegate Norton introduced H.R.1291 – Washington, D.C. Admission Act.[25] The bill has been referred to the Committee on Government Oversight and Reform and to the House Rules Committee. Unfortunately for the District, the bill is once again based solely on partisan politics. All 117 cosponsors of the bill are Democrats. The official position of the Republican Party is opposed to statehood.[26]

> Statehood for the District can be advanced only by a constitutional amendment. Any other approach would be invalid. A statehood amendment was soundly rejected by the states when last proposed in 1976 and should not be revived.

The District of Columbia issue highlights the intense desire of people for representation.[27] In an advisory referendum in the 2016 general election, 86% of voters in the District voted for statehood. It also highlights the strength of partisan politics and why Congress is so ineffective.

Section 5.8.3   Clemons v. Department of Commerce

In November 2008 Apportionment.US was founded as a non-profit organization by Scott Scharpen.[28] The mission statement for Apportionment.US contains three items.[29]

- Achieve equal and appropriate representation in the U.S. House of Representatives for current and future generations,
- Educate American citizens about the Constitution in general, and House apportionment in particular, and
- Promote the benefits of smaller congressional districts resulting from an increase in House membership.

Mr. Sharpen was convinced that a huge disparity in one person, one vote is caused by the size of the House of Representatives being too small. Mr. Sharpen led a court action to have the size of the House increased for apportionment based on the 2010 census. Accordingly, on 17 September 2009 Michael Farris, the lead lawyer, filed a lawsuit in Northern Mississippi District Court in Oxford, Mississippi.[30] Mr. Farris is an expert in constitutional law and is chair of the Home School Legal Defense Association.[31] The District Court convened a three-judge panel to hear the case.

---

[24] https://statehood.dc.gov/.

[25] https://www.congress.gov/bill/115th-congress/house-bill/1291.

[26] Republican Platform, Government Reform, Preserving the District of Columbia; accessed from https://www.gop.com/platform/reforming-government/ (bottom of page).

[27] http://dcstatehoodyeswecan.org/j/.

[28] http://www.apportionment.us/index.html.

[29] Ibid, About.

[30] Clemons et al v. United States Department of Commerce et al, Case No. 3:09-cv-00104; https://www.plainsite.org/dockets/j6ivokuy/mississippi-northern-district-court/clemons-et-al-v-united-states-department-of-commerce-et-al/.

[31] Peter Baker, *Suit Seeks to Double Size of House*, New York Times, 12 July 2010; accessed from https://thecaucus.blogs.nytimes.com/2010/07/12/suit-seeks-to-double-size-of-house/?_r=0.

On 8 July 2010 the District court issued a ruling against the complaint. The District Court ruled in favor of Congress's discretion to set the size of the House within the constraints stated in the Constitution. The ruling was appealed to the Supreme Court on 26 August 2010. The appeal asked the Court to consider the following questions.

- Does the Constitution's requirement of one-person, one-vote apply to the interstate apportionment of the U.S. House of Representatives?
- Does the current level of inequality violate this standard?
- Does Congress need to increase the size of the House to remediate this inequality?

The motivation for the case is stated in the Jurisdictional Statement of the appeal.[32]

> This action challenges the constitutionality of the current interstate apportionment of Congress under the principle of one-person, one-vote. While the Supreme Court has required meticulous precision in the apportionment of congressional districts within a state, by freezing the size of Congress at 435 seats for approximately 100 years, the interstate apportionment is now grossly out of compliance with the requirement of Article I, Section 2 and Amendment XIV, Section 2 that "Representatives shall be apportioned among the several States according to their respective numbers." This action asks this Court to declare the current apportionment system to be unconstitutional.

On 13 December 2010 the Supreme Court dismissed the appeal for "lack of jurisdiction."[33] Although Apportionment.US lost its case in court, it inspired renewed academic interest about the legal aspects of the size of the House. In particular, Professor Jeffrey Ladewig concluded:[34]

> the constitutional requirement of "one person, one vote" can only be constitutionally addressed—to any considerable degree—by reconsidering the twentieth century statutory requirement that fixed the size of the House at 435 seats.

The merits of the case were also picked up in some corners of the press. For example, Jeff Jacoby writing in The Boston Globe began an op-ed article, "Large families need larger houses. A larger nation does, too."[35] The website Apportionment.US has not made a posting since the Supreme Court decision dismissing their appeal. However, the website is still available and remains a valuable resource in learning current day issues facing congressional apportionment. The set of 19 videos are especially enlightening and the linked resources are informative. In particular, Apportionment.US makes a strong case for increasing the size of the House.

---

[32] http://www.apportionment.us/Complaint.pdf.

[33] 10-291, CLEMONS, JOHN T., ET AL. V. DEPT. OF COMMERCE, ET AL., 13 December 2010; accessed from https://www.supremecourt.gov/orders/courtorders/121310zor.pdf.

[34] Jeffrey Ladewig, *One Person, One vote, 435 Seats: Interstate Malapportionment and Constitutional Requirements*, Connecticut Law Review, 43(4), May 2011: 1125-1156.

[35] Jeff Jacoby, *A House poorly divided*, The Boston Globe, 26 December 2010; http://archive.boston.com/bostonglobe/editorial_opinion/oped/articles/2010/12/26/a_house_poorly_divided/.

Section 5.9:   Reapportionment Based on the 2020 Census

Section 5.9.1   Automatic Reapportionment

The Census Bureau announced the apportionment results based on the 2020 census at a news conference on 26 April 2021.[1][2] This census is the first in which Americans could respond to the census survey online. Just over half of American households availed themselves of this opportunity.

Table 5.16 (next page) displays the apportionment of the House of Representatives based on the 2020 census by each of the five modified divisor methods: LD (largest divisor, Jefferson), HM (harmonic mean, Dean), GM (geometric mean, Huntington-Hill; equal proportions), AM (arithmetic mean, Webster; major fractions), and SD (smallest divisor, Adams). In addition Hamilton's quota method is displayed in the Quota and Hamilton columns. For comparison, the Seats column next to each state gives the apportionment based on the 2010 census. The bottom line is that seven seats changed hands. Texas gained two seats while Colorado, Florida, Montana, North Carolina, and Oregon each gained one seat. In contrast, California, Illinois, Michigan, New York, Ohio, Pennsylvania, and West Virginia each lost one seat.

The workable interval of divisors for each modified divisor method is provided below along with an easy rounded figure to use. The divisor represents the national average district size for each method. By comparison, the total U. S. apportionment population divided by 435 yields an average constituency of 761169. The only historical methods consistent with the national divisor are Webster's and Hamilton's.

- LD   [721212, 721659]   721500
- HM   [764699, 767240]   765000
- GM   [762995, 762997]   762996
- AM   [758008, 761300]   760000
- SD   [801422, 804149]   803000

Based on the 2020 census Webster's method is the only modified divisor method in agreement with Hamilton's quota method. The method of equal proportions displays a small-state bias to Rhode Island and Montana at the expense of New York and Ohio. Equal proportions uses a divisor of 762996 producing a quotient for Montana of 1.4226. The geometric mean for 1 (round down) and 2 (round up) is 1.4142; hence, Montana is allocated two seats. The quotient for New York is 26.495225, but the geometric mean of 26 and 27 is 26.495283; hence, New York narrowly settled for 26 seats. The case clearly shows that it is easier for a small state to get the round-up option in comparison to a larger state. In addition the method of harmonic means awards a seat to Idaho at the expense of Minnesota.

---

[1] 2020 Census Apportionment Results Delivered to the President.
[2] 2020 Census Apportionment Results.

State	Seats	Population	LD	HM	GM	AM	SD	Quota	Hamilton
Alabama	7	5030030	6	7	7	7	7	6.6083	7
Alaska	1	736081	1	1	1	1	1	0.9670	1
Arizona	9	7158923	9	9	9	9	9	9.4052	9
Arkansas	4	3013756	4	4	4	4	4	3.9594	4
California	53	39576757	54	52	52	52	50	51.9947	52
Colorado	7	5782171	8	8	8	8	8	7.5964	8
Connecticut	5	3608298	5	5	5	5	5	4.7405	5
Delaware	1	990837	1	1	1	1	2	1.3017	1
Florida	27	21570527	29	28	28	28	27	28.3387	28
Georgia	14	10725274	14	14	14	14	14	14.0905	14
Hawaii	2	1460137	2	2	2	2	2	1.9183	2
Idaho	2	1841377	2	3	2	2	3	2.4191	2
Illinois	18	12822739	17	17	17	17	16	16.8461	17
Indiana	9	6790280	9	9	9	9	9	8.9209	9
Iowa	4	3192406	4	4	4	4	4	4.1941	4
Kansas	4	2940865	4	4	4	4	4	3.8636	4
Kentucky	6	4509342	6	6	6	6	6	5.9242	6
Louisiana	6	4661468	6	6	6	6	6	6.1241	6
Maine	2	1363582	1	2	2	2	2	1.7914	2
Maryland	8	6185278	8	8	8	8	8	8.1260	8
Massachusetts	9	7033469	9	9	9	9	9	9.2404	9
Michigan	14	10084442	13	13	13	13	13	13.2486	13
Minnesota	8	5709752	7	7	8	8	8	7.5013	8
Mississippi	4	2963914	4	4	4	4	4	3.8939	4
Missouri	8	6160281	8	8	8	8	8	8.0932	8
Montana	1	1085407	1	2	2	1	2	1.4260	1
Nebraska	3	1963333	2	3	3	3	3	2.5794	3
Nevada	4	3108462	4	4	4	4	4	4.0838	4
New Hampshire	2	1379089	1	2	2	2	2	1.8118	2
New Jersey	12	9294493	12	12	12	12	12	12.2108	12
New Mexico	3	2120220	2	3	3	3	3	2.7855	3
New York	27	20215751	28	26	26	27	26	26.5588	27
North Carolina	13	10453948	14	14	14	14	14	13.7341	14
North Dakota	1	779702	1	1	1	1	1	1.0243	1
Ohio	16	11808848	16	15	15	16	15	15.5141	16
Oklahoma	5	3963516	5	5	5	5	5	5.2071	5
Oregon	5	4241500	5	6	6	6	6	5.5724	6
Pennsylvania	18	13011844	18	17	17	17	17	17.0946	17
Rhode Island	2	1098163	1	2	2	1	2	1.4427	1
South Carolina	7	5124712	7	7	7	7	7	6.7327	7
South Dakota	1	887770	1	1	1	1	2	1.1663	1
Tennessee	9	6916897	9	9	9	9	9	9.0872	9
Texas	36	29183290	40	38	38	38	37	38.3401	38
Utah	4	3275252	4	4	4	4	5	4.3029	4
Vermont	1	643503	1	1	1	1	1	0.8454	1
Virginia	11	8654542	11	11	11	11	11	11.3701	11
Washington	10	7715946	10	10	10	10	10	10.1370	10
West Virginia	3	1795045	2	2	2	2	3	2.3583	2
Wisconsin	8	5897473	8	8	8	8	8	7.7479	8
Wyoming	1	577719	1	1	1	1	1	0.7590	1
USA	435	331108434	435	435	435	435	435	435.0000	435

Table 5.16. Apportionment based on the 2020 census.

Reapportionment based on the 2020 census presents a solid case that apportionment methodology needs reform. It supplies evidence that the current House size of 435 is too small to clearly satisfy the constitutional mandate that "Representatives shall be apportioned among the several States according to their respective numbers, counting the whole number of persons in each State."[3]

For example, based on the 2010 census, California had 66 times the population of Wyoming, but the representation ratio was 53 to 1. Based on the 2020 census, this disparity increased to California having 68.5 times the Wyoming population, but the representation ratio decreased to 52 to 1. This disparity can be removed by including the Wyoming Rule (Section 6.2.4) into the apportionment algorithm, thereby increasing the size of the House to 573.

The small House of 435 with respect to the national population also concerns small states with only 2 seats. For example, based on the 1990 census, Montana lost a seat going from 2 seats to 1 (see Section 5.6.2). Accordingly, Montana was jubilant to regain that lost seat based on the 2020 census.[4] Based on projections of the 2020 census, Rhode Island braced itself to lose a seat. Rhode Island was overjoyed that the projection did not materialize and that Rhode Island retained both its seats.[5][6] However, both Montana and Rhode Island were lucky beneficiaries of a small-state bias intrinsic with the method of equal proportions used today.

The small-state bias permitted Montana to gain a seat and Rhode Island to retain its two seats. Because the size of the House is fixed, these advantages came at the expense of a seat each to New York and Ohio. Based on the 2020 census, the calculations for the method of equal proportions may be illustrated for a House with 435 seats as follows. First, consider a divisor (average district size) of 762996. Divide 762996 into each state's population to obtain each state's quotient, a decimal number. Round that decimal by geometric mean rounding: if the quotient is greater than or equal to the geometric mean of the round-down, round-up options (GM), then round the quotient up; otherwise, round the quotient down. Table 5.17 displays the calculations of the affected states. Table 5.16 also includes the calculations for Minnesota, which received the 435th seat in the House using the Census Bureau technique of awarding congressional seats by priority.

The worry for states like Montana and Rhode Island is another indicator that the 435 House size is too small. They deserve better. Appropriately increasing the House size, say to 573, would alleviate their justified concerns for losing a seat.

Table 5.17. Apportionments from the 2020 census.

State	Quotient	GM	Seats
Minnesota	7.483331	7.483315	8
Montana	1.422559	1.414214	2
New York	26.49523	26.495283	26
Ohio	15.47695	15.491933	15
Rhode Island	1.439278	1.414214	2

---

[3] U. S. Constitution, Fourteenth Amendment, Section 2.

[4] Blackfoot Valley Dispatch, *Montana regains second Congressional seat.* 6 May 2021; available at Montana regains second Congressional seat - Blackfoot Valley Dispatch.

[5] Ted Nesi, *Nesi's Notes: May 1*, WPRI.COM12; available at Nesi's Notes: May 1 | WPRI.com.

[6] Philip Marcelo, *Census surprise: Rhode Island keeps both US House Seats*, Associated Press, 26 April 2021; available at Census surprise: Rhode Island keeps both US House seats (apnews.com).

The House first reached 435 seats in 1912. At that time, based on the 1910 census, a congressperson represented, on average, about 210000 people. Now, that figure is about 766000, ranking the U. S. among the least representative among the world's democracies.

Although the automatic reapportionment of Congress went smoothly, the decade produced several stories relevant to congressional apportionment. Such stories include Article the First, Extreme Partisanship, and the Electoral College.

Section 5.9.2   Article the First

As reported in Chapter 1: Reapportionment Based on the 1790 Census, Article the First is an "only in America" story. Shortly after the United States began operations under the newly ratified Constitution, Congress submitted twelve amendments to the States for ratification. These amendments were submitted as Article the First through Article the Twelfth in 1789.[7] Article the Third through Article the Twelfth were quickly ratified by 1791 and subsequently became enshrined as the Bill of Rights. Article the Second was eventually ratified on 5 March 1992 and is now attached to the Constitution as the Twenty-Sixth Amendment. Of the original proposed twelve amendments, eleven were ratified. What happened to Article the First?

> Article the First . . . After the first enumeration required by the first Article of the Constitution, there shall be one Representative for every thirty thousand, until the number shall amount to one hundred, after which, the proportion shall be so regulated by Congress, that there shall be not less than one hundred Representatives, nor less than one Representative for every forty thousand persons, until the number of Representatives shall amount to two hundred, after which the proportion shall be so regulated by Congress, that there shall not be more than two hundred Representatives, nor more than one Representative for every fifty thousand persons.

Article the First stipulated that the initial ratio of representation is to be 30000. When that ratio yields a House size 100 or greater, then the ratio may be increased up to 40000 but the House size must be retained at 100 or larger. Similarly, the ratio may be increased up to 50000 for a House exceeding 200 members. The first reapportionment, based on the 1790 census, was in conformity with Article the First. The ratio of 30000 yielded a House size of 112. Accordingly, the ratio could be increased up to 40000 as long as the resulting House size was at least 100. The 1792 reapportionment act used a ratio of 33000 yielding a House size of 105.

Officially, Article the First was never ratified, failing ratification by only one state. The Article would be irrelevant today since its operative clause is that the size of the House could not be less than 200 nor more than one representative for every 50000 persons. Since the size of the House today is 435 and each congressperson on average represents 760000 based on the 2020 census, then the adoption of this amendment would have little relevance today.

---

[7] http://avalon.law.yale.edu/18th_century/resolu02.asp.

However, Eugene Martin LaVergne brought suit in 2011 that Connecticut actually ratified Article the First but that the paperwork was misfiled by a Connecticut official and hence Congress was never notified. LaVergne claimed he found the authentic documents in the Connecticut state archives and so Article the First should be declared as ratified. After losing this suit, LaVergne again brought suit in 2017 claiming that the original Article the First contained a misprint and that the correct wording would make the operative clause for today read that the size of the House cannot be *less than* one representative for every 50000 persons. This would make the *minimum allowable size* of the House 6163 today. LaVergne lost both suits in Federal court. Rather than retelling the LaVergne story here, we refer the reader to the story as told by Nowell Frances in his recent, comprehensive book about apportionment.[8] Also, one may consult Mr. LaVergne's own detailed story.[9] Mr. Lavergne's case is interesting because it relates to a relevant question: what should be the size of the House?

Section 5.9.3　　　Extreme Partisanship

In summarizing the decades since 1940, Jared Diamond (Pulitzer prize-winning author of *Guns, Germs, and Steel*) offers, "the current decade of the 2010's really is the one offering the most cause for anxiety."[10] He expanded, "the most ominous of the fundamental problems now threatening American democracy is our accelerating deterioration of political compromise."[11] Diamond presented this "most ominous problem" in Chapter 9 of his most recent book, *Upheaval*. In Chapter 10 he presented three more accompanying serious problems: American elections, inequality, and declining investment in our human capital and public purposes.

Diamond's concerns especially connect with congressional apportionment and the census. Paralyzing gridlock occurred during the attempt at reapportionment based on the 1920 census, the only decade where there was no reapportionment. A posterchild issue for this paralysis was Prohibition since dries would not yield on anything giving wets more power. What was interesting was the people coalition supporting Prohibition, an uncanny alliance of white supremacy and religious fundamentalism as recalled today by groups such as the Ku Klux Klan and the Women's Christian Temperance Union.

The Klan is remembered today primarily as a white terrorist group lynching Blacks in the South. However, the Klan was much more than that. The Klan had extensive influence in the entire nation. In 1925 their March on Washington drew 40000.[12] The political agenda of the Klan was summarized in a position pamphlet known as The Evans Plan.[13] As one reads the

---

[8] Nowell Frances, *Reclaiming the People's House*, Depot Pond Publishing, 2019: Chapter 6.

[9] Martin Eugene LaVergne, *How Less is More: The Story of the Real First Amendment to the United States Constitution*, First Amendment Free Press, Inc., 2017.

[10] Jared Diamond, *Upheaval: Turning Points for Nations in Crisis*, Little, Brown and Company, 2019: 326.

[11] Ibid: 341.

[12] Frederic D. Schwarz, *The Klan on Parade*, American Heritage, Vol. 51(4), July/August 2000; accessed on 1 September 2019 from https://www.americanheritage.com/klan-parade.

[13] https://en.wikipedia.org/wiki/Hiram_Wesley_Evans.

political debates in Congress and related sources, one notices a similarity of positions held by the wets of yesterday and alt-right "conservatives" of today.

Then, as now, the operative, fundamental forces were fueled by white supremacy and religious fundamentalism, often united rather than separated. A telling volume is told by a photograph of the Klan's March on Washington in 1925 (Figure 5.5).[14] For more, see the

Figure 5.5. *A konklave of klansmen in the March on Washington, 1925.*

moving documentary by CNN's Fareed Zakaria, *State of Hate: The Explosion of White Supremacy*.[15] A report from the Center on Extremism, "New Hate and Old: The Changing Face of American White Supremacy," is informative.[16]

Diamond's problems are manifestations of the fact that the Republican Party today has been hijacked by a cult mentality of alt-right advocates formed by an uncanny but staunch alliance. The Republican Party is fully aware that it is in the minority and is faced with the challenging problem: how can a minority maintain power and rule? While being in the minority they have no choice but intransigence. They cannot compromise and advance their agenda, and they have been successful in maintaining power in the face of being the minority. Main tools have included Senator Mitch McConnell, Attorney General William Barr, gerrymandering, voter suppression, foreign meddling in partisan politics, pay-to-play politics, the National Rifle Association, the American Legislative Exchange Council (ALEC), and Donald Trump as President.

---

[14] https://allthatsinteresting.com/ku-klux-klan-march-on-washington#1 (click View Gallery).
[15]

https://archive.org/details/CNNW_20190706_010000_CNN_Special_Report_State_of_Hate_The_Explosion_of_White_Supremacy/start/480/end/540.
[16] https://docs.house.gov/meetings/JU/JU00/20190409/109266/HHRG-116-JU00-20190409-SD011.pdf.

Although the Ku Klux Klan and the Women's Christian Temperance Union have mostly faded into history, motivating forces such as white supremacy and religious fundamentalism have not. New organizations, with similar motivations but modern social media and political skills, have replaced them. Perhaps the most noticeable to the general public is CPAC (Conservative Political Action Conference), an annual conference of political activists hosted by the American Conservative Union, and conspiracy story groups like QAnon.

Although such venues supply voting armies, the power behind the scenes lies with an oligarchy of the wealthy. There is another issue of supreme national importance that accompanies Jared Diamond's top concern of bitter, uncompromising partisanship: the inequitable distribution of wealth, resources, and opportunity. There are many technical ways to measure the inequitable distribution of wealth in America, but however it is done, the conclusion is staggering.[17] [18] For example, Pedro Nicolaci da Costa, writing in *Forbes*, "In 2018, the richest 105 held 70% of total household wealth, up from 60% in 1989. The share funneled to the top 1% jumped to 32% last year from 23% in 1989."[19]

These two problems, uncompromising partisanship and inequitable resources, form a chicken and egg situation. They are intimately united. An oligarchy of the wealthy is highly motivated to use the political system to protect, maintain, and enhance its wealth. Three examples, the Kochs, Mercers, and Adelsons, all major donors to the Republican party, have had an enormous effect on the direction of the GOP. Heather Timmons, writing for the business organization *Quartz*, concluded, "The influence of these three families offers a stark illustration of how extreme wealth can distort a democracy."[20]

The structure of American government also favors their cause by giving weighted advantages to smaller states with "rural values" across the entire spectrum of government operations. The structure of the Senate overwhelmingly favors the small states. The small state advantage also exists in the House of Representatives because of the low House size for today's national population, and the method of equal proportions has a slight bias towards smaller states. This congressional small-state advantage is carried over into the electoral system for selecting the President. Hence, control the small states and one can control the country, a methodology successfully exploited, for example, by Project RedMap.

---

[17] Christopher Ingraham, Wealth concentration returning to 'levels last seen during the Roaring Twenties,' according to new research, *The Washington Post*, 8 February 2019.

[18] Isabel V. Sawhill and Christopher Pullman, Six facts about wealth in the United States, *The Brookings Institution*, 25 June 2019; https://www.brookings.edu/blog/up-front/2019/06/25/six-facts-about-wealth-in-the-united-states/.

[19] Pedro Nicolaci da Costa, America's Humongous Wealth Gap is Widening Further, *Forbes*, 29 May 2019; https://www.forbes.com/sites/pedrodacosta/2019/05/29/americas-humungous-wealth-gap-is-widening-further/#228a6d9242ee.

[20] Heather Timmons, The three ultra-rich families battling for control of the Republican party, *Quartz*, 5 December 2017; accessed 27 September 2019 from https://qz.com/1085077/mercers-vs-kochs-vs-adelsons-the-three-ultra-rich-families-battling-for-control-of-the-republican-party/.

Especially troubling is the Republican orchestration of gerrymandering, voter suppression, social media, and attempts at census manipulation. Evidence obtained from the estate of the late Dr. Thomas Hefeller proves that the proposed addition of the citizenship question for the 2020 census was motivated by pure partisan gain for "Republicans and Non-Hispanic Whites."[21]

The citizenship issue has been replayed in every decade in the recent past. For the 2010-2020 decade, on 22 June 2017 Warren Davidson (R-OH) introduced House Joint Resolution No. 106, a proposed constitutional amendment: "Representatives shall be apportioned among the several States according to their respective numbers, which shall be determined by counting the number of persons in each state who are citizens of the United States."[22] The proposal was cosponsored by Representatives Doug Lamborn (R-CO) and Mo Brooks (R-AL).[23] The bill was sent to the House Committee on the Judiciary and then referred it to the Subcommittee on the Constitution and Civil Justice, the equivalent of sending the proposal to a legislative mortuary. Later, Representative Brooks filed suit in court that only documented residents should be counted in the census.[24] The argument over who should be counted in the census as a basis for congressional apportionment continues to this day with increasing partisanship and bitterness.

Section 5.9.4   The Electoral College

The analysis given below was made on 4 November 2020, based on returns at that time where there were still five uncalled swing states in the 2020 presidential election: Pennsylvania, North Carolina, Georgia, Nevada, and Arizona (although the Associated Press and Fox had called Arizona for Biden). At the time Trump had clear leads in Pennsylvania, North Carolina, and Georgia. Biden had credible leads in Arizona and Nevada. This analysis, aided by the Pew Research Center projection of the 2020 census (the 2020 census was not released until almost six months later), assumes that these results would hold.

Assuming that Pennsylvania, North Carolina, and Georgia go to Trump, and Arizona and Nevada go to Biden, then the final Electoral College result would be Biden 270 and Trump 268. Even though this scenario did not hold, the analysis reveals five surprising and disturbing consequences about the electoral system this country uses to decide the winner of a presidential election.

---

[21] https://www.commoncause.org/press-release/new-evidence-from-common-cause-partisan-gerrymandering-case-reveals-plot-to-add-citizenship-question-to-2020-census-for-republican-and-white-redistricting-advantage/.

[22] Congressional Record, 115th Congress, 1st Session, Vol. 163, No. 107: H5109; accessed 29 August 2019.

[23] https://davidson.house.gov/media-center/press-releases/davidson-introduces-amendment-apportion-representation-citizen.

[24] Tara Bahrampour, The census citizenship question failed. But Alabama is seeking to exclude undocumented immigrants in apportioning congressional seats, *The Washington Post*, 11 August 2019. Accessed 28 August 2019 from https://www.washingtonpost.com/local/social-issues/the-census-citizenship-question-failed-but-an-alabama-lawsuit-seeks-to-exclude-undocumented-immigrants-in-apportioning-congressional-seatsopponents-decry-the-effort-as-unconstitutional-and-an-attempt-by-republicans-to-normalize-the-concept-with-the-public/2019/08/14/1887f190-b777-11e9-b3b4-2bb69e8c4e39_story.html.

Consequence 1

The Electoral College winner is an artifact of the method of apportioning the U. S. House of Representatives. For apportionment of the House based on the 1930 census, there were two methods in competition for distributing the seats in the House: major fractions (also known as Webster's method) and equal proportions (also known as the Huntington-Hill method). The default method based on the census/apportionment act of 1929 was to distribute the current House size by major fractions. 55 Stat 470 (1941), passed on a party-line partisan vote and approved into law by President Franklin Roosevelt, established equal proportions as the method for House apportionment.

The Electoral College result of 270-268 is a result of distributing the seats in the House, and thus the electoral votes among the states, by the method of equal proportions. If the method of major fractions were used, then the result would be a 269-269 tie. The two methods of apportionment agreed except for one seat where equal proportions gave the seat to Rhode Island, whereas major fractions would have awarded the seat to North Carolina. This would result in one less Rhode Island electoral vote and one more North Carolina electoral vote, flipping a Biden vote to Trump. Hence, changing the method of House apportionment from major fractions to equal proportions in 1941 has the effect in 2020 of taking the election from Biden and creating a tie. In the event of a tie, the decision for who wins the election goes to the U. S. House of Representatives.

Consequence 2

One faithless Biden elector will create an Electoral College no decision because neither Biden nor Trump will have an electoral majority of 270 votes. In that event, the decision for who wins the election goes to the U. S. House of Representatives.

This scenario is of consequence because the possibility of a faithless elector needs to be considered. In the 2016 presidential election there were seven faithless electors of consequence. Five of them were pledged to the Democrat candidate. Of these, three voted for Colin Powell, one for Bernie Sanders, and one for Faith Spotted Eagle. However, for the 2020 presidential election, this point became moot since there were no faithless electors.

Consequence 3

The Electoral College winner is an artifact of the size of the House of Representatives. Recall that the number of electoral votes, as prescribed in the Constitution, equals the number of national members in Congress: 2 (since each state has two senators) plus the number of representatives (seats in the House). This formula applies to the nation as a whole and to each of the fifty states individually. Further, the Twenty-third Amendment elevates Washington D.C. to the status of an electoral state, giving D.C. three electoral votes. Since there are currently 435 seats in the House, 100 senators, and 3 D.C. electoral votes, then there are 538 electoral votes. Note that the size of the Electoral College depends on the size of the House.

Why does the House have 435 seats? This figure was basically frozen into law by the census/apportionment act of 1929. The House first reached 435 in 1912. The 1929 act was a result of the failure of Congress to reapportion the House based on the 1920 census. To prevent this from happening again, the law institutes an automatic apportionment feature in the event Congress does not act within the first session after the decennial census results are reported. Ever since 1930, Congress has simply deferred to this automatic reapportionment feature. Consequently, the House size has not changed due to lack of congressional action. The House size will remain at 435 until Congress changes it.

In 1912 when the House first reached 435, the national population was such that on average a congressperson represented about 210,000 people. Now, a congressman represents about 760,000 people. This makes the U. S. the least represented democracy in the world, an outlier among democratic nations. The Fourteenth Amendment to the Constitution directs that "Representatives shall be apportioned among the several States according to their respective numbers, counting the whole number of persons in each State." A constant House size of 435 is out of alignment with the intention of this mandate. For example, based on the 2010 census, California has 66 times the population of Wyoming, yet the representative ratio is 53 to 1. Congress needs to address the situation of the size of the House in order to align apportionment "according to their respective numbers." House size will also have a direct impact on the size of the Electoral College.

The results of the 2020 election for House sizes 435 to 510 using equal proportions (the current method of apportionment), and assuming the 270-268 scenario described above for the 2020 election for the current make-up of the Electoral College, are as follows.

- Biden wins for the following House sizes: 435-436, 438-440, 442, 444-450, 454, 456-466, 472, 478-482, 488-490, 492-498.
- Trump wins for the following House sizes: 452, 468, 470, 474, 476, 484, 486, 500-506, 508-510.
- Tie for the following House sizes: 437, 441, 443, 451, 453, 455, 467, 469, 471, 473, 475, 477, 483, 485, 487, 491, 499, 507.

Thus, for House sizes 435-510, Biden wins 41 times, Trump wins 17 times, and there are 18 ties. It is a dramatic consequence that in the modern era that the winner of our presidential election may be simply an artifact of the size of the House of Representatives.

Consequence 4

With so many realistic situations producing a tie, it is of interest to note that for the Electoral College to decide a presidential winner, a candidate must get a majority of the electoral votes. If not, then the decision is made by the House where each state gets one vote. The slate of presidential candidates consists of the top three candidates from the Electoral College. In this case of the 2020 election, there would be two candidates: Donald Trump and Joe Biden.

The most probable scenario in the House is that the vote would be partisan. This view is predominant because of the partisan behavior in virtually every aspect in Congress. As a result, if the decision goes to the House and is made along these partisan lines, then Trump wins: 27-21-2. This is because 27 states have a majority Republican delegation, 21 states have a majority Democrat delegation, and two states, Minnesota and Michigan, have a split delegation in the House of the 117th Congress that met on 6-7 January 2021.

There were two previous times the election of the President was sent to the House: 1800 and 1824. Both were disasters. If this election were sent to the House, it would be another disaster which would only intensify the bitter partisan divide in this country.

Consequence 5

The **Wrong Winner Effect** is an effect that can take place in a presidential election held in a census year since the distribution of the seats in the House, and thus the corresponding distribution of the electoral votes, is based on the previous census. Hence, the distribution of most electoral votes is based on a population census that is 10-years old.

I am thankful to the Pew Research Center for allowing me the use of their projected 2020 census for apportionment. If the make-up of the Electoral College would be based on this projected 2020 census, then Trump wins in the Electoral College, 271-267. The situation illustrates a devastating flaw in the current presidential election system: the winner of the electoral system simply may be an artifact of the Wrong Winner Effect.

Two Pew Research Center articles of relevance to the 2020 census are:

- D'Vera Cohn, *What to know about the citizenship question the Census Bureau is planning to ask in 2020*, 30 March 2018.
- Jeffrey S. Passel and D'Vera Cohn, *How removing unauthorized immigrants from census statistics could affect House reapportionment*, 24 July 2020.

Passel and Cohn note that the projected 2020 census shifts ten House seats. States that gain are Texas 3, Florida 2, and 1 each for Arizona, Colorado, Montana, North Carolina, and Oregon. These are offset by a loss of 1 seat each from Alabama, California, Illinois, Michigan, Minnesota, New York, Ohio, Pennsylvania, Rhode Island, and West Virginia. For these ten seats, the 2020 make-up is 7 red and 3 blue whereas the 2010 make-up is 4 red and 6 blue.

However, the above electoral scenario did not prevail. Trump's early lead in several swing states did not hold and Biden won the Electoral College 306-232. Since the 2020 census was not announced until April 2021, the Electoral College could not have been formulated based on the 2020 census. Even if the Electoral College could have been formulated based on the 2020 population, the final count would be Biden 303 and Trump 235.[25]

---

[25] Hansi Lo Wang, Connie Hanzhang Jin, Zach Levitt, *Here's How the 1st 2020 Census Results Changed Electoral College, House Seats*, NPR; 1st 2020 Census Results: What You Need To Know About The Count : NPR.

Section 5.9.5   The 2020 Road Ahead

Fortunately, the early electoral possibility presented in the previous section did not materialize. After each state certified its vote, Biden won a majority in the Electoral College, 306-232. Even though this final result appeared decisive, the election exposed severe and ominous problems.

The 2020 presidential election was about the soul of the nation. The election exposed a serious flirtation with changing the form of national government from a constitutional, democratic, republican federation of states into a "constitutional" dictatorship. The four years of the Trump administration put on display a realization of Jared Diamond's fears of how a transformation from democracy to dictatorship happens in the United States. As it became clear that Trump was losing the 2020 presidential election, his forces went into full dictatorship mode to invalidate the election. When cult leader Jim Jones leading the Peoples Temple in Jonestown, Guyana, saw the end coming, Jones set out a table of Kool-Aid for the faithful. In similar style Trump laid out a table of kookies to sow the seeds of alienation and mistrust with the electoral system. The most ominous part of this debacle is the vast size and support for the Trump cult following. The behavior of a contrived "stop-the-steal" kookies buffet, from Rudy Gulliani to Sidney Powell, is cause for alarm.

There are three arenas at work for the establishment of a dictator in America. One arena is a cult leader who can serve as a savior for an audience who will take the message. Trump serves as that cult leader. Second is a cadre of supporters from political, social, and media groups who serve as active acolytes and apostles for the cult leader. A key role of the cadre is to radicalize the base and suppress the opposition. Much of the GOP, "conservative" evangelicals, gun lobby groups, white nationalists, and right-wing media climbed aboard, transforming themselves into the GQP. Many of these groups actively participated because it served as a convenient conveyance to advance their own agendas. Third is a mass audience that adopts the message as a major component of their own personal identity.

The dangers of the operative interaction of these components was on vivid display on 6 January 2021 during the routine certification of the states' certificates of electoral votes in a joint session of Congress. The riot of people who consumed the "stop-the-steal" kookies displayed the results of pathological cognitive dissidence on the impact of following their cult leader. This group can now be proclaimed as the most dangerous domestic terror group in the country. Equally unsettling was the display of two particular people who perceived a potential fall of the cult leader and boldly moved to fill the vacuum: Senator Josh Hawley (R-MO) and Senator Ted Cruz (R-TX).

Mr. Cruz declared himself a leader and proposed to have a 10-day commission study voter "irregularities" of the 2020 presidential election. He made an appeal citing the 1876 Tilden-Hayes election. He failed to mention that, in that election, four states (Florida, Louisiana, Oregon, and South Carolina) presented competing electoral slates of electors. The commission was created to decide which of the competing slates would be certified. In the 2020 election, no state offered competing certificates of votes. The certificates of vote for all 50 states were certified by appropriate state officials.

Cruz deserves special condemnation for presenting his proposed commission about "irregularities" in the context of electoral vote certification while appealing to Congress to consider the concerns of those protesting the election results. Cruz, with his education, should know that the 1876 commission he appealed to specifically ruled that their function was to decide among the competing electoral slates offered by four states. The commission also ruled that it was not their role to investigate even known electoral fraud. In technical terms it was not the position of the commission "to go behind the certificates authenticated by the State executive." The interested reader may consult a variety of fascinating resources about this commission.[26] [27] [28] [29] [30] [31]

Mr. Hawley gave the prestige of his signature as a U. S. Senator to give credence to conspiracy stories and cult propaganda. The actions of both men needs to be confronted and condemned in the strongest possible terms by those who want to preserve American democracy and prevent the transformation of the government of this country into a "constitutional" dictatorship.

In the spirit of accolades for the defense of American democracy, special thanks and appreciation need to be awarded. Senator McConnell (R-KY) deserves recognition for his finest time in his long political career for his leadership of directing the operations in the Senate regarding the certification of electoral certificates of vote. Senator Romney (R-UT) deserves recognition for his exposure of Cruz's antics. There were several members of Congress, in this special crunch time for American democracy, who bravely and successfully faced the immediate challenge of Hawley and Cruz. Unfortunately, this bi-partisan effort was short-lived.

With the inauguration of Joe Biden and Kamala Harris as President and Vice-President, the GOP shifted into overdrive and transformed itself into the GQP, spending most of its energy into QAnon-type conspiracy stories. Fueled by a "stop-the-steal" mentality, the GQP has focused on local voter suppression legislation. They have dressed in verbal white robes and hats with a mantra of "voter integrity." However, the fraudit of the 2020 presidential election authorized by the GQP legislature in Arizona for Maricopa County, Arizona, in 2021 displays stark proof of the real objective: voter suppression, which is the personification of the antithesis of election integrity.[32]

---

[26] Philip W. Kennedy, *The Pacific Northwest Quarterly*, 60(3), July 1969: 135-144.

[27] Michael F. Holt, *By One Vote: The Disputed Presidential Election of 1876*, University Press of Kansas, 2008.

[28] Proceedings of the Electoral Commission (309 pages):
A Century of Lawmaking for a New Nation: U.S. Congressional Documents and Debates, 1774 - 1875 (loc.gov)

[29] You Think This Is Chaos? The Election of 1876 Was Worse - The New York Times (nytimes.com).

[30] Ted Cruz is wrong about the 2020 election - The Washington Post.

[31] Disputed Election of 1876 | Miller Center.

[32] Caitlin Huey-Burns, Adam Brewster, *The Arizona COP's Maricopa County audit: What to know about it*, 8 May 2021; The Arizona election audit: What to know about the GOP's efforts in Maricopa County - CBS News.

However, the stark and greatest danger is the large cult following that Trump has amassed. Americans, in general, need a refresher course in the rise of recent dictators: Hitler (Germany), Mussolini (Italy), Pinochet (Chile), Putin (Russia), Erdoğan (Turkey), Duarte (Philippines), Orban (Hungary), Lukashenko (Belarus), to start a modern list. The electorate, in each case, played a significant role in their rise to power. Jared Diamond used the example of Pinochet to illustrate and ask the question, can this happen here? The sad answer to Diamond's question is that it did happen here. We are fortunate that here, however, the process was not finalized—Trump was not re-elected. Americans owe much to aware voters, especially in Arizona, Nevada, Wisconsin, Michigan, Pennsylvania, with a special applause of appreciation to Georgia.

Motivated by all the inherent problems exposed by the current presidential electoral system, one steady indicator manifested in the background is the National Popular Vote. Accordingly, in November 2020, the National Popular Vote launched a new initiative: 270 by 2024. In November the National Popular Vote Compact had a membership of 16 electoral states controlling 196 electoral votes. The Compact's goal is to attract enough states controlling another 74 electoral votes. Then, the final decision mechanism for who wins the presidency will be the national popular vote, an idea whose time has come. The national popular vote is a better decision mechanism for who wins than the current electoral system with its weighted system of electoral votes distributed by a statewide winner-take-all rule. It would be in the best interests of the country if every state would simply join the National Popular Vote Compact.[33]

---

[33] National Popular Vote

Chapter 6

An Historical Overture

Chapter 6
An Historical Overture

Table of Contents

Reference The chapter photo is courtesy of the public domain. Large opera room is available from ABSFreePic.com; http://absfreepic.com/free-photos/download/opera-4000x2664_22620.html.

Section 6.1: The Great Teacher

History (or its equivalent, Experience) is a great teacher. An historical overview of congressional apportionment needs two mathematical skills to comprehend and appreciate it: how to average two different nonnegative integers and how to round a positive decimal number.[1] The history itself had three movements: the basic divisor period, the quota period, and the modified divisor period. In this section we apply the gift of hindsight to organize the lessons that History has given us about congressional apportionment.

Section 6.1.1   The Mathematical Skills

The mathematical skill needed for understanding congressional apportionment is the average. Given two different positive numbers, say $0 < a < b$, we ask, what is the average of a and b? The response is denoted by ave(a,b). History provides five ways to present an average appropriate for congressional apportionment.

- The minimum: ave(a,b) = min(a,b) = a.
- The maximum: ave(a,b) = max(a,b) = b.
- The arithmetic mean: ave(a,b) = AM(a,b) = $(a + b)/2$.
- The geometric mean: ave(a,b) = GM(a,b) = $\sqrt{a \times b}$.
- The harmonic mean: ave(a,b) = HM(a,b) = $2/(1/a + 1/b)$ = $2ab/(a + b)$.

The necessity of understanding this concept of average is immediately evident from the current computational technique of distributing congressional seats by priority. First, one seat is given to each state. Then seats are distributed, one at a time, by priority which is established by calculating a list of priority numbers. The priority number, A_n, for a given state to receive an additional seat is given by dividing the state's population by ave($n,n+1$) given that the state has n seats. Hence, if a state has n seats, then its priority number for an additional seat is given by A_n = (state population)/ave($n,n+1$).

The five historical ways to take an average describe the five historical divisor methods of apportionment when viewed by the priority technique of calculation. Each method is identified with an historical and an operational name. The historical name represents a person significant in

Table 6.1. Nomenclature for congressional apportionment.

Historical Name	Operational Name	Average
Jefferson	Largest Divisor (LD)	max($n,n+1$)
Dean	Harmonic Mean (HM)	HM($n,n+1$)
Huntington-Hill	Geometric Mean (GM)	GM($n,n+1$)
Webster	Major Fractions (MF)	AM($n,n+1$)
Adams	Smallest Divisor (SD)	min($n,n+1$)

some historical sense and is frequently used by authors writing about apportionment primarily from a mathematical point of view. An operational name is used to describe a sense of methodology and is often used by the Census Bureau and authors writing primarily from an historical or political point of view. These names are summarized in Table 6.1.

---

[1] Charles Biles, *An Average Lesson*; an open resource available from Humboldt State University digital commons http://digitalcommons.humboldt.edu/apportionment/ or the author's website http://nia977.wixsite.com/drbcap/resources.

The second mathematical skill needed for understanding congressional apportionment is how to round a decimal. One starts with a constituency question, how many people should a congressperson represent? The answer, d, is called the constituency, ratio of representation, or the divisor. One divides this ratio into a state's population to obtain the state's quotient. The quotient is the number of seats a state merits based on its population. If the quotient is a whole number, then there is no further problem. But invariably this quotient is a non-integer decimal. Since congresspersons do not come in fractional parts, then the quotient must be rounded. Hence, one is faced with the problem: how to round the quotient decimal?

Suppose that q is a non-negative, non-integer decimal number. Let n be the integer part of q. Then, $n < q < n+1$. The problem is whether to round q down to n or up to $n+1$. The default is to round q down to n. However, the task of rounding carries a round-up criterion, i.e., round up if a certain criterion is met. This round-up criterion may be specified as follows: round up if and only if $q \geq$ ave$(n,n+1)$. This succinct criterion provides a way to unify the arithmetic problem of rounding the decimal with the five historical methods of congressional apportionment for a divisor method.

- Jefferson: round up if and only if $q \geq$ max$(n,n+1)$.
- Dean: round up if and only if $q \geq$ HM$(n,n+1)$.
- Huntington-Hill: round up if and only if $q \geq$ GM$(n,n+1)$.
- Webster: round up if and only if $q \geq$ AM$(n,n+1)$.
- Adams: Jefferson: round up if and only if $q \geq$ min$(n,n+1)$.

Note that the Jefferson round-up criterion is never satisfied since $q < n+1$. Hence, Jefferson's criterion is always round down. Similarly, the Adams criterion is always satisfied; hence, Adams's criterion is always round up. The Webster criterion is the usual method of rounding that most students learn in the fifth grade.

Section 6.1.2   The Basic Divisor Method Period

All apportionment acts based on the census from 1790 through 1840 were fabricated using a basic divisor method. The method is simple, easy to understand, and uses the following steps.

Step 1.   How many people does a congressperson represent? Answer: d.

Step 2.   Divide d into a state's population to obtain its quotient, q.

Step 3.   Round q to obtain the state's apportionment; however, if q rounds to zero, then award the state 1 seat (the constitutional minimum requirement).

Note that a rounding criterion is an essential part of the basic divisor algorithm. From 1790 through 1830 Jefferson's method of rounding was applied; i.e., the quotient decimal was rounded down. The first mutation in methodology occurred with apportionment based on the 1840 census in which Jefferson's rounding criterion was replaced by Webster's.

Two other methods of rounding were proposed during the debates based on the 1830 census: Dean and Adams. Hence, there were four different criteria on the apportionment debate table based on the 1830 census. The Adams criterion was never used for an actual congressional apportionment. The Dean criterion was used once in constructing an apportionment supplement act based on the 1870 census. The rationale for Dean's method, the equalization for interstate congressional district size, has been the most appealed to fairness criterion among all the apportionment methods. The Huntington-Hill rounding criterion was not introduced until the early 1900s.

A basic divisor method is named according to its rounding criterion. Hence, there is Jefferson's basic divisor method, Dean's basic divisor method, etc. If the basic divisor method has already been specified, then one can shorten the reference to Jefferson's method, Dean's method, etc. Suppose that we denote the rounding of the quotient, q, by round(q). Then round(q) is either n or $n+1$ where round(q) = $n+1$ if and only if $q \geq$ ave($n,n+1$). Accordingly, the apportionment, a, specified in Step 3 above, may be provided as a = max(1,round(q)).

Section 6.1.3   The Quota Period

A major mutation in methodology occurred for apportionment based on the census of 1850. Congress abandoned the basic divisor method because of excessive partisan politics that occurred when deciding what divisor to use. Politicians discovered that a divisor leaving their state with a quotient whose decimal part was close to zero was advantageous to their state. The intolerable divisor game played during apportionment based on the 1840 census doomed the basic divisor method.

The quota method was launched by the Vinton Act approved just before the 1850 census. The method uses the House size approach to apportionment rather than the constituency approach. It was used for apportionment based on the census from 1850 through 1890.

The initiating question for the quota method is, how many seats should there be in the House? The answer, h, was used to establish each state's quota, i.e., fair share of h seats in the House. The quota was originally calculated using the rule of three introduced by Fisher Ames in the apportionment debates based on the 1790 census. Through the next several censuses Congress used the basic divisor method and so was accustomed to the contingency approach to apportionment. Hence, rather than using the rule of three, Congress used the equivalent concept of the national divisor, (national population)/h, to obtain each state's quota.

The better algorithm for a quota method contains the following steps.

- Step 1. Determine the House size, h.
- Step 2. Apply the rule of three to obtain each state's quota.

$$state\ quota = h \times \frac{state\ population}{national\ population}$$

- Step 3. Give each state its lower quota (the quota rounded down).

- Step 4.   Step 3 distributes most but not all of the *h* seats. Create a priority list and then accordingly distribute additional seats to bring the House size to *h*.

American history has proposed four different methods for constructing the priority list needed in Step 4.

Hamilton:	The quota decimal fractions.
Lowndes:	State constituency determined by (state population)/(lower quota).
Seaton:	Highest priority is given to the state with the lowest disparity between the national divisor and the state constituency using the upper quota.
Hill:	(state population)/GM(lower quota, upper quota).

Variations in the quota method arise in Step 4 regarding how to create the priority list. The simplest list is obtained by Hamilton's method of using the decimal fraction component of the quota, i.e., quota – lower quota. Earlier, William Lowndes proposed a priority list based on the state constituency resulting from using the lower quota from in Step 3. However, Lowndes's proposal went nowhere.

Unexpected mathematical paradoxes started appearing with Hamilton's method beginning with the 1870 census. The Alabama Paradox eventually became a deal-breaker for Hamilton's method. Seaton and Hill sought to rescue Hamilton's method from paradoxes by applying a different way to construct the priority list. Neither recognized that this was an impossible task. Congress manually adjusted results from using Hamilton's method based on the census of 1890, and in the process decided they needed a better method.

Section 6.1.4   The Modified Divisor Period

History taught Congress that there are only two approaches to congressional apportionment: the constituency approach and the house size approach. The constituency approach led to the basic divisor method which was abandoned in 1850. The House size approach led to the Hamilton quota method which was abandoned because of deal-breaking paradoxes. So Congress sought to keep the favorable parts of both methods while avoiding their resulting problems. This led to the modified divisor method period which began for apportionment based on the census of 1900 and continues to this day.

House size is easier to decide than constituency. Hence, the modified divisor method begins with fixing the House size. However, rather than applying the rule of three and calculating each state's quota, the House size was set aside as an answer to a basic divisor method. This took the political partisanship out of deciding what the divisor should be. The modified divisor method was merely a basic divisor method with a pre-set answer. One simply needs to find a divisor that works to produce the predetermined House size.

History at this point provided Congress with four methods of rounding the quotient decimal in the divisor method. Huntington and Hill provided a fifth: geometric mean rounding. Hill originally proposed the geometric mean as a device for constructing a quota method priority list. Huntington adapted Hill's idea and incorporated it into a divisor method, now known as the Huntington-Hill method.

Up to this point apportionment computations were made on an ad-hoc basis. First, one fixed the House size and then determined the apportionment for that given House size. If one wanted to know the apportionment for a different House size, then one had to run the apportionment algorithm again for that specific House size. For apportionment based on the 1910 census, Census Bureau statistician Walter Willcox introduced an ingenious priority method of computation. One first allocates one seat to each state. Then additional seats are serially awarded, one at a time, based on priority. A Willcox priority computational technique is equivalent to an ad-hoc computational technique for a modified divisor method.

Since there are now five different methods for rounding the quotient decimal, there are five historical variations for the modified divisor method.

Jefferson:	round down
Adams:	round up
Dean:	harmonic mean rounding
Huntington-Hill:	geometric mean rounding
Webster:	arithmetic mean rounding (round normally)

It is impressive how much of the history of congressional apportionment turns on the arithmetic skill of how to round a decimal.

As a result of the non-apportionment based on the census of 1920, Congress enacted a process which is automatic unless Congress takes specific action to the contrary. Since reapportionment based on the 1930 census, Congress has been content to let the automatic process take over. The automatic process has left the House size fixed at 435. Consequently, average congressional district size has increased exponentially. Many people are becoming unsatisfied with an apportionment process that is fixed in a growing world of rapid change.

A trendline of the exponential growth of average national constituency, (national population)/435, is given in Figure 6.1 (next page). The equation for the exponential curve of best fit shows an average decade growth rate of 12.01% for the decade beginning with 1910 (Decade 0 = 1910, Decade 2 = 1930, Decade 4 = 1950, etc.). In 1912 when Arizona and New Mexico were admitted to the union bringing the House size to 435, on average a congressman represented about 210,000 people. By 2021 this ballooned to just over 760000.

An important nuance is to note that the Census Act of 1929 is not what fixes the House size at 435, but congressional inactivity. The Census Act of 1929 prevents a reoccurrence of the debacle where Congress failed to reapportion the House based on the 1920 census. The Act protects the nation from congressional failure by specifying that if Congress does not reapportion within 60 days of receiving the census report from the President, then the House will be apportioned with the House size *last used*. A 1941 amendment specified that this apportionment will be accomplished using the Method of Equal Proportions (Huntington-Hill method). As a result, after the census the Census Bureau reports to the President apportionment for the House size last used (currently 435) by the Method of Equal Proportions. The President transmits the report to Congress which has 60 days to act. Hence, the result of the Census Act of 1929 has been to fix the House size at 435 as a consequence of its automatically going into effect from congressional inaction on apportionment.

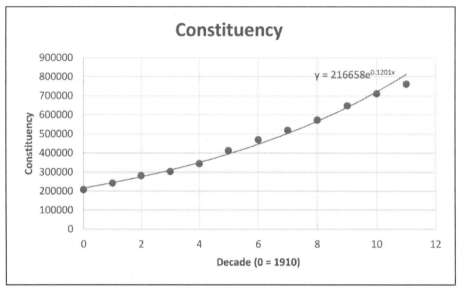

Figure 6.1. National average constituency trendline: 1920-2020.

Section 6.2:   A Future Overture

The practice of government is always an evolutionary process. Congress regularly visited the matter of congressional apportionment based on the first census in 1790 until reapportionment based on the 1910 census. Congress failed its constitutional duty to reapportion based on the 1920 census. Since the 1930 census Congress has defaulted to the automatic feature of reapportionment as specified in the apportionment act of 1929 and its 1941 amendment. The automatic feature is presently encoded in Title 2 §2 of the U. S. Code.[1] Court cases of the past four decades indicate that there are forces massing for reform to make the House more representative. In this section we examine four proposals for such reform: Title 2 Reform, Agreeable House Size, Article the First, and The Wyoming Rule.

Section 6.2.1   Title 2 Reform

The two key features of automatic congressional apportionment specified in Title 2 of the U. S. Code are that the House size is 435 and the distribution of those seats will be made using the method of equal proportions, i.e., the Huntington-Hill modified divisor method.

The simplest most basic reform would be to replace the method of equal proportions with the method of major fractions, i.e., Webster's method. The work of Balinski and Young has conclusively verified that *"Webster's method is the one and only unbiased divisor method."*[2] In comparison the method of largest divisors (Jefferson's method) has an intrinsic bias towards larger states. The other three historical methods (harmonic mean, Dean; equal proportions, Huntington-Hill; least divisors, Adams) all have an intrinsic bias towards smaller states.

The bias in the methods of Dean and Huntington-Hill is evident from considering the mechanics of the methods. One selects the ratio of representation and divides it into a state's apportionment population. This produces a quotient which for most practical purposes is a non-integer decimal number. The problem is whether to round the decimal up or down to obtain the state's apportionment. Webster's criterion is to round normally, i.e., round up if and only if the decimal part is greater than or equal to .5. But the methods of Dean and Huntington-Hill have round up criteria that are easier to satisfy. For example, consider a quotient whose decimal part is .436. If the state is small and the quotient is 2.436, then the state is awarded 3 seats by Dean's method since the harmonic mean of 2 and 3 is 2.400. However, if the state is larger and the quotient is 8.436, then the state is awarded 8 seats since the harmonic mean of 8 and 9 is 8.471; similarly for the method of equal proportions.

Hence, a simple reform would be to make the method of apportionment neutral regarding the size of the state. Representation in the national government is already biased in favor of the smaller states in the Senate and in the Electoral College. Using the method of equal proportions only adds another touch of bias in the direction of smaller states.

---

[1] https://www.law.cornell.edu/uscode/text/2/2a.
[2] Michel Balinski and H. Peyton Young, *Fair Representation: Meeting the Ideal of One Man, One Vote*, Brookings Institution Press, Second Edition, 2001: Chapter 9, *Eliminating Bias*: 71-78; Theorem 5.3: 125-6.

The major Title 2 reform is to reconsider the House size. Already, much has been written on the case for increasing the size of the House. We refer the interested reader to the literature on this subject. Three especially good sources are the works of Brian Frederick (book)[3], Christopher Yates (article)[4], and Apportionment.US (Supreme Court Case)[5].

An obvious question to pursue is, how many seats should there be in a representative assembly? Guidelines in the Constitution are minimal: each state must have at least one representative and the size of the House shall not exceed one representative for every thirty thousand people. Based on the 2020 census the minimum size of the House is 50 seats. But would a House of 50 be constitutional? The Constitution also states that apportionment of the House shall be based on population as enumerated by a decennial census. Does the mere fact that a state has population mean that a seat is based on population? If so, then why the need for an enumeration? A House with 50 seats would only be a mini-Senate.

Based on the 2020 census the maximum size of the House is either 11036 or 11013 depending on whether one adopts Hamilton's or Washington's interpretation of the 30000 constraint in the Constitution. Hamilton applies the 30000 constraint to the national population, Washington to each state. In either case the 2020 House size of 435 is on the low side of what is constitutionally allowable.

Is there an ideal House size? Another variant of the question is, how many politicians do we really need?[6] A recent model in wide use is the cube root law: the optimal size of a legislature is the cube root of the population.[7] The cube root law suggests that the size of the House based on the 2020 census should be around 692 since the cube root of the national population, 331108434, is 691.815. The national divisor for House size 692 is 478480. To produce House size 692, Webster's method needs to modify the national divisor to 478000. The methods of Hamilton and Webster are identical for House size 692. Table 6.2 shows the results of apportioning a House with 692 members using Hamilton's and Webster's methods.

Increasing the House size from 435 to 692 would reduce the average district size from the current 708000 to 478000. Alaska, Delaware, Montana, North Dakota, Rhode Island, and South Dakota would each have two representatives. The state of Vermont would then become the largest congressional district in population. However, there is a population to representation disparity since California has 68.5 times the population of Wyoming but the representation ratio is 83 to 1.

---

[3] Brian Frederick, Congressional Representation and Constituents: The Case for Increasing the U. S. House of Representatives, Taylor and Frances, New York, 2010.

[4] Christopher Yates, A House of Our Own or a House We've Outgrown? An Argument for Increasing the size of the House, *Columbia Journal of Law and Social Problems*, 25(2) 1992: 157-196; available at http://www.thirty-thousand.org/documents/Yates_1992.pdf.

[5] Clemons v. Department of Commerce; http://www.apportionment.us/.

[6] Kristof Jacobs and Simon Otjes, Explaining reforms of assembly sizes: Reassessing the cube root law relationship between population and assembly size, 6 September 2014; available at https://ecpr.eu/Filestore/PaperProposal/3bc100be-56fe-4efc-8d8c-a1f0b85e7f24.pdf.

[7] Jeffrey Ladewig and Mathew Jasinski, On the Causes and consequences of and Remedies for Interstate Malapportionment of the U. S. House of Representatives, *Perspectives on Politics*, 6(1) March 2008: 98.

State	Seats	Population	Quota	Hamilton	Quotient	Webster
Alabama	7	5030030	10.5125	11	10.5231	11
Alaska	1	736081	1.5384	2	1.5399	2
Arizona	9	7158923	14.9618	15	14.9768	15
Arkansas	4	3013756	6.2986	6	6.3049	6
California	53	39576757	82.7134	83	82.7966	83
Colorado	7	5782171	12.0844	12	12.0966	12
Connecticut	5	3608298	7.5412	8	7.5487	8
Delaware	1	990837	2.0708	2	2.0729	2
Florida	27	21570527	45.0813	45	45.1266	45
Georgia	14	10725274	22.4153	22	22.4378	22
Hawaii	2	1460137	3.0516	3	3.0547	3
Idaho	2	1841377	3.8484	4	3.8523	4
Illinois	18	12822739	26.7989	27	26.8258	27
Indiana	9	6790280	14.1913	14	14.2056	14
Iowa	4	3192406	6.6720	7	6.6787	7
Kansas	4	2940865	6.1463	6	6.1524	6
Kentucky	6	4509342	9.4243	9	9.4338	9
Louisiana	6	4661468	9.7422	10	9.7520	10
Maine	2	1363582	2.8498	3	2.8527	3
Maryland	8	6185278	12.9269	13	12.9399	13
Massachusetts	9	7033469	14.6996	15	14.7144	15
Michigan	14	10084442	21.0760	21	21.0972	21
Minnesota	8	5709752	11.9331	12	11.9451	12
Mississippi	4	2963914	6.1944	6	6.2007	6
Missouri	8	6160281	12.8747	13	12.8876	13
Montana	1	1085407	2.2684	2	2.2707	2
Nebraska	3	1963333	4.1033	4	4.1074	4
Nevada	4	3108462	6.4965	7	6.5031	7
New Hampshire	2	1379089	2.8822	3	2.8851	3
New Jersey	12	9294493	19.4250	19	19.4445	19
New Mexico	3	2120220	4.4312	4	4.4356	4
New York	27	20215751	42.2499	42	42.2924	42
North Carolina	13	10453948	21.8482	22	21.8702	22
North Dakota	1	779702	1.6295	2	1.6312	2
Ohio	16	11808848	24.6799	25	24.7047	25
Oklahoma	5	3963516	8.2835	8	8.2919	8
Oregon	5	4241500	8.8645	9	8.8734	9
Pennsylvania	18	13011844	27.1941	27	27.2214	27
Rhode Island	2	1098163	2.2951	2	2.2974	2
South Carolina	7	5124712	10.7104	11	10.7212	11
South Dakota	1	887770	1.8554	2	1.8573	2
Tennessee	9	6916897	14.4560	14	14.4705	14
Texas	36	29183290	60.9916	61	61.0529	61
Utah	4	3275252	6.8451	7	6.8520	7
Vermont	1	643503	1.3449	1	1.3462	1
Virginia	11	8654542	18.0876	18	18.1057	18
Washington	10	7715946	16.1259	16	16.1421	16
West Virginia	3	1795045	3.7516	4	3.7553	4
Wisconsin	8	5897473	12.3254	12	12.3378	12
Wyoming	1	577719	1.2074	1	1.2086	1
USA	435	331108434	692.0000	692		692

Table 6.2. Apportionment based on the 2010 census for a House with 676 seats using Webster's method.

Section 6.2.2   An Agreeable House Size

In 1992 Michael Neubauer, a mathematics professor at California State University Northridge, and his master's student, Margo Gartner, published a proposal for apportioning the House. Their work was motivated by problems associated with a constant House size over the past century. A suitable solution to those problems is hampered by the Balinski and Young Impossibility Theorem: divisor methods are subject to quota rule violations and quota methods are subject to unacceptable paradoxes. Accordingly, Neubauer and Carr examined the divisor methods of Dean, Huntington-Hill, and Webster in contrast with the Hamilton quota method.[8]

> As we see it, the problem of finding a "good" House size and the "right" apportionment method are best considered together. While the four methods discussed here result in different apportionments for many House sizes, they also agree for many House sizes. If we can find a House size for which they agree, then we will have eliminated the possibility of either an Alabama Paradox or quota violations.

Neubauer and Carr defined that a House size is **agreeable** means that the distribution of seats by the methods of Dean, Huntington-Hill, Webster, and Hamilton all agree. Accordingly, they proposed, *"after each census, increase the House size to the first agreeable House size larger than the existing House size."* They noted that if the proposal had been adopted for reapportionment based on the 1960 census, then the House size would be 445; 1970, 727; 1980, 735; 1990, 818; 2000, 862.

A simple alteration could be to first determine if the existing House size is agreeable. Is so, then keep it; otherwise, increase to the first agreeable larger House size. For example, based on the 2000 census the House size 435 was not agreeable—the first agreeable size larger than 435 was 477.[9] Based on the 2010 census 435 was not agreeable—the first agreeable size larger that 435 was 871.[10] This indicates that the criterion of agreeable may be too strong since it can lead to a major increase in House size in one decade.

One solution is first to replace the method of equal proportions by the method of major fractions (Webster's method). Then replace the criterion of agreeable with acceptable where a House size is **acceptable** means that the methods of Hamilton and Webster agree. In this event Neubauer and Carr noted that the increase in House size only would have been from 435 to 451 between 1960 and 2000.

An application of the cube root law yields a House size of 692 as described in the previous section. Further, 692 is an acceptable House size. An amended form of the Neubauer and Carr proposal is to use an acceptable House size consistent (nearest) with the cube root law. This would yield a House size of 692 based on the 2020 census.

---

[8] Michael Neubauer and Margo Gartner, A Proposal for Apportioning the House, *PS: Political Science and Politics,* Volume 44, Issue 01, January 2011, pp 77 -79.

[9] Ibid: 79.

[10] Michael Neubauer, private communication, 29 August 2014.

Section 6.2.3 thirty-thousand.org

The foundation for thirty-thousand.org is Article the First as originally passed in the House of Representatives.[11]

> Article the First . . . After the first enumeration required by the first Article of the Constitution, there shall be one Representative for every thirty thousand, until the number shall amount to one hundred, after which, the proportion shall be so regulated by Congress, that there shall be not less than one hundred Representatives, nor less than one Representative for every forty thousand persons, until the number of Representatives shall amount to two hundred, after which the proportion shall be so regulated by Congress, that there shall not be less than two hundred Representatives, nor less than one Representative for every fifty thousand persons.

The recommendations of thirty-thousand.org for the House size are based on a premise as if the House version of Article the First were ratified. Hence, thirty-thousand.org recommends apportionment be accomplished by using a basic divisor method with 50000 as the ratio of representation.[12] However, thirty-thousand.org does not specify the specific rounding criterion to be used in conjunction with a basic divisor method with ratio 50000. Table 6.3 (next page) presents a spreadsheet showing apportionment using the five historical methods of rounding a quotient decimal: Down (Jefferson), HM (harmonic mean, Dean), GM (geometric mean, Huntington-Hill), AM (arithmetic mean, Webster), and Up (Adams).

In an interesting coincidence based on both the 2010 and 2020 censuses, the basic divisor methods using the ratio of 50000 produce the same apportionment using the Dean, Huntington-Hill, and Webster criteria for rounding the quotient decimal. Hence, thirty-thousand.org is proposing a House with 6623 seats based on the 2020 census. We leave it to the reader's imagination to picture how such a House would function. We caution not to dismiss thirty-thousand.org merely because the House size proposal may at first appear more bizarre than practical. The website contains a wealth of information about the concerns of representation and House size.

Section 6.2.4 The Wyoming Rule

Most reapportionment reform proposals focus on increasing House size. However, there are two approaches to congressional apportionment, the constituency approach and the House size approach. The constituency approach is launched by asking, how many people should a congressman represent? Although thirty-thousand.org proposes an answer of 50000, the main motivation is to maximize the House size via the conditions specified in Article the First.

---

[11] https://www.thirty-thousand.org/.
[12] See Question 4 with Answer on the above website.

Table 6.3. Thirty-Thousand.org apportionment proposal based on the 2020 census.

State	Seats	Population	Quotient	Down	HM	GM	AM	Up
Alabama	7	5030030	100.6006	100	101	101	101	101
Alaska	1	736081	14.7216	14	15	15	15	15
Arizona	9	7158923	143.1785	143	143	143	143	144
Arkansas	4	3013756	60.2751	60	60	60	60	61
California	53	39576757	791.5351	791	792	792	792	792
Colorado	7	5782171	115.6434	115	116	116	116	116
Connecticut	5	3608298	72.1660	72	72	72	72	73
Delaware	1	990837	19.8167	19	20	20	20	20
Florida	27	21570527	431.4105	431	431	431	431	432
Georgia	14	10725274	214.5055	214	215	215	215	215
Hawaii	2	1460137	29.2027	29	29	29	29	30
Idaho	2	1841377	36.8275	36	37	37	37	37
Illinois	18	12822739	256.4548	256	256	256	256	257
Indiana	9	6790280	135.8056	135	136	136	136	136
Iowa	4	3192406	63.8481	63	64	64	64	64
Kansas	4	2940865	58.8173	58	59	59	59	59
Kentucky	6	4509342	90.1868	90	90	90	90	91
Louisiana	6	4661468	93.2294	93	93	93	93	94
Maine	2	1363582	27.2716	27	27	27	27	28
Maryland	8	6185278	123.7056	123	124	124	124	124
Massachusetts	9	7033469	140.6694	140	141	141	141	141
Michigan	14	10084442	201.6888	201	202	202	202	202
Minnesota	8	5709752	114.1950	114	114	114	114	115
Mississippi	4	2963914	59.2783	59	59	59	59	60
Missouri	8	6160281	123.2056	123	123	123	123	124
Montana	1	1085407	21.7081	21	22	22	22	22
Nebraska	3	1963333	39.2667	39	39	39	39	40
Nevada	4	3108462	62.1692	62	62	62	62	63
New Hampshire	2	1379089	27.5818	27	28	28	28	28
New Jersey	12	9294493	185.8899	185	186	186	186	186
New Mexico	3	2120220	42.4044	42	42	42	42	43
New York	27	20215751	404.3150	404	404	404	404	405
North Carolina	13	10453948	209.0790	209	209	209	209	210
North Dakota	1	779702	15.5940	15	16	16	16	16
Ohio	16	11808848	236.1770	236	236	236	236	237
Oklahoma	5	3963516	79.2703	79	79	79	79	80
Oregon	5	4241500	84.8300	84	85	85	85	85
Pennsylvania	18	13011844	260.2369	260	260	260	260	261
Rhode Island	2	1098163	21.9633	21	22	22	22	22
South Carolina	7	5124712	102.4942	102	102	102	102	103
South Dakota	1	887770	17.7554	17	18	18	18	18
Tennessee	9	6916897	138.3379	138	138	138	138	139
Texas	36	29183290	583.6658	583	584	584	584	584
Utah	4	3275252	65.5050	65	66	66	66	66
Vermont	1	643503	12.8701	12	13	13	13	13
Virginia	11	8654542	173.0908	173	173	173	173	174
Washington	10	7715946	154.3189	154	154	154	154	155
West Virginia	3	1795045	35.9009	35	36	36	36	36
Wisconsin	8	5897473	117.9495	117	118	118	118	118
Wyoming	1	577719	11.5544	11	12	12	12	12
USA	435	331108434		6597	6623	6623	6623	6647

Internet Research

The internet is a wonderful research tool. Reference research is much faster than old-fashioned library hardcopy searches. Video resources, such as YouTube, can be engaging as well as informative. However, it is important to fact check specifics. Sometimes a general explanation is excellent, but an illustrating example uses incorrect data. For example, one YouTube video illustrating the Wyoming Rule for the 2010 census uses 563626 for the population of Wyoming. However, that is the resident population. The apportionment population, 568300, consists of the resident population plus the state's overseas population. Other sites confuse decimal rounding methods, always rounding normally and thereby mistakenly apply Webster's rounding criterion when another criterion is appropriate. Other sites confuse fairness criteria for the five historical divisor methods claiming that a certain method equalizes absolute district sizes as much as possible not realizing that this is the fairness criterion defining Dean's method.

The Wyoming Rule applies the constituency approach by proposing that the average congressional district size be the population of the smallest state.[13] Wyoming has the smallest population since the 1990 census; hence, the name of the rule. The apportionment population for Wyoming in the 2020 census is 577719. The Wyoming Rule is a basic divisor method but the rule itself does not specify a quotient rounding criterion. The resulting House size will vary due to two factors: the population of Wyoming and the criterion used to round the quotient decimals. So, the resulting House size depends on the choice for how to round the quotient decimal. A summary for the last three censuses is presented in the following Table 6.4

Table 6.4. House size applying the Wyoming Rule.

Census	Jefferson	Dean	Huntington-Hill	Webster	Adams
2000	544	571	570	569	593
2010	523	543	542	540	572
2020	550	574	573	573	599

Table 6.5 (next page) shows the result of using the Wyoming Rule based on the 2020 census applying the five historic apportionment rounding criteria to the resulting quotient. For comparison the Hamilton quota method for House size 573 is also provided (Q573 is the quota column for House size 573, LQ573 is the corresponding lower quota, and Ham is the Hamilton apportionment). The Seats column gives the number of seats in the House based on the 2010 census so that one can compare the results of the old and new apportionments.

Another feature of the Wyoming Rule is that the size of the House may decrease from decade to decade even though the population increases. This occurs when the population increase for the smallest state occurs at a faster rate than the population as a whole. Those who argue that an increase in population should be accompanied by a corresponding increase in House size should bear this in mind when advocating the Wyoming Rule.

---

[13] Steven Taylor, *Representation in the House: The Wyoming Rule*, Outside the Beltway, 14 December 2010; accessed from http://www.outsidethebeltway.com/representation-in-the-house-the-wyoming-rule/.

Table 6.5. *Apportionment based on the 2000 census and the Wyoming Rule.*

State	Seats	Population	Quotient	LD	HM	GM	AM	SD	Q573	LQ573	Ham
Alabama	7	5030030	8.7067	8	9	9	9	9	8.7047	8	9
Alaska	1	736081	1.2741	1	1	1	1	2	1.2738	1	1
Arizona	9	7158923	12.3917	12	12	12	12	13	12.3889	12	12
Arkansas	4	3013756	5.2166	5	5	5	5	6	5.2155	5	5
California	53	39576757	68.5052	68	69	69	69	69	68.4896	68	69
Colorado	7	5782171	10.0086	10	10	10	10	11	10.0063	10	10
Connecticut	5	3608298	6.2458	6	6	6	6	7	6.2443	6	6
Delaware	1	990837	1.7151	1	2	2	2	2	1.7147	1	2
Florida	27	21570527	37.3374	37	37	37	37	38	37.3289	37	37
Georgia	14	10725274	18.5649	18	19	19	19	19	18.5606	18	19
Hawaii	2	1460137	2.5274	2	3	3	3	3	2.5268	2	3
Idaho	2	1841377	3.1873	3	3	3	3	4	3.1866	3	3
Illinois	18	12822739	22.1955	22	22	22	22	23	22.1904	22	22
Indiana	9	6790280	11.7536	11	12	12	12	12	11.7509	11	12
Iowa	4	3192406	5.5259	5	6	6	6	6	5.5246	5	6
Kansas	4	2940865	5.0905	5	5	5	5	6	5.0893	5	5
Kentucky	6	4509342	7.8054	7	8	8	8	8	7.8036	7	8
Louisiana	6	4661468	8.0687	8	8	8	8	9	8.0669	8	8
Maine	2	1363582	2.3603	2	2	2	2	3	2.3597	2	2
Maryland	8	6185278	10.7064	10	11	11	11	11	10.7039	10	11
Massachusetts	9	7033469	12.1746	12	12	12	12	13	12.1718	12	12
Michigan	14	10084442	17.4556	17	17	17	17	18	17.4516	17	17
Minnesota	8	5709752	9.8833	9	10	10	10	10	9.8810	9	10
Mississippi	4	2963914	5.1304	5	5	5	5	6	5.1292	5	5
Missouri	8	6160281	10.6631	10	11	11	11	11	10.6607	10	11
Montana	1	1085407	1.8788	1	2	2	2	2	1.8784	1	2
Nebraska	3	1963333	3.3984	3	3	3	3	4	3.3976	3	3
Nevada	4	3108462	5.3806	5	5	5	5	6	5.3794	5	5
New Hampshire	2	1379089	2.3871	2	2	2	2	3	2.3866	2	2
New Jersey	12	9294493	16.0883	16	16	16	16	17	16.0846	16	16
New Mexico	3	2120220	3.6700	3	4	4	4	4	3.6691	3	4
New York	27	20215751	34.9924	34	35	35	35	35	34.9844	34	35
North Carolina	13	10453948	18.0952	18	18	18	18	19	18.0911	18	18
North Dakota	1	779702	1.3496	1	2	1	1	2	1.3493	1	1
Ohio	16	11808848	20.4405	20	20	20	20	21	20.4358	20	20
Oklahoma	5	3963516	6.8606	6	7	7	7	7	6.8591	6	7
Oregon	5	4241500	7.3418	7	7	7	7	8	7.3401	7	7
Pennsylvania	18	13011844	22.5228	22	23	23	23	23	22.5177	22	23
Rhode Island	2	1098163	1.9009	1	2	2	2	2	1.9004	1	2
South Carolina	7	5124712	8.8706	8	9	9	9	9	8.8686	8	9
South Dakota	1	887770	1.5367	1	2	2	2	2	1.5363	1	2
Tennessee	9	6916897	11.9728	11	12	12	12	12	11.9700	11	12
Texas	36	29183290	50.5147	50	51	51	51	51	50.5032	50	51
Utah	4	3275252	5.6693	5	6	6	6	6	5.6680	5	6
Vermont	1	643503	1.1139	1	1	1	1	2	1.1136	1	1
Virginia	11	8654542	14.9805	14	15	15	15	15	14.9771	14	15
Washington	10	7715946	13.3559	13	13	13	13	14	13.3528	13	13
West Virginia	3	1795045	3.1071	3	3	3	3	4	3.1064	3	3
Wisconsin	8	5897473	10.2082	10	10	10	10	11	10.2059	10	10
Wyoming	1	577719	1.0000	1	1	1	1	1	0.9998	1	1
USA	435	331108434		550	574	573	573	599	573.0000	550	573

Ann Lousin, professor of law at The John Marshall Law School, and Leona Mirza, professor of mathematics at North Park University, both in Chicago, proposed using the Wyoming Rule as a method of avoiding a Bush vs. Gore result as occurred in the 2000 presidential election.[14] The specific objective of the proposal is that "the best, easiest and cleanest way to change the composition of the Electoral College would be to replace the Huntington-Hill method of determining the total number of U.S. representatives every decade with a process using the smallest-populated state as its key."

Lousin and Mirza further described the details given that Wyoming is given one representative. Then, "a state that had twice Wyoming's population would be awarded two U.S. representatives; a state with three "Wyomings" would have three representatives, and so forth." This implies Jefferson's method of rounding down the quotient decimal.

See Table 6.5, LD column, for reapportionment based on the 2020 census to analyze an application of the Wyoming Rule with Jefferson's method of rounding. Table 6.6 (next page) displays a similar analysis based on the 2000 census and shows that a notable drawback of Jefferson's Wyoming Rule is a clash with the quota rule. Jefferson's method creates a House with 544 members. California is awarded two seats above quota. Florida, New York, and Texas are each awarded one seat above quota. Further, the large state favoritism is evident when viewing the quota against the actual apportionment. From the viewpoint of the quota the favoritism for the larger states Illinois and New Jersey is glaring in comparison with the smaller Iowa, Montana, New Mexico, Oklahoma, Oregon, and West Virginia.

Lousin and Mirza stated they have "no quarrel with the Huntington-Hill method" and that it "works superbly." Since Jefferson's Wyoming Rule is a basic divisor method, the House size is merely a result of the algorithm. One does not know the House size until the apportionment process is completed. Jefferson's Wyoming Rule creates a House with 544 members based on the 2000 census. This leads to the question, how would the Huntington-Hill method distribute those 544 seats? For the result see Table 6.7 (next page), $h = 544$, H-H column. In comparison there is a substantial difference in the distribution of the 544 seats affecting 20 states. Most notably Jefferson's Wyoming method allocates three more seats to California than Huntington-Hill. Further, Jefferson allocates two more seats to New York and Texas than Huntington-Hill.

The result of applying Jefferson's basic divisor method with the Wyoming Rule illustrates the rationale of Balinski and Young's recommendation to use Webster's method of rounding the quotient decimal. Based on the 2020 census, Webster's Wyoming Rule yields a House with 573 members (see Table 6.6, AM column). There are no quota rule violations and there is no large state vs. small state favoritism. Further, the Wyoming-Webster method and the Hamilton quota method are in perfect agreement. Hence, 573 is an acceptable House size.

---

[14] Ann Lousin and Leona Mirza, *Rethink reapportionment*, The National Law Journal, 22 February 2010; accessed from http://buildabiggerhouse.org/wp-content/uploads/2016/03/con-law.pdf.

State	Seats	Population	Quotient	Jefferson	Quota	H-H
Alabama	7	4461130	9.0069	9	8.6235	9
Alaska	1	628933	1.2698	1	1.2157	1
Arizona	6	5140683	10.3788	10	9.9371	10
Arkansas	4	2679733	5.4103	5	5.1800	5
California	52	33930798	68.5050	68	65.5891	65
Colorado	6	4311882	8.7055	8	8.3350	8
Connecticut	6	3409535	6.8837	6	6.5907	7
Delaware	1	785068	1.5850	1	1.5176	2
Florida	23	16028890	32.3617	32	30.9842	31
Georgia	11	8206975	16.5696	16	15.8643	16
Hawaii	2	1216642	2.4564	2	2.3518	2
Idaho	2	1297274	2.6191	2	2.5077	3
Illinois	20	12439042	25.1140	25	24.0450	24
Indiana	10	6090782	12.2971	12	11.7736	12
Iowa	5	2931923	5.9194	5	5.6675	6
Kansas	4	2693824	5.4387	5	5.2072	5
Kentucky	6	4049431	8.1756	8	7.8277	8
Louisiana	7	4480271	9.0455	9	8.6605	9
Maine	2	1277731	2.5797	2	2.4699	3
Maryland	8	5307886	10.7164	10	10.2603	10
Massachusetts	10	6355568	12.8317	12	12.2855	12
Michigan	16	9955829	20.1004	20	19.2449	19
Minnesota	8	4925670	9.9447	9	9.5214	9
Mississippi	5	2852927	5.7600	5	5.5148	6
Missouri	9	5606260	11.3188	11	10.8370	11
Montana	1	905316	1.8278	1	1.7500	2
Nebraska	3	1715369	3.4633	3	3.3159	3
Nevada	2	2002032	4.0420	4	3.8700	4
New Hampshire	2	1238415	2.5003	2	2.3939	2
New Jersey	13	8424354	17.0085	17	16.2845	16
New Mexico	3	1823821	3.6822	3	3.5255	4
New York	31	19004973	38.3703	38	36.7371	36
North Carolina	12	8067673	16.2883	16	15.5950	15
North Dakota	1	643756	1.2997	1	1.2444	1
Ohio	19	11374540	22.9648	22	21.9873	22
Oklahoma	6	3458819	6.9832	6	6.6860	7
Oregon	5	3428543	6.9221	6	6.6275	7
Pennsylvania	21	12300670	24.8346	24	23.7775	24
Rhode Island	2	1049662	2.1192	2	2.0290	2
South Carolina	6	4025061	8.1264	8	7.7805	8
South Dakota	1	756874	1.5281	1	1.4631	2
Tennessee	9	5700037	11.5082	11	11.0183	11
Texas	30	20903994	42.2044	42	40.4079	40
Utah	3	2236714	4.5158	4	4.3236	4
Vermont	1	609890	1.2313	1	1.1789	1
Virginia	11	7100702	14.3360	14	13.7258	14
Washington	9	5908684	11.9294	11	11.4216	11
West Virginia	3	1813077	3.6605	3	3.5047	4
Wisconsin	9	5371210	10.8443	10	10.3827	10
Wyoming	1	495304	1.0000	1	0.9574	1
US	435	281424177		544	544.0000	544

Table 6.6. Spreadsheet analysis of apportionment based on the 2000 census using the Wyoming Rule with Jefferson's method in comparison with the Huntington-Hill method for the same House size.

Lousin and Mirza's proposal is a good example of growing awareness of the interconnectedness of the components of representation. The proposal is motivated by a problem with the election of the President of the United States connected to the Electoral College connected to the size of the House of Representatives connected to congressional district size connected to the congressional apportionment problem. And it illustrates the importance of the missing arithmetical component with its surprising political consequences: how to round a decimal.

Section 6.2.5   The Bottom Line

What lesson and advice does the history of congressional apportionment have for today? There are two key items that should be foremost for updating the method of apportionment. The first evident item is that the current size of the House, 435, is too small to accommodate the large U. S. population following the constitutional mandate that apportionment be based on population. The second evident item is that the method of equal proportions carries an intrinsic small state bias.

The history of congressional apportionment, especially in the modern era, suggests the following specifics. First, based on the 2020 census, raise the size of the House to a figure around 573. This House size will make the seat proportion of a given state in the House as near as possible to its population proportion. Second, the method of equal proportions should be replaced by the method of major fractions since it is the only way of rounding a quotient decimal that is neutral to the population size the state. Both reforms may be accomplished by updating the census/apportionment act of 1929 which established the automatic apportionment mechanism in effect today.

The 1929 act was established to prevent another reapportionment failure as occurred with the 1920 census. That act basically established that if Congress does not reapportion the House based on a new census within the session that the Congress receives the census report, then Congress will retain the last House size distributed by the method last used and based on the current census. This has had the effect of fixing the House size since Congress does not act. The automatic apportionment mechanism should be revised to reflect the Wyoming Rule, re-establish the method of major fractions, and adjust the resulting House size to conform to the Quota Rule

The final lesson applicable to the 2020 decade is the major political decision as to whether the people want to proceed with the establishment of a "constitutional" dictatorship under the GQP, which may be summarized as the Putinization of America.

Professor Johnston often said that if you didn't know history, you didn't know anything. You were a leaf that didn't know it was part of a tree.

Michael Crichton[1]

Epilogue

Congressional apportionment is only one component in a large political ecosystem: representation. Representation is at the very heart of American government. The concept may at first appear simple and most people take its meaning as a given. However, its practice is anything but easy. An entire academic program could be devoted to the basic question, what is representation? The narrower notion of congressional representation is intertwined with many other related components, including the census, districting, suffrage, and voting.

The first related component for representation as envisioned in congressional apportionment concerns a census question, who is to be represented? In proportional representation there are many problems for obtaining an enumeration of those to be represented. Several issues remain contentious.

- Should enumeration of the population be based on residency or citizenship?
- Which overseas people should be enumerated?
- Should statistical sampling techniques be used?
- What techniques should be used to correct for difficulties in enumeration; for example, homeless, transient, or uncooperative people?
- Should people other than residents of states, like territories or the District of Columbia, be represented by voting members in Congress?

Congressional apportionment is merely the process of determining how many seats in Congress each state gets. Apportionment does not specify how those seats are to be filled. Currently, a seat is filled by electing a representative from a congressional district. However, the make-up of these districts is up to each individual state. Arguably the single greatest problem for fair representation today is gerrymandering of congressional districts.[2][3] Like apportionment and voting, gerrymandering is a serious mathematical and political problem.[4]

---

[1] Michael Crichton, *Timeline*, Balantine Books, New York, 1999: 85.

[2] Matthew Frankel, *U. S. Congress: Gerrymandering is the Problem:*, Brookings, 15 June 2010; accessed from https://www.brookings.edu/blog/up-front/2010/06/15/u-s-congress-gerrymandering-is-the-problem/.

[3] http://www.fairvote.org/gerrymandering#gerrymandering_key_facts; accessed 19 April 2017.

[4] Google: mathematics and gerrymandering.

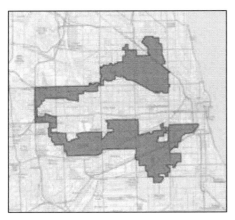

Figure E1. Illinois 4th congressional district.

Gerrymandering is a technique used to obtain goals of certain partisan political activities.[5] One such successful activity was Project RedMap[6] orchestrated in 2009-2010 by Chris Jankowski who won Rachel Maddow's choice as the "unsung political genius of our time."[7] Congressional apportionment is a two-sided coin involving fairness on one side and power on the other. Gerrymandering of congressional districts is an effective technique for engaging power over fairness. One merely needs to examine the shape of congressional districts in many states to see blatant gerrymandering.[8] The shape of the 4th district in Illinois (Figure E1), a Democrat stronghold, still serves as a poster child for gerrymandering.[9]

Suffrage is the process of determining who is allowed to vote in a given election. Suffrage relates to the fundamental question, how are representatives selected? For example, state legislatures selected members of the Senate for most of the nation's history. The Seventeenth Amendment, ratified on 8 April 1913, finally specified that senators will be "elected by the people."[10] In early American history suffrage was usually restricted to residents of a given locale who were white, Protestant, propertied, male, and at least 21 years of age. Of course there were exceptions; however, they were notable because they were exceptions. Now, for the most part citizens age 18 or older may register to vote. However, some states driven by power politics are advancing registration suppression laws white-robed as election security laws. In general, once a congressional district is drawn, the key question is, who can participate in the process of selecting the representative?

Voting is perhaps the single most identifiable component of the democratic process for most people. Once apportionment, districting, and suffrage are in place, then an election is held to determine who the representative will be. There are many components to this process.

- Ballot access, i.e., the process of determining who can be on the ballot. Ballot access laws vary widely from state to state.
- Ballot structure: vote for one, approval voting, ranked choice, cumulative voting.
- Who wins: plurality, majority, instant run-off options for ranked-choice voting.
- Election mechanics: absentee, mail-in, voting machines, paper trail.

---

[5] Christopher Ingraham, *Americas most gerrymandered congressional districts*, The Washington Post, 15 May 2014; accessed from https://www.washingtonpost.com/news/wonk/wp/2014/05/15/americas-most-gerrymandered-congressional-districts/?utm_term=.8a5ad766c44c.

[6] http://www.redistrictingmajorityproject.com/.

[7] The Rachel Maddow Show, 2 March 2015; http://www.msnbc.com/rachel-maddow/watch/how-the-gop-gave-itself-a-ten-year-advantage-407234115988.

[8] https://en.wikipedia.org/wiki/List_of_United_States_congressional_districts.

[9] https://en.wikipedia.org/wiki/Illinois%27_congressional_districts.

[10] https://www.archives.gov/legislative/features/17th-amendment.

Unfortunately, the ballot box is still being used to engineer power politics. This is illustrated by the shameful behavior of the chair of the Montana Republican Party, Jeff Essmann, in his opposition to a mail-in voting mechanism in a special election for Montana's seat in the House of Representatives schedule for 25 May 2017.[11] In addition to election mechanics, this Montana election also spotlights a ballot access problem as illustrated by Thomas Breck (Green Party) along with Steve Kelly and Doug Campbell (Independents) who filed suit in the 9th Circuit Court of Appeals.[12]

FairVote is an "organization that seeks to make democracy fair, functional, and more representative."[13] Their website is a good place to start in studying modern problems about representation. The two problems that FairVote highlights as most influential are polarization and gerrymandering. Both problems are illustrative of the two-sided coin conjoining fairness and power.

[11] Kira Lerner, *Montana Republicans are fighting to make it harder to vote in special Congressional election*, ThinkProgress, 11 April 2017; https://thinkprogress.org/montana-republicans-are-fighting-to-make-it-harder-for-democrats-to-elect-their-next-congressman-774659d058d0 accessed on 19 April 2017.

[12] Matt Volz, *Judge won't halt Montana special election ballots for appeal*, Missoulian, 11 April 2017; http://missoulian.com/news/government-and-politics/judge-won-t-halt-montana-special-election-ballots-for-appeal/article_7496f825-0665-5ce5-b47d-8ebf4202386b.html accessed 19 April 2017.

[13] http://www.fairvote.org/about.

Discussion Items

1. There are two approaches to congressional apportionment: constituency and House size. The constituency approach is launched with the question, how many people should a congressperson represent? The answer is called the ratio of representation (ratio), the constituency, or the divisor. The House size approach is launched with the question, how many seats should the House have? Which approach do you prefer?

2. Part of the reason for the apportionment impasse following the 1920 census was that Congress was split into three factions over the House size: decrease, no change, and increase. None of the three factions could garner a majority. In today's world, do you think that the size of the House of Representations should remain at 435 or should it be changed? If changed, should the House be increased or decreased; if so, to what?

3. The 1920 census was the first census to reveal that most U. S. residents were associated with an urban rather than a rural area. The book *Democracy Delayed* advanced the view that although a majority of U. S. residents were associated with urban areas, most members of Congress were associated with rural areas resulting in an urban vs. rural clash of values. What were these conflicting values? Is America experiencing a similar culture/values clash today?

4. Who or what does a representative in the U. S. House of Representatives represent? Who or what should a representative represent?

5. Should the President of the United States be elected using the current electoral system?

6. Suffrage (right to vote) is a major topic in U. S. history. What were the key aspects of suffrage in American history? Do problems in suffrage still exist today?

7. The congressional apportionment process only determines how many representatives each state gets in the House. After apportionment it is up to the states to determine their congressional districts. The main abuse of the district process is gerrymandering. What is gerrymandering? Is it a problem? If so, what should be done about it?

   The apportionment act based on the 1910 census had five sections. Section 3 states, "That in each State entitled under this apportionment to more than one Representative to the Sixty-third and each subsequent Congress shall be elected by districts composed of a contiguous and compact territory, and containing as nearly as practicable an equal number of inhabitants. The said districts shall be equal to the number of Representatives to which such State may be entitled in Congress, no district electing more than one Representative." Subsequent apportionment acts dropped national guidelines for congressional districts. Should Congress adopt national fairness guidelines for Congressional districts, such as compact, contiguous, or with an equal number of inhabitants?

A good discussion starter is *America's Most Gerrymandered Congressional Districts* by Christopher Ingraham, The Washington Post, 15 May 2014.[1] Wikipedia in this case is an excellent resource to obtain a state-by-state picture.[2]

8. Do you think that the courts should get involved in resolving redistricting disputes? Do you think that gerrymandering violates the principle of equal protection under the law? For the latest on court involvement, see Professor Justin Levitt's guide.[3]

9. Given a fixed House size, intuitively the Hamilton quota method seems obvious and most natural. The following two examples illustrate surprising consequences of Hamilton's quota method.

Example A. The Emerald school district has three schools: Shamrock, Pine, and Forest. The school enrollments are Shamrock 41, Pine 106, and Forest 253. Each year the school board apportions teachers to the schools based on enrollment using the Hamilton quota method.

1. The county allocates 24 teachers to the Emerald school district. How does the district allocate the 24 teachers among the three schools?
2. Just before announcing the results the county decides to give the district another teacher. How does the district allocate the 25 teachers among the three schools?
3. Is anything weird about the resulting apportionments? Explain.

Example B. The nation of Zebulon has four provinces: Azcula, Brinth, Crevan, and Darcon. The Zebulon Constitution specifies a national assembly of 100 members to be distributed based on population as enumerated by a decennial census using the Hamilton quota method. The 2000 and 2010 census results are provided below.

Province	2000	2010
Azcula	5,525,381	5,657,564
Brinth	3,470,152	3,508,474
Crevan	3,864,226	3,885,049
Darcon	201,203	201,049

1. What is the distribution of seats in the Zebulon national assembly based on the 2000 census?

---

[1] https://www.washingtonpost.com/news/wonk/wp/2014/05/15/americas-most-gerrymandered-congressional-districts/?utm_term=.9c8e7b221bf9.

[2] https://en.wikipedia.org/wiki/List_of_United_States_congressional_districts.

[3] Justin Jevitt, All About Redistricting: http://redistricting.lls.edu/index.php.

2. What is the distribution of seats in the Zebulon national assembly based on the 2010 census?
3. Is anything weird about the resulting apportionments? Explain.

INDEX

Made in the USA
Coppell, TX
09 December 2021

67732349R00203